2:01

STARS AND STELLAR SYSTEMS
Compendium of Astronomy and Astrophysics

(IN NINE VOLUMES)

GERARD P. KUIPER, *General Editor*
BARBARA M. MIDDLEHURST, *Associate General Editor*

I
TELESCOPES

II
ASTRONOMICAL TECHNIQUES

III
BASIC ASTRONOMICAL DATA

IV
CLUSTERS AND BINARIES

V
GALACTIC STRUCTURE

VI
STELLAR ATMOSPHERES

VII
NEBULAE AND INTERSTELLAR MATTER

VIII
STELLAR STRUCTURE

IX
GALAXIES AND THE UNIVERSE

CONTRIBUTORS

G. O. ABELL

W. BECKER

G. VAN BIESBROECK

A. BLAAUW

W. H. VAN DEN BOS

G. M. CLEMENCE

W. DIECKVOSS

CECILIA PAYNE-GAPOSCHKIN

SERGEI GAPOSCHKIN

JOHN S. HALL

D. L. HARRIS III

H. L. JOHNSON

PHILIP C. KEENAN

ROBERT P. KRAFT

B. V. KUKARKIN

WILLEM J. LUYTEN

R. L. MINKOWSKI

P. P. PARENAGO

R. M. PETRIE

F. P. SCOTT

K. SERKOWSKI

STEWART SHARPLESS

K. Aa. STRAND

BENGT STRÖMGREN

S. VASILEVSKIS

A. N. VYSSOTSKY

FRANK BRADSHAW WOOD

C. E. WORLEY

BASIC
ASTRONOMICAL
DATA

Edited by

K. Aa. STRAND

THE UNIVERSITY OF CHICAGO PRESS

CHICAGO AND LONDON

This publication has been supported in part by the

NATIONAL SCIENCE FOUNDATION

Library of Congress Catalog Card Number: 63-11402

THE UNIVERSITY OF CHICAGO PRESS, CHICAGO & LONDON
The University of Toronto Press, Toronto 5, Canada

© *1963 by The University of Chicago. Published 1963*
Second Impression 1966. Printed in the United States
of America

Preface to the Series

THE SERIES "Stars and Stellar Systems, Compendium of Astronomy," comprising nine volumes, was organized in consultation with senior astronomers in the United States and abroad early in 1955. It was intended as an extension of the four-volume "Solar System" series to cover astrophysics and stellar astronomy. In contrast to the "Solar System" series, separate editors have been appointed for each volume. The volume editors, together with the general editors, form the editorial board that is responsible for the over-all planning of the series.

The aim of the series is to present stellar astronomy and astrophysics as basically empirical sciences, co-ordinated and illuminated by the application of theory. To this end the series opens with a description of representative telescopes, both optical and radio (Vol. 1), and of accessories, techniques, and methods of reduction (Vol. 2). The chief classes of observational data are described in Volume 3, with additional material being referred to in succeeding volumes, as the topics may require. The systematic treatment of astronomical problems starts with Volume 4, as is apparent from the volume titles. Theoretical chapters are added where needed, on dynamical problems in Volumes 4, 5, and 9, and on astrophysical problems in Volumes 6, 7, and 8. In order that the chapters may retain a greater degree of permanence, the more speculative parts of astronomy have been de-emphasized. The level of the chapters will make them suitable for graduate students as well as for professional astronomers and also for the increasing number of scientists in other fields requiring astronomical information.

The undersigned wish to thank both the authors and the volume editors for their readiness to collaborate on this series, which it is hoped will stimulate the further growth of astronomy.

The editors wish to acknowledge the support by the National Science Foundation both in defraying part of the costs of the editorial offices and in providing a publication subsidy.

GERARD P. KUIPER
BARBARA M. MIDDLEHURST

Preface to Volume 3

THE basic astronomical data that have been collected over the years are the results of large numbers of observations that in general have been processed into catalogues, tabulations, and classifications by statistical means.

While the classification of data is a useful empirical method of bringing order to large masses of observations, it has been in many cases a necessary step toward explaining a natural phenomenon. We find that stellar astronomy is no exception in this respect because classification processes have led to a better understanding of the physical nature of the stars, their positions, and their motions within the systems to which they belong.

This volume was organized for the purpose of describing the chief classes of astronomical data that are available from ground-based observatories with an evaluation of the completeness and accuracy of these data where appropriate. No attempts have been made to describe instrumentation, observational techniques, and methods of reduction, as these subjects are covered elsewhere in the series (Vols. 1 and 2). Neither does this volume concern itself with the systematic treatment of astronomical problems, which will be dealt with in the volumes that follow in the series.

The twenty-two chapters and two appendixes are essentially independent of one another. Each author, an active worker and authority in the subject covered by his chapter, was invited to present the subject as he thought it should be presented. This has resulted in some overlap, omissions, and different levels of presentation which the editor did not consider necessary to adjust, in view of the fact that no two astronomers, equally competent, would be in full accord as to what should be included and what should be omitted.

The first chapter deals with the definition of the fundamental system of reference. It is followed by chapters 2–7, within which observational data related to the positions and the motions of the stars are discussed, together with the reliability and completeness of data in the various types of star catalogues in use at the present time.

Chapters 8–11 review data on classification of the stars from their spectra and from various methods of photometric observation.

Chapters 12–13 discuss interstellar absorption as a function of interstellar reddening and the use of multicolor photometry to separate the intrinsic colors of the stars from the apparent ones affected by interstellar reddening.

Empirical physical data on the stars are discussed in chapters 14 and 15, while chapter 16 is concerned with the relatively new field of polarization of starlight caused by interstellar particles.

Chapters 17–19 describe surveys and empirical data on double stars and on variable stars, while chapters 20–22 discuss luminosity calibrations.

The first appendix is a brief account of star catalogues and charts generally used in astronomical research, while the second one describes in more detail the National Geographic Society–Palomar Observatory Sky Survey, which has resulted in a Sky Atlas that has become of great importance in many current astronomical research projects.

This volume was organized between 1957 and 1958, and most of the material was received during 1960, although several manuscripts were not received until well into 1962. The early contributors were given an opportunity to modify their chapters to include new data.

The editor wishes to acknowledge the friendly co-operation and patience of the many authors who have so generously contributed to this volume.

The editor had the privilege of sharing the early problems of getting the volume under way with his coeditor, the late Dr. Daniel L. Harris III, who, he regrets, had to withdraw because of other commitments when they both moved to Washington, D.C. Dr. Harris did, however, from time to time continue to give valuable advice until his untimely death on April 29, 1962.

I am grateful to Barbara Middlehurst for her editorial assistance and to my colleagues in the Astrometry and Astrophysics Division of the U.S. Naval Observatory who so faithfully participated in the editorial work by reading proof, checking references, and preparing the index.

K. Aa. Strand

Table of Contents

1. ASTRONOMICAL REFERENCE SYSTEMS   1
    G. M. Clemence

    1. Introduction   1

    2. Equatorial Co-ordinates   2

    3. Precession and Nutation   3
       3.1. Definition   3
       3.2. Dynamical Theory of Precession and Nutation   4
       3.3. Determination of the Speed of the Precession   5

    4. Aberration   6

    5. Reduction from Apparent to Mean Place   7

    6. The Galactic System of Co-ordinates   8

    7. Galactic Rotation   9

    8. Polar Motion   9

    References   9

2. THE SYSTEM OF FUNDAMENTAL PROPER MOTIONS 11
    F. P. Scott

    1. Introduction 11

    2. The Basis of the Celestial Co-ordinate System 12

    3. Catalogues of Observed Positions of the Stars 13

    4. Compiled Fundamental Star Catalogues 16

    5. Sources of Fundamental Proper Motions 23

    6. Projects on the Improvement of Fundamental Proper Motions . . 26

    References 28

3. THE REFERENCE SYSTEM OF BRIGHT, INTERMEDIATE, AND FAINT STARS
    AND OF GALAXIES 30
       S. Vasilevskis

    1. Introduction 30

2. Bright Stars 31

3. Intermediate Stars 33

4. Faint Stars 35

5. Galaxies 36

References 38

4. PHOTOGRAPHIC PROPER MOTIONS 40
     W. Dieckvoss

1. Introduction 40

2. Reduction of Relative Proper Motions to Absolute 40

3. Photographic Errors 41

4. Catalogues 42

References 45

5. PROPER-MOTION SURVEYS 46
     Willem J. Luyten

1. Introduction and Technique 46

2. The Principal Surveys 49
   2.1. Surveys by Wolf and Innes 49
   2.2. Surveys by Ross 50
   2.3. Surveys by Luyten 50
   2.4. Miscellaneous Surveys 51
   2.5. Future Surveys 52

3. Advantages and Disadvantages of Blink Surveys 53

References 54

6. TRIGONOMETRIC STELLAR PARALLAXES 55
     K. Aa. Strand

1. Introduction 55

2. Internal Accuracies 56

3. External Probable Errors 58

4. Systematic Corrections 60

5. Present and Future Parallax Programs 61

6. Bibliography 62

References 62

7. RADIAL VELOCITIES 64
     R. M. Petrie

   1. Catalogues of Radial Velocities 64

   2. Systematic Differences between Observatories 65

   3. Absolute Accuracy of the *General Catalogue* System 69
      3.1. A Standard Velocity System 69
      3.2. Solar-Type Stars 69
      3.3. A-Type Stars 71
      3.4. B-Type Stars 72

   4. Frequency of Spectroscopic Binaries 73

   References 76

8. CLASSIFICATION OF STELLAR SPECTRA 78
     Philip C. Keenan

   1. Principles of Spectral Classification 78

   2. Physical Theory of Spectral Classification 80

   3. Systems of Classification 83
      3.1. Introduction 83
      3.2. The *Henry Draper* System (HD Types) 83
      3.3. The Recognition of Differences in Luminosity 85
      3.4. The Mount Wilson Classification (MW Types) 85
      3.5. The MK Classification 88

   4. Spectral Types and Criteria 93
      4.1. Introduction 93
      4.2. Type O 93
      4.3. Type B 95
      4.4. Type A 95
      4.5. Type F 96
      4.6. Types G and K 96
      4.7. Type M 98
      4.8. Type S 102
      4.9. Carbon Stars 102

   5. Spectral Characteristics of Population Groups 105
      5.1. Introduction 105
      5.2. Types B and A 107
      5.3. The Main Sequence, Types G–M 107
      5.4. Giants and Subgiants of Types G and K 108

   6. Classification of Spectrograms of Very Small Scale 112

   7. Conclusions—the Technique of Classification 118

   References 118

9. QUANTITATIVE CLASSIFICATION METHODS 123
    Bengt Strömgren

  1. General Considerations 123

  2. Spectral Classification through Wide-Band Photometry 125

  3. Spectral Classification through Photometry in Bands of Intermediate
    Width 131

  4. Spectral Classification through Narrow-Band Photometry 146
    4.1. Quantitative Photographic Methods Utilizing the Lindblad
       Criteria 146
    4.2. Quantitative Photographic Methods Based on the Use of the Ultra-
       violet Criteria of Barbier and Chalonge 151
    4.3. Photographic Methods Utilizing Measures of the Balmer Discon-
       tinuity and Balmer Line Strengths 159
    4.4. Photographic Methods Based on Quantitative Determination of
       Line Ratios for a Considerable Number of Absorption-Line Pairs 161
    4.5. Methods Based on Photoelectric Narrow-Band Photometry . . 162
    4.6. O. C. Wilson's Method of Determining Absolute Magnitudes from
       Measures of the Widths of H and K Emission Lines 179

  5. Accuracy and Limiting Magnitude Obtainable in Quantitative Spectral
    Classification 180

  6. Applications of the Theory of Model Stellar Atmospheres to Results
    Obtained through Quantitative Spectral Classification 184

  References 186

10. SPECTRAL SURVEYS OF K AND M DWARFS 192
    A. N. Vyssotsky

  1. Discovery of Red Dwarf Stars 192

  2. Absolute Magnitudes 193

  3. Distribution by Spectral Class and Apparent Magnitude; Luminosity
    Function 194

  4. Colors of Red Dwarfs 196

  5. Kinematic Characteristics 197

  6. Population Groups among Red Dwarf Stars 200

  7. Concluding Remarks 201

  References 201

11. PHOTOMETRIC SYSTEMS 204
   H. L. Johnson

   1. Introduction 204

   2. General Considerations 204

   3. The U, B, V System 207

   4. The P, V System 216

   5. The Cape Systems 217

   6. The C_1 System 218

   7. The R, I System 218

   8. The Six-Color Photometry 221

   9. Conclusion 221

   References 222

12. INTERSTELLAR REDDENING 225
   Stewart Sharpless

   1. The Law of Interstellar Reddening 225
      1.1. The Reddening-Curve 225
      1.2. The Ratio of Total to Selective Absorption 229
      1.3. Reddening Measured in Two- and Three-Color Systems . . . 231

   2. Variations in the Law of Interstellar Reddening 233
      2.1. Photometric Studies 233
      2.2. The Orion Nebula Region 236
      2.3. Conclusions 237

   References 239

13. APPLICATIONS OF MULTICOLOR PHOTOMETRY 241
   W. Becker

   1. General Remarks 241

   2. Multicolor Systems in Use at Present 244

   3. Diagrams of Three-Color Photometry and Their Application . . . 246
      3.1. General 246
      3.2. Color Difference, Balmer Discontinuity, and Spectral Type . . 247
      3.3. Color Difference and Color Index 248
      3.4. Color Differences and Absolute Magnitude 250
      3.5. Color Index and Absolute Magnitude 252
      3.6. The Relation between the Two-Color Indices 253

   References 261

14. THE STELLAR TEMPERATURE SCALE AND BOLOMETRIC CORRECTIONS . . 263
     D. L. Harris III

   1. Introduction 263

   2. Empirical Bolometric Corrections for Late-Type Stars 264

   3. Theoretical Bolometric Corrections 266

   4. Fundamental Effective Temperatures 266

   5. The Effective-Temperature–Spectral-Type Relationship 268

   6. Color Temperatures 270

   7. Summary and Conclusions 271

   References 272

15. EMPIRICAL DATA ON STELLAR MASSES, LUMINOSITIES, AND RADII . . 273
     D. L. Harris III, K. Aa. Strand, and C. E. Worley

   1. Introduction 273

   2. Orbits of Visual Binaries 273

   3. Mass Ratios of Visual Binaries 281

   4. The Empirical Mass-Luminosity Relation 284

   5. The Radii of the Stars 288

   References 291

16. POLARIZATION OF STARLIGHT 293
     John S. Hall and K. Serkowski

   1. Introduction 293

   2. Methods of Measuring Polarization 293
       2.1. Parameters Describing Polarization 293
       2.2. Photographic Measurements of Polarization 296
       2.3. Photoelectric Measurements of Polarization 297

   3. Basic Observational Results 299
       3.1. Polarization and the Milky Way 299
       3.2. Wavelength Dependence of Polarization and Extinction . . . 301

   4. Optical Properties of Interstellar Dust 302
       4.1. Distribution Parameter 302
       4.2. Scattering by Cylindrical and Ellipsoidal Grains 304
       4.3. Quantum-mechanical Dust Grains 307

5. Alignment Mechanisms 308

6. Interstellar Polarization and Galactic Magnetic Fields 310
   6.1. Magnetic Fields in Spiral Arms 310
   6.2. Structure and Density of Magnetic Fields 311

7. Polarization and Extinction 313
   7.1. Depolarization 313
   7.2. Correlation between Polarization and Extinction 313

References 315

17. SURVEYS AND OBSERVATIONS OF VISUAL DOUBLE STARS 320
    W. H. van den Bos

1. Random Searches 320

2. The Lick Survey 322

3. Southern Surveys 323

4. Special Surveys 324

5. General Catalogues 325

6. Current Files of Measurements 326

7. Conclusion 326

References 326

18. SURVEYS AND OBSERVATIONS OF PHYSICAL AND ECLIPSING VARIABLE STARS   328
    B. V. Kukarkin and P. P. Parenago

1. Introduction 328
   1.1. Definition 328
   1.2. The Importance of Variable Stars 328

2. Historical Summary 329

3. The Nomenclature of Variable Stars 332
4. Literature on Variable Stars 333
   4.1. Catalogues and Lists of Variable Stars 333
   4.2. The Number of Known Variable Stars 335
   4.3. Bibliography of Variable Stars 336

5. Classification of Variable Stars 337
   5.1. Historical 337
   5.2. General Classification 338
   5.3. Eruptive Variable Stars 339
   5.4. Pulsating Variable Stars 346
   5.5. Eclipsing Variable Stars 356

6. Statistics on Variable Stars 359
    6.1. Probability of Discovery 359
    6.2. Observed Distribution According to Type 360
    6.3. Special Surveys of Variable Stars 360
    6.4. Estimate of the Total Number of Variables in the Galactic System 364

Monographs on Variable Stars 365

References   367

19. EMPIRICAL DATA ON ECLIPSING BINARIES   370
    Frank Bradshaw Wood

1. History   370

2. Catalogues and Publications   371

3. Period and Period Changes 373

4. Tables of Eclipsing Binaries   375

References   381

20. THE CALIBRATION OF LUMINOSITY CRITERIA   383
    A. Blaauw

1. Introduction 383

2. The Spectral Types A to M 384
    2.1. The Early Mount Wilson Work 384
        2.11. The Nature of the Systematic Errors in the Early Mount
              Wilson Spectroscopic Absolute Magnitudes 387
        2.12. The Analyses of Russell and Moore 391
        2.13. The Analyses of van Rhijn and of Strömberg . . . 392
        2.14. Modern Use of the Early Mount Wilson Catalogue . . 394
    2.2. The Yerkes MK System 397
        2.21. Miss Roman's Work on the F5–K5 Stars of Luminosity
              Classes II–V 397
        2.22. Other Data for Late-Type Main-Sequence Stars . . . 400
        2.23. Osawa's Work on the Main-Sequence A-Type Stars . . 400
        2.24. Summary of Calibrations for Classes A–M, II–V . . 400
    2.3. Calibration Procedures in Some Other Modern Systems . . 400
        2.31. Oke's Work on F5–K2 Stars 402
        2.32. The Work by Hossack and Halliday on G8–K1 Stars . . 404
        2.33. The Method of Wilson and Bappu for Types G, K, and M 404
3. Types O and B and Supergiants 406
    3.1. The Fundamental Data on Absolute Magnitudes 406
        3.11. The Main-Sequence Fitting Procedure, Starting from the
              Hyades 406

      3.12 Application to h and χ Persei   409
      3.13. Direct Connection of h and χ Persei with the Scorpio-
            Centaurus Association   409
      3.14. Evaluation of Systematic Errors   411
    3.2. The MK System for the Early Types and Supergiants . . .   413
      3.21. Luminosity Classes I and II   414
      3.22. Luminosity Classes III–V   414
      3.23. Remarks to Table 3   415
    3.3. The Calibration of Hydrogen-Line Intensities for O and B Stars .   415
      3.31. The Hγ Intensities   415
      3.32. Other Hydrogen Lines   417

  References   417

21. THE ABSOLUTE MAGNITUDES OF CLASSICAL CEPHEIDS   421
      Robert P. Kraft

  1. Introduction   421

  2. The Period-Color and Period-Luminosity Relations for Cepheids in the
     Vicinity of the Sun   423
    2.1. The Period-Color Relation   423
    2.2. The Period-Luminosity Law   428

  3. Properties of the Color-Magnitude Diagram for Galactic Cepheids .   434

  4. A Comparison of Cepheids in the Small Magellanic Cloud with Those
     in the Vicinity of the Sun   437

  5. Some Anomalous Classical Cepheids of the Distant Northern Milky
     Way   442

  References   445

22. THE LUMINOSITIES OF VARIABLE STARS   448
      Cecilia Payne-Gaposchkin and Sergei Gaposchkin

  1. Introduction   448

  2. Variable Stars in Stellar Groups   450
    2.1. Luminosities Referred to Galactic Clusters   450
    2.2. Luminosities Referred to Globular Clusters   451
    2.3. Luminosities of Variable Stars in Spiral Galaxies   452
    2.4. Luminosities of Variable Stars in Irregular Galaxies   453
    2.5. Luminosities of Variable Stars in Elliptical Galaxies . . .   453
    2.6. Variable Stars in Binary Systems   453

  3. Luminosities of Intrinsic Variables   453
    3.1. Classical Cepheids   453
    3.2. The RR Lyrae Stars   455

3.3. Intrinsic Variables Associated with Cepheids 458
3.4. Intrinsic Variables Referred to RR Lyrae Stars 461
3.5. Intrinsic Variables in Binary Systems 464
3.6. Long-Period Variables 465
3.7. Beta Canis Majoris Stars 466
3.8. Delta Scuti Stars (Dwarf Cepheids) 467

References 467

APPENDIXES

I. STAR CATALOGUES AND CHARTS 471
   G. Van Biesbroeck

1. Early Star Catalogues 471

2. Survey Catalogues 471

3. Zone Catalogues 472

4. The Carte du Ciel Catalogue 474
   4.1. General Description 474
   4.2. Transformation of Co-ordinates 474

5. Fundamental Catalogues 478

6. Star Charts 479

References 479

II. THE NATIONAL GEOGRAPHIC SOCIETY–PALOMAR OBSERVATORY SKY SURVEY 481
    R. L. Minkowski and G. O. Abell

1. The Program 481

2. The Telescope 481

3. The Sky Survey 482

4. The Reproduction 484

5. The Sky Atlas 486

6. Disposition of the Plates 486

References 487

CHAPTER 1

Astronomical Reference Systems

G. M. CLEMENCE

U.S. Naval Observatory, Washington, D.C.

§ 1. INTRODUCTION

SINCE distances are not directly measured in astronomy but have to be inferred by indirect methods that are often laborious and prolix, the systems of co-ordinates in common use are those that specify only directions. The co-ordinates of any celestial object are those numbers that specify the direction of the line of sight from the observer to the object. Sometimes direction cosines are used, referring the direction of the line of sight to a system of three rectangular axes with origin at the observer. Spherical co-ordinates have, however, the advantage that they are two in number instead of three and that they can be read directly from graduated circles attached to telescopes; these are most commonly used.

All celestial objects may be imagined to be seen projected on the inside surface of a sphere, of radius greater than the distance to any of them. The position of any object is then specified by its latitudinal and longitudinal co-ordinates on the sphere, which is termed the *celestial sphere*.

For most purposes not related to the solar system, it is immaterial whether the center of the celestial sphere is considered to be at the observer, at the center of the earth, or at the center of the sun. Only a few hundred of the stars are near enough that they would have perceptibly different positions relative to the others as seen from the sun and from the earth. For definiteness, the center is taken at the observer.

Of the innumerable systems of spherical co-ordinates that may be imagined, three are of special importance. They are the equatorial system of declination and right ascension, the ecliptic system of celestial latitude and celestial longitude (sometimes called *ecliptic latitude* and *ecliptic longitude*, to avoid confusion with other latitudes and longitudes), and the galactic system of galactic latitude and galactic longitude. The fundamental planes of the three systems are the plane of the earth's equator, the plane of the ecliptic, and the

1

plane of the Galaxy. These three planes intersect the celestial sphere in three great circles—the equator, the ecliptic, and the galactic equator—from which the three latitudinal co-ordinates are measured. The ecliptic approximates the path that the sun traces on the celestial sphere, and the plane of the Galaxy approximates the Milky Way. In all three systems the north pole is the one that would be visible to an observer located at the North Pole of the earth. Right ascension and ecliptic longitude are measured from a common origin, which is the intersection of the equator and the ecliptic that the sun appears to reach in March; it is called the *vernal equinox* or simply the *equinox*. Right ascensions and ecliptic longitudes are reckoned through the entire circumference in the eastward direction, which is the direction of the sun's apparent motion against the background of stars; right ascensions are commonly expressed in time instead of arc, 1 hour being precisely equal to 15°. Galactic longitude was formerly (before 1958) measured in the direction of increasing right ascension, from the intersection of the celestial equator and the galactic equator (the galactic pole being taken by definition to be in right ascension 12^h40^m, declination $+28°$), but now from an origin more nearly in the direction of the galactic center, near right ascension 17^h40^m, declination $-29°$.

§ 2. EQUATORIAL CO-ORDINATES

The equatorial system owes its importance to the high precision with which the declination of an object and the difference between the right ascensions of two objects can be measured, by means of the simplest geometrical principles and without recourse to any theory. Imagine a graduated circle to be mounted with its plane in the plane of the observer's meridian, with a fixed index against which the graduations may be read as the circle is rotated in its own plane. Also imagine a telescope rigidly attached to the circle so that the line of sight sweeps out the meridian as the circle is rotated. Now if a close circumpolar star is observed at upper and lower culminations on the same night, the mean of the two circle readings is the reading corresponding to declination 90°. The declination of any star as it transits the meridian may then be determined by reading the circle. To measure differences of right ascension, a clock is provided, so regulated as to measure 24 hours between meridian transits of the same star. The difference between the right ascensions of two stars is then simply the difference between the clock times of meridian transit. The origin of right ascensions may be fixed by imposing the condition that when the declination of the sun is observed to be zero in March, its right ascension is also zero. Of course, the actual procedure is very much more refined than that described, but the basic principles are not altered.

With such an instrument, called a *transit circle* (see Vol. 1), it is possible to measure declinations and differences of right ascension with a precision of about $0''.1$ for a single observation. If the same stars are observed on successive nights, it will be found that their declinations and right ascensions are changing in a systematic fashion by amounts that are often perceptible in a single day. The greater part of the change is caused not by the motions of the stars but by the motions of the equator and equinox. To make allowance for them, it is necessary to have recourse to gravitational theory. The rapidly changing declinations and right ascensions that are immediately observed are named *apparent co-ordinates*.

§ 3. PRECESSION AND NUTATION

3.1. DEFINITION

The gravitational couples between the moon and the earth and between the sun and the earth affect the earth's motion of translation and, because the earth differs from a concentrically homogeneous spherical body, also affect the orientation in space of the earth's axis of rotation. The latter effect is, for convenience, separated into two parts: *luni-solar precession* and *nutation*. The luni-solar precession may be roughly described as a progressive, nearly circular, counterclockwise motion of the north pole of the equator around the north pole of the ecliptic, with radius about 23° and period about 26,000 years. It causes the equinox to move westward along the ecliptic about 50″ per year. The nutation may be thought of as a smaller, irregular motion superimposed on the precession, moving the equinox ahead or behind its mean position as much as 17″, with a principal period of 18.6 years.

The gravitational couples between the center of mass of the earth and the other planets produce a progressive motion of the pole of the ecliptic, named the *planetary precession*, the effect of which is to move the equinox eastward about 0″.11 per year and to diminish the angle between the ecliptic and the equator (about 23°) by 0″.47 per year. These couples, as well as the lunar couple, also produce small irregular motions analogous to the nutation, which, however, are conventionally not attributed to the ecliptic but are called *perturbations of the sun's latitude;* they never exceed 1″. The ecliptic then, speaking precisely, is a mathematical fiction, corresponding not to the actual plane of the earth's orbit but to one with the minor irregularities of the actual motion smoothed out. No lack of rigor is thus introduced. What is wanted in the end is the positions of the sun and stars in a non-rotating frame of reference; the notion of the ecliptic is introduced merely to facilitate the calculations. The ecliptic system of co-ordinates has, then, no simple and exact geometrical or dynamical significance; it is simply a computational convenience.

The sum of the luni-solar precession and the planetary precession is named the *general precession*. In consequence of the way the ecliptic is defined, the general precession causes the ecliptic longitudes of all celestial objects to increase at the same speed and has no effect on ecliptic latitudes. Nutation may be conveniently divided into two components, one of which—the nutation in longitude—affects the ecliptic longitudes of all objects equally without affecting the ecliptic latitudes, while the other—the nutation in obliquity (of the ecliptic)—

likewise does not affect latitudes but changes declinations and right ascensions in addition to the changes caused by the nutation in longitude.

The conventionally adopted value of the general precession per tropical century in longitude is (Newcomb 1905)

$$p = 5025\overset{\prime\prime}{.}64 + 2\overset{\prime\prime}{.}22\ T\ ,$$

where T is reckoned in tropical centuries from 1900.0. The notation 1900.0 is the conventional way of indicating the beginning of the tropical year 1900. The beginning of any tropical year, defined as the instant when the sun's mean longitude is 280°, during the twentieth century occurs on December 31 or January 1. A tabulation is given by Newcomb (1906, p. 403), to which 0.5 day must be added to obtain Universal Time. The tropical year is used for convenience in precessional calculations on account of the irregular length of the calendar year. The general precession per tropical century in right ascension is, for a star at the equinox,

$$m = 4608\overset{\prime\prime}{.}50 + 2\overset{\prime\prime}{.}79\ T\ ,$$

and, in declination,

$$n = 2004\overset{\prime\prime}{.}68 - 0\overset{\prime\prime}{.}85\ T\ .$$

For any star at right ascension a and declination δ,

$$\frac{da}{dT} = m + n\ \sin a\ \tan \delta\ ,$$

$$\frac{d\delta}{dT} = n\ \cos a\ ,$$

from which, by integration, the right ascension and declination of a star may be reduced from any epoch to any other, so far as precession is concerned. The validity of the reduction diminishes with the time before or after 1900 but is amply accurate for several centuries. Over much longer periods of time and for stars very near the pole, more rigorous methods must be employed (Newcomb 1906). Tables to facilitate these reductions will be found in any of the principal national ephemerides.

The theory of the nutation (Woolard 1953) gives rise to periodic terms with coefficients as great as $0\overset{\prime\prime}{.}0002$ having 69 different arguments and periods varying from 5.5 days to 18.6 years. The sums in longitude and obliquity are tabulated for every day in the national ephemerides.

3.2. Dynamical Theory of Precession and Nutation

The elements of the orbits of the planets being known at some fundamental epoch (as 1850.0) from observations, the planetary theory (Newcomb 1895) gives the speed of rotation of the ecliptic about an axis in its own instantaneous plane and the ecliptic longitude of that axis as power series in the time. Those series may be resolved into rotations about the line of equinoxes and a second axis 90° from them. The first rotation, denoted $\kappa \cos L$, is then the rate of change of the obliquity of the ecliptic, and the second one, $\kappa \sin L$, is identical with $\lambda \sin \theta$, where λ is the rate of the planetary precession and θ is the instantaneous value of the obliquity, which must be determined at the fundamental epoch by observation. Then (de Sitter 1938), if we use the symbols p, m, and n as earlier in this chapter and put p_0 for the luni-solar precession and p_g for the so-called geodesic precession, which is a small, relativistic, direct motion of the equinox along the ecliptic amounting to $1''915$ per century, the various precessional quantities satisfy the following relations:

$$m = p_1 \cos \theta - \lambda, \qquad\qquad p = p_1 - \lambda \cos \theta,$$

$$n = p_1 \sin \theta, \qquad\qquad P = p_0 \sec \theta ,$$

$$p_0 = p_1 + p_g ,$$

where P is very nearly an absolute constant, diminishing only $0''004$ per century; it is called the *constant of precession*.

If we denote by N the principal coefficient in the expression for the nutation in obliquity, it is connected with P by the relations

$$P = (A + B\mu')H, \qquad N = C\mu'H \cos \theta, \qquad \mu' = \frac{\mu}{1+\mu},$$

where μ is the ratio of the mass of the moon to that of the earth, H is the mechanical ellipticity of the earth, and A, B, and C are known functions of the elements of the orbits of the earth and moon.

The values of A, B, C, and θ are known with high precision. If H and μ were known with equal precision, then the precession could be calculated without recourse to astronomical observations. The same would not be true for the nutation, since Jeffreys (1948–1957; Jeffreys and Vicente 1957) has shown that the relation given here is not exact, owing to the deformation of the earth under the action of the moon. In fact, the values of H and μ are not known with sufficiently high precision, and the formula is therefore not used for the derivation of P; instead, it serves as an equation of condition between μ and H, once P is known.

3.3. DETERMINATION OF THE SPEED OF THE PRECESSION

The determination of P with high precision is at once one of the most important and one of the most difficult tasks connected with stellar astronomy. It is equivalent to determining the absolute speed of rotation of the frame of reference, that is, to determining an invariable direction in space; but that is not what makes it interesting to astronomers. The determination of P is of practical importance because the precession for any star must be subtracted from the star's observed motion, in order to get the proper motion; for any star the proper motion μ_a in right ascension and μ_δ in declination are defined by the equations

$$\mu_a = \frac{da}{dT} - (m + n \sin a \tan \delta), \qquad \mu_\delta = \frac{d\delta}{dT} - n \cos a ,$$

the derivatives da/dT and $d\delta/dT$ being the observed motions relative to the moving co-ordinate system.

Evidently any error in the assumed value of P is carried over into m and n, and thus into μ_a and μ_δ. If the error is large enough that its effect predominates over the motions of the stars themselves, then it can be determined by analysis of the proper motions of a sufficient number of stars well distributed over the sky. This method of determining the precession has been the one most used in the past. It is, however, open to several objections. It has to be assumed that the stars themselves have no systematic component of intrinsic motion parallel to the ecliptic, an assumption that seems permissible. More drastically, it is assumed, at least in the methods of analysis so far used, that the proper motions of the stars have a Gaussian distribution, so that analysis by least squares is valid. The proper motions do not, in fact, have a Gaussian distribution, and the results depend to an appreciable extent on how the stars are selected and on the inclusion or exclusion of a few stars having large motions. It is found, furthermore, that the values of m and of n determined by the analysis are not reconcilable with each other. For further discussion of these questions and others related to the subject see Newcomb (1895), Wilson and Raymond (1938), van de Kamp and Vyssotsky (1936), and Morgan and Oort (1951).

In any case the individual motions of the stars set a limit (van de Kamp 1939) on the precision with which the precession can be determined by the method just described. It appears that the limit is about $0\overset{''}{.}1$ per century and that it has been nearly reached, if not quite.

Another method of determining the precession, which may be called the *dynamical method*, depends on motions within the solar system. The ecliptic longitudes of the nodes and perihelia of the planets are determined by observation, referred to the moving equinox, at different epochs. The planetary theory gives the portions of the motions that are not due to precession; whence the difference between the observed and computed motions is the precession. This method is free from the objections to which the older one is subject, but it has not yet been applied with a high degree of completeness, because of the great amount of calculation required. It has lately been revived by Clemence (1949) and Brouwer (1950). The results, as far as they go, agree with those of the classical method in indicating that Newcomb's value of p, given earlier in this chapter, requires a correction of $+0\overset{''}{.}8$.

A third method of determining the precession depends on the frame of reference constituted by the extragalactic nebulae (Wright 1950). It is now (1961) being applied both at the Lick Observatory and in the U.S.S.R., using somewhat different observational procedures; results cannot be expected for at least a decade or two.

§ 4. ABERRATION

Besides precession and nutation, there is another local effect producing changes in declinations and right ascensions that is called *aberration*. The principle of aberration may be stated as follows: two neighboring observers in relative motion will see the same object in different directions, the angular difference being the ratio of their relative velocity to the velocity of light (at least to the first order), multiplied by the sine of the angle between the line of sight to the object and the observer's relative velocity vector and in the direction of the velocity vector. Thus an observer will see a star in the ecliptic displaced 20″.47 eastward when it is opposite the sun, as compared with its direction 3 months earlier or later, when the earth is moving away from or toward the star. Similar displacements, amounting at most to 0″.008, are produced by the earth's velocity around the center of mass of the earth and moon and, also amounting to 0″.008, by the earth's velocity around the center of mass of the earth and Jupiter. Meridian observations must be freed from these effects before being combined with one another. The corrections are facilitated by tables of the earth's velocity components published in the national ephemerides, together with formulae for easy application.

It is worthy of note that, by convention, the corrections for aberration omit the annual variation of the earth's velocity that is due to the eccentricity of the orbit. The error thus committed amounts to 0″.3 at most, and, depending on the longitude of the earth's perihelion, it is very nearly constant for a particular star throughout several centuries, changing by about 2 per cent of its amount in a century. Thus the proper motions are not sensibly affected. The convention was adopted to facilitate calculation in a day when calculations were much more arduous than they are now; it is still advisable to perpetuate it, so that current star catalogues will be comparable with earlier ones.

It is also worth noting that no allowance is made for the real motion of a star during the time required for light to travel from it to the observer. The making of such corrections would serve no practical purpose and would merely complicate the work of the astronomer.

§ 5. REDUCTION FROM APPARENT TO MEAN PLACE

The declinations and right ascensions of stars that are immediately observed are named *apparent declinations* and *apparent right ascensions*, or simply *apparent places*. If the effects of aberration (conventionally limited as already described) are removed from apparent places, the co-ordinates are then said to be referred to the true equator and equinox. If those are further corrected by removing the effect of nutation, the co-ordinates, are by definition, referred to the mean equator and equinox of date. If still further corrected for precession from a specified epoch—as 1950.0, for example—the co-ordinates are referred to the mean equator and equinox 1950.0; for brevity, they may be indicated simply as Dec. and R.A. (1950.0).

In practice, the reductions for aberration, nutation, and precession to the nearest beginning of a tropical year are combined in a single short calculation for every observation of every star, the reduction to a standard equator and equinox being made separately over an integral number of years. A good reason for the procedure is that the proper motion of a star, though it may be and often is sensible in a fraction of a year, is never so large that it has to be taken into account in rotating the frame of reference over a few years. During 10 or 20 years, the effect of proper motion may, however, be large enough that it must be allowed for in calculating the precession; for this reason, observational star catalogues are referred to some equator and equinox not many years removed from their mean epoch. Also, for a similar reason, a distinction is made between the *equinox* of a stellar catalogue position, which is always the beginning of a tropical year, and its *epoch*, which is usually given as a year and decimal and is the mean of the actual times of observation. Stellar positions are given in this form when the proper motions are not known, as in the case of observational catalogues. In such cases, further reductions for precession must be made from the stated *equinox* and reductions for proper motions from the stated *epoch*.

§ 6. THE GALACTIC SYSTEM OF CO-ORDINATES

Although galactic co-ordinates have been in use for well over a century, no single system was in general use before about 1932, when Ohlsson's (1932) conversion tables were published. In that system the galactic north pole was at declination $+28°$, right ascension $12^h 40^m$, equator and equinox 1900.0, and the origin of galactic longitude was the ascending node of the galactic equator on the celestial equator (1900.0), near right ascension 18^h.

In 1958 at the General Assembly of the International Astronomical Union it was decided to adopt a new standard system of galactic co-ordinates, basing the pole primarily on the distribution of neutral hydrogen in the inner parts of the Galaxy and taking the origin of longitude near the galactic center. The precise specification of the new system (Blaauw *et al.* 1960) puts the north galactic pole in declination $+27°.4$, right ascension $12^h 49^m$, equator and equinox 1950.0, and the origin of galactic longitude at position angle $123°$ with respect to the pole of the equator 1950.0. Thus, denoting galactic longitude in the old system by l^I and in the new system by l^{II}, there exists the approximate relation $l^{II} = l^I + 32°.31$.

The galactic system of co-ordinates, unlike the equatorial and ecliptic systems, is thus related to intragalactic dynamics, but it is precisely defined in terms of the equatorial system, making it possible to transform equatorial co-ordinates to galactic co-ordinates with entire precision, so long—and only so long—as Newcomb's numerical value of the precession continues to be used in reducing the equatorial co-ordinates of stars from the epoch of observation to 1950.0. Otherwise an ambiguity will be created, which might have been avoided by specifying the galactic system of co-ordinates in terms of the mean equator and equinox of date. However, such a specification, involving power series in the time, would have resulted in intolerably laborious transformations and is not worthwhile from a purely practical point of view.

§ 7. GALACTIC ROTATION

The stars in the Galaxy (at least some thousands of them in our own neighborhood) are known (Oort 1927*a, b, c,* 1928) to be moving in orbits not greatly inclined to the galactic equator. The stars between us and the galactic center are moving faster than those that are more distant. The observed motions are consistent with the supposition that the principal force governing them is gravitation, with the center of mass near the galactic center. The period of rotation is, at the sun, about 2×10^6 centuries.

Whether the plane of the Galaxy, considered as the plane of maximum orbital momentum, and whether the invariable plane of the solar system, defined in a similar way, are rotating as the equator and ecliptic are, is not known. The motions, if they exist, are too slow to have been observed.

§ 8. POLAR MOTION

The polar motion plays no part in stellar astronomy as such. It is entirely without influence on all classes of astronomical observations excepting those involving reference to the direction of the vertical, which are predominantly those in which astronomical latitudes and longitudes play a role, such as the determination of Universal Time.

The axis of rotation of the earth is not fixed in the solid earth. The two points where it intersects the surface of the earth move about on the surface in a roughly circular fashion, with varying amplitude and phase and a period approximating 14 months. During the period while the motion has been observed, about two centuries, the movements have been confined to an area about 100 feet square. The motion is best regarded as a motion of the body of the earth about the axis of rotation and not as a motion of the axis of rotation in space. For a discussion of the dynamics of the process see Jeffreys (1959). The motion is not predictable but must be inferred from observed changes in the latitudes and longitudes of places on the earth.

REFERENCES

BLAAUW, A., GUM, C. S., PAWSEY, J. L., and WESTERHOUT, G.	1960	*M.N.,* **121**, 123.
BROUWER, D.	1950	*Bull. Astr.,* **15**, 3.
CLEMENCE, G. M.	1949	*Proc. Amer. Phil. Soc.,* **93**, 532.
JEFFREYS, H.	1948	*M.N.,* **108**, 206.
	1949	*Ibid.,* **109**, 670.
	1950	*Ibid.,* **110**, 460.
	1959	*The Earth* (4th ed.; Cambridge: Cambridge University Press).
JEFFREYS, H., and VICENTE, R. O.	1957	*M.N.,* **117**, 142, 162.

KAMP, P. VAN DE	1939	*A.J.*, **48**, 21.
KAMP, P. VAN DE, and		
VYSSOTSKY, A. N.	1936	*A.J.*, **45**, 161.
MORGAN, H. R., and		
OORT, J. H.	1951	*B.A.N.*, **11**, 379.
NEWCOMB, S.	1895	*Astr. Papers Amer. Ephem.*, Vol. **5**, Part 4.
	1905	*Ibid.*, Vol. **8**, Part 1.
	1906	*A Compendium of Spherical Astronomy* (reprinted by Dover Publications, 1960).
OHLSSON, J.	1932	*Ann. Lund Obs.*, No. 3.
OORT, J. H.	1927a	*B.A.N.*, **3**, 275.
	1927b	*Ibid.*, **4**, 79.
	1927c	*Ibid.*, p. 91.
	1928	*Ibid.*, p. 269.
SITTER, W. DE	1938	*B.A.N.*, **8**, 213 (edited and completed by D. BROUWER).
WILSON, R. E., and		
RAYMOND, H.	1938	*A.J.*, **47**, 49, 132.
	1939	*Ibid.*, **48**, 86.
WOOLARD, E. W.	1953	*Astr. Papers Amer. Ephem.*, Vol. **15**, Part 1.
WRIGHT, W. H.	1950	*Proc. Amer. Phil. Soc.*, **94**, 1.

CHAPTER 2

The System of Fundamental
Proper Motions

F. P. SCOTT

U.S. Naval Observatory, Washington, D.C.

§ 1. INTRODUCTION

A FUNDAMENTAL proper motion is the time rate of change of a star's position with respect to a fundamental reference system. It is a composite of all the angular displacements caused by the star's own motion and the motion of the solar system that are capable of changing the direction in which the star is seen on the celestial sphere. Such characteristics make proper motions invaluable for a number of basic astrometric researches. They have made important contributions to the determination of the solar motion and the peculiar motions of stars and stellar systems, the derivation of statistical parallaxes, the calibration of the cosmic scale of distance, and, more recently, the search for expanding associations. It is through them that the kinematic and physical properties of stars may eventually be related, to provide a better understanding of the evolutionary processes in our Galaxy.

Strictly speaking, fundamental proper motions are found only in fundamental star catalogues. They are an integral part of such volumes and were derived so as to be compatible with the catalogue positions and the adopted value of the constant of precession. These three elements—positions, proper motions, and constant of precession—define the fundamental co-ordinate system at its initial epoch and with respect to its initial equinox, and they preserve its characteristics as it is projected to other epochs and referred to other equinoxes.

In a broader sense, however, it is customary to regard any proper motion as fundamental if, directly or indirectly, it has been computed from displacements of the position of a star measured with respect to the fundamental co-ordinate system. In any event, the outcome of any research based on proper motions will be directly related to their quality and homogeneity in our fundamental star

11

catalogues. The precision of these proper motions and their freedom from systematic errors fix the degree of confidence that may be attached to the results of any investigation in which they are used. In a large measure, any improvement that may be hoped for in these investigations will have to come through an improvement in our fundamental star catalogues, which, in turn, will depend on the quality of the catalogues produced by positional astronomers.

§ 2. THE BASIS OF THE CELESTIAL CO-ORDINATE SYSTEM

From a theoretical approach, any set of celestial objects for which the laws of motion are known could serve as a co-ordinate system for investigating the events, motions, and phenomena of space. The configuration of the bodies at some instant could be taken as the initial co-ordinate system. The laws of motion would then prescribe exactly how the co-ordinates represented by each object should be changed with time as the bodies take up new positions with respect to the reference axes.

Among the objects upon which a co-ordinate system might be based are distant galaxies, stars, and members of the solar system. Initially, of course, the motions of these objects are unknown. The establishment of a co-ordinate system based on any of them requires that their motions be derived in the process.

Inasmuch as the historical approach to a celestial co-ordinate system was made from the direction of the practical applications of astronomy, galaxies and faint stars were removed from consideration quite early. Their extreme faintness put them far beyond the reach of the telescopes commonly used by practicing astronomers, geodesists, and time services.

No one of the remaining classes of objects, by itself, was regarded as constituting a suitable reference system for all types of astronomical work. Although members of the solar system could have provided a reference system based rigidly on the laws of dynamics, the result would have been objectionable to all those who needed to have reference objects in view at all hours of the day and from all parts of the earth. To the practicing astronomer, bright stars were the ideal objects on which to base an astronomical co-ordinate system. These objects however, required the existence of a set of reference axes for the study of their motions prior to their use as a co-ordinate system.

In the course of its development, the problem of the astronomical co-ordinate system was resolved by combining the best features of the systems offered by bright stars and members of the solar system. From the former came the requisite number of reference objects and from the latter the means for establishing the all-important reference frame by dynamical methods. This solution of the problem, however, has made it imperative that the positions of members of the solar system be determined in the same manner as those of the stars during every program directed at the improvement of the fundamental co-ordinate system. Afterward an analysis of the differences between the observed positions of the sun and planets and those computed from their laws of motion provides the adjustment that is needed by the observed positions of all other objects to bring them into conformity with the equinox and equator demanded by dynamical theory (Brouwer 1941; Morgan 1941).

The construction of the astronomical co-ordinate system began with a series of approximations that have not yet ended. First, the sun and planets were observed among the "fixed" stars. From these observations came the first approximation of a representation of the motions of the solar system by the laws of dynamics, an estimate of the precession, and preliminary positions of the stars. Successive repetitions of the observational series have led to a continuous improvement in our knowledge of the motions in the solar system and to an ever increasing series of positions of the principal stars. From the latter has gradually evolved whatever knowledge we now possess of the motions of the stars with respect to a fundamental frame of reference (Newcomb 1906, chap. xii ff.; Kopff 1936; Morgan 1937, 1943, 1946; Fricke 1957; Böhme 1960).

§ 3. CATALOGUES OF OBSERVED POSITIONS OF THE STARS

The results of the observational series which eventually decide the nature of the celestial co-ordinate system are usually exhibited in the form of catalogues of observed positions. The vast majority of these catalogues has been based on meridian circle observations, only a few having been derived from other types of telescopes, such as the vertical circle, the altazimuth, the transit, and the azimuth instrument.

In conducting fundamental observations with a meridian circle the procedures are made to conform, as nearly as possible, with the principles laid down for such work in chapter 1. For the measurement of declinations, the pole point is located, the atmospheric refraction accounted for even to the determination of a local constant of refraction, calibrations carried out for the divided circle, and the yielding of the instrument to the force of gravity accounted for as far as facilities for the determination of the flexure will permit. For the establishment of right ascensions, the most modern clocks are used, the irregularities of the pivots measured, the orientation of the instruments frequently checked by application of laboratory and astronomical methods, and the observations so arranged and discussed that residual errors in the provisional right ascensions are minimized in the determination of the clock correction and the azimuth of the instrument.

The resulting positions of the objects are usually quite independent of the provisional positions adopted at the beginning of the program. The independence of the declinations stems from the fact that the provisional positions never enter the process at any step. The degree of independence of the right ascension determinations depends on how well the effects of systematic and random errors in the provisional positions of the stars have been eliminated from the clock corrections and the azimuth of the instrument (Scott 1957).

Although the observed declinations are independent of the provisional positions, they may be affected by systematic errors which show trends with declination, zenith distance, or even right ascension. Some of the systematic trends may have arisen from application of an erroneous correction for the flexure, faulty refractions, unknown seasonal variations in these quantities, or even discontinuities in the behavior of the instrument.

As with the declinations, the observed right ascensions may also include systematic trends, some of which may have arisen from inadequate corrections for the irregularities of the pivots, from shifts in the collimation axis as the instrument swept out the meridian, or even from the circumstance that instrumental constants as determined may not necessarily apply to the observations. A few studies of possible causes of systematic errors in meridian-circle work are listed in the references (van Herk 1952; Gething 1954; Scott 1955; van Herk and van Woerkom 1961), the last being the most comprehensive.

TABLE 1

PROBABLE ERROR OF A SINGLE FUNDAMENTAL OBSERVATION

U.S. NAVAL OBS. TRANSIT CIRCLE	EPOCH	PROB. ERROR		TYPE OF R.A. MICROMETER	CIRCLES	No. OF DECL. BISECTIONS
		R.A.	Decl.			
6-Inch........	1930	±0″25	±0″34	Hand drive	Visual	2 Usually
6-Inch........	1935	.19	.31	Motor drive	Mixed	2 Usually
6-Inch........	1945	.19	.30	Motor drive	Photo.	2 Usually
9-Inch........	1920	.28	.27	Key	Visual	2–4
9-Inch........	1940	.22	.28	Motor drive	Visual	2–4
7-Inch........	1960	(0.19)	(0.22)	Motor drive	Photo.	4 Usually

Among the characteristics of a fundamentally observed catalogue which may be evaluated are its internal probable errors and its apparent freedom from systematic errors as exhibited by comparisons with contemporary catalogues. Table 1 lists a few estimates of the probable error of a single observation obtained from fundamental observations made between $+30°$ and $-15°$ declination with three transit circles at the U.S. Naval Observatory. The results for the 7-inch transit circle are preliminary, having been based on only a few nights' work.

It is of interest to note the improvement in right ascension observations that resulted from the introduction of the motor-driven, traveling-thread micrometer. It may also be noted that the moving co-ordinate—right ascension—appears always to have been determined with greater precision than the stationary co-ordinate. This is because the greater part of the night error is removed from the right ascensions through the application of the clock correction, whereas, in fundamental work, no adjustment of this form is applied to the declination observations.

In Figure 1 are shown curves of the systematic differences, $15\Delta\alpha \cos \delta$ and

$\Delta\delta$, between each of three U.S. Naval Observatory fundamentally observed catalogues and the *FK3, Dritter Fundamental-Katalog des Berliner astronomischen Jahrbuchs* (Kopff 1934). A striking feature of these curves is their spread in some parts of the sky, indicating the presence of systematic differences of the order of 0″.10 or 0″.15, even at convenient zenith distances. It is this type of error in an observed catalogue and not its internal accuracy that will eventually determine the systematic character of the fundamental reference system.

The agreement of both sets of curves near the pole is a consequence of combining observations made at both culminations and, to a further extent, in the declination-curves by the forcing exerted on the observations in the solution for the pole point. The lack of complete agreement of the declination-curves near the equator cannot be ascribed to a drift of the *FK3* equator. It is presumably due to the difficulty in deriving the day-minus-night corrections that are needed

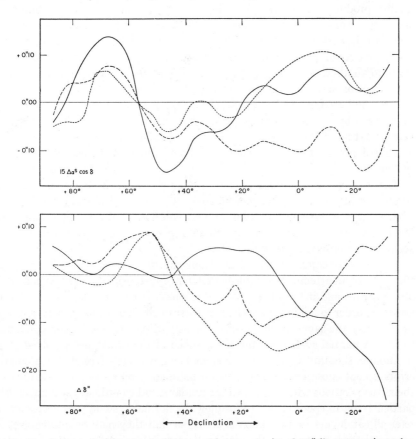

Fig. 1.—Systematic differences in $15\Delta\alpha^s$ cos δ (*upper curves*) and $\Delta\delta''$ (*lower curves*) varying with declination, for the Washington catalogues minus *FK3*. Nine-inch transit circle, 1942 (————); 6-inch transit circle, 1939 (– – – – –); 6-inch transit circle, 1945 (·--------·).

to reduce the sun and day planet observations to the system of the night stars. The average value of a deficiency in this reduction in declination becomes interpreted in the solution of observations of these objects as a correction to the instrumental declinations. Perhaps the spread in the declination-curves near the equator is a measure of the precision of the sun and planet solutions for $\Delta\delta_0$.

The systematic behavior of the instruments just described is typical of what may be expected of modern transit circles. The point to be emphasized is that results from modern instruments are subject to systematic errors, which may influence the proper motions in a compiled fundamental star catalogue.

§ 4. COMPILED FUNDAMENTAL STAR CATALOGUES

At intervals of a few decades, fundamentally observed star catalogues of high quality produced during the preceding half-century or more are combined for the purpose of compiling a fundamental catalogue of precision. The methods used in this work are complex and exacting. Although designed to accomplish the same over-all purpose, they vary considerably from one fundamental catalogue to another, depending on the observational data available and the views of the author on the problem of constructing a fundamental reference system. The method used in compiling a particular fundamental catalogue will be best understood by referring to the explanatory remarks in the catalogue itself. The general nature of the problem may be readily obtained from the description of a method proposed by Brouwer (1960) for revising an existing fundamental system.

The task facing an investigator in forming a fundamental system is that of combining the available observational data so that they will yield the best possible, error-free system of positions and proper motions. In principle, the problem is solved when a straight line of the form $p = p_0 + \mu t$ has been fitted to the accumulated observations of each star.

Each fundamentally observed catalogue entering the discussion is, by itself, the result of an attempt to establish a reference system at the mean epoch of its observations, and it would be regarded as one if it were not for its systematic errors. In order to minimize the effect of these errors, catalogues observed at approximately the same epoch on different instruments are sometimes combined to form a normal system for the mean epoch of the catalogues involved. The positions of the stars in the normal system, being relatively free of all systematic errors except those characteristic of all meridian circles, may be regarded as their true positions with respect to the fundamental co-ordinate system at that particular mean epoch. Prior to forming the normal system, it is necessary to refer all catalogues to a common equinox, so that they may be intercompared for the purpose of deriving the systematic corrections and the weights needed to combine them into a normal system.

If two or more such normal systems can be formed, the constant term in the equation of the straight line fitted to the normal positions of each star is its position at the mean epoch of the normals, and the slope of the line is its proper motion. The proper motion derived in this manner is the residue of the star's time rate of change of position that was not accounted for by the applications of precession in reducing all catalogues to a common equinox.

A catalogue of positions and proper motions obtained in this manner is the best representation of a fundamental reference system that may be had from the data discussed. It should be remarked that the process just described has been very greatly simplified for the sake of illustrating the principle involved.

The three compiled star catalogues now in use—the *FK3, Dritter Fundamental-Katalog des Berliner astronomischen Jahrbuchs* (Kopff 1934); the *GC, General Catalogue of 33,342 Stars for the Epoch 1950* (Boss 1937); and the *N30, Catalog of 5,268 Standard Stars, 1950.0* (Morgan 1952)—were designed for quite different purposes and according to somewhat different concepts. Two of them—the *FK3* and *GC*—are said to be fundamental in character according to classical standards. Both are third-generation members of their respective series, and both represent revisions and enlargements of their immediate predecessors.

These catalogues differ in two respects, viz., the method by which their equators were fixed and the number of stars contained in them. The equator of the *FK3* is based on observations of the sun and planets according to the dynamical method mentioned earlier, whereas that of the *GC* was established according to an entirely different, but perhaps equally sound, method. It was the opinion of its authors that the uncertainties in the sun and day planet observations were so high that they would vitiate any result based on them. Therefore, in establishing the declination system of the *GC*, they chose instead a method which consisted of combining observations made in the Northern and Southern hemispheres wherein the refraction was the only unknown to be considered. The method is based on the principle that the combined polar distances of a star observed in both hemispheres should be 180° if properly corrected for the refraction.

It has been the policy of the authors of the *FK* series of catalogues, in striving to attain fundamental star catalogues of the highest precision, to restrict the number of stars to those having the most favorable observational histories. Thus the *NFK*, the predecessor of the *FK3*, contained 925 stars; this number was increased to 1535 for the *FK3* and for the *FK4*, the successor to the *FK3*, soon to be released.

The authors of the *GC* were guided by the needs of stellar astronomers in establishing the size of their catalogue. This work, containing 33,342 stars, is said to be complete to 7.0 mag. and includes thousands of fainter stars for which there was promise that a fairly reliable proper motion could be obtained. The inclusion of so many stars has made the work somewhat heterogeneous from the standpoint of internal accuracy and from the standpoint of the rigor with which stars of all magnitude classes are related to the basic system.

The *N30* catalogue is the result of a completely independent attack on the problem of establishing a consistent set of positions and proper motions of recent epoch. To make the outcome as free as possible of the systematic errors of the old observations, the proper motions were derived by comparing the *GC* positions at their mean epochs, after correction for some well-recognized systematic errors, with a new normal position at about 1930 based on independent observational catalogues accumulated between 1917 and 1950.

This process has been criticized (Kopff 1954) as not being fundamental on two counts—first, because of the neglect of the weight of the *GC* proper mo-

TABLE 2

MEAN ERRORS OF THE *FK3*

	POSITIONS				CENTENNIAL PROPER MOTIONS	
DECL.	Mean Epoch		1959			
	R.A.	Decl.	R.A.	Decl.	15Δμ cos δ	Δμ'
+75°......	±0ˢ008	±0″03	±0ˢ026	±0″11	±0″16	±0″17
+65......	.005	.04	.018	.11	.19	.18
+55......	.004	.04	.013	.11	.19	.17
+45......	.004	.04	.011	.11	.21	.18
+35......	.003	.04	.011	.12	.24	.21
+25......	.003	.04	.008	.11	.19	.18
+15......	.002	.04	.008	.11	.20	.18
+ 5......	.002	.04	.008	.12	.21	.20
− 5......	.002	.04	.009	.12	.25	.23
−15......	.003	.04	.010	.14	.28	.27
−25......	.004	.05	.013	.17	.31	.31
−35......	.005	.06	.018	.21	.40	.37
−45......	.007	.07	.024	.24	.47	.42
−55......	.008	.07	.028	.23	.44	.40
−65......	.011	.07	.037	.22	.40	.38
−75......	0.016	0.06	0.060	0.22	0.40	0.39

tions and, second, because the revision of the *GC* was insufficiently carried out. No question has been raised as to correctness of the *N30* positions at their mean epochs.

The useful life of a fundamental star catalogue seldom exceeds 25 years. By that time the positions at epoch have become so contaminated by accumulated errors of the proper motions that they are useless for the most precise applications. This is the present condition of the *GC* and *FK3* and is the reason for the revision of the *FK3* now in progress.

The simplest characteristics to examine in passing judgment on compiled fundamental star catalogues are their internal accuracies and their apparent freedom from systematic errors. Table 2 lists the mean errors of the positions of the *FK3* at their mean epochs and at 1959, as well as the mean errors of its proper motions. Table 3 shows the distribution of the probable errors of the *GC* proper motions with declination for four different magnitude groups of stars, and Table 4 shows the distribution of the weights in $N30$ according to the same arguments. Table 5 has been added as a means for making an approximate transfer from the $N30$ weighting system to probable errors. It might be noted here that Barney (1949) is of the opinion that the stated probable errors of the GC proper motions are too low by at least 15–20 per cent of their amount. The most noticeable feature of Tables 2, 3, and 4 is the marked drop in the precision of the positions and motions south of $-30°$ declination. It will also be noted that the positions of the bright stars, upon which the system of each of the catalogues is primarily based, are by far the best determined of all.

Curves such as those in Figure 2 and analytical expressions such as those in

TABLE 3

PROBABLE ERRORS OF THE *GC* CENTENNIAL PROPER MOTIONS

DECL.	$m<5.5$		$5.5<m\leq6.5$		$6.5<m\leq7.5$		$7.5<m$	
	R.A.	Decl.	R.A.	Decl.	R.A.	Decl.	R.A.	Decl.
+82°5........	0″09	0″08	0″28	0″24	0″38	0″39	0″60	0″64
+67.5........	.23	.19	.35	.35	.63	.65	0.68	.72
+52.5........	.19	.15	.41	.34	.75	.64	0.74	.59
+37.5........	.21	.20	.48	.40	.72	.60	0.70	.54
+22.5........	.17	.15	.41	.36	.65	.59	0.65	.56
+ 7.5........	.18	.18	.47	.41	.69	.60	0.69	.56
− 7.5........	.22	.19	.50	.45	.69	.63	0.67	.57
−22.5........	.22	.21	.53	.50	.79	.72	0.89	.79
−37.5........	.39	.30	.64	.53	.86	.73	1.05	.95
−52.5........	.42	.33	.66	.51	.88	.70	1.04	.87
−67.5........	.37	.32	.64	.52	.80	.67	0.91	.81
−82.5........	0.30	0.26	0.46	0.39	0.71	0.64	0.81	0.76

TABLE 4

WEIGHTS OF $N30$ POSITIONS AND
CENTENNIAL PROPER MOTIONS

Decl.	$m<5.5$	$5.5<m\leq6.5$	$6.5<m\leq7.5$	$7.5<m$
+82°5..........	81	59	38	15
+67.5..........	64	38	19	12
+52.5..........	51	26	16	14
+37.5..........	52	28	18	14
+22.5..........	65	33	18	10
+ 7.5..........	65	32	20	11
− 7.5..........	60	34	22	15
−22.5..........	52	32	19	14
−37.5..........	16	12	11	10
−52.5..........	13	11	10	3
−67.5..........	13	11	10	8
−82.5..........	13	13	11	12

Table 6 are sometimes used to illustrate the dependence of systematic differences between fundamental star catalogues on the arguments declination and right ascension. A part of the systematic differences in positions shown in Figure 2 is undoubtedly due to systematic errors in both catalogues at their respective mean epochs. The greater part, however, is due to the multiplication of the systematic errors of the *FK3* proper motions by the time interval between the mean epochs of the *FK3* and the *N30*. Such systematic errors are introduced in the proper motions when the average of all the instrumental error-curves of the

TABLE 5

RELATION OF *N30* WEIGHTS TO PROBABLE ERRORS

WEIGHT	POSITIONS		PROPER MOTION	WEIGHT	POSITIONS		PROPER MOTION
	1930	1950			1930	1950	
100.....	±0″026	±0″030	±0″08	36......	±0″048	±0″066	±0″24
81.....	.032	.040	.11	25......	.052	.072	.25
64.....	.032	.040	.13	16......	.070	.105	.40
49.....	0.041	0.052	0.17	9......	0.09	0.13	0.46

TABLE 6

SYSTEMATIC DIFFERENCES, *N30* − *FK3*, BETWEEN +30° AND −30°
VARYING WITH RIGHT ASCENSION*

DIFFERENCE	COEFFICIENT OF			
	sin a	cos a	sin $2a$	cos $2a$
Δa............	−0″051	+0″015	−0″036	−0″015
$\Delta\delta$............	− .013	− .051	+ .003	− .009
$\Delta\mu$............	− .070	+ .063	− .123	− .054
$\Delta\mu'$............	−0.013	−0.144	+0.002	−0.007

* From *N30*, p. xxiii.

type shown in Figure 1 changes from one epoch to another because of a different combination of instruments or because of changes in the systematic behavior of the individual instruments. Since such changes probably vary with both right ascension and declination, warps may exist in the proper-motion system in different parts of the sky. That individual instruments do undergo inexplicable changes in their behavior was found by Gliese (1960), the notable exception being the U.S. Naval Observatory 6-inch transit circle, which has given a fairly consistent performance since 1910.

   For some uses, these systematic errors do but little harm, even though their presence may be regretted. There are areas of research, however, in which systematic errors in the proper motions can have disastrous effects on the end results. Since there is usually no way to assess the systematic errors in proper motions in a quantitative sense until an opportunity arises to test them against new observations, it is advisable that each investigator devise a control to apply to his results which will warn him of their presence.

One type of control is that illustrated by van Herk (1959), wherein, in checking the expansion rate of the B stars in Lacerta, a comparison was made with the "expansion rate" indicated by other types of stars in the same region. His investigation showed that the *N30* proper motions probably underwent a change in systematic error between $+36°.5$ and $+52°.5$ declination. This type of error is what one might expect in this part of the sky, as it is in the troublesome

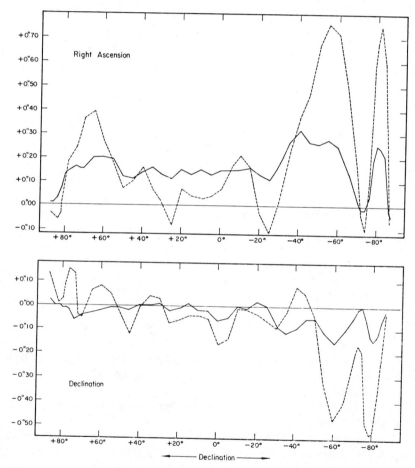

FIG. 2.—Systematic differences between the *N30* and *FK3* catalogues (*N30* − *FK3*) varying with declination for the epoch 1930. The upper curves are $15\Delta\alpha^s \cos \delta$ (————), and $15\Delta\mu^s \cos \delta$ (----------). The lower curves are $\Delta\delta''$ (————) and $\Delta\mu''$ (----------).

zenith zone of nearly all the instruments contributing to the northern *N30* proper motions. Another type of control which may be useful in some cases is that applied by Kopff (1954*a*) in testing whether the *FK3* stars and non-*FK3* stars in *N30* showed the same systematic relationship with the *GC*. Insofar as the proper motions are concerned, the two types of *N30* stars show excellent agreement between $+50°$ and $-40°$ and strong divergences in the regions $+50°$ to $+70°$ and $-40°$ to $-60°$.

The periodic terms in the systematic differences in the proper motions shown in Table 6 are of particular interest because they are of the same form as those that one might expect in the proper motions because of an error in the precession constant. It is therefore important that observational procedures at all epochs be devised to eliminate this type of error in both the right ascension and the declination results.

The general practice of using good clocks is a guard against periodic errors of the annual type in our present right ascensions. This was not always the practice, and some of the periodicities in our present proper motions in right ascensions are due to insufficient elimination of daily and annual terms from the clocks used at earlier epochs. Our present right ascensions are probably not free from all errors of a periodic type due to temperature or annual changes in the instrument and the room refraction. In the same manner, the practice of correcting declination observations for variations in the latitude and in the refraction due to water-vapor pressure tends to diminish annual terms in the declinations. This practice, however, was not always carried out. In fact, the large cosine term in $\Delta\mu'$, Table 6, was shown by Oort (1950) to be due to the neglect of a correction for the variation in the latitude in the observations prior to 1900 used in computing the *FK3* proper motions.

It is quite certain that the proper motions of the *FK4* will be an improvement over those of the *N30* because of the inclusion of additional observational material, especially that for the second Cape catalogue for 1950. The system of the *FK4* positions will be based on observational catalogues produced since 1920. The exclusion of earlier catalogues will advance the mean epochs to about 1935 and 1928 in right ascension and declination, respectively. In the equatorial sections of the sky the system of the *FK4* will be quite close to that of the *FK3* and *N30*, as shown in a preliminary report by Fricke (1960) and as may be inferred from Figure 2. To the north of $+40°$ and to the south of $-40°$ declinations, as suggested by Figure 2, the *FK4* will differ by large amounts from the *FK3*, the differences in the right ascension being greatest around $+75°$ and $-80°$ declinations.

The proper motions of the *FK4* system will be more dependent than those of the *FK3* on observational series conducted since 1900 with the instruments at the Cape, Greenwich, Pulkovo, and Washington Observatories. This will effectively free them from the uncertainties of the systematic errors of the older observations and should result in a decidedly improved system.

§ 5. SOURCES OF FUNDAMENTAL PROPER MOTIONS

The best sources for fundamental proper motions are, of course, the fundamental star catalogues, and, whenever possible, preference should be given to
them. Extensive tables have been prepared to facilitate the transfer of positions
and proper motions from the system of one fundamental star catalogue to that
of another. Thus, if required, the proper motions of the entire *GC* could be
systematically reduced to the systems of the *N30* or *FK3* by application of corrections of the form *N30* minus *GC*, or *FK3* minus *GC*, prepared by Morgan
(1951) and Kopff (1939). Likewise, the *N30* proper motions could be reduced
to the system of the *FK3* and vice versa, by proper use of the tables, *FK3* minus
N30, prepared by Nowacki (1953).

The need to transfer proper motions from one system to another comes from
the fact that the systematic accuracy of one system may be better than that of
another. The question naturally arises as to which of the present systems—the
GC, *FK3*, and *N30*—is likely to be the best for a particular research. This matter was given very careful consideration by Morgan and Oort (1951) in their
determination of the precession and the constants of galactic rotation. In their
opinion, the best system of proper motions presently available is that formed
by correcting the average of the proper motions in the *FK3* and *N30* systems by
the Δk and Δn found in their paper. They also advise that the term in the *FK3*
proper motions in declination due to the neglect of variation of latitude before
1900 should be removed before averaging them with the *N30* proper motions.
Thus they find the best values of the centennial proper motions to be

$$\mu = \tfrac{1}{2}(\mu_{FK3} + \mu_{N30}) + 0^s\!.021 - 0^s\!.020 \sin \alpha \tan \delta \,,$$

$$\mu' = \tfrac{1}{2}(\mu'_{FK3} + \mu'_{N30}) - 0''\!.37 \cos \alpha \,.$$

These formulae may be used to reduce *GC* proper motions to the "best system,"
provided that, beforehand, the tables by Morgan and Kopff mentioned earlier
are used to reduce them separately to the *N30* and *FK3* systems. The question
of the best system will undoubtedly be reopened as soon as the *FK4* becomes
available.

Transferring a set of proper motions to a new system may not improve their
accidental errors because of small uncertainties in the systematic reductions applied. A decrease in accidental error may be obtained if the investigator includes observational data accumulated after the proper motions were originally
derived. The greatest increase in accidental accuracy will be obtained for stars
fainter than magnitude 5.5. Considerable observational data are now on hand
which could be used for the improvement of the proper motions of the fainter
GC stars. The most important of recent meridian-circle star catalogues containing observations of the *GC* stars are those with mean epochs later than 1925
given on page ix of the *N30* catalogue. This list may be supplemented, if the in-

vestigator desires, by including the photographically derived positions between the North Pole and $-2°$ declination published in the 15 volumes of the *AGK2* (Schorr and Kohlschütter 1951) and the positions for another large group of stars given in the Yale and Cape photographic catalogues to be discussed next. The formulae for improving both the position and the proper motion of a star by including an additional observation, as well as a numerical example, are given on page 49 of the first volume of the *GC*. Proper motions on a fundamental system for nearly 200,000 stars are given in the photographic catalogues of the Cape and Yale Observatories listed in Tables 1 and 2 of chapter 4.

The positions in these catalogues are related to a fundamental system through the reference stars used in the reduction of the plates; the reference stars in most cases have been related to the fundamental system by meridian-circle observations. The proper motions depend on a comparison of the photographic positions with an earlier observation, usually visual. Thus the early epoch positions for the Yale proper motions were usually obtained from one of the A.G. catalogues, *Katalogs der Astronomischen Gesellschaft, Leipzig*, (*AGK1*) and those for the Cape proper motions from some combination of positions from early catalogues of the Albany, Cape, Córdoba, La Plata, Perth, San Luis, and Sydney Observatories. The large probable errors and general lack of knowledge of the systematic errors of the early catalogues have resulted in rather high uncertainties in the proper motions under discussion. The probable errors range from $0\rlap{.}''15$ to $1\rlap{.}''5$ per century, depending on the early catalogue used and the epoch difference between it and the photographic position. The average probable error is around $1\rlap{.}''0$ per century. The deleterious effect of the uncertainties of the early positions on the proper motions may be roughly estimated when it is noted that the probable error of a centennial proper motion is $1\rlap{.}''2$ when a photographic position at 1933 (Yale $-14°$ to $-18°$) is compared with an A.G. position at 1895 (Washington) and that it drops to $0\rlap{.}''7$ when two photographic positions at 1936 and 1914 (Yale $+1°$ to $-2°$) are compared.

Fundamental proper motions may also be obtained by computing them from observational data which have been reduced to a fundamental system. If such a task is undertaken, the search for positions of the stars observed before 1900 will be greatly facilitated if use is made of the *GFH, Geschichte des Fixstern-himmels* (Berlin: Akademie der Wissenschaften, 1922–1960). Abteilung I of this work covering the northern sky is complete, and all except the volumes for 17^h, 18^h, and 19^h of Abteilung II for the southern sky have been published. These volumes, eventually to be 48 in all, contain a collection of all the observations that are known to have been made of stars brighter than the ninth magnitude during the eighteenth and nineteenth centuries. The positions listed in them were referred to the equinox of 1875.0 by use of precessions based on Struve's constant of precession. The centennial values of M and N in the precession formulae based on Struve's constant differ from those based on Newcomb's constant by the following amounts:

$$M_N - N_S = -0\overset{s}{.}0382 - 0\overset{s}{.}00363 \, T \, ,$$

$$N_N - N_S = -0\overset{s}{.}0348 + 0\overset{s}{.}00065 \, T = -0\overset{''}{.}522 + 0\overset{''}{.}0097 \, T \, ,$$

where T is counted in centuries from 1900. Since it is the current practice to make all proper motions compatible with Newcomb's constant of precession, corrections for these differences should be applied to the reductions to the equinox of 1875.0. Likewise, the precessions given in the *GFH* should be adjusted to Newcomb's constant before using them to refer the positions to another equinox.

The *Index der Sternörter* (Schorr and Kruse 1928) is helpful in locating sources in which the positions of the stars observed during the period 1900–1925 may be found. A continuation of the *Index* covering the period from 1925 to 1960 is nearly ready for publication by the Rechen-Institut in Berlin, Germany.

The systematic reductions to the *GC* for about 240 of the older catalogues, about half before and half after 1900, are given in Appendix III of Volume 1 of the *GC*. Similar reductions for an additional 108 catalogues have been published by Gyllenberg (1948). Recent meridian-circle star catalogues usually contain a comparison of the catalogue with the *GC* which may be used for reducing the catalogue to the system of the *GC*.

In order to continue the *GC* method for computing proper motions, it is necessary that each observation enter the least-squares solution with the weight assigned it by the *GC* or by Gyllenberg. The weight of an observation in a subsequent catalogue may be estimated from the average probable error of an observation in the catalogue, using $0\overset{''}{.}30$ as the probable error equivalent to weight 1.

The computation of proper motions by reducing observational data to the system of a fundamental star catalogue is, in principle, an extension of the fundamental catalogue to include other stars. If the other stars are at the faint end of the magnitudes included in a fundamental catalogue—the *GC*, for example—then the process is subject to every risk (*GC*, **1**, 22) that is associated with extrapolating to the faint stars the magnitude equation determined principally by the bright stars. These and other errors depending on the reaction of the observer are so poorly determined for observations before 1850 that it is advisable to avoid them whenever possible. The observations from 1850 to 1900, although an improvement over those of earlier epochs, nevertheless have large and, as yet, insufficiently studied systematic errors that may seriously affect any proper motions based on them.

It was not until after 1900 that a progressive campaign was started for the elimination of systematic errors depending on magnitude and personal equation. The gradual adoption of the impersonal micrometer and the use of screens and reversing prisms have reduced these types of systematic errors to a point where they are now practically negligible. The general experience of astronomers in dealing with proper motions of bright stars is that the increase in precision during the last 50 years outweighs the extended epoch difference gained by including the observations of the entire preceding century.

§ 6. PROJECTS ON THE IMPROVEMENT OF FUNDAMENTAL
PROPER MOTIONS

A number of important projects specifically directed at the improvement of fundamental proper motions are either in progress or about to commence. Among these projects are the following:

1. The introduction of the *FK4* will insure an adequate reference system for at least the next quarter of a century. Because this catalogue and the *N30* represent quite independent approaches to a fundamental system, it will be of interest to compare both with observations for the next decade, to test the relative freedom of their proper-motion systems from systematic errors.

2. Observational programs are in progress for improving the positions of 1987 stars (Kopff 1953) prior to absorbing them into the fundamental system. These stars, called the "*FK3* Suppl. Stars," range in magnitude from 5.0 to 7.0 and were selected to fill the gaps and increase the density of the *FK3* and *FK4* network of stars over the sky. The addition of these objects will increase the number of stars in the *FK* system to 3522 and will greatly facilitate the comparison of observations of the brighter stars with the fundamental system.

3. A further extension of the *FK3* to include 931 stars between magnitudes 7.0 and 8.5, north of $-30°$ declination, has been undertaken by meridian-circle observers of the U.S.S.R. The plan has been extended to the Southern Hemisphere by the Cape and La Plata Observatories. Although the work is still in progress, the *PFKSZ*, *Preliminary General Catalogue of Faint Fundamental Stars*, containing 587 stars north of $-20°$ declination, has been published (Zverev and Plozhentsev 1958). This catalogue is based on 14 catalogues produced by 10 observatories and is regarded as one of the most accurate of modern catalogues containing faint stars. The centennial proper motions are on the *FK3* system and have probable errors of $0\overset{''}{.}29 \cos \delta$ and $0\overset{''}{.}33$ in right ascension and declination, respectively.

4. In view of the great wealth of observational data accumulated over the last 30 years and with the prospect of more becoming available in the near future, a resolution was adopted at the Second Astrometric Conference (*A.J.*, **65**, 167) to revise the *GC*. If this plan comes to fruition, thousands of highly accurate and systematically consistent fundamental proper motions will be available for astrometric researches.

5. Two extensive programs involving the closest co-operation on the international level are directed at the production of upward of 400,000 proper motions on the fundamental system. It is expected that the probable errors of these motions will be of the order of $0\overset{''}{.}6$ per century.

The first of the programs, the *AGK3—Trans. I.A.U.*, Vol. 9 and subsequent Comm. 8 and Sub-Comm. 8a—has been in progress since 1956. Its goal was a photographic reobservation by 1960 of all stars brighter than the ninth magnitude north of $-2°$ declination. Proper motions will be derived from a comparison with the *AGK2* (Schorr and Kohlschütter 1951), observed about 1930. The photographic observations are being made at the Hamburg-Bergedorf Observatory, and the meridian-circle observations of over 21,000 reference stars are being contributed by the instruments at the Babelsberg, Bergedorf, Bordeaux, Heidelberg, Herstmonceux, Nicolaiev, Ottawa, Paris, Pulkovo, Strasbourg, and the U.S. Naval Observatories and will form a catalogue named *AGK3R*.

The second program, directed at a similar improvement of the proper motions in the Southern Hemisphere—*Trans. I.A.U.*, **11**, Comm. 8 and Sub-Comm. 8a—is now about to commence.

The completion of these programs will immediately make it possible to project accurate current positions of the stars back to the epoch of the principal catalogues of the latter half of the last century. A star-by-star comparison with the early observations should yield the systematic corrections needed to reduce them to the system of the fundamental catalogue for use in the derivation of even more accurate proper motions. The same process could be used, when necessary, to re-reduce the plates of many of the astrographic catalogues and thereby redeem their high intrinsic value for proper-motion work.

6. Intensive observational programs—*Trans. I.A.U.*, Vol. **11**, Comm. 8 and Sub-Comm. 8a—directed at the improvement of the positions and proper motions of miscellaneous star lists have been organized during the last few years. Among the lists under observation or about to be observed are the stars brighter than the 6th magnitude, the O- and B-type stars and the cepheids (Blaauw 1955), and the stars around associations (Parenago 1954).

7. It is hoped that the proposal (Danjon 1960) to establish a chain of astrolabes at 15° or 20° intervals of latitude between the North and South poles will be realized. These instruments and the horizontal transit circles now under construction at Herstmonceux, Ottawa, Porto, and Pulkovo, combined with the present active meridian circles, should be very effective in reducing the systematic errors of the fundamental star catalogue.

8. With the major problems arising from the observer—i.e., magnitude and personal equation—out of the way, it may be expected that serious attention will be given to the causes of the characteristic systematic errors that still remain in meridian-circle catalogues. The improvement in observing and recording techniques over the last thirty years has reduced the random error of an observation to a point where investigation of more subtle errors may profitably be made.

Inasmuch as the remaining errors are probably not going to be susceptible to a simple method of elimination, removing them is likely to be slow. The magnitude of the systematic errors, Figure 1, is such that they could easily be produced by an adverse temperature gradient of a tenth of a degree per foot in a path distance of 20 feet or by a shift of less than a micron in the relative positions of the objective and micrometer in passing through the zenith. The causes of troubles of this kind are hard to find and usually much harder to correct.

REFERENCES

BARNEY, I.   1949   *A.J.*, **54**, 150.

BLAAUW, A.   1955   *I.A.U. Symposium*, No. 1: *Coordination of Galactic Research* (Cambridge: Cambridge University Press), Appendix.

BÖHME, S.   1960   *Mitt. Astr. Rech.-Inst., Heidelberg*, Ser. B, No. 3.

BOSS, B.   1937   *General Catalogue of 33,342 Stars for the Epoch 1950*, Vols. **1–5** (Washington, D.C.: Carnegie Institution of Washington).

BROUWER, D.   1941   *Ann. New York Acad. Sci.*, **42**, 133.

     1960   *A.J.*, **65**, 186.

DANJON, A.   1960   *A.J.*, **65**, 169 and 180.

FRICKE, W.   1957   *Mitt. Astr. Rech.-Inst., Heidelberg*, Ser. B, No. 2.

     1960   *A.J.*, **65**, 177.

GETHING, P. J. D.   1954   *M.N.*, **114**, 415.

GLIESE, W.   1960   *M.N., Astr. Soc. South Africa*, **19**, 2.

GYLLENBERG, W.   1948   *Medd. Lund Astr. Obs.*, Ser. 2, No. 122.

HERK, G. VAN   1952   *B.A.N.*, **11**, 489.

     1959   *A.J.*, **64**, 348.

HERK, G. VAN, and
WOERKOM, A. J. J. VAN   1961   *A.J.*, **66**, 87.

KOPFF, A.   1934   *Dritter Fundamental-Katalog des Berliner astronomischen Jahrbuchs* (Anh. Berliner astr. Jahrbuchs 1936, Berlin Akad.).

     1936   *M.N.*, **96**, 714.

     1939   *A.N.*, **269**, 160.

     1940   *Abh. Preuss. Akad. Wiss.*, No. 18, p. 1939 (Berlin, 1940).

     1953   *Astr. Geodät. Jahrb.*, 1954, p. [1] (Karlsruhe).

     1954   *M.N.*, **114**, 478.

MORGAN, H. R.   1937   *Science*, **85**, 1.

     1941   *Ann. New York Acad. Sci.*, **42**, 117.

     1943   *Pop. Astr.*, **51**, 527.

     1946   *Ibid.*, **54**, 2.

     1951   *A.J.*, **56**, 97.

     1952   *Catalogue of 5,268 Standard Stars, 1950* ("Astr. Papers of the American Ephemeris," Vol. **13**, Part 3).

MORGAN, H. R., and
OORT, J. H.   1951   *B.A.N.*, **11**, 379.

NEWCOMB, S.   1906   *A Compendium of Spherical Astronomy* (New York: Macmillan Co.).

     1960   *Ibid.* (reprint; New York: Dover Publications).

NOWACKI, H.   1953   *Nachr. d. Astr. Zentralstelle*, Vol. **7**, No. 6.

OORT, J. H.   1950   *Constantes fondamentales de l'astronomie, Colloques internationaux*, **25**, 55 (Paris: Centre National de la Recherche Scientifique).

PARENAGO, P. P.   1954   *Trans. Xth Astrometric Conference Soviet Union,*
                                         p. 256.

SCHORR, R., and
    KOHLSCHÜTTER, A.   1951   *Zweiter Katalog der Astr. Gesellschaft,* Vols. **1–10**
                                         (Hamburg Sternwarte), **11–15** (Bonn).

SCHORR, R., and
    KRUSE, W.   1928   *Index der Sternörter, 1900–1925,* Vols. **1** and **2**
                                         (Bergedorf).

SCOTT, F. P.   1955   *A.J.,* **60**, 93.

                                 1957   *Trans. I.A.U.,* **9**, 713.

ZVEREV, M. S., and
    PLOZHENTSEV, D. D.   1958   *Pub. Astr. Obs. Pulkovo,* Ser. 2, Vol. **72**.

CHAPTER 3

The Reference System of Bright, Intermediate, and Faint Stars and of Galaxies

S. VASILEVSKIS

Lick Observatory, University of California, Mount Hamilton, California

§ 1. INTRODUCTION

THE astrometric history of a star and the method of its observation depend on its brightness. Bright stars have the longest history of frequent observation and form a fundamental reference of positions and proper motions. With decreasing brightness, the number of stars increases, and the average frequency of their observations decreases. The difficulty of visual observation increases with the faintness of stars until photography takes over completely.

Although the observational history and the method of observation, visual or photographic, can serve as criteria for a grouping of stars according to their brightness, no sharp limit exists between separate groups, and the grouping is more or less arbitrary. Let us choose the following groups for the present discussion.

Bright stars are those having positions and proper motions that depend almost entirely on visual observations with meridian circles or with vertical circles and transit instruments (Pulkovo Observatory), which have been used in the formation of the fundamental catalogues. Since there are several fundamental systems of positions and proper motions, the approximate limiting magnitude depends on the chosen system. No fundamental catalogue contains a complete list of all stars down to a certain magnitude; therefore, the bright stars will be defined here as those contained in fundamental catalogues and, in general, brighter than $m_v = 8$.

The magnitude limits between 8 and 12, approximately, will be chosen for *intermediate stars*. In this group there is a close co-ordination between visual and photographic programs. A selected group of brighter stars, down to approx-

30

imately the tenth magnitude, are usually observed visually, in order to provide a position reference for photographic observations. Then these stars are observed photographically, together with fainter stars, thus tying in the latter to the system of visual observations.

Stars fainter than the twelfth magnitude will be assigned to the group of *faint stars;* their positions and proper motions can be determined only photographically.

External galaxies constitute a separate group of objects. Although the positions of many bright galaxies were observed visually (Bigourdan 1892–1911) long ago, the galaxies achieved their prominence in astrometry only recently, after initiation of two photographic proper-motion programs—the Russian (Deutsch 1954) and the Lick (Wright 1950). The Russian program is based on brighter galaxies, such that many of them would belong to our intermediate-brightness group, while all galaxies in the Lick program are faint, of the order of the sixteenth magnitude.

§ 2. BRIGHT STARS

The present fundamental catalogues have been formed from observations of bright stars, and each is a careful and critical combination of various observational catalogues into a reference system of stellar positions and proper motions. Since each observational catalogue is affected by accidental and systematic errors, it is impossible to build a fundamental system completely free of systematic errors, in spite of a thorough investigation and evaluation of each catalogue by comparison with others. The systematic errors are functions of position, i.e., of α and δ, and, particularly in older catalogues, of stellar magnitude m:

$$\Delta\alpha = f(\alpha, \delta, m), \qquad\qquad \Delta\delta = F(\alpha, \delta, m).$$

Usually these errors are split into three components:

$$\Delta\alpha_\alpha = f_1(\alpha), \qquad \Delta\alpha_\delta = f_2(\delta), \qquad \Delta\alpha_m = f_3(m);$$
$$\Delta\delta_\alpha = F_1(\alpha), \qquad \Delta\delta_\delta = F_2(\delta), \qquad \Delta\delta_m = F_3(m).$$

In many cases some of the errors can be neglected, particularly $\Delta\delta_m$, while in other cases it is impossible to split the total error into components, which depends on only one argument each. For instance, a sizable $\Delta\alpha_\alpha$ may be different in different zones of declination. In most cases the above functions are not expressed in an analytical form, but their values are tabulated. Since proper motions are functions of positions, variable with time, they are also affected by systematic errors of a similar character. A detailed discussion of the errors can be found in every fundamental catalogue.

It is obvious that accurate observations extending over a long period of time are necessary for the derivation of reliable positions and proper motions. On the other hand, systematic errors of old observational catalogues are large, and in many cases the loss of precision due to these errors is greater than the gain of a longer time interval for the determination of proper motions. In forming a fundamental catalogue, one has to decide which observational catalogues are to be used and what procedure is to be followed in combining the selected catalogues. For this reason, different fundamental catalogues have different systems. Let us describe briefly the various fundamental catalogues, past and present.

Newcomb, Boss, and Auwers, each independently, laid the foundations of the modern fundamental catalogues. The first catalogue by Newcomb (1873) contains only right ascensions of 32 equatorial stars. Although this number of stars is much too small for the reference system, the catalogue is valuable because of a rigorous discussion of errors and a derivation of the position of the equinox. The final catalogue by Newcomb (1898b) contains positions and proper motions of 1257 stars; the positions are reduced to 1875 and 1900 by use of the precession constant derived by Newcomb (1898a) and, by an international agreement, used since then in all catalogues.

The *General Catalogue* (*GC*) by B. Boss (1937) is the final product of several fundamental catalogues constructed by his father, L. Boss, starting with 1877; the history is outlined in Volume 1 of the *GC*. The aim was to make use of as many observational catalogues as possible and to put all the observations on a homogeneous fundamental system. Since many stars had not been observed enough for reliable positions and proper motions, L. Boss organized special meridian-circle observations at Albany (Boss 1931), and an expedition was sent to San Luis (Boss and Boss 1928), Argentina, for the same purpose. The total number of stars in the *GC* is 33,342, their positions and proper motions being derived from 238 observational catalogues. Although all the positions and proper motions are reduced to a good and uniform system, the accidental errors increase in general for the fainter stars because of few observations and a short observational history.

Dritter Fundamental-Katalog des Berliner astronomischen Jahrbuchs (*FK3*) (Kopff 1934) is the internationally adopted catalogue used in all astronomical ephemerides. The catalogue is a recent step in the development and improvement of a series of fundamental catalogues originated by Auwers (1879), and it is being improved at present (Fricke 1960) to obtain an *FK4*. The original Auwers catalogues were formed for reference in meridian-circle observations of stars down to the ninth magnitude; these observations were organized by the Astronomische Gesellschaft. In the process of making his catalogues, Auwers investigated the systematic errors of observational catalogues and derived corrections to his fundamental catalogues. These corrections were taken into account, and a new catalogue, *Neuer Fundamental-Katalog* (*NFK*), was published by Peters (1907). Contrary to the practice of Boss, Auwers selected only stars with long and good observational history; hence the number of entries was only 925. In forming the *FK3* (Kopff 1937, 1938), some of the Auwers stars were omitted, and several hundred new stars were added for uniformity of distribution.

Auwers' catalogues have been criticized for the inclusion of old observational catalogues with large systematic errors. Subsequently, the older catalogues were omitted and new ones taken into account, and it is generally believed that the *FK3* is the best catalogue at present, while *FK4* will probably be generally adopted in the near future.[1] Eichelberger (1925) went to an extreme by using only four modern catalogues in building a fundamental system. Morgan (1952) formed a catalogue by using 60 observational catalogues, none of them older than 1917; the system obtained is called "*N30*" because of the mean epoch around 1930. (For further details see chapter 2, p. 18.)

§ 3. INTERMEDIATE STARS

As mentioned in the introduction, stars of magnitudes between approximately 8 and 12 not contained in fundamental catalogues will be called "intermediate stars" in the present chapter. It should be noted that these stars are usually called "faint" by meridian-circle observers, and actually only the brighter end of the group can be observed visually.

Near the end of the last century, two large programs were initiated and carried out under international co-operation: the Astronomische Gesellschaft catalogues (*AGK1*) and the *Astrographic Catalogue (Carte du Ciel)*. On the Astronomische Gesellschaft program all the BD stars down to the ninth magnitude were observed, while the astrographic program called for photographic observations of stars in both hemispheres down to approximately the eleventh magnitude.

The *AG* catalogues have different precision in different zones, and the magnitude equation is appreciable in many of them. The discussion of the catalogues can be found in Volume 1 of the *GC;* their value is not very high at present. An improvement in these catalogues may be expected, as will be outlined later.

The *Astrographic Catalogue* is still not quite completed (progress reports can be found in *Trans. I.A.U.*, Comm. 23), and, although intrinsically it is very precise in all zones, it is not homogeneous regarding position reference, magnitude zero point and scale, and limiting magnitude. One of the main reasons for the delay in completion is the relatively small field, $2° \times 2°$, of the normal astrograph used for taking the photographs.

Schlesinger and Hudson (1916) proposed the use of a larger field in astronomical photography, and their success prompted a photographic repetition of the Astronomische Gesellschaft zones, published in many volumes of Yale University Observatory *Transactions* (see chapter 4, Table 1). Here again, although the Yale catalogues are very precise internally, they are not quite homogeneous in their reference system. New reduction of some zones is in progress.

The first photographic catalogue rigorously referred to a fundamental system

---

[1] [The *FK4* was introduced as the basis of ephemerides in 1962 (*Trans. I.A.U.*, **11A**, 1962). —EDITOR.]

was initiated by the Astronomische Gesellschaft. Six German observatories and Pulkovo carried out meridian-circle observations of stars intended for photographic position reference. These observations took a relatively short time, from 1928 to 1932, and they were carefully tied into the system of the *FK3;* the result is a catalogue of 13,747 stars, *AGK2A* (Kopff 1943). Photographic observations north of $-2°5$ were carried out by three observatories in 1930, i.e., the mean epoch of the reference catalogue, in order to have photographic positions independent of possible proper-motion errors in the reference catalogue. Instruments known as "A.G. astrographs," which covered a $5° \times 5°$ field, were used. The result of the photographic observations is *AGK2* (Schorr and Kohlschütter 1951–1958), a homogeneous catalogue of positions in the *FK3* system. Since errors in the *AGK1* are large and not always known, particularly for the fainter stars, no proper motions are given in *AGK2.*

In order to obtain accurate proper motions in a fundamental system, Heckmann (1954) proposed a new photographic repetition, *AGK3*, which is now in progress (Dieckvoss 1960). After the *AGK3* is completed, positions and proper motions for all stars to approximately the ninth visual magnitude in the system *FK4* will be available for galactic research and for reference in photographic positions and proper motions of faint stars.

Another program—a catalogue of faint stars (*KSZ*)—has been proposed (Gerasimovitch and Dneprovskii 1932) and initiated by the Russians (Zverev 1940) with the intention of tying the positions of the stars to a fundamental system and determining their motions with reference to external galaxies (Deutsch 1954). The list of *KSZ* stars north of $-20°$ (Zverev 1956) contains 15,690 stars, with visual magnitude between 7.5 and 9.1 with a few exceptions. Every effort has been made to select late-type stars; therefore, they are fainter photographically. Approximately 900 stars were selected for absolute meridian observations, to form a fundamental catalogue of faint stars (*FKSZ*); a preliminary fundamental catalogue (*PFKSZ*) of 587 stars north of $-20°$ has already been published (Zverev and Polozhentsev 1958).

The number of active meridian circles had decreased since the *AGK2A* was observed; therefore, it was necessary to co-ordinate internationally the programs of meridian observations and to distribute the effort more or less uniformly between the programs of *AGK3* and *KSZ*. An astrometric conference was called for this purpose in Brussels in 1955, and at present the observations are in progress (Scott 1960; Zverev 1960).

All these catalogues, except the *Astrographic Catalogue* and a few zones of the Yale catalogue, do not extend beyond the sky observable from the Northern Hemisphere. The Cape Observatory has been the only one to develop and to carry out programs similar to those of *AG* and *KSZ* (Stoy 1960). There are efforts to increase the astrometric activity in the Southern Hemisphere, and conferences in Cincinnati (*A.J.*, **65**, 167, 1960) and La Plata (*A.J.*, **65**, 235, 1960) were held with a special emphasis on urgent astrometric work in the southern sky. In addition, the Russians are planning an expedition to the Southern Hemisphere (Nemiro and Zverev 1960).

Proper motions of intermediate stars, with reference to external galaxies, will also be determined in the course of the Lick proper-motion program (Vasilevskis 1954); a similar program for the Southern Hemisphere is being planned by the observatories of Yale and Columbia universities.

All the astronomical work outlined above will not only yield reliable positions and proper motions of many stars but also permit new reductions of *AGK1* and the *Astrographic Catalogue* and the extension of the time base for proper motions in a modern system of reference.

§ 4. FAINT STARS

There is no general catalogue of positions for stars fainter than approximately the twelfth magnitude, and there are only a few catalogues of proper motions in special fields. Determination of proper motions in regions of clusters is usually done with the intention of segregating the cluster members, and only relative proper motions are derived in most cases. Although there are many programs in progress for stars in Selected Areas (*Trans. I.A.U.*, **9**, 1957), only the Radcliffe (Knox-Shaw and Scott-Barrett 1934) and Pulkovo (Deutsch 1940) catalogues give proper motions for faint stars, but they are not tied into a fundamental system.

Since astrometry of faint stars is a problem of the future, it may be appropriate to inquire whether there is any need to determine positions of faint stars, particularly in a fundamental system of reference. Historically, position comes before proper motion; change of position during a long time interval led Halley to the discovery of proper motions. This historical tradition, however, is not a justification for the position determination of bright and intermediate stars. Positions are necessary for studies of planetary motions, for time service, geodesy, nautical astronomy, and other problems within our solar system. Faint stars do not serve these purposes, and their astrometry can be justified only by the needs of galactic research, where an astrometrically precise position is not required.

There is no need, however, to review the problems in which precise proper motions are necessary in galactic research; no complete picture of structure and dynamics of our Galaxy can be obtained without proper motions of faint stars, both nearby dwarfs and distant giants. Determination of an accurate position was considered as a first necessary step in the derivation of proper motion until programs were initiated to use external galaxies as a reference system. Differential measurements with respect to the fixed frame of galaxies yield the proper motions of stars directly, without determination of their precise positions.

In the course of the Lick program, proper motions of stars beyond the sixteenth magnitude will be measured (Vasilevskis 1954). Since intermediate stars will also be included in the measurements, the proper motions in a fundamental system will be directly compared with those referred to the fixed frame of galaxies. This comparison will permit the study of systematic errors of fundamental catalogues and a determination of a correction to the constant of precession. The first results are expected before 1970.

§ 5. GALAXIES

Galaxies constitute a separate group of objects of astrometric programs because of their large distances and non-stellar appearance. If the redshift of galaxies is caused by their radial velocities and if it is assumed that their tangential velocities may approach the radial, then the maximum tangential velocity is $v_t = Hd$ km/sec, where H is the Hubble constant and d is the distance in millions of parsecs. After recent revisions of the cosmic distance scale, the original value of the Hubble constant has decreased and is now equal to 75 km/sec per million parsecs. With this value the proper motions of a galaxy would not exceed $0''00002$ per annum. Since there is no reason to assume that the tangential velocities of galaxies would approach the radial ones derived from redshifts, the actual proper motions are expected to be much smaller, and their effect can be neglected for centuries, even in the most precise measurements. This absence of proper motion suggests that galaxies could form an ideal reference system for positions, and authorities in extragalactic research (Lundmark 1954) and in positional astronomy (Kopff 1936) have advocated the construction of a catalogue of positions of galaxies.

The non-stellar appearance of galaxies makes them less suitable for position reference. Although many galaxies have almost stellar nuclei, all of them are diffuse and extended objects, asymmetrical in a majority of cases. Let us first define the position of an extended and asymmetric object with more or less pronounced central condensation.

If there is a stellar nucleus, it seems logical to suppose that the position of this nucleus represents the position of the galaxy. The measured position of the nucleus may depend, however, on the method and means of observation, if the immediate surroundings are not also symmetric. A small emission spot close to the nucleus may influence a visual observation differently from a photographic one, depending on the effective wave length of the emission. Moreover, the same photograph will give different positions, depending on whether settings are made with a visual microscope or by an electronic scanner, such as that developed by the Watson Computing Laboratory (Lenz and Bennett 1954). The scanner will set on the opacity center, which may be different from the subjective visual center. The aperture of a telescope and its focal ratio are also important factors; the exposure time and properties of a plate produce or conceal significant features of an image. It is quite often that a galaxy measurable on one plate cannot be used on a different plate. Let us illustrate this fact by some statistical figures.

The Russian program (Deutsch 1954) calls for observations of bright galaxies, most of them listed in the *New General Catalogue of Nebulae and Clusters of*

Stars (NGC) (Dreyer 1888). The proposed instrument is the normal astrograph of 33-cm aperture and $f/10.4$. A catalogue of 1508 galaxies has been published by the Pulkovo Observatory (Deutsch *et al.* 1955), with careful estimates of measurability on plates of 1-hour exposure with the normal astrograph. Galaxies are grouped into 10 classes, with 10 assigned to the best images and 1 to those which cannot be measured; class 6 and lower represent galaxies with measurability appreciably lower than that of stars. For comparison, 130 galaxies of quality 10–7, assigned by Pulkovo, were inspected on Lick plates of 2-hour exposure obtained with the 20-inch (50-cm), $f/7.4$, astrograph. The number and percentage of galaxies in various groups of measurability, estimated at Lick, are given in the accompanying table.

| | MEASURABILITY ESTIMATED AT PULKOVO | | | | | | | |
| | 10 | | 9 | | 8 | | 7 | |
INSPECTION AT LICK	No.	Per Cent	No.	Per Cent	No.	Per Cent	No.	Per Cent
Nucleus:								
Stellar....................	12	67	3	19	4	21	10	13
Poorly defined..............	2	11	5	31	3	16	7	9
Cannot be discerned........	4	22	8	50	12	63	60	78
Surrounding:								
Symmetric.................	4	22	11	69	11	58	56	73
Asymmetric...............	14	78	5	31	8	42	21	27
Measurability:								
Good......................	3	17	2	12	1	5	11	14
Doubtful.................	10	56	6	38	10	53	36	47
Impossible...............	5	28	8	50	8	42	30	39
Total no. inspected........	18	......	16	......	19	......	77	......

The table does not imply any criticism of the Pulkovo selection; it merely demonstrates the sensitivity of the image quality to the instrument and exposure used and shows that it is impossible to select a sufficient number of common galaxies suitable for different programs. Pulkovo group 10 contains mostly galaxies with a stellar nucleus but with an asymmetric surrounding. On the one hand, the nucleus permits an accurate setting on a particular image; on the other hand, these galaxies are sensitive to instrument and exposure because of the surrounding asymmetry. Let us describe a few particular galaxies contained in the table.

NGC 224 (M31) has a stellar nucleus, but there is no trace of it on Lick plates because the large central region is overexposed. NGC 1068 shows a stellar nucleus and a small and asymmetric area of spiral structure on short exposures. On longer exposures this small area looks like an elongated nucleus, and a large area of spiral structure appears around it. The positions of this galaxy on two different exposures will be quite different. NGC 205 has a stellar nucleus and a symmetrical elliptical nebulosity around it; the Lick astrograph plates show some absorption spots on the outskirts of this nebulosity. Photographs with the 120-inch telescope show asymmetric obscuration quite close to the nucleus, and it seems reasonable to suppose that this asymmetry takes part in forming the image of the nucleus and that its contribution depends on the instrument and exposure.

It may be concluded from the foregoing discussion that galaxies cannot serve as position references. Although many visual observations of them have been made in the past, particularly by Bigourdan (1892–1911), it would be difficult to justify new programs of photographic position determination to build a precision catalogue of galaxies in a fundamental system.

Galaxies, however, can serve as an excellent reference for proper motions, if some precautions are followed. It does not matter which point in the image represents the position of a galaxy, as long as the same point is measured at both epochs. The minimum conditions are that the same exposure time with the same instrument has to be made at the same hour angle on plates of the same properties and that measurement of both plates has to be made with the same engine and method. This is particularly important in the Russian program, where there is only a single or a few galaxies on each plate; the effect of an inexact repetition may be minimized in the Lick program, where more than 50 galaxies per plate will be selected, if errors due to asymmetry of galaxies are distributed at random. Both programs have been critically reviewed by the Russians (Fatchikhin 1960) and at Lick (Vasilevskis 1957), and it is certain that each program will supplement the other and that both combined will contribute to investigations of the dynamics of the solar system, as well as of our Galaxy.

REFERENCES

Auwers, A.	1879	*Pub. Astr. Gesellschaft*, Vol. **14**.
Bigourdan, M. G.	1892–	
	1911	*Observations de nébuleuses et d'amas stellaires* (Paris: Gauthier-Villars), Vols. **1–5**.
Boss, B.	1931	*Albany Catalogue of 20,811 Stars* (Washington, D.C.: Carnegie Institution of Washington).
	1937	*General Catalogue of 33,342 Stars for the Epoch 1950* (Washington, D.C.: Carnegie Institution of Washington).
Boss, L., and Boss, B.	1928	*San Luis Catalogue of 15,333 Stars* (Washington, D.C.: Carnegie Institution of Washington).
Deutsch, A. N.	1940	*Pub. Pulkovo Obs.*, Ser. 2, Vol. **55**.
	1954	*Trans. I.A.U.*, **8**, 789.
Deutsch, A. N., Lavdovskii, V. V., and Fatchikhin, N. V.	1955	*Bull. Pulkovo Obs.*, Vol. **20**, Part 1, p. 14.

DIECKVOSS, W.   1960   *A.J.*, **65**, 171.
DREYER, J. E.   1888   *New General Catalogue of Nebulae and Clusters of Stars* (*Mem. R.A.S.*, Vol. **49**, Part 1).
EICHELBERGER, W. S.   1925   *Astr. Papers Amer. Ephem.*, **10**, 1.
FATCHIKHIN, N. V.   1960   *Proc. 14th Astrometric Conf. U.S.S.R.*, p. 169.
FRICKE, W.   1960   *A.J.*, **65**, 177.
GERASIMOVITCH, B., and
  DNEPROVSKII, N.   1932   *Circ. Pulkovo Obs.*, No. 3, p. 3.
HECKMANN, O.   1954   *A.J.*, **59**, 31.
KNOX-SHAW, H., and
  SCOTT-BARRETT, H. G.   1934   *Radcliffe Catalogue of Proper Motions in Selected Areas 1 to 115* (London: Oxford University Press).
KOPFF, A.   1936   *M.N.*, **96**, 714.
                          1937   *Veröff. Astr. Rech.-Inst. Berlin-Dahlem*, No. 54 (Auwers' stars).
                          1938   *Abh. Preuss. Akad. Wiss., phys.-math. Kl.*, No. 3 (*Zusatzst*).
                          1943   *Veröff. Astr. Rech.-Inst. Berlin*, No. 55.
LENZ, J., AND
  BENNETT, R.   1954   *Electronics*, **27**, 158.
LUNDMARK, K.   1954   *Trans. I.A.U.*, **8**, 798.
MORGAN, H. R.   1952   *Astr. Papers Amer. Ephem.*, Vol. **13**, Part 3.
NEMIRO, A. A., and
  ZVEREV, M. S.   1960   *A.J.*, **65**, 226.
NEWCOMB, S.   1873   *Washington Astr. and Met. Obs. 1870*, Appendix 3.
                          1898a   *Astr. Papers Amer. Ephem.*, **8**, 1.
                          1898b   *Ibid.*, p. 77.
PETERS, J.   1907   *Veröff. Astr. Rech.-Inst. Berlin*, No. 33.
SCHLESINGER, F., and
  HUDSON, C. J.   1916   *Pub. Allegheny Obs.*, **3**, 59.
SCHORR, R., and
  KOHLSCHÜTTER, A.   1951–
                          1958   *Zweiter Katalog der Astr. Gesellschaft* (Hamburg and Bonn).
SCOTT, F. P.   1960   *A.J.*, **65**, 175.
STOY, R. H.   1960   *A.J.*, **65**, 199.
VASILEVSKIS, S.   1954   *A.J.*, **59**, 40.
                          1957   *Ibid.*, **62**, 126.
WRIGHT, W. H.   1950   *Proc. Amer. Phil. Soc.*, **94**, 1.
ZVEREV, M. S.   1940   *A.J. (U.S.S.R.)*, **17**, No. 5, 54.
                          1956   *Catalogue of Faint Stars.*
                          1960   *Proc. 14th Astrometric Conf. U.S.S.R.*, Vol. **11**.
ZVEREV, M. S., and
  POLOZHENTSEV, D. D.   1958   *Pub. Pulkovo Obs.*, Vol. **77**.

CHAPTER 4

Photographic Proper Motions

W. DIECKVOSS

Hamburg Observatory, Germany

§ 1. INTRODUCTION

THE traditional method of deriving the proper motions of the stars consists of determining their positions at two or more epochs in a clearly defined system. The method can be employed for either visual or photographic work and usually covers large areas of the sky divided into zones between certain values of declination. The absolute proper motions derived in this way are limited to the brighter stars.

Another method which has been used is to take two or more plates of the same area of the sky with the same telescope at different epochs. In this case the procedure consists of measuring either the plate co-ordinates or their differences by some suitable procedure. Since the method does not necessarily require photographic plates covering large fields, larger telescopes can be employed for programs of faint stars in selected regions. The proper motions derived in this way are relative proper motions and require further reductions for transformation into absolute proper motions in a rigorously defined fundamental system.

In this chapter, we shall briefly discuss procedures for reducing relative proper motions to absolute, the errors introduced by the photographic method, and the more important catalogues containing photographic proper motions.

§ 2. REDUCTION OF RELATIVE PROPER MOTIONS TO ABSOLUTE

The procedures for reducing relative proper motions to absolute depend on the number of stars on the plate with known absolute proper motions. If the absolute proper motions are known for a sufficient number of stars in the field to permit the use of plate constants, absolute proper motion can be obtained for all stars appearing on the plate.

If the number of known absolute proper motions on the plate is not sufficient for the procedure just described, the differences in scale value and orientation of the plates for different epochs can be determined by assuming the average proper motion of the faint stars to be zero. With these faint stars, preferably symmetrically distributed, used as reference stars, relative proper motions can be obtained, and reduction to absolute can be achieved by either statistical corrections to the mean proper motion of the faint stars as a consequence of solar motion and galactic rotation or by using the absolute proper motions, if known, for one or more stars in the field.

§ 3. PHOTOGRAPHIC ERRORS

The systematic and accidental errors of the derived proper motions arise from various sources. In addition to the errors inherent in the catalogue of reference stars, there are errors introduced by the process of measuring the star images on the photographic plate and by the lens of the telescope producing the images.

The errors introduced by the measuring machine are easily controlled. They can be derived from the determinations of the errors of the measuring screws or scales, the guiding errors of the measuring microscope and the plate carriage. Errors introduced by the actual structure of the photographic image of the star are much more serious. The asymmetric distribution of intensity arising from defects or faulty adjustment of the telescope objective and from guiding errors of the telescope becomes obvious to the eye only in extreme cases. The residual errors arising from these sources depend on the magnitude of the star, together with the length of the exposure, the type of emulsion, the kind of development and, especially for the larger telescopes, the seeing during the exposure. In addition to these well-known magnitude errors, there are also errors arising from prismatic defects in the objective and from atmospheric dispersion, which depend on the color of the stars.

Although these errors are in most cases small in comparison with the average random errors of the co-ordinates, they are of a systematic nature which prevents the use of many plates of the same area for the purpose of increasing the accuracy. As a result, they produce fictitious astronomical effects which become dangerous in investigations of stellar motions as functions of magnitude, spectral type, and luminosity.

As far as the errors depending on the telescope are concerned, they can, in principle, be determined by reversing the objective or the whole telescope with respect to the sky, since the resulting error will change its orientation in the opposite sense. The error becomes zero for the means derived from the two positions of the telescope, provided that no new errors are introduced during this process.

Magnitude errors become especially dangerous in work with large objectives. Particularly if the lenses have been taken out of their cell between two epochs, serious systematic errors may be introduced, as far as strictly differential measurements are concerned. It is also possible that small changes in the adjustment of a lens system will take place spontaneously in the course of time. Changes of the type just mentioned become especially dangerous in proper-motion and other programs requiring long intervals of time between epochs. It therefore seems advisable to establish a number of standard fields of star positions determined with the highest precision and preferably by international co-operation, as advocated by a resolution of the Second Astrometric Conference (*A.J.*, **65**, 170, 1960).

§ 4. CATALOGUES

Most modern catalogues give proper motions found from a comparison of the new positions with those of the older catalogues.

The Yale catalogues by Schlesinger and his associates obtain their positions from a repetition of the meridian catalogues of the Astronomische Gesellschaft, usually referred to as the *AGK1*. The zones of declination are covered by a series of plates taken with a wide-angle camera. The fields range from $5° \times 5°$ to $10° \times 14°$. Each star is measured on two adjacent plates, and, in order to reduce the magnitude errors for the new photographic epoch, a coarse grating is placed in front of the objective, giving diffraction spectra of the brighter stars. The magnitude errors in many of the old meridian catalogues have been especially troublesome, and special care has been taken by the authors to eliminate this error from the published proper motions.

In a number of zones a third epoch has been added from a repetition of the photographic work, and in some zones results were combined with the results of the second catalogue of the Astronomische Gesellschaft (*AGK2*). Details of the Yale zone catalogues published up to 1962 are given in Table 1.

Another large proper-motion program is carried out at the Cape Observatory. In addition to the photographic work, the observatory is also responsible for the meridian observations of the reference stars. The Cape catalogues contain proper motions derived from comparisons with older meridian-circle catalogues. Together with the Yale catalogues, they will ultimately cover the whole Southern Hemisphere (*Trans. I.A.U.*, **10**, 125, 1960). Of special value to the users of the Yale and Cape catalogues is the inclusion of the spectral types of the stars. For details of the published Cape catalogues see Table 2.

The new international program of the *AGK3*, now in progress (Dieckvoss 1960), will, when completed, contain proper motions with a high degree of homogeneity. The first-epoch photographic plates for the proper motions are the plates taken at Bonn and Bergedorf for the formation of the *AGK2*. The second-epoch plates were all taken in Bergedorf, but with the same centers as those of the first epoch. A coarse objective grating was used, and the plates were taken with the telescope both east and west of the pier, in order to eliminate the magnitude-color errors that had shown up in the *AGK2*. In addition, the objective was tested at regular intervals. The differences between the co-ordinates in the sense of "new *minus* old" are transferred into relative proper motions, and the reduction to absolute proper motions will be carried out by means of the proper motions obtained from the international meridian-circle program for the reference stars, called the *AGK3R*, which is discussed in chapter 2 (p. 27). The catalogues just mentioned deal with proper motions of stars brighter than the ninth magnitude. For the stars fainter than this, there exist no general catalogues of proper motions.

An important source for deriving proper motions of the fainter stars is the combination of the early plates of the *Astrographic Catalogue (CdC)* with recent ones taken with the same telescopes. Many of the early plates have epochs prior to 1900 and have limiting photographic magnitudes between 11 and 13. With a

TABLE 1

DATA ON YALE ZONE CATALOGUES

ZONE	EPOCH OF PLATES	EPOCH(S) OF EARLY CATALOGUE(S)	MEAN ERROR OF		YALE PUB. VOL.
			Position	Proper Motion	
+90° to +85°......	1951	1900, 1930	±0".13	±0".006	26, Part I
+60 +55.......	1947	1875, 1916, 1930	.12	.008	27
+55 +50.......	1947	1876, 1916, 1930	.12	.008	26, Part II
+30 +25.......	1928, 1930	1880, 1910	.14	.009	24
+25 +20.......	1928, 1930	1881, 1900	.14	.007	25
+20 +15.......	1940	1870	.17	.008	18
+15 +10.......	1940	1872	.17	.011	19
+10 + 9.......	1940	1884	.17	.011	22, Part II
+ 9 + 5.......	1936	1884	.17	.011	22, Part I
+ 5 + 1.......	1936	1879	.17	.010	20
+ 1 − 2.......	1936	1884, 1914	.17	.011	21
− 2 − 6.......	1933	1890	.16	.013	17
− 6 −10.......	1933	1894	.16	.012	16
−10 −14.......	1933	1891	.16	.017	11
−14 −18.......	1933	1895	.16	.018	12, Part I
−18 −20.......	1933	1893	.16	.016	12, Part II
−20 −22.......	1933	1893	.16	.016	13, Part I
−22 −27.......	1933	1893	.16	.018	14
−27 −30.......	1933	1893	0.16	0.018	13, Part II

TABLE 2

DATA ON CAPE ZONE CATALOGUES

ZONE	EPOCH OF PLATES	EPOCH(S) OF EARLY CATALOGUE(S)	MEAN ERROR OF		CAPE ANN. VOL.
			Position	Proper Motion	
−30° to −35°......	1932	1895, 1898	±0".22	$\mu < 0".021$	17
−35 −40......	1936	1900, 1903, 1912	.18	$0".009 \leq \mu \leq .035$	18
−52 −56......	1938	1875, 1900, 1910, 1925	.16	$.006 \leq \mu \leq .022$	19
−56 −64......	1945–46	1875, 1925	0.14	$0.006 \leq \mu \leq 0.020$	20

time interval of 60 years, these plates will yield annual proper motions with an internal mean error of the order of 0″.003 (Vyssotsky 1954).

Astrographic Catalogue zones which have been repeated for proper motions are the Helsinki zone (+40° to 46° decl.) for right ascensions between 3ʰ and 6ʰ (Furuhjelm 1916, 1926, 1947) and the Toulouse zone (+4° to +12° decl.) between right ascensions 0ʰ and 6ʰ (Paloque 1952). In the Southern Hemisphere the Cape zone (−41° to −51° decl.) has been repeated and the proper motions published (Jones and Jackson 1936). Other work completed or in progress in regard to proper motions derived from the *Astrographic Catalogue* plates is reported in the *Transactions of the I.A.U.* in the progress reports of the Commission de la Carte du Ciel (Comm. No. 23).

Among proper-motion programs of the fainter stars which cover smaller areas of the sky, but still lead to statistically important data, can be mentioned the McCormick catalogues and the proper-motion programs in Kapteyn's Selected Areas (S.A.). The McCormick catalogues contain the results of measurements of parallax plates combined with repetitions of these fields. The parallax star or a star with known absolute proper motion on the individual plates was used to reduce the relative proper motions to absolute. The first McCormick catalogue (van de Kamp and Vyssotsky 1937) includes 341 fields with a total of 17,900 stars brighter than 13.3 (visual) mag. with a mean error of the annual proper motions equal to ±0″.009. The second McCormick catalogue (Vyssotsky and Williams 1948) covers 441 fields with a total of 11,300 stars brighter than 12.5 (visual) mag., and the annual proper motions have a mean error of ±0″.008. The program on Kapteyn's Selected Areas includes the derivation of proper motions for a large number of stars by photographic means.

Several observatories are engaged in this work, and among the major contributions published so far can be mentioned those by Radcliffe, Pulkovo, and Groningen. Radcliffe (Knox-Shaw and Scott-Barrett 1934) has published data on 115 S.A. containing 32,400 stars to a limiting photographic magnitude of 15.2 and with annual proper motions having a mean error of ±0″.006. Pulkovo (Deutsch 1940) has published proper motions of 18,000 stars brighter than 14.8 (photographic) mag. in 74 S.A. The annual proper motions have a mean error of ±0″.007. Proper motions of 5200 stars in 24 S.A. at the equator derived from plates taken at the Alger Observatory have been published by Groningen (van Rhijn and Plaut 1955). The limiting magnitude is 11.5 photographic, and the annual proper motions have a mean error of ±0″.005.

A bibliography of the earlier work in this field has been published by van Rhijn (1957), and reports on further progress can be found in *Transactions of the I.A.U.*, Volume 10, in the progress report of Commission 32 (Selected Areas). In the future, work in this field will be reported in Commissions 24 (Stellar Parallaxes and Proper Motions) or 33 (Galactic Structure), since Commission 32 was discontinued in 1958.

The latest development in regard to obtaining absolute proper motions is the use of galaxies as frames of reference. According to our present knowledge, it may be assumed that the positions of the galaxies are unchanged with time. Accordingly, they can be considered fixed reference frames against which the absolute proper motions of the stars can be determined. At the present time, two programs using galaxies as frames of reference are in progress, as described in chapter 3.

In conclusion, it might be mentioned that any collection of old plates taken with instruments of not too short focal length and with well-defined stellar images can be used for the purpose of deriving proper motions of special objects or areas if new plates were taken with the same centers as the old. Work of this kind would form a very valuable supplement to the study of galactic structure from proper motions. So far studies of this kind have been based primarily on the classical meridian-circle catalogues.

REFERENCES

DEUTSCH, A. N.	1940	*Pub. Obs. Cent. Pulkovo,* Ser. 2, Vol. **55**.
DIECKVOSS, W.	1960	*A.J.,* **65**, 171.
FURUHJELM, R.	1916	*Acta Soc. sci. Fenn.,* Vol. **48**, No. 1.
	1926	*Ibid.,* Vol. **50**, No. 7.
	1947	*Ibid.,* Nov. Ser. A, Vol. **3**, No. 12. (Completed and edited by V. R. ÖLANDER.)
JONES, H. SPENCER, and JACKSON, J.	1936	*Proper Motions of Stars in the Zone Catalogue of 20,843 Stars, Zones −40° to −52°* (London: H.M. Stationery Office).
KAMP, P. VAN DE, and VYSSOTSKY, A. N.	1937	*Pub. Leander McCormick Obs.,* **7**, 1.
KNOX-SHAW, H., and SCOTT-BARRETT, H. G.	1934	*Radcliffe Catalogue of Proper Motions in Selected Areas* (Oxford: Oxford University Press).
PALOQUE, M. E.	1952	*Mouvements propres des étoiles des catalogues photographiques de Toulouse* (Paris: Centre Nationale de la Recherche Scientifique).
RHIJN, P. J. VAN	1957	*Trans. I.A.U.,* **9**, 469.
RHIJN, P. J. VAN, and PLAUT, L.	1955	*Pub. Kapteyn Astr. Lab. Groningen,* No. 56.
VYSSOTSKY, A. N.	1954	*A.J.,* **59**, 52.
VYSSOTSKY, A. N., and WILLIAMS, E. T. R.	1948	*Pub. Leander McCormick Obs.,* **10**, 1.

CHAPTER 5

Proper-Motion Surveys

WILLEM J. LUYTEN

Department of Astronomy, University of Minnesota

§ 1. INTRODUCTION AND TECHNIQUE

THE problem of surveying the sky for stars of large proper motion received a powerful stimulus by the introduction of a new technique, employing the "blink microscope." Actually, the first instrument used for this purpose was slightly different and was known as the "stereocomparator"; but in practice it did not prove very successful and was fairly quickly superseded by the blink microscope. First introduced by C. Pulfrich (1902) of Carl Zeiss, Jena, the principle of the blink microscope may be briefly described as follows.

Two photographic plates taken with the same telescope centered at about the same point in the sky and with the same equivalent exposure, but several years apart in time, are placed side by side in the instrument. A separate objective is used to scan each plate, but the light-beams are subsequently united so that they can be observed through the same eyepiece. By means of the usual slow-motion adjustments, the plates are then carefully lined up so that the star images from the two plates coincide as closely as possible when seen through the eyepiece. The "blink" arrangement then consists of a simple shutter—operated either by hand or mechanically (electrically), according to the observer's preference—which alternately occults one plate or the other and is operated at any speed desired by the observer.

Those stars which have not moved appreciably in the interval—and these constitute the majority—show a steady image, but any star that *has* moved will appear to "jump." Human physiology and psychology being what they are, the eye "catches" this jump much more easily than it would notice a difference in position shown by merely superimposing the images of the two plates in the same field of view.

A modification of this design was introduced by F. Schlesinger at Yale and W. P. Gerrish at Harvard (Schlesinger 1926). In this new type of comparator the two plates are placed horizontally, film down, and a microscope containing

46

but a single objective is put between them. A compound prism precedes the objective and unites the two beams before they reach that objective and pass from there to the single eyepiece. Since the upper plate is now viewed through the film and the lower plate through the glass, one more reflection has to be introduced into the beam from the latter, but a penta prism can easily accomplish this. For further details of the optical arrangement in both cases, reference may be made to articles by Pulfrich (1902) for the Zeiss type and by Schlesinger (1926) for the horizontal-type machine.

The choice of instrument is, of course, entirely up to individual preference, and it appears that the Zeiss type with two objectives is almost universally chosen. While it is true that, because of the two objectives, it is possible to bring into sharp focus at the same scale the images from two plates with slightly differing scale (though taken with the same telescope), it has been the writer's experience that if such original difference in scale is small, the single-objective instrument can cope with it; but if the scale difference becomes large, the plates do not blink well anyway. To the writer, with more than thirty-five years of experience, the horizontal type, single-objective instrument is preferable partly because of its greater simplicity of construction and operation (and hence the much lower concomitant cost) and partly because of the much greater ease of marking horizontal plates. One should not forget that a blink microscope is not a high-precision measuring machine but a survey instrument.

It may also be interpolated here that the blink microscope has been found invaluable in the detection of variable stars. For this purpose, plates taken in rapid succession are used—taken continuously during the night if one is interested in flare stars, cluster variables, or eclipsing binaries; with intervals of days if one is looking for cepheids; and with intervals of months if long-period variables are sought. In this case, of course, the star image does not "jump" but contracts and expands, and this, in turn, demands a much closer concordance between the plates in effective length of exposure than for proper-motion work. If the plates are well matched, variations of half a magnitude can be seen easily. A further adaptation of the method is in the search for stars of extreme color, such as the faint blue star searches originated by Zwicky and Humason and expanded by the writer. For this purpose, two plates are taken right after one another, one in blue light, the other in yellow or red, and the exposures are so adjusted as to give identical images for stars of, say, spectral class G. Very blue stars can then be found easily in blinking because the pulsation of their images goes contrariwise to that of the majority of the stars, which are redder than G.

Another technique, although basically different from blinking, should also be briefly mentioned. Here one uses the original negative of one plate but superimposes on it a positive copy of another plate taken with the same center. If proper care is used to match exposures and density of background and the plates are accurately lined up, stars which do not differ or change show a uniform grayness, but those which have moved or changed brightness or differ much in color from the average (if blue and red pairs are used) stand out because of a very different pattern of light and dark. Originally used by E. C. Pickering at Harvard and J. C. Kapteyn at Groningen, the method had fallen into disuse until revived recently by F. Zwicky (1955) at Palomar and J. Borgman (1959) at Groningen, especially as it appears to be more amenable to automation by the introduction of photoelectric scanners and automatic registration than is the blink method. It is in use chiefly for variable-star and color work and has not yet been used extensively for proper-motion work.

When the blink microscope is employed for the detection of proper motions, the plates used are necessarily taken many years apart. Changes in the optical adjustment of the telescope are almost bound to have occurred, and rarely do the field and images of the two plates appear identical. Generally, all the stars in the field will quiver a little in blinking, but this has not been found much of a handicap.

If a general proper-motion survey is to be executed efficiently, i.e., if large parts of the sky are to be searched in not too long a time, one cannot use too high magnification or plates of too large a scale. It has been the writer's experience that, with a magnification of only 6 or so, one can just see displacements of 15 μ on ordinary plates of good quality. Displacements of twice this amount become fairly easy, 50 μ become glaring, and, by the time 100 μ is reached, the observer gets the feeling that all stars with such a large motion will be discovered. Actually, this is not true: blinking plates is a very subjective procedure, and the time of day, the observer's alertness, and a number of other personal factors probably enter into it. Furthermore, the figures just given hold only for images of optimum quality, some 2–4 mag. above the plate limit. For brighter stars and for stars close to the plate limit, as well as for stars in the corners of the plate where the images are distorted, all numbers given above must be raised by a factor—sometimes a large factor. On the other hand, when using Schmidt plates, with their very small, sharp images, all the numbers quoted above should probably be reduced considerably—perhaps halved. At the other end of the scale, stars of even optimum quality image but with excessively large motion might be overlooked, in theory, since in this case the image often clearly jumps out of the field. Such objects should, however, be picked up as double variables, and the danger that they would really be overlooked is very slight indeed.

As an illustration, quantitative figures derived from the writer's *Bruce Proper Motion Survey* may be quoted. The plates used had a scale of 1 mm = 1', and an average interval of 30 years; a displacement of 50 μ, therefore, corresponds to a proper motion of 0".1 annually. The blinkable area of the plates amounted to about 30 square degrees, though the images in the corners were atrocious. Most plates reached to the sixteenth magnitude photographic, some long-exposure plates to the eighteenth, but a few poor-quality plates reached only to 14.5. From overlapping plates it was found (Luyten 1939) that the discovery chance of a star between 10.6 and 12.5 and with a proper motion between $0''.1$ and $0''.2$ annually was 0.48 but that for stars with the same motion and between 12.6 and 14.5 it was 0.67. For motions as large as $0''.2$–$0''.4$ the discovery chance increased, even for the brighter group, to 0.74 at the lower to 0.96 at the upper limit of the motion. Near the center of plates of good quality many stars were found whose motions, after measurement, proved to be no larger than $0''.030$ annually, corresponding to a displacement of 15 μ.

§ 2. THE PRINCIPAL SURVEYS

2.1. SURVEYS BY WOLF AND INNES

Before discussing the advantages and disadvantages of blink surveys for proper motion, it may be well to describe briefly the principal surveys made to date. Pioneers in the field were M. Wolf for the Northern, and R. T. A. Innes for the Southern Hemisphere. Wolf, who actually used the "stereocomparator" arrangement rather than a "blink," used plates taken with the 40-cm Bruce telescope at Heidelberg, which had a scale of 1 mm = 102''. The plate limit varied considerably, but occasionally stars of magnitude 17 were observed. Wolf's results were published in 51 lists in the *Astronomische Nachrichten*. Data from the first 20 lists were combined into a single publication (Wolf 1919) giving information for 1053 stars, arranged in order of right ascension; the later lists range from *A.N.*, No. 5033 (1920) to *A.N.*, No. 5658 (1929) (Wolf 1920–1929). Wolf's searches were made in scattered regions mostly in the Northern Hemisphere and covered a total area of some 2000 square degrees. His results were of greater importance, in that they not only constituted the first extensive search of this kind but also produced the first list of faint stars with large proper motion—the only one for many years. Among the Wolf stars thus found are many interesting objects: W 359, one of the nearest and faintest of known red dwarfs; W 489, the yellowest white dwarf known; W 28, perhaps better known as "van Maanen's star"; and many others.

Practically simultaneously, Innes, at the Union Observatory, Johannesburg, began blinking large numbers of plates taken with the Franklin Adams camera (1 mm = 4') or with various Carte du Ciel instruments from Greenwich to Melbourne. The most spectacular find made by Innes was that of the faint companion to α Centauri, which is still the nearest star known and now generally designated as "Proxima Centauri." Data for many hundreds of proper-motion stars found by Innes were published in the *Circulars of the Union Observatory* (Innes 1915–1927), but unfortunately Innes did not number his stars serially, and it has therefore become very difficult to refer to or identify Innes' stars in our present publications. In general, Innes' limit was the thirteenth magnitude, though a few stars fainter than this were found. His lower limit of motion was smaller than that of Wolf. All in all, Innes covered several hundred square degrees in his searches, mainly in the Southern Hemisphere, and published data for about 3000 proper-motion stars.

2.2. Surveys by Ross

Around 1925, F. E. Ross at the Yerkes Observatory began his blink survey, using plates taken with the 25-cm Bruce telescope (1 mm = 161″), which generally had intervals of around 20 years. Each plate covered an area of 170 square degrees, but the plates were of greatly varying quality and showed great distortion in the corners. Although, altogether, 233 fields were examined, the total area blinked—also because of considerable overlaps among the plates—was probably not more than about 20,000 square degrees. The results of this important survey were published in 12 lists in the *Astronomical Journal* (Ross 1925–1939) and gave data for a total of 1069 stars, generally brighter than the fifteenth magnitude and with motions exceeding 0″.2 annually.

2.3. Surveys by Luyten

The next extensive search for large proper motions was begun by the present writer, utilizing the magnificant plate material of the Harvard Observatory. At first in 1923, pairs of plates taken with the 8-inch Bache (1 mm = 3′) or the 8-inch Draper telescope (1 mm = 2′.7) were blinked. The older plates did not, in general, show many stars fainter than the twelfth magnitude, and, because of their small scale, only the larger motions could be found. Several lists, totaling some 683 stars with large proper motion, were published in several *Harvard Circulars* (Luyten 1927–1928).

Preliminary searches were then carried out on a few pairs of plates taken with the 61-cm Bruce telescope (1 mm = 1′); on these it was found that, with intervals of around 30 years, motions much below 0″.1 annually could be detected (Luyten 1928). Since at Harvard there was available an almost complete coverage of the Southern Hemisphere on about 1000 plates of this kind—the 1-hour exposures generally going a little beyond magnitude 16 and some 100 plates with 4 hours' exposure going to almost 18, with most plates having been taken around 1900—it was decided to repeat these plates and thus cover the Southern Hemisphere almost completely.

The new plates were taken at the Harvard Southern Station near Bloemfontein between 1929 and 1935; they were blinked by the writer at Minnesota, and more than 100,000 stars of appreciable motion were found. These now have all been measured; the data for 28,535 stars south of declination −50° were published in mimeographed form (Luyten 1941); subsequently, data for some 38,000 stars between −50° and −20° were similarly published (Luyten 1960a). After the southern survey had been completed, some 300 similar pairs of plates covering scattered regions between 0° and +40° were blinked, and another 17,000 proper-motion stars found. Data for these and for the remaining 18,000 stars between declinations −20° and 0° are now being prepared for publication. For further details on the entire program, reference may be made to the "First Report" and the "Final Report" of the *Bruce Proper Motion Survey* (Luyten 1938, 1960b). Some brief comments on the accomplishments of this survey may be added.

First of all, it is the only survey made to date which covers a very large part of the sky (96 per cent of the Southern Hemisphere and more than 20 per cent of the Northern Hemisphere) in an almost homogeneous manner. For stars with the largest motions, larger than $0''.3$ annually, the survey may be considered to be nearly complete down to $m_{pg} = 14.5$, whereas for the much smaller area of the long-exposure plates (about 1500 square degrees) this limit must lie close to $m_{pg} = 16.5$. As such, this survey provides the only material at present on the frequency in space of stars of very low luminosity and therefore on the faint end of the luminosity function. Second, after suitable statistical analysis, it will provide better data than were available heretofore on the numbers of stars of different brightness and proper motion—down to $0''.05$ annually—and hence ultimately on the kinematics of the galactic system. Third, among the 100,000 stars for which data are being published, there are a number of objects of great individual interest, such as (a) some 300 white dwarfs, constituting at least 80 per cent of all those now known; (b) the 30-odd wide binaries composed of a red-white dwarf pair and the only two double white dwarfs now known, these stars constituting the only objects from which, eventually, the masses of white dwarfs may be derived; (c) a number of white dwarfs of the lowest luminosity group (L 97–12, L 879–14) with extremely peculiar spectra and the first two helium white dwarfs (L 930–80 and L 1573–31), as well as the smallest known white dwarf (L 886–6); and (d) the prototype of the flare stars (L 726–8B = UV Ceti) and the first one in which the complete progress of a flare was observed, this being also the star of smallest known mass.

The vast majority of the 100,000 proper-motion stars found in this survey have motions so small that they possess only statistical value. The small minority with large motions, however, would seem to be of individual interest. For this reason three special catalogues have been published for these stars of large motion, viz., a catalogue of 1849 stars with motions exceeding $0''.5$ annually (LFT Catalogue, 1956) and two catalogues for the Northern and Southern Hemispheres separately, with data for stars with motions larger than $0''.2$. The Southern Hemisphere catalogue, containing 9867 entries, was published in 1957 (LTT Catalogue); the Northern Hemisphere section contains more than 7000 entries (Luyten 1961).

2.4. MISCELLANEOUS SURVEYS

In addition to these four large, general surveys, a number of smaller and more specialized searches have been made, notably by E. Hertzsprung (1918), using Potsdam astrographic plates; R. Furuhjelm (1916), similarly using Helsingfors plates; van Maanen and Willis (1930); and Oosterhoff (1936), who blinked Mount Wilson Selected Area plates taken with the 60-inch telescope; Bhaskaran (1932–1938), who used astrographic plates taken at Hyderabad; and G. Van Biesbroeck (1944, 1961) who made a search for faint companions to large proper-motion stars on plates taken with the 82-inch McDonald telescope. From this last survey came the discovery of the faint companion to BD+ $4°.4048$, a star of absolute magnitude $+19.5$.

Perhaps the most extensive survey of all as far as area and magnitude limit are concerned was started by H. Giclas at the Lowell Observatory in 1956. This survey aims to use the plates originally taken for the Pluto search with the 13-inch telescope, beginning in 1927, and covering the sky completely from the north pole to declination $-40°$, or about 80 per cent of the entire sky, and down to the seventeenth photographic magnitude. The plates have a scale of 1 mm = $2'$, and it is intended to take the new plates at such times as to make the intervals as uniform as possible. Since the images on the Lowell plates are considerably better than those on the Harvard Bruce plates, it should be possible to make the survey more complete than the Bruce survey and to go down to the same limit of proper motion. To date, about one-third of the survey has been completed and published (Giclas 1958), and motions as well as approximate colors have been published for 3358 stars. Among these are 18 new stars with motions exceeding $1''$ annually and another 298 with motions between $0''.5$ and $1''.0$ annually. Forty-eight white dwarf suspects and seventy pairs of proper-motion stars are listed. Only motions larger than $0''.27$ annually are being published.

2.5. FUTURE SURVEYS

The ultimate in proper-motion surveys of this kind—as we can now visualize it—will become possible when the Palomar 48-inch Schmidt survey plates are old enough to be repeated and blinked. This survey covers about 77 per cent of the entire sky down to magnitudes 21 photographic and 20 red. Since most of the very faint proper-motion stars we are looking for are probably red (a typical white dwarf of $21.0\ m_{\mathrm{pg}}$ could be expected to have a proper motion only of the order of $0''.010$ annually) and probably have color indices exceeding 1.5 on the average, it would now appear most feasible to repeat and blink only the red plates. There should be no difficulty in blinking any pair of plates in high galactic latitude, but, until some kind of automatic blinking methods or servo-mechanisms have been developed which could take over the tedious job of examining the plates, human-eye blinking should probably not be carried to galactic latitudes lower than 15° or 20°, except for a few, small, isolated, heavily obscured regions.

The writer has blinked a few pairs of these same plates, using duplicate negatives for the old plates and originals for the new, having intervals of only 8–9 years. While any conclusions drawn now should be considered extremely preliminary, it might be mentioned that (a) even with these short intervals, motions as small as $0''.1$ for stars fainter than the fifteenth magnitude are fairly easily seen—though this does not mean that any single examination of a pair of plates necessarily approaches completion for motions of this size—and many stars with motions half this size were picked up (the latter corresponding to a displacement of only 7 μ) and (b) few very faint stars with large motions were found (18–19 pg and with motions larger than $0''.5$ annually). If this latter point is substantiated, it will mean that we have really passed the maximum of the luminosity function and that stars with luminosities fainter than $M = 17$ are of rapidly decreasing frequency. It is this latter point that now seems the most important to settle and that alone would render the colossal amount of work involved in repeating and blinking the Palomar plates worthwhile. Our present guess is that, with the beautiful images of the Palomar Schmidt, optimum conditions would be reached for an interval of from 12 to 15 years, since for longer intervals the number of proper-motion stars found would become unmanageably large. It may be mentioned that, among the 1000 or so proper-motion stars found to date, there is one with $m_{red} = 20.2$, $m_{pg} = 22^+$, $\mu = 1''$, probably the star of lowest luminosity now known.

§ 3. ADVANTAGES AND DISADVANTAGES OF BLINK SURVEYS

As compared with other methods of finding and determining stellar motions wholesale, the blink method has the great advantage of speed. With it we can search a large area in the sky fairly thoroughly in a reasonably short time. Thus in the Bruce proper-motion survey the writer completed the examination of some 1000 pairs of plates, covering almost the entire Southern Hemisphere to at least the sixteenth magnitude (and down to 18 for 10 per cent of the plates) in less than 6 academic years, while carrying a more than normal teaching load at the same time. In general, far fewer than 1 per cent of the stars in any part of the sky are found to have appreciable motion with the blink microscope. The disadvantages of the blink method are mainly twofold: (a) it is probably not feasible to extend any blink survey to motions smaller than $0''.05$ annually, and perhaps in the future, among the very faint stars, it should be restricted to $0''.2$ or even $0''.3$ as a lower limit; and (b) the motions obtained are *relative*, as in all photographic work.

That the second objection is not too serious results largely from the first. For very faint stars the systematic motion of the neighboring stars used for measuring is almost negligible compared with that of the proper-motion star itself. Thus, for a star of magnitude 16 with a motion of $0''.1$ annually, the correction from relative to absolute motion will rarely amount to more than $0''.008$.

One further point seems important enough to be mentioned here. In most blink surveys, especially those of Wolf and Ross, measurements were carried out at the eyepiece of the blink microscope itself, and, as the "zero" or stationary background, there is generally used either a single star or the average of a few stars, which, according to the blink, possess no appreciable motion. The standard method of measuring proper motions, of course, consists of measuring the image of the motion star relative to three or more comparison stars on both plates, in a measuring machine in which either the plate or the microscope is moved in its entirety by the screw. A simple linear reduction then suffices to derive the motion. While the former—"optical"—method is unquestionably much faster, experience has shown that it is also much more inaccurate and, in fact, does not come close to utilizing the accuracy inherent in the plates. Eventually, the proper motions found with the blink microscope must be determined with as much accuracy as possible, and it would seem to the writer to be more sensible to do this immediately rather than to measure the motions optically first and with lower accuracy, in order to save some time.

REFERENCES

BHASKARAN, T. P. 1932–
1938 *A.N.*, Nos. 5867, 6097, 6332, 6386.

BORGMAN, J. 1959 *Electronics*, **32**, 66 (No. 19).

FURUHJELM, R. 1916 *Recherches sur les mouvements propres des étoiles dans la zone photographique de Helsingfors* (Helsingfors: Universitet. Astronomiska Observatoriet).

GICLAS, H. 1958 *Lowell Obs. Bull.*, No. 89.

HERTZSPRUNG, E. 1918 *A.N.*, No. 4959.

INNES, R. T. A. 1915–
1927 *Union Obs. Circ.*, Nos. 25, 28, 30, 35, 37, 39, 43, 45, 46, 47, 48, 53, 54, 55, 58, 59, 69, 73.

LUYTEN, W. J. 1927–
1928 *Harvard Circ.*, Nos. 310, 324.
1928 *Ibid.*, Nos. 325, 326, 327.
1938 *Pub. Obs. Minnesota*, Vol. 2, No. 5.
1939 *Ibid.*, No. 8, p. 165.
1941 *Bruce Proper Motion Survey, The General Catalogue*, Parts A, B, C (Minnesota: University of Minnesota Press).
1960a *Ibid.*, Parts D, E.
1960b *Pub. Obs. Minnesota*, Vol. 2, No. 15.
1961 *A Catalogue of 7127 Stars in the Northern Hemisphere with Proper Motions Exceeding 0".2 Annually* (Minneapolis, Minn.: Lund Press).

MAANEN, A. VAN, and
  WILLIS, H. C. 1930 *Mt. W. Contr.*, No. 412.

OOSTERHOFF, P. T. 1936 *Mt. W. Contr.*, No. 542.

PULFRICH, C. 1902 *Zs. f. Instrumentenk.*, **22**, 65, 133, 178, 229.

ROSS, F. E. 1925–
1939 *A.J.*, Nos. 853, 856, 862, 871, 886, 900, 926, 935, 957, 1073, 1101, 1118.

SCHLESINGER, F. 1926 *A.J.*, **37**, 45.

VAN BIESBROECK, G. 1944 *A.J.*, **51**, 61.
1961 *Ibid.*, **66**, 528.

WOLF, M. 1919 *Veröff Sternw. Heidelberg*, **7**, 195.
1920–
1929 *A.N.*, Nos. 5033, 5035, 5039, 5050, 5074, 5079, 5084, 5089, 5090, 5120, 5128, 5153, 5214, 5243, 5262, 5281, 5289, 5293, 5305, 5307, 5319, 5374, 5388, 5391, 5396, 5422, 5451, 5470, 5495, 5516, 5658.

ZWICKY, F. 1955 *Pub. A.S.P.*, **67**, 232.

CHAPTER 6

Trigonometric Stellar Parallaxes

K. Aa. STRAND

U.S. Naval Observatory, Washington, D.C.

§ 1. INTRODUCTION

THE principal catalogue of trigonometric parallaxes is the *General Catalogue of Trigonometric Stellar Parallaxes* by Miss Louise F. Jenkins, published in 1952. We shall refer to it in this chapter as the *"General Catalogue"* or the *"Catalogue."*

The *Catalogue* lists the parallaxes of 5822 stars as obtained from approximately 10,000 individual determinations. A nearly equal number of these determinations was produced by the Allegheny, Cape, McCormick, and Yale Observatories and comprises 70 per cent of the total, while the Greenwich, Mount Wilson, and Yerkes Observatories contributed another 20 per cent on a nearly equal basis.

The *Catalogue* includes all parallaxes that had been published or received in manuscript form by Miss Jenkins prior to June, 1950. Excluded from the *Catalogue* were all the early parallaxes determined from visual observations and several short series of photographic determinations which were omitted because of their small weight as compared with the more modern series.

At the end of this chapter is given a bibliography which contains references to parallaxes published since the appearance of the *General Catalogue*. The combined number of parallax determinations in the supplementary list is 970 and shows that the accumulated number of determinations during recent years falls far short of the average for the first 50 years of photographic determination of trigonometric parallaxes of stars.

An examination of the parallaxes collected in the *Catalogue* shows that the material is deficient in certain aspects, as outlined below. A considerable number of the published parallaxes, especially those originating from early series, have such large accidental errors that it is questionable whether they can be used individually or for statistical purposes. This is due to the limited material on which the determinations were based.

55

Parallaxes are missing for stars of certain spectral classifications by reason of the selectivity of the observing programs. When the original observing program was drawn up by Schlesinger, it called for parallax determinations of all stars brighter than 5.5 mag. except stars of spectral class earlier than A and late-type giants. After the completion of this program, most recent programs have concentrated on faint stars which show dwarf characteristics as discovered from proper motions or spectral types.

The median parallax of the *Catalogue* is 0″.018, which is less than twice the average accidental error of ±0″.011 for one of the smaller parallaxes (Hertzsprung 1952). This means that far too many stars with small parallaxes were included in the observing programs, especially during the earlier period when Schlesinger's program was in effect.

With the exception of the Mount Wilson Observatory parallaxes, which were obtained from photographic material taken with the 60- and 100-inch reflectors, all other parallaxes were based on photographs taken with long-focus refractors, which limit the observations to stars brighter than 13.5 mag. As a result, parallaxes are missing for the majority of the stars of low luminosity in the solar neighborhood. As these stars are late-type M dwarfs, subdwarfs, and white dwarfs, the lack of trigonometric parallaxes to determine their intrinsic brightness poses a serious problem in the interpretation of their physical characteristics.

§ 2. INTERNAL ACCURACIES

The small size of a trigonometric parallax, often constituting only a few microns in terms of the scale on the photographic plates, makes it important to evaluate the sources contributing to the published probable error of a parallax. Only a few of the many extensive investigations that have been published on this subject can be mentioned in the following brief summary.

The internal probable error, $e(i)$, of a plate of unit weight (a plate with two images rated of good quality) is related to the focal length of the telescope, F, by the following formula:

$$e(i)^2 = \left(\frac{0″.12}{F}\right)^2 + (0″.025)^2.$$

This formula was first developed by Schlesinger (1937), but the constants have been modified to relate to internal rather than external plate errors and to a slightly different system of weighting the plates. However, taking these changes into account, we find excellent agreement between the Schlesinger constants and the present ones, which were based on data obtained from more recent parallax series (Land 1944, 1949; Strand and Hall 1951; Wagman 1956; Lippincott 1957).

On the basis of this formula, one finds that relatively little loss in accuracy is incurred if one goes from the refractor of largest focal length used in parallax work—the Yerkes refractor of 19.4 meters in focal length—to the refractors of shortest focal length of 6.9 meters, at the Cape and Greenwich Observatories. For the Yerkes refractor, $e(i) = \pm 0\rlap{.}''026$, while, for the other telescopes mentioned, $e(i) = \pm 0\rlap{.}''030$.

The term in the Schlesinger formula varying inversely with the focal length must originate largely from the surface of the photographic plate, indicating a distortion in the photographic emulsion which contributes a probable error amounting to $\pm 0.7 \; \mu$. From the following discussion it will be seen that this error varies with the size of the configuration of the reference frame. It is also present in very small configurations of two adjacent images with separations ranging from a few tenths up to not more than 2 mm. Based on the results of 1014 multiple-exposure plates of binaries photographed with the Dearborn, Lick, Lowell, and Sproul refractors, the corresponding error is $\pm 0.3 \; \mu$ for the mean result of a plate.

The average error $e(i)$ may be considered as composed of three average errors, the accidental error, $e(a)$; the shift error, $e(s)$; and a night error, $e(n)$ (Land 1944); and we have

$$e(i)^2 = e(a)^2 + e(s)^2 + e(n)^2 \; .$$

It may be assumed that $e(a)$ is composed of accidental errors due to random refraction oscillations, photographic image formations, and the process of measuring. Quoting the results obtained at the Sproul Observatory (van de Kamp 1945), the error of measurement of a plate of unit weight is $\pm 0\rlap{.}''015$ (p.e.), while the combined effect of the two other sources contributing to $e(a)$ is $\pm 0\rlap{.}''023$ (p.e.).

The error $e(s)$ was found by Schilt (1939) to increase with the size of the configuration of the reference frame up to a limit of 150 cm^2 of the sum of the squares of the x- and y-co-ordinates of the reference stars. For larger values of this sum, there was no increase in the value of $e(s)$ and sometimes a decrease. These results were based on Yale parallax plates and were later confirmed by Land (1942) from a study of Sproul plates. He concluded that the shift error, ranging from $\pm 0\rlap{.}''009$ to $\pm 0\rlap{.}''017$ (p.e.), is caused principally by relative displacements of the emulsion, the central region being shifted relative to the outer region. Further studies by Land (1948) based on a large number of Yale parallaxes showed that the probable error of unit weight increased from $\pm 0\rlap{.}''023$ for $\Sigma x^2 = 60$ cm^2 to $\pm 0\rlap{.}''028$ for $\Sigma x^2 = 160$ cm^2, in good agreement with his previous results. The effect of $e(s)$ may be reduced through the use of "double plates," obtained by turning the plate 180° in its own plane between two successive sets of exposures. This method has been adopted in several of the current parallax programs. It appears that the shift error is not entirely eliminated by this process, and the remaining error, which increases with the size of the field, may therefore be caused by optical distortion (Lippincott 1957).

The average night error for a plate, $e(n)$, appears to be constant during all exposures of one and the same star field within the period of observation on the same night but shows variations from one night to another. At least part of this error originates from refraction anomalies in the atmosphere. This was first explained by Schlesinger and Blair (1905) as caused by small inclinations to the earth's surface in the strata of uniform atmospheric density.

Another factor contributing to the night error may originate in the optical system. Land (1944) has shown that the night error ranges from $\pm 0''.009$ to $\pm 0''.017$ (p.e.), with an average value of $\pm 0''.012$ (p.e.), for the measured position of the central star relative to the reference system. This error limits the gain in accuracy to the point that it becomes impractical to take more than two double plates with a total of eight to twelve exposures on any given night.

In the discussion of the errors it was assumed that effects due to atmospheric dispersion were, as far as possible, eliminated by restricting the observations to small hour angles; that the exposures were of sufficient length to give well-exposed images, as underexposed images appear to increase the error of unit weight (Alden 1949); and that the effective magnitude of the parallax star was reduced to the average magnitude of the comparison stars. The latter should have little dispersion in their magnitudes, possibly less than 0.3 mag.

In cases where proper magnitude compensation has not been employed or where very small sector openings, giving reductions of 5 mag. or more, have been used, it has been found that the resulting probable errors are larger and that systematic effects have been introduced that are far more serious.

From the foregoing, it is seen that the accidental error of a parallax plate of unit weight is of the order of $\pm 0''.028$ (p.e.) and varies little in size for refractors of from 7 to 20 meters in focal length, provided that all sources contributing to the accidental error, including emulsion shifts, are kept to a minimum.

§ 3. EXTERNAL PROBABLE ERRORS

In problems involving the use of trigonometric parallaxes, accurate estimates of the external probable error are generally needed. This then requires the establishment of a relationship between the internal and the external mean error. The internal probable error of a parallax in the published lists is derived from a least-squares solution and is determined from the internal agreement of the plate material, the parallax factors, and the weight of the measures. Because of the small number of plates used in the earlier parallax series, large fluctuations are found in the values of the probable error of unit weight, with a similar effect on the resulting probable errors listed for the parallaxes.

Certain practices in some of the earlier parallax series also affected the published probable errors. Among these may be mentioned the rejection of measures which gave large residuals in the solutions and the discontinuation of a series if the first preliminary solution based on a small number of plates was found to be very consistent.

The effects of these various practices on the published internal mean errors, together with methods to reduce them to external ones, have been discussed by Schlesinger (1928, 1935). In the *General Catalogue* the following formula has been used to relate the internal probable error, $r(i)$, with the external probable error, $r(e)$:

$$r(e) = a + \tfrac{1}{2} r(i) ,$$

where the values for a range from $0\overset{\prime\prime}{.}0036$ for Allegheny to $0\overset{\prime\prime}{.}018$ for Uppsala (see *General Catalogue*, p. 6).

The mean external probable errors for the various series were determined from the comparison of the parallaxes common to two or more series, using the relation

$$0.455 \langle (\pi, A - \pi, B)^2 \rangle = \langle r^2(e, A) \rangle + \langle r^2(e, B) \rangle .$$

An independent determination of the mean external probable errors for the Allegheny and the McCormick series has been published by Harris (1954), who confirmed the *General Catalogue* precepts for the external mean errors. He also examined the variation in the weights within the two series and showed that the results for Allegheny were essentially correct with regard to the precepts but that the McCormick values showed less variation than the precepts allowed for. He pointed out that this might be ascribed to the correlation between the probable error of unit weight and the number of plates in a series, as has been mentioned above. Although only two of the long series were investigated, it might be assumed from the results that the precepts applied in the *General Catalogue* for determining the relative weights have been confirmed.

For the parallax determinations dependent on forty or more plates made at the Sproul and Yerkes Observatories, the *General Catalogue* has reduced the constant a for both series from $0\overset{\prime\prime}{.}008$ to $0\overset{\prime\prime}{.}004$. Hence, for a parallax determined at these two observatories with approximately fifty plates, the internal probable error of the parallax dependent on an average parallax factor of 0.8 would be of the order of $\pm 0\overset{\prime\prime}{.}005$, which would lead to an external probable error of $\pm 0\overset{\prime\prime}{.}007$, using the above precept.

The author of this chapter recently made a comparison between Allegheny, Sproul, and Yerkes parallaxes based on not less than thirty-six plates for each determination. While the material is somewhat limited, the results of the investigation appear consistent with the precept adopted by the *General Catalogue* for the long series. The investigation showed the following relation between the internal and external probable errors:

$$r(e)^2 = r(i)^2 + b ,$$

where b was equal to $4'' \times 10^{-6}$ for the Sproul series, $6'' \times 10^{-6}$ for the Yerkes, and $8'' \times 10^{-6}$ for Allegheny. The slightly larger value for Allegheny may be caused by the somewhat smaller number of plates used in each determination. Again assuming a parallax determined from fifty plates, the external probable error on the basis of the above precept would be $\pm 0\overset{\prime\prime}{.}006$, for all three observatories, compared with the average internal probable error of $\pm 0\overset{\prime\prime}{.}005$. Perhaps the most significant result was that there were no systematic differences between the series.

§ 4. SYSTEMATIC CORRECTIONS

In preparation for the *General Catalogue*, the longer trigonometric series of parallaxes were compared with each other by a least-squares solution. On the basis of this investigation, precepts were established to reduce the relative parallaxes to absolute. Since the parallax of a star is determined relative to a set of comparison stars, it follows that the mean parallax of the comparison stars must be added to the relative parallax, in order to reduce it to absolute.

The mean parallax of the comparison stars is small, under normal circumstances, and may be derived from a statistical parallax based on knowledge of magnitude and preferably also on spectrum or color. Frequently used in modern determinations are the tables by Vyssotsky and Williams (1948) and Binnendijk (1943). For a field star of the eleventh photovisual magnitude, the annual parallax is of the order of $+0\rlap{.}''002$ for low galactic latitude and $+0\rlap{.}''005$ above galactic latitude 41°. For stars in the visual magnitude group between 8.5 and 9.5, the corresponding values are $+0\rlap{.}''004$ and $+0\rlap{.}''007$.

The *General Catalogue* adopted a value of $+0\rlap{.}''003$ for reducing all published Allegheny parallaxes to absolute. The corrections to the other series were derived from comparisons with Allegheny. As a result, corrections were obtained for these series, using Allegheny as the standard. This procedure was investigated by Schilt (1954), who came to the conclusion that the precepts of systematic correction, as applied in the *General Catalogue*, should not be used. From his investigation, Schilt finds that the systematic corrections applied in the *Catalogue* are those in the accompanying table. The table shows that all series,

Observatory	Systematic Correction	No. of Parallaxes
Allegheny.........	$0\rlap{.}''000$	1800
McCormick......	$-.001$	1881
Yale............	$-.005$	1728
Cape............	$-.006$	1667
Greenwich.......	$-.001$	760
Mt. Wilson......	$-.004$	550
Yerkes..........	$-.005$	427
Sproul..........	-0.006	400
Mean.......	-0.0035	....

except Allegheny, require a negative correction and that there is essential agreement between Allegheny, McCormick, and Greenwich, or 45 per cent of the individually determined parallaxes, while the remaining observatories on the list, having 50 per cent of the parallaxes, require corrections of from $-0\rlap{.}''004$ to $-0\rlap{.}''006$. Since the systematic difference between two stations can be determined with a probable error of $\pm 0\rlap{.}''0015$ (Harris), provided that they have 100 parallaxes in common, the difference between the two northern stations— Allegheny and McCormick—and the two southern stations—Cape and Yale—

must be considered real. At the present time, there is no satisfactory explanation of this difference. The question also arises whether these same corrections should be applied to the parallaxes which are observed only from the southern stations. For the remaining stations, the systematic differences from Allegheny are quite likely not real, owing to lack of sufficient material. This is perhaps best shown in the case of the Yerkes parallaxes, where the systematic difference with Allegheny changed from $0''000$ in the 1935 *Catalogue* to the present value of $-0''005$ by adding 53 parallaxes, or 14 per cent, to the total available in 1935.

The large systematic difference of $0''005$ between Allegheny and McCormick, on the one side, and Cape and Yale, on the other, is very disturbing because there is no satisfactory explanation for its existence. Of the four programs, the programs at the southern observatories were the latest to be started and benefited from the experience gathered on earlier programs, both in observational procedures and in statistical treatment of the measures, contrary to the early parallaxes, where the mean values were affected by the omission of negative and otherwise unacceptable results (Schilt 1954). Traces of this effect are undoubtedly present in the over-all statistical treatment of the Allegheny and McCormick programs from their inception, as are possible systematic effects of observing the bright stars with very narrow sector openings.

Since there appears to be considerable doubt as to the validity of the precepts for systematic corrections in the *General Catalogue*, it seems advisable not to use them. Instead, the relative parallaxes as published and listed for each star on the right-hand pages of the *Catalogue* should be used. Reductions to absolute may, in general, be assumed to be $+0''003$ for galactic latitudes less than 45°; $+0''004$ for 45°–70°; and $+0''005$ for 70°–90°. A more refined reduction may be obtained from the tables by Vyssotsky and Williams (1948) or Binnendijk (1943) on the basis of the known magnitudes of the comparison stars.

§ 5. PRESENT AND FUTURE PARALLAX PROGRAMS

At present the Allegheny, Greenwich (Herstmonceux), and Sproul Observatories are actively engaged in parallax work in the Northern Hemisphere and the Cape Observatory in the Southern Hemisphere. Their programs are summarized in the progress report of Commission 24 of the I.A.U. (*Trans. I.A.U.*, Vol. **11A**, 1962). The remaining observatories previously contributing to the parallax work either have no active programs at the present time or their future activities in this field are uncertain.

One of the drawbacks in the parallax programs has been the slow process of measuring the photographic plates, which requires personnel with a special skill for this work. It is hoped that present developments in automatic measuring machines, promising speedup in plate measurements by a factor of at least five times, will encourage observatories to re-enter this field. Their active participation is urgently needed to secure the required number of parallaxes for the brighter stars and solve the problem of existing discrepant values in the *General Catalogue*.

For stars fainter than the thirteenth magnitude, there is at the present time no telescope in operation suitable for high-precision astrometric problems such as trigonometric parallax determinations, requiring a large number of plates of each star field. Within the next few years this lack of instrumentation will be remedied for the Northern Hemisphere, when the 60-inch astrometric reflector at the Flagstaff Station, Arizona, of the U.S. Naval Observatory, becomes operational. By incorporating the latest developments in automation, in both observing, measuring, and reduction of the data, it is expected that parallaxes for a representative sample of intrinsically faint stars will be available within a not too distant future.

§ 6. BIBLIOGRAPHY

PARALLAX DETERMINATIONS PUBLISHED SINCE THE *GENERAL CATALOGUE*

Observatory	Year	Publication	No. of Parallaxes*
Allegheny.............	1952 1953 1957 1957 1960	*A.J.*, **56**, 201 *Ibid.*, **57**, 123 *Ibid.*, **62**, 280 *Ibid.*, p. 281 *Ibid.*, **65**, 106	50 52 (21) 34 (10) 55 52
Cape................	1954 1958	*M.N.*, **114**, 610 *Ibid.*, **118**, 31	100 (24) 19 (1)
London..............	1950 1956	*M.N.*, **110**, 618 *Ibid.*, **116**, 258	20 17
McCormick..........	1959 1960	*A.J.*, **64**, 268 *Pub. McCormick Obs.*, **14**, 2	† 270
Sproul‡..............	1951–1961	*A.J.*, Vols. **55–66**	37
Van Vleck...........	1956 1959	*A.J.*, **61**, 396 *Ibid.*, **64**, 269	28 20
Yale................	1956 1956 1958	*A.J.*, **61**, 199 *Ibid.*, p. 394 *Ibid.*, **63**, 340	90 57 34
Yerkes..............	1951	*A.J.*, **56**, 106	32

* Numbers in parentheses indicate number of parallaxes in series included in the *General Catalogue*.

† Contains corrections to previously published parallaxes from the Leander McCormick Observatory.

‡ The parallax determinations from the Sproul Observatory are based on extensive series of plates and are mainly of nearby single and double stars. The published parallaxes are contained in 25 articles in *A.J.*, Vols. **55–66**.

REFERENCES

ALDEN, H. L.	1949	*Trans. Yale U. Obs.*, Vol. **15**, Part 2.
BINNENDIJK, L.	1943	*B.A.N.*, **10**, 9.
HARRIS, D. L.	1954	*A.J.*, **59**, 59.
HERTZSPRUNG, E.	1952	*Observatory*, **72**, 242.

JENKINS, L. F.   1952   *General Catalogue of Trigonometric Stellar Parallaxes* (New Haven: Yale University Observatory).

KAMP, P. VAN DE   1945   *A.J.*, **51**, 159.
LAND, G.   1942   *A.J.*, **50**, 51.
                              1944   *Ibid.*, **51**, 25.
                              1949   *Trans. Yale U. Obs.*, Vol. **15**, Part 2.
LIPPINCOTT, S. L.   1957   *A.J.*, **62**, 55.
SCHILT, J.   1939   *A.J.*, **48**, 53.
                              1954   *Ibid.*, **59**, 55.
SCHLESINGER, F.   1928   *A.J.*, **38**, 189.
                              1935   *General Catalogue of Trigonometric Stellar Parallaxes* (2d ed.; New Haven: Yale University Observatory).
                              1937   *A.J.*, **46**, 85.
SCHLESINGER, F., and
    BLAIR, G. B.   1905   *Misc. Sci. Papers, Allegheny Obs.*, N.S., No. 18.
STRAND, K. AA., and
    HALL, R. G.   1951   *A.J.*, **56**, 106.
VYSSOTSKY, A. N., and
    WILLIAMS, E. T. R.   1948   *A.J.*, **53**, 78.
WAGMAN, N. E.   1956   *Pub. Allegheny Obs.*, Vol. **10**.

CHAPTER 7

Radial Velocities

R. M. PETRIE

Dominion Astrophysical Observatory, Victoria, B.C.

§ 1. CATALOGUES OF RADIAL VELOCITIES

THE principal radial-velocity catalogue—and indeed the one to which we shall chiefly refer in this chapter—is that compiled by R. E. Wilson (1953) (referred to herein as the *"General Catalogue"* or the *"Catalogue"*). It contains radial velocities of 15,106 stars, including the material listed in previous general catalogues, and velocities published up to the closing date of January 1, 1951. One need consult the literature, therefore, only for lists published after the closing date, in order to supplement the material of the *General Catalogue.* Extensive lists appearing since 1951 include the following: "Radial Velocities of 360 Stars" by R. E. Wilson and A. H. Joy (1952); "The Radial Velocities of 166 Red Dwarf Stars" by E. R. Dyer, Jr. (1954); "Radial Velocities of Southern B Stars Determined at the Radcliffe Observatory, I," by M. W. Feast, A. D. Thackeray, and A. J. Wesselink (1955); "The Measurement of Objective-Prism Radial Velocities" by Marcelle Duflot and C. Fehrenbach (1956); "The Radial Velocities, Spectral Classes, and Photographic Magnitudes of 1041 Late-Type Stars" by J. F. Heard (1956); "Radial Velocities of Southern B Stars Determined at the Radcliffe Observatory, II," by M. W. Feast, A. D. Thackeray, and A. J. Wesselink (1957); "Fundamental Data for Southern Stars (First List)" by David S. Evans, A. Menzies, and R. H. Stoy (1957); and "The Measurement of Objective-Prism Radial Velocities, Third List," by J. Boulon, Marcelle Duflot, and C. Fehrenbach (1959).

A number of shorter lists have been published, and a catalogue of radial velocities of 570 B stars has been prepared by Petrie and Pearce (1962). It is estimated that some 2500 radial-velocity determinations have become available since the compilation of the *General Catalogue;* nevertheless, the production of radial velocities by use of conventional slit spectrographs is decreasing and is likely to continue to decline. The withdrawal of several observatories from routine radial-velocity work and the faintness of the stars now to be observed are the chief causes. It is evident that the *General Catalogue* will serve as the standard source of radial velocities for a considerable time, and it is important, therefore, to study its internal and absolute accuracy both for the purpose of employing the *Catalogue* values and for comparison with new lists.

The unsatisfactory rate of accumulation of radial velocities may be improved in the near future by the use of slitless spectrographs. One may refer to the important advances made in this connection by Fehrenbach and his colleagues (Barbier and Fehrenbach 1955; Fehrenbach 1955; Duflot and Fehrenbach 1956; Boulon, Duflot, and Fehrenbach 1959), by Schalén (1954), and by Panaiotov (1955). A number of observatories are now contemplating the installation of equipment for objective-prism radial velocities. It is perhaps premature to discuss the velocities obtained by the new method until more comparison material is available, and no such discussion will be included here. One may hope that the objective-prism method will soon supply the radial velocities of faint stars, which are necessary if we are to investigate the dynamics of the Galaxy at large distances from the sun.

§ 2. SYSTEMATIC DIFFERENCES BETWEEN OBSERVATORIES

The *General Catalogue*, like its predecessor compiled by Moore (1932), tabulates systematic corrections to be applied to radial velocities from different observatories. The corrections to the institutional values generally vary with spectral type, and they are derived so as to reduce all velocities to the system of the Mills three-prism observations made at the Lick Observatory. The choice of the Lick system as the standard is a logical one because of its reliability, because of the large number of radial velocities obtained directly with the Mills spectrograph, and because of the care used by Campbell and his colleagues in defining and maintaining their velocity system.

It is difficult to be sure of the systematic corrections because of the changes in instruments and procedures introduced in most observatories during the past few decades. The difficulty is emphasized by Wilson: "Differences between instrumental combinations and the effects of revisions in systems of wave-lengths do not in general appear in the published results, and a compiler would face an enormous and probably unprofitable task should he attempt to untangle the observations." These remarks are, unfortunately, too true; it cannot be too strongly urged that radial-velocity workers give all relevant details in publishing results and, furthermore, that they observe standard stars, in order to ascertain systematic differences with other observatories and other equipment. Radial-velocity work can attain its greatest usefulness and significance only by meticulous adherence to these principles.

The systematic corrections given in the *Catalogue* are valuable, especially where long programs were executed without changes in equipment or procedures. Yet the corrections must be regarded merely as average values to be applied with some discrimination. For example, Wilson tabulates a correction of $+1.0$ km/sec to the radial velocities of A stars determined at Ottawa (prior to 1920). However, a detailed examination by Pearce (unpublished) shows different corrections to two series of Ottawa spectrograms. He analyzed 374 spectra of 11 stars observed with the Ottawa three-prism spectrograph and found a negligible correction, viz., -0.2 ± 0.5 km/sec. On the other hand, he established a correction of $+3.6 \pm 0.4$ km/sec for Ottawa single-prism observations of A stars based on some 2100 spectrograms of 63 stars. Obviously, the *General Catalogue* entry is some kind of average between the above-quoted values, and its indiscriminate application would not always yield the best radial velocities.

In the Introduction to the *General Catalogue* it is stated: "In agreement with Moore we found no significant differences for the stars of class B, . . ." and yet differences are in fact found among the *Catalogue* entries if one divides the stars into magnitude groups. The influence of spectroscopic purity on the effective wavelengths of blended features and the peculiarities of different spectro-

TABLE 1

SYSTEMATIC DIFFERENCES FOR BRIGHT B STARS

	Mean Difference (km/sec)	No.
Mount Wilson−Lick.........................	$+0.1 \pm 0.7$	84
Dominion Astrophysical−Lick.................	$- .2 \pm .6$	61
Mount Wilson−Dominion Astrophysical........	-0.1 ± 0.7	66

graphs appear to affect the velocities. The systematic corrections given in the *General Catalogue* rest on comparisons necessarily restricted to the brighter stars, which were generally observed with spectrographs giving relatively high purity and dispersion. It does not follow that radial velocities of fainter B stars share the zero systematic correction.

Comparisons have been made between the velocities of B stars determined at the Lick, Mount Wilson, and Dominion Astrophysical Observatories, and the results serve to illustrate the comments made above. Table 1 gives the differences found for stars between spectral types B0 and B7 and brighter than apparent magnitude 6.5. These comparisons are extremely satisfactory, proving that the early work on bright B stars, employing relatively powerful spectrographs, gave highly consistent results.

Comparisons between the results for fainter stars are less satisfactory. Still employing *General Catalogue* entries, spectral types B0–B7, for apparent magnitudes between 6.6 and 8.1, one finds the differences shown in Table 2. A similar comparison for B stars fainter than apparent magnitude 8.0 is given in Table 3.

Some of the comparisons are not well established because of the small number of stars available, but nevertheless it is clear that systematic differences exist.

In particular, the Lick Observatory velocities are more negative than those from Mount Wilson and Victoria. This conclusion is supported by an independent comparison published by Feast and Thackeray (1958) and by the results of an extensive program recently completed at Victoria (Petrie and Pearce 1962). The latter provides the material for the comparisons in Table 4 with *General Catalogue* values and with those of the Radcliffe Observatory, among B stars between apparent magnitudes 7.5 and 9.0.

It appears to be established that systematic differences do in fact exist between the velocities of the fainter B stars determined at various institutions, although corrections for such differences are not applied in the mean velocities of the *General Catalogue*.

Smaller residual differences are found among the velocities of later-type stars. As an illustrative example, the *General Catalogue* velocities of stars of

TABLE 2

SYSTEMATIC DIFFERENCES FOR B STARS BETWEEN
MAGNITUDES 6.6 AND 8.1

	Mean Difference (km/sec)	No.
Mount Wilson−Lick...........................	+3.4±1.5	54
Dominion Astrophysical−Lick..................	+2.6±1.2	20
Mount Wilson−Dominion Astrophysical.........	−0.4±1.1	52

TABLE 3

SYSTEMATIC DIFFERENCES FOR B STARS FAINTER
THAN MAGNITUDE 8.0

	Mean Difference (km/sec)	No.
Mount Wilson−Lick...........................	+ 5.2±1.9	54
Dominion Astrophysical−Lick..................	+10.5±2.3	4
Mount Wilson−Dominion Astrophysical.........	+ 3.2±1.6	6

TABLE 4

SYSTEMATIC DIFFERENCES FOR FAINT B STARS

	Mean Difference (km/sec)	No.
Dominion Astrophysical−Lick..................	+10.7±0.9	52
Mount Wilson−Dominion Astrophysical.........	+ 1.0±0.9	47
Radcliffe−Dominion Astrophysical.............	+ 1.5±0.9	22

spectral type K have been separated into two groups, those stars of magnitude 6.0 and brighter and those stars fainter than 6.0. Table 5 gives the results.

The corrections given by Wilson to reduce velocities to the system of the *Catalogue* are as follows: for Mount Wilson, −0.5 km/sec; for Dominion Astrophysical, +0.5 km/sec; and for David Dunlap, −1.0 km/sec. The systematic differences for the brighter K stars, tabulated in Table 5, are very satisfactorily dealt with by the *Catalogue* corrections. This is not so, however, for the fainter K stars, the mean differences after application of the systematic corrections being, for example, Dominion Astrophysical − Lick = −1.5 km/sec and Mount Wilson − David Dunlap = −1.9 km/sec. The comparisons for the fainter stars are not very numerous, it is true, but nevertheless it appears that averaging the results over stars of all magnitudes may not give the best *Catalogue* system of radial velocities.

TABLE 5

SYSTEMATIC DIFFERENCES FOR K-TYPE STARS

	BRIGHTER STARS		FAINTER STARS	
	Mean Difference (km/sec)	No.	Mean Difference (km/sec)	No.
Mount Wilson−Lick.....................	+0.8±0.2	162	−1.6±1.1	9
Dominion Astrophysical−Lick............	−0.6±0.2	112	−2.0±1.9	20
Mount Wilson−Dominion Astrophysical...	+1.2±0.2	125	+1.2±0.4	34
Mount Wilson−David Dunlap..........	−0.3±0.2	25	−2.4±0.4	22

It is probable that, were enough comparisons available, one would arrive at corrections for each institution and for each spectral interval, depending on the dispersion used and even on the particular program being considered. As the compiler of the *General Catalogue* pointed out, it is virtually impossible to recover the full details of some of the earlier programs and properly to assign systematic corrections. The corrections given in the *Catalogue* are the best average values available and, with the possible exception of the B stars, should lead to reliable statistical results. The systematic differences in the case of the B stars are worth special attention, since the velocities are more complete to certain magnitude limits and systematic differences large enough to be important appear to exist.

The systematic corrections tabulated by Wilson could be improved if certain comparisons were now made with instruments of well-known behavior. This would require a substantial volume of observation and measurement, and it is unlikely that radial-velocity workers will, at present, be able to devote much effort to this task. Perhaps it will be sufficient to ask that all extensive programs now under way, or contemplated, include enough comparison material for a firm assessment of systematic differences.

§ 3. ABSOLUTE ACCURACY OF THE *GENERAL CATALOGUE* SYSTEM

3.1. A STANDARD VELOCITY SYSTEM

The velocity system of the *General Catalogue* is essentially that of the Lick Observatory as defined by the Mills three-prism spectrograph. It is of interest and importance, therefore, to assess the absolute accuracy of that system of radial velocities. The problem is difficult and involved, including, as it does, matters of instrumental errors, wavelength assignments, and measuring procedures. Some progress may be made, however, by comparing observed radial velocities with line-of-sight speeds calculated independently of spectroscopic data, i.e., from the results of positional astronomy.

The best source of standardizing material is obviously the solar system, since the radial velocities of the sun, moon, and planets can be computed without referring to spectroscopic observations. This method was, in fact, used in forming the Lick system for the programs which culminated in the catalogue of radial velocities of stars brighter than 5.51 apparent magnitude (Campbell and Moore 1928).

One may then accept the zero point of the Lick three-prism radial velocities of stars whose spectra resemble that of the sun, say in the range F4–G9. One expects the system to be valid over such a range because of the rather small variation in the stellar temperature and the excitation. Thus the spectral lines and blends known to be valid for radial-velocity measures in the solar system (type G2) may be used over a limited spectral range, especially in view of the dispersion and purity given by the Mills spectrograph.

3.2. SOLAR-TYPE STARS

The reliability of the wavelengths chosen may be tested by means of comparisons between the radial velocities of components of visual binaries of appropriate spectral types. Such an inspection has been made by using pairs in which one component lies in the range F8–G4, while the other is slightly outside that range in either direction. Unfortunately, Lick three-prism velocities are almost entirely lacking for this test, and one must use *Catalogue* values (mostly Mount Wilson observations), assuming that the systematic corrections suffice, on the average, to reduce the published velocities to the Lick system. The following results are obtained from the *General Catalogue*: 16 stars, mean type = F5, velocity residual = $+0.4 \pm 0.5$ km/sec; 10 stars, mean type = G7, velocity residual = -2.2 ± 0.7 km/sec. The result from the F stars confirms the constancy of the zero point. That given by the late G stars is in agreement with the systematic difference found for K stars fainter than magnitude 6.0 (see Table 5). The visual-binary data then indicate that the Lick system is constant between at least F5 and G7.

A quite independent test may be obtained by utilizing moving clusters in which the radial velocities of member stars may be calculated from proper motions and trigonometric parallaxes. This is a powerful and attractive method; it is greatly to be deplored that only the Taurus and the Ursa Major clusters can qualify as control objects, and even in these two cases the observational material needs to be improved. All other clusters are so remote that the errors in the trigonometric parallaxes produce intolerable uncertainties in the calculated radial velocities.

The space motion of the Taurus Cluster has been calculated from sixteen members having parallaxes listed in the Yale catalogue (Jenkins 1952) and proper motions given in the *N30* catalogue (Morgan 1952). The space motion, S, is given by

$$S = 4.74 \frac{\mu}{\pi} \csc \lambda ,$$

where μ is the annual proper motion, π is the trigonometric parallax, and λ is the angular distance of the star from the convergent. The convergent was taken

TABLE 6

VELOCITY RESIDUALS FOR TAURUS CLUSTER STARS

Star	Type	Observed Velocity (km/sec)	O−C (km/sec)
γ Tauri......	G9	+38.5±0.3	−1.1
δ Tauri......	G8	+38.5± .2	−0.1
ε Tauri......	G8	+39.1± .3	+0.2
θ¹ Tauri......	G8	+37.7±0.6	−1.6

at $A = 91°.8 \pm 0°.6$ and $D = +9°.1 \pm 0°.2$ from a determination by Pearce (1955). The individual values were weighted according to $(\pi/\delta\pi)^2$, where $\delta\pi$ is the probable error in the parallax, other sources of observational error being negligible by comparison. The weighted mean from the 16 stars is

$$S = 44.8 \pm 3.5 \text{ km/sec} ,$$

a value entirely independent of spectroscopic observations, although its usefulness is marred by the large probable error. An improvement in the accuracy of the parallaxes would at once enhance the importance of this cluster as a valuable control on radial-velocity data.

Four members of the Taurus Cluster of approximately solar type have been observed for radial velocity with the Mills three-prism spectrograph. The comparison with the computed velocities is tabulated in Table 6. The mean residual from the computed motion is -0.6 ± 0.3 km/sec, which is very satisfactory in view of the uncertainty in the calculated space motion.

We may conclude from the foregoing comparisons that the zero point of the Lick system and also of the *General Catalogue* may be accepted as accurate between F5 and G9. There is, of course, some reservation attached to this conclusion because of the Taurus Cluster comparison, which can be improved, as mentioned above, only by the provision of better parallaxes.

3.3. A-Type Stars

The Ursa Major and Taurus clusters are useful for testing the velocity system for the A stars. The Ursa Major Cluster is especially favorable because the proper motions and parallaxes of the individual members are relatively large. There are eleven members, the convergent is located at $A = 299°6 \pm 2°2$, $D = -32°4 \pm 2°1$, and the calculated space motion, relative to the sun, is 15.2 ± 0.8 km/sec (Petrie and Moyls 1953). Seven A-type members, excluding two stars with variable velocity, are available for comparison with the Lick Observatory three-prism velocities. The comparison is given in Table 7. The weighted mean residual is -1.0 ± 0.5 km/sec, weights having been assigned according to the number of plates measured and the quality of the spectral

TABLE 7

VELOCITY RESIDUALS FOR A-TYPE URSA MAJOR STARS

Star	Type	Observed Velocity (km/sec)	O−C (km/sec)	Wt.
HD 91480....	A8	−13.0	−0.7	2
HD 95418....	A3	−11.4	+0.4	10
HD 103287....	A0n	−12.9	−2.3	1
HD 106591....	A0n	−15.8	−5.9	1
HD 113139....	A4n	− 9.2	−0.6	2
HD 116657....	A8s	−10.8	−2.9	2
HD 116842....	A1n	−12.5	−4.7	1

lines. The unweighted average value is -2.4 ± 0.6 km/sec. It may be remarked that the Victoria revised velocity system is in slightly better accord with the computed value, the mean residual being -0.3 ± 0.4 km/sec.

The Taurus Cluster supplies a number of A-type comparisons. For this we adopt a space motion calculated from the accurate radial velocities of the four solar-type members mentioned earlier. The Lick and Victoria high-dispersion results give the space motion as 43.1 ± 0.2 km/sec. The Lick Observatory three-prism velocities provide the comparison in Table 8. The weighted mean residual is -0.7 ± 0.9 km/sec and the unweighted average is -1.5 ± 1.1 km/ sec. The existence of one large residual in the tabulation rather spoils the comparison and, of course, causes the large probable error of the mean residual.

The above comparisons, for what they are worth, suggest a small positive correction to the *Catalogue* velocities of A stars. Some support for this conclusion is found in the Lick Observatory three-prism velocities of the A-type members of the visual binaries, θ Aurigae, ADS 5559, μ Bootis, and ξ Cephei. The mean residual, with reference to the solar-type component, is -2.4 ± 1.6 km/sec, but again the large probable error obscures the interpretation.

In order to obtain a direct comparison from the *General Catalogue* itself, velocity differences were formed between A-type and solar-type components of visual binaries. Binaries were chosen if one component, designated "solar type," had a spectrum between F4 and G9, while the other component lay between A0 and F2. In all, 48 pairs were found in the *Catalogue* and were divided into two groups according to the spectral type of the earlier component. The mean residuals (from the velocity of the solar-type component) are found to be as follows: 20 stars, mean type = A2, mean residual = -1.2 ± 1.1 km/sec; 28 stars, mean type = F0, mean residual = -0.3 ± 0.7 km/sec.

Although these residuals are not significantly different from zero, they agree in sign with the residuals derived directly from moving clusters. Furthermore, most of the visual binaries in this comparison are faint, and the majority

TABLE 8

VELOCITY RESIDUALS FOR A-TYPE TAURUS STARS

Star	Type	Observed Velocity (km/sec)	$O-C$ (km/sec)	Wt.
HD 25570.	F2	+36.0	− 0.8	4
HD 27934.	A5	+41.3	+ 3.6	5
HD 27962.	A3	+36.3	− 2.0	4
HD 28355.	A6	+38.5	− 0.5	5
HD 28546.	A7	+41.1	+ 2.2	3
HD 28556.	F1	+39.0	0.0	3
HD 28910.	A5	+25.4	−13.8	2
HD 30034.	A6	+39.0	− 1.1	3
HD 33254.	A9	+40.8	− 0.8	4

of the velocities were obtained at the Mount Wilson Observatory. Therefore, referring again to Table 5, we should have expected the above residuals of the A-type components to be positive rather than negative. We may conclude that the Lick and the *General Catalogue* velocities of the A stars probably require a small positive correction, but its exact amount cannot be found without more comparison material.

3.4. B-TYPE STARS

The system of velocities of the B stars can be investigated only by indirect comparisons. Galactic clusters and visual binaries may be used, the control velocities being assigned from observations of solar-type members or A-type members, once the velocity system of the latter is related to the former. We must proceed by steps from the solar system to the A stars and finally to the B stars. A long program of such standardization has been undertaken at Victoria (Petrie 1946, 1947, 1948, 1953; McDonald 1948; Petrie, Andrews, and McDonald 1958), resulting in a revised system forming a consistent and homogeneous series between spectral types O9 and K8.

In the course of the work, standard control stars of type B were selected, and these allow one to make some comparisons. The number of control stars is small, but it could easily be increased by the addition of secondary standards integrated into the fundamental system. The control stars now available give the comparisons in Table 9, the material including largely the B stars brighter than apparent magnitude 7.0. The stars included in the comparison are too few for much weight to be attached to the mean residuals, but the tabulation suggests that the *Catalogue* velocities of the B stars are too positive. The correction of −2.9 km/sec, in Table 9, would remove the larger part of the K term usually found in general solutions of the solar motion employing the brighter B stars.

In concluding this section, one may remark that it is not the intention here to derive definitive corrections to the *General Catalogue* velocities but rather to indicate, with numerical examples, how corrections may eventually be determined. It appears that the *Catalogue* velocities are very good for solar-type stars

TABLE 9

COMPARISON OF VELOCITIES OF BRIGHT B STARS

Comparison	Velocity Difference (km/sec)	No.
General Catalogue − revised . . .	+2.9±0.6	14
Mount Wilson − revised	+1.8±0.3	6
Lick − revised	+5.0±0.9	5
Yerkes − revised	−0.8±1.6	6

and will require only minor adjustment. The situation is not clear for the A stars, for which a small positive correction of about 1 km/sec may be required, or for the B stars for which a negative correction of about 3 km/sec is suggested for the brighter stars. Acceptable numerical values must await the addition of more comparison material; it would be well worth the effort to increase substantially the material required to assign corrections to the *Catalogue* system. The full value of the large volume of radial velocities now available will be realized in the study of galactic problems only when we are sure of the absolute corrections.

§ 4. FREQUENCY OF SPECTROSCOPIC BINARIES

The relatively frequent occurrence of spectroscopic binaries and their interesting apparent distribution with spectral type demonstrate their importance in studies of stellar origin and evolution and of the origin of double stars. It is difficult to estimate the number of spectroscopic binaries from catalogue entries because individual plate velocities cannot be given and are not always available in the literature. Assignment of variable velocity depends on a number of factors: the number and quality of lines measured on the spectrograms, the number and quality of the plates available, the stability of the spectrograph, and the observed velocity range.

Ordinarily, the decision as to the reality of variable velocity rests with the observer, who is best acquainted with the material and the relevant sources of error. When the spectra contain many well-defined lines, the range among individual plate velocities is a reliable guide and may be used with confidence. Sometimes the decision is based on arbitrary and subjective criteria, but it may be preferable to adopt more formal and objective tests, based on internal and external plate errors and levels of significance. A good example of the application of an objective criterion is given by Heard (1956) in an analysis of the David Dunlap Observatory radial velocities.

A reliable assignment of binary motion is particularly difficult for most velocity measures of A and B stars. The spectral lines are generally diffuse and few in number, so that plate velocities are subject to substantial errors. Furthermore, the hotter stars tend to exhibit variable velocity from physical causes, such as β Cephei variation, and the near-instability of the outer atmospheric layers to which the radial-velocity measures refer.

The following procedure is helpful in the difficult cases. The probable error of a single velocity is estimated. This can best be done by obtaining duplicate or multiple spectra in succession upon a sufficient number of the stars being studied, but it may also be done by noting the scatter among individual velocities of a star considered not to be variable. If r_0 be the probable error of a single velocity and R be the greatest deviation of single velocities from the mean, we may consider the velocity to be variable if $R \geq 3r_0$. This criterion, for a normal distribution of errors, gives a 95 per cent chance that the observed range is not caused by observational error. In these matters much depends on the successful estimation of the observational error, and the conscientious observer is apt to overestimate this. Thus the number of stars of variable velocity tends to be underestimated.

It appears that a reliable estimate of the proportion of stars varying in velocity may be made from the frequency distribution of observed ranges or probable errors, provided that one is dealing with a homogeneous series of velocities. The distribution is expected to be a combination of a (nearly) normal error-curve, with its mode located at the average probable error, and a much flatter and more irregular curve giving the distribution caused by variable velocity. One may be able to remove the observational error portion of the distribution and so estimate the fraction of the stars whose velocities vary.

An example is provided by the radial velocities of some 500 B stars, generally B0–B5, published by the Dominion Astrophysical Observatory (Petrie and Pearce 1962). Mean velocities and probable errors are available, the spectrograms were taken with a single-prism instrument kept at the same adjustment throughout the observations, while the radial-velocity measures were made largely by one person without changes in procedures. It may confidently be expected that the observational errors remained constant during the execution of the program.

The frequency-curve of the probable errors of a single velocity is shown in Figure 1. It will be noted that the distribution has marked asymmetry. There is a sharp rise from very small probable errors to a maximum at about ±4.5 km/ sec, followed by an irregular decline extending to quite large values. One may assume that the portion of the curve to the left of its maximum value gives a reasonably good representation of the observational-error distribution and thus remove this part from the whole.

Assuming a normal distribution, a good representation is given by

$$N = 11.4 \, e^{-0.14(x-4.5)^2} \, ,$$

where N is the frequency, in percentage, of the probable error, x. It may be noted that the average probable error for similar radial velocities was found

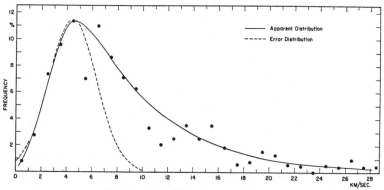

FIG. 1.—Probable error of one plate

from an entirely independent method to be ±4.3 km/sec (Petrie 1953), thus supporting the above interpretation. We may now remove the observational error-curve and obtain the distribution of variances for stars which are varying in radial velocity. There would be little hesitation in assuming probable errors in excess of, say, ±10 km/sec to indicate variable velocity, but in the region ±5 to ±10 one would be in some doubt when considering the stars individually. The present treatment avoids this difficulty but, of course, tells us nothing regarding any individual star.

The fraction of stars of variable velocity according to this example is 49 per cent. Too much emphasis should not be given to the exact numerical value, because of the assumptions made; yet we may conclude that approximately half the stars of this program vary in radial velocity. Sporadic atmospheric variations are largely included in the observational error, and β Cephei varia- tion does not appear to be very common among B stars generally. We are faced, then, with a high incidence of binaries among the stars of class B. It would be possible to apply this treatment to much of the data of the *General Catalogue*. A preliminary investigation suggests that binary motion is much less common among the solar-type stars; but a more complete tabulation should be made and the work extended to the A stars as well.

REFERENCES

BARBIER, M., and FEHRENBACH, C.	1955	*J. d. Obs.*, **38**, 180.
BOULON, J., DUFLOT, M., and FEHRENBACH, C.	1959	*J. d. Obs.*, **42**, 1.
CAMPBELL, W. W., and MOORE, J. H.	1928	*Pub. Lick Obs.*, Vol. **16**.
DUFLOT, M., and FEHRENBACH, C.	1956	*J. d. Obs.*, **39**, 104.
DYER, E. R., JR.	1954	*A.J.*, **59**, 218.
EVANS, D. S., MENZIES, A., and STOY, R. H.	1957	*M.N.*, **117**, 534.
FEAST, M. W., and THACKERAY, A. D.	1958	*M.N.*, **118**, 125.
FEAST, M. W., THACKERAY, A. D., and WESSELINK, A. J.	1955	*Mem. R.A.S.*, **67**, 51.
	1957	*Ibid.*, **68**, 1.
FEHRENBACH, C.	1955	*J. d. Obs.*, **38**, 165.
HEARD, J. F.	1956	*Pub. David Dunlap Obs.*, **2**, 107.
JENKINS, LOUISE F.	1952	*General Catalogue of Trigonometric Stellar Parallaxes* (New Haven: Yale University Observatory).
McDONALD, JEAN K.	1948	*J.R.A.S. Canada*, **42**, 220; *Contr. Dom. Ap. Obs.*, No. 12.
MOORE, J. H.	1932	*Pub. Lick Obs.*, Vol. **18**.
MORGAN, H. R.	1952	*Astr. Papers Amer. Ephem.*, Vol. **13**, Part 3.
PANAIOTOV, L. A.	1955	*A.J., U.S.S.R.*, **32**, 305.
PEARCE, J. A.	1955	*Pub. A.S.P.*, **67**, 23.
PETRIE, R. M.	1946	*J.R.A.S. Canada*, **40**, 325; *Contr. Dom. Ap. Obs.*, No. 4.
	1947	*J.R.A.S. Canada*, **41**, 311; *Contr. Dom. Ap. Obs.*, No. 10.
	1948	*J.R.A.S. Canada*, **42**, 213; *Contr. Dom. Ap. Obs.*, No. 11.
	1953	*Pub. Dom. Ap. Obs.*, **9**, 297.
PETRIE, R. M., ANDREWS, D. H., and McDONALD, JEAN K.	1958	*Pub. Dom. Ap. Obs.*, **10**, 415.

PETRIE, R. M., and
   MOYLS, B. N.   1953   *M.N.*, **113**, 239; *Contr. Dom. Ap. Obs.*, No. 31.
PETRIE, R. M., and
   PEARCE, J. A.   1962   *Pub. Dom. Ap. Obs.*, **12**, 1.
SCHALÉN, C.   1954   *Ark. f. astr.*, **1**, 545.
WILSON, R. E.   1953   *General Catalogue of Stellar Radial Velocities* (Washington, D.C.: Carnegie Institution of Washington).

WILSON, R. E., and
   JOY, A. H.   1952   *Ap. J.*, **115**, 157.

CHAPTER 8

Classification of Stellar Spectra

PHILIP C. KEENAN
Perkins Observatory, Delaware, Ohio

§ 1. PRINCIPLES OF SPECTRAL CLASSIFICATION

Spectral classification may be defined as the direct estimation of the physical characteristics of stars by comparison of their spectral features. We speak of "direct estimation" because the method consists essentially in placing the spectrum of a given star in a sequence of spectra of stars in which the physical conditions are known, however incompletely. The corresponding characteristics of the given star can thus be inferred immediately without going through the process of first measuring line equivalent widths and then interpreting them through a detailed physical theory of line absorption. The latter process is essential for the study of the structure of an individual atmosphere, while spectral classification is limited to the more modest aim of estimating those integral properties of a star (e.g., effective temperature) that determine the main features of its spectrum. Within these limits the method of classification has proved to be a powerful tool, both because it can be applied to small-scale spectrograms on which faint stars can be recorded and because the classification of a group of stars often provides the clues leading later to detailed atmospheric analysis.

A system of classification is just a particular way of carrying out this ordering of the spectra. The setting-up of a scheme of classification involves (1) choice of criteria (these are the features—relative intensities of lines or bands, etc.—that are used in ordering the spectra); (2) arrangement of enough spectra by means of these criteria to provide a good set of standard-type stars (the assigned spectral types are merely the numbers or other symbols used to describe the positions of the stars of the sequence); and (3) calibration of the types in terms of the physical characteristics of the stars.

Actually, an observer now rarely faces the necessity of setting up a quite new system of classification. Rather, one usually is concerned either with modifying an existing scheme of classification to fit a special group of stars or with making the types assigned from plates of a different dispersion or spectral region con-

78

sistent with existing classifications. Any of these processes is made up essentially of the three steps outlined above, though they are frequently combined in practice. Sometimes, though, it is important to separate them—particularly the final step of calibration, as W. W. Morgan (1937) has pointed out. If the types assigned are symbols purely descriptive of what is actually seen on the spectrograms, the spectral catalogue will not need to be revised whenever the data on which the calibrations rest are improved. The *Henry Draper Catalogue* is a good example; the HD types essentially order the spectra according to their effective temperatures. If, instead of using types represented by letter, the Harvard observers had attempted to give actual temperatures as estimated at the time of preparation (1911–1924), the figures for many of the stars (e.g., type O and supergiants of most types) would have needed drastic revision after only a few years. It is true that more recent systems modify the HD types by adding subdivisions indicating increased accuracy or by additional symbols defining other variables besides temperature, but the important point is that the HD types as originally published are still useful for many purposes; this is so because they do a good job of representing the most striking differences that can be noticed on any small-scale spectrograms similar to the original *Henry Draper* plates.

It is not possible to lay down rigid rules for setting up a system of classification that will have lasting usefulness. For one thing, the extent of our physical knowledge of the objects to be classified does much to determine the line of attack on the problem. When spectroscopists first began trying to fit the complicated spectra of the most common stars into meaningful patterns, it was necessary to start in an almost purely empirical way. The criteria had often to be chosen without knowledge of the physical factors that were causing the differences or even what elements were responsible for all the observed lines. The *Henry Draper* system again furnishes a good example. When it was first introduced in 1890 (Pickering 1890; also Pickering and Fleming 1897), it was simply an arrangement of spectra in order of decreasing ratios of intensities of the Balmer lines of hydrogen to the intensities of a number of other lines. Some of these lines—those which are strongest in types O and B—were not identified as due to helium until the work of Vogel in 1895. At about the same time it became apparent to Pickering, Miss Maury, and Miss Cannon that temperature was the primary variable reflected in the HD criteria and that the hydrogen lines actually go through a maximum at intermediate temperatures (later found to be about 11,000° K). Accordingly, the Harvard observers rearranged the HD types, which had originally been in alphabetical order, into their present sequence—O, B, A, F, G, K, M.

The situation today is quite different. It is practically necessary for the classifier to take into account all the physical information available for the group of stars with which he is working. He must use all these clues in developing an arrangement that will separate the physical parameters as sharply as possible, but he must also be careful to use as criteria only features that can be resolved on the spectrograms available.

§ 2. PHYSICAL THEORY OF SPECTRAL CLASSIFICATION

The physical variables that determine a star's spectrum are essentially the same for stars of all populations, i.e., stars with differing structure and composition. The relations connecting them, however, are known to vary from one group of stars to another. For this reason we shall find it convenient to write down the general functional equations first and then consider how the functions depend on the stellar models. The essential features of the argument were actually given by Russell, Dugan, and Stewart (1927 or 1938, p. 874), who considered specifically the case of typical stars near the sun (Population I).

The criteria of classification which describe the spectrum of a star are usually ratios of intensities of absorption lines or bands. Since line absorption is a monotonically increasing function of the number of atoms capable of absorbing that line, we have, for each line,

$$\text{Line absorption} = w = f_1 (N_{a, r, s}) , \tag{1}$$

where the subscript a specifies the abundance of element a; r the stage of ionization; and s the level of excitation of the lower state of the transition giving the line observed. Then $N_{a, r, s}$ is the number of atoms in the stellar atmosphere per square centimeter of surface that are capable of absorbing the given line. If the total absorption, w, is measured in units of angstroms, the function f_1 is that represented by the usual curve of growth. The theory of absorption lines shows that this can quite generally be written as

$$w = f_1 (N_{a, r, s}, T, p) , \tag{2}$$

where the temperature, T, enters through the influence of thermal Doppler effect and turbulence on line shape. The gas pressure, p, is involved if the line profile is also affected by any kind of pressure broadening. Here the temperature and pressure should refer to the weighted "mean" of the depths which contribute to the formation of the line, but we shall assume that, for all lines, T and p are proportional to their photospheric values. Then we write for T the effective temperature, T_e, of the star. This assumption introduces no error in the specification of the number of variables involved, so long as we do not attempt classification by ratios involving two lines formed at very different atmospheric levels or in the detached shells surrounding some large stars.

To a similar approximation, we write

$$N_{a, r, s} = f_2 (n_{a, r, s}, p, T_e, A_a), \tag{3}$$

where $n_{a, r, s}$ is the number of suitable atoms per cubic centimeter at the photosphere and A_a is the relative abundance of element a. Specifically, this assumes that the opacity in the atmosphere and the gradients of temperature and pressure are completely determined by the photospheric value of T and p and the chemical composition of the star.

The mean molecular weight, μ, of the atmospheric gas is determined by the sum of all the atomic abundances. Conversely, we can write

$$A_a = f_3 (\mu) \tag{4}$$

and use μ as the variable specifying chemical composition. Combining these steps, we have

$$w = f_4 (n_a, r, s, p, T_e, \mu) . \tag{5}$$

Further, $n_{a, r, s}$ is related to the particle density, n_a, of element a by the equations of ionization and excitation (Saha and Boltzmann equations if thermal equilibrium holds) and to the total number of particles per cubic centimeter by the definition $n_a = A_a n$; hence

$$w = f_5 (n, p, T_e, \mu). \tag{6}$$

One variable can be eliminated by the equation of state, which, for thermal equilibrium, has the familiar and simple form, $p = nkT$.

Thus equation (6) simplifies to

$$w = f_6 (p, T_e, \mu) \tag{7}$$

if we choose to eliminate n, the particle density. This equation might have been written down intuitively, for any spectroscopist would expect line intensities to be fixed by some sort of mean temperature and pressure and the chemical composition.

Up to this point we have not shown how the spectrum depends on the total luminosity of the star. To do this, we must take account of the fact that if the atmosphere is to be mechanically stable, the pressure must be related to the downward force of gravity. If there are no turbulent currents, the relation is the usual equation of hydrostatic equilibrium:

$$dp = - g\rho dh = \frac{g}{k} d\tau,$$

where k is the mass coefficient of absorption, g is the acceleration of gravity, and ρ is the density. If the variation of k with depth is neglected, the pressure $p(\tau)$ at optical depth τ is

$$p = \frac{g}{k} \tau .$$

We already have made the assumption that $k = f(T_e, p, \mu)$, from which it follows that $p = f(g, T_e, \mu)$ near the photosphere. If the equilibrium is partly dynamic (i.e., involving turbulent currents), the same variables are involved, and we can write generally

$$w = f_7 (g, T_e, \mu) . \tag{8}$$

The surface gravity, however, is defined by

$$g = \frac{G\,\mathfrak{M}}{R^2} ,\tag{9}$$

where $\mathfrak{M}$ and R are the mass and radius of the star and G is the constant of gravitation. Further,

$$R^2 = \frac{L}{4\pi a T_e^4} = f(L, T_e) .\tag{10}$$

Introducing equations (9) and (10) into equation (8), we have the relation

$$w = f_8\,(\mathfrak{M}, L, T_e, \mu) .\tag{11}$$

Equation (11) is the general expression stating the four physical variables that determine the absorption spectrum of a star. Insofar as this expression alone is concerned, a star with given T_e and μ could have any number of pairs of values of $\mathfrak{M}$ and L leading to the same set of $N_{a,\,r,\,s}$ and hence to the same observed spectrum. Then we should not expect the line intensities to be used without knowledge of the mass to establish the luminosity—we should have no dependable spectroscopic absolute magnitudes.

The fact that consistent luminosities can be determined spectroscopically for large numbers of stars implies an additional condition. This condition is the mass-luminosity relation. Then only can we eliminate the mass and write

$$w = f_9\,(L, T_e, \mu) .\tag{12}$$

For stars of constant composition this becomes

$$w = f_9\,(L, T_e) ,\tag{13}$$

and we can expect a two-dimensional classification to determine the temperature and the luminosity.

The two conditions imposed to establish equation (13) are not independent, for in at least some cases a difference in chemical composition between two stars implies a difference in the nuclear processes in their interiors and, correspondingly, in their structures. Thus stars of different compositions will, in general, obey different mass-luminosity laws. Populations apparently differ in composition; hence there is no reason to expect them all to follow the same mass-luminosity relation.

The implications of these relations for spectral classification are as follows: (1) Since the two-dimensional classification for most of the stars of types B–M in the vicinity of the sun (e.g., those included in the Mount Wilson catalogue; Adams *et al.* 1935) has been confirmed as generally consistent by the statistical tests that have been applied, the same $f_9(L, T_e)$ must apply to these stars. This, then, is another way of saying that most of the stars in our small portion of the Galaxy have nearly the same chemical composition, as direct determinations of abundance have confirmed independently. (2) For the smaller groups of stars which, both from the presence of discrepant features ("peculiarities") in their small-scale spectra and from the abundance measurements on large-scale spectrograms, appear to differ in composition from the normal solar-type stars, differing functions $f_9(L, T_e)$ are to be expected. If they show only slight spectral peculiarities, as in the "weak CN" group of F-, G-, and K-type stars, they can often be classified by many of the normal criteria, but the calibration of the types in terms of temperature and luminosity must always be done independently for such a group. Where the peculiarities are more extreme and the differences in composition greater (S-type and carbon stars), the usual classification in two dimensions may be impracticable. Thus the carbon stars have never been separated into luminosity classes; this implies that the dispersion in composition within the group alters their spectra so strongly that the effects of any dispersion in luminosity are masked.

§ 3. SYSTEMS OF CLASSIFICATION

3.1. INTRODUCTION

We shall have space to describe only those schemes of classification that have proved useful enough to remain in widespread use. It would be misleading, however, not to mention the lasting importance of the pioneer visual work of Secchi, Vogel, and others at the end of the nineteenth century and the later development of several systems which helped to clarify our understanding of the physical conditions in stellar atmospheres, even though the special notations of these systems may have dropped out of use. Among the investigators to whose work it is not possible to do full justice in this chapter are Lockyer, Miss Maury, Lindblad, Schwassmann, and Vyssotsky. A comprehensive account of the development of spectral classification will be found in the fine historical article by R. H. Curtiss in the *Handbuch der Astrophysik*, Volume 5, Part 1 (1932).

It happens that the history of classification has not been one of revolution in which radically different systems have overthrown one another but rather one of evolution from the relatively simple *Henry Draper* system toward classifications of greater precision and more definite separation of variables. Just how many of these modifications should be called "separate systems" is a matter of rather arbitrary definition, but we shall use the term freely as a matter of convenience.

3.2. THE "HENRY DRAPER" SYSTEM (HD TYPES)

The criteria of classification used by Miss Cannon are described in the Introductions to each of the nine volumes of the *Henry Draper Catalogue* (*Harvard Ann.*, Vols. **91–99**) (Cannon and Pickering 1918–1924), though it will be noted that type S was not introduced until the first seven volumes had appeared. The sequence of HD types in order of decreasing temperature is P, O, B, A, F, G, K, M, with class P referring to spectra of gaseous nebulae. Types S, R, and N describe stars overlapping types K and M in temperature range but differing in the molecules responsible for the strongest bands in their spectra. The HD stellar types O–M are summarized in Table 1, in which there is space in the fourth column to list only the most characteristic among the criteria.

The original nine volumes give HD types for 225,300 stars; to these, 46,850 stars were added in the *Henry Draper Extension* (*Harvard Ann.*, Vol. 100), and about 32,000 more HD types were published at Harvard and elsewhere in miscellaneous special lists. Later Miss Cannon and her associates classified about 87,000 additional stars, and these types were marked on field charts published in *Harvard Annals*, Vol. 112 (1949). Thus a total of over 391,000 stars were classified on the HD system at Harvard—an extraordinary achievement. The sheer extent of the catalogue has contributed much to its enduring value.

TABLE 1

THE "HENRY DRAPER" CLASSIFICATION—TYPES O–M

Type	Main Characteristics	Sub-types	HD Criteria	Typical Stars
O	Hottest stars, continuum strong in UV	Oa	O II λ 4650 dominates	BD+35°4013
		Ob	He II λ 4686 dominates ⎱ emission	BD+35°4001
		Oc	Lines narrower ⎰ lines	BD+36°3987
		Od	Absorption lines dominate; only He II, O II in emission	ζ Pup, λ Cep
		Oe	Si IV λ 4089 at maximum	29 CMa
		Oe5	O II λ 4649, He II λ 4686 strong	τ CMa
B	Neutral helium dominates	B0	C III λ 4650 at maximum	ε Ori
		B1	He I λ 4472 > O II λ 4649	β CMa, β Cen
		B2	He I lines are maximum	δ Ori, α Lup
		B3	He II lines are disappearing	π⁴ Ori, α Pav
		B5	Si λ 4128 > He λ 4121	19 Tau, φ Vel
		B8	λ 4472 = Mg λ 4481	β Per, δ Gru
		B9	He I λ 4026 just visible	λ Aql, λ Cen
A	Hydrogen lines decreasing from maximum at A0	A0	Balmer lines at maximum	α CMi
		A2	Ca II K = 0.4 Hδ	S CMa, ι Cen
		A3	K = 0.8 Hδ	α PsA, τ³ Eri
		A5	K > Hδ	β Tri, α Pic
F	Metallic lines becoming noticeable	F0	K = H + Hδ	δ Gem, α Car
		F2	G band becoming noticeable	π Sgr
		F5	G band becoming continuous	α CMi, ρ Pup
		F8	Balmer lines slightly stronger than in sun	β Vir, α For
G	Solar-type spectra	G0	Ca λ 4227 = Hδ	α Aur, β Hya
		G5	Fe λ 4325 > Hγ on small-scale plates	κ Gem, α Ret
K	Metallic lines dominate	K0	H and K at maximum strength	α Bov, α Phe
		K2	Continuum becoming weak in blue	β Cnc, υ Lib
		K5	G band no longer continuous	α Tau
M	TiO bands	Ma	TiO bands noticeable	α Ori, α Hya
		Mb	Bands conspicuous	ρ Per, γ Cru
		Mc	Spectrum fluted by the strong bands	W Cyg, RX Aqr
		Md	Mira variables, Hγ, Hδ in emission	χ Cyg, o Cet

The limiting magnitude to which the catalogue is complete varies locally according to the image quality and the overlapping in rich fields and depends systematically on the declination. In the northern half of the sky, practically all stars down to $m_v = 8.25$ are included, while in the south the limit is about $\frac{1}{2}$ mag. fainter, at $m_v = 8.75$ (Shapley and Cannon 1921).

3.3. The Recognition of Differences in Luminosity

Long before the *Henry Draper Catalogue* had been published, there were observations indicating that stars of a given temperature might differ widely in luminosity and that these differences affected the appearance of their spectra. Indeed, the types introduced by Miss Maury at Harvard (Maury and Pickering 1897) represented a first attempt at a classification in two dimensions. She introduced small prefixes, *a*, *b*, *c*, to describe parallel temperature sequences distinguished by different line widths. Her general classification was replaced by the simpler HD notation, partly because the characteristics used by Miss Maury were due to several different physical variables, including axial rotation. Nevertheless, her prefix *c* continued to be used in several catalogues (Mount Wilson, etc.) to designate stars of types B, A, or F which on small-scale spectrograms appeared to have unusually sharp and narrow lines. Hertzsprung suspected that these *c* stars had higher luminosities than most stars of the same types with normal lines and confirmed this (1905, 1907) by comparing their trigonometric parallaxes and motions. He announced his discovery of the supergiant character of the *c*-stars in 1909 in these words: "Wir müssen hieraus schliessen, dass die *c*-Sterne, selbst die, welche zu den hellsten Sternen des Himmels gehören, sehr entfernt und absolut ausserordentlich hell sind."[1]

3.4. The Mount Wilson Classification (MW Types)

The next step was taken at Mount Wilson, where Adams and Kohlschütter (1914) used slit spectrograms of somewhat greater scale than the *Henry Draper* plates to show that some lines were stronger in the more luminous stars (positive luminosity effect), while others were weaker. They made the first application of these differences to estimate spectroscopic absolute magnitudes of individual stars. For the next twenty years, work along these lines continued at Mount Wilson, culminating in the publication of the catalogue "The Spectroscopic Absolute Magnitudes and Parallaxes of 4179 Stars" (Adams *et al.* 1935). The catalogue was made up mostly of stars later than A5 and situated north of declination −26°.

The criteria used for classification by the Mount Wilson observers were visual estimates of the relative intensities of selected pairs of lines. Such estimates have often been called "line ratios," but, since they are normally ex-

---

[1] An illuminating picture of the situation in spectral classification just at the time that Hertzsprung, Russell, and others had come to appreciate the importance of investigating luminosity effects will be found in an exchange of "Correspondence Concerning the Classification of Stellar Spectra," published in 1911 in the *Astrophysical Journal*, **33**, 260.

pressed in a step scale that reflects the logarithmic response of the eye, it would be more consistent to call them line differences."[2]

At Mount Wilson, spectral temperature types were assigned first, and then curves were drawn for each type relating the line differences to absolute magnitudes as found independently from trigonometric parallaxes or mean motions. The number of line pairs used for stars of any one type was about 10, and among the pairs found most sensitive to luminosity for types G–M were Sr II λ 4077/ Fe λ 4071; Sr II, Fe λ 4215/Fe λ 4250; λ 4340 (Hγ)/Fe λ 4325; Sc II, Y II λ 4375/Fe λ 4404; Ca λ 4454/Fe λ 4461. The first line of each pair shows a positive luminosity effect, while the iron lines used for comparison change very little with luminosity. These same pairs of lines have been among those used most frequently as luminosity criteria by later observers also.

The usefulness of the Mount Wilson types has been much greater for the cooler stars than for those of types A–F. Stars of these early types show large

TABLE 2

CLASSIFICATION OF As AND An STARS

HD	MOUNT WILSON		HD	MOUNT WILSON	
	As	An		As	An
A0..........	A2	A0	A5..........	A7.5	A4
A2..........	A4	A1.5	F0..........	A8	A5.5
A3..........	A6	A3			

differences in their rate of rotation, and the rapidly rotating stars have spectra in which the metallic absorption lines are very wide and shallow. In the Mount Wilson catalogues the A-type stars with fairly sharp lines (slow rotation) were marked with the subscript "s," while those with wide, shallow lines due to rapid rotation were marked "n." It is easy to see that, as one increases the scale of the spectrograms, it becomes difficult to make direct comparisons of the wide lines in "n" stars and the sharp lines in "s" stars; the observer is obliged to set up separate sequences of the stars of the two groups. Systematic differences between the Harvard and Mount Wilson classifications of the two groups were noticed independently by Lindblad (1924) and by Fairfield (1924), in the sense that the "n" stars were classified as relatively earlier at Mount Wilson. Table 2 represents the differences with sufficient accuracy, for individual stars show large departures from the mean relation. Later discussions (see Hynek 1936) showed that the HD types were the more consistent with the color temperatures

[2] The analogy with the magnitude scale and with Argelander's "light-steps" for comparing the brightness of variable stars is not perfect, for, in judging the strength of an absorption line, the eye is presumably influenced by its width, its depth, and its shape rather than by its total absorption alone.

of both groups, and more recent classifications have adhered rather closely to the Harvard scale.

It is for the G-, K-, and M-type stars that the Mount Wilson types and absolute magnitudes have proved most useful, partly because the greater resolution of the slit spectrograms allowed the relative intensities of the narrow metallic lines of these stars to be compared more accurately than on most slitless spectrograms. The Mount Wilson observers replaced the groups Ma, Mb, and Mc of the original HD classification by the decimal subdivisions M0, M1, M2, M3, M4, M5, and M6. As described by Adams, Joy, and Humason (1926), "The system of classification . . . is based almost entirely on the intensities of the bands of titanium oxide, only minor consideration being given to other features of the spectrum." Actually, experience has shown that classification by either molecular bands or atomic lines gives a consistent scale of temperature types, at least for stars of the giant M branch. The Mount Wilson classification of late-type stars was extended to groups of variable stars, including semiregular and irregular variables (Joy 1942), and Mira variables (Merrill 1923, 1941).

The Mount Wilson spectroscopic absolute magnitudes have been examined statistically by Öpik (1929), Russell and Moore (1938, 1940), and Strömberg (1939). From comparisons with the trigonometric parallaxes of the *Yale Catalogue* (Jenkins 1952), Russell and Moore found no appreciable systematic errors in the mean absolute magnitudes of stars of the main sequence and the ordinary giant branch. On the other hand, the method of calibration by plotting line ratios (which are affected by errors of observation) against absolute magnitude gives regression-curves which must lead to an underestimation of the deviations of the individual absolute magnitudes from the means for each spectral type. Russell and Moore (1940) estimated the mean error of the Mount Wilson spectroscopic absolute magnitudes in the giant branch as $\pm 0^{m}\!.53$ and the true dispersion of the stars of the giant branch as $\pm 1^{m}\!.04$.

These statistical effects (in the estimation of errors and dispersions) appear, of course, in any calibration converting observed estimates of spectroscopic luminosity criteria to absolute magnitudes by means of group means. They can be allowed for by statistical analysis giving unbiased estimates (as above), or they can be made quite small in amount if enough calibration stars are observed to allow the intervals over which the averages are taken to be kept small.

In the practical use of the Mount Wilson catalogue, the absolute magnitudes of stars close to the main sequence or the giant branch can be read without correction. For other stars (e.g., subgiants or supergiants), corrections have been given by Russell and Moore (1940, Table 12), but for many purposes it is a satisfactory rule of thumb to multiply the negative absolute magnitudes given for supergiants by a factor of 2.

In the years following the first work of Adams and Kohlschütter, several observatories undertook somewhat similar programs of classification in two dimensions. Among the more important and extensive catalogues is the list of types

and absolute magnitudes of 1105 stars of types F, G, K, and M published by
Young and Harper (1924a) at Victoria. Their method was similar to that of
Mount Wilson in the use of curves connecting estimated intensity ratios with
absolute magnitude. The appreciable systematic differences between the Victoria and Mount Wilson types were summarized in a separate paper (Young
and Harper 1924b). The later classification carried out by Young (1939–1945)
at Toronto on the stars included in the program of radial velocities at David
Dunlap Observatory was essentially on the Victoria system.

For stars brighter than the fifth magnitude, Hoffleit (1937) extended to the
South Pole a classification based on that of Mount Wilson. As she pointed out,
her absolute magnitudes implied a smaller dispersion among the giants than was
found at Mount Wilson, and this could be a reflection of the difficulty in evaluating small differences in the luminosity criteria on her slitless spectrograms,
as compared with slit spectrograms of slightly better resolving power.

3.5. The MK Classification

The problem of developing an accurate classification on slit spectrograms of
sufficiently low dispersion (≈ 115 A/mm) to permit its extension to relatively
faint stars was taken up by Morgan (1937) at the Yerkes Observatory. For the
reasons given at the beginning of this chapter (§ 1), he preferred to return
to a classification expressed directly in terms of the empirical criteria observed
on the spectrograms, the two dimensions being given by spectral type and luminosity class. The system as developed by Morgan, Keenan, and Kellman
(1943) for stars of types O9–M3 employed five main luminosity classes: I
(sometimes subdivided into Ia and Ib), II, III, IV, and V.

A revised list of types for standard stars was published by Johnson and
Morgan (1953). Some additional stars for which Morgan determined types were
included in the list of 108 photometric standard stars for which Johnson and
Harris (1954) published three-color measures. The supergiants noted as c stars
by C. Payne Gaposchkin were given MK types by Bidelman (1951). MK types
for the brighter stars in the Southern Hemisphere were estimated by Evans and
were included in the catalogues of "Fundamental Data for Southern Stars" by
Evans, Menzies, and Stoy (1957, 1959), and a list of standard southern stars
was prepared by Buscombe (1959, 1962). Catalogues of stars of particular types
will be discussed in the following section, in which the criteria are summarized.
Plate 1 illustrates the main features of the sequence of giants from B2 to K5.

The use of Roman numerals to represent the major classes of luminosity has
been widely adopted, for there is no danger of confusing them with the types
representing temperatures. They have the disadvantage of making it difficult
to add finer subdivisions in luminosity when desired, however, and this is a
problem that must be faced now. In some areas of the luminosity-spectrum
diagram, particularly between types G5 and K2, it is already possible to improve
on the accuracy of classification of the Yerkes *Atlas of Stellar Spectra*. The gain

comes partly from the use of spectrograms of slightly higher dispersion and partly from the identification of enough of the cooler supergiants to establish better sequences among them.

If we look ahead to Table 6 (p. 92), it is evident that near K0 the luminosity classes Ia, Ib, II, III, IV, and V are separated by very roughly equal intervals of absolute magnitude. This makes it rather convenient to leave the main classes as now defined, with class III corresponding to about the middle of the giant branch. Luminosities midway between these classes have generally been designated Ib–II, III–IV, etc., but the difficulty lies in making smaller subdivisions.

The notation presently suggested by Morgan and Keenan is shown in Table 3, where the second column lists only the original main classes that are likely to be distinguished by observers working with small-scale spectrograms. The finer

TABLE 3

LUMINOSITY CLASSES

Description	Luminosity Classes		Description	Luminosity Classes	
Supergiants.............	0	0 Ia0 Ia Iab Ib	Subgiants.............	IV	IVa IVab IVb
	I		Main sequence (dwarfs).	V	Va Vab Vb
Bright giants...........	II	IIa IIab IIb			
Giants................	III	IIIa IIIab IIIb	Subdwarfs.............	VI	VI

subdivisions in the third column are distinguished by letters a and b, as had been done earlier for class I supergiants.[3] Thus if a giant star is classified K0 III by one observer and K0 IIIab by another, it indicates that the first observer can tell merely that it belongs in the giant branch, while the second observer is estimating that it lies within about half a magnitude of the middle of the giant branch. Further subdivision is possible but will not often be needed. Luminosity class 0 is added to provide a place for the very brightest stars, with $M_v \approx -9$, observed in galaxies. The question of introducing and subdividing class VI to describe subdwarfs is left open for future consideration.

As examples of the use of the notation in the last column, Table 4 gives revised types for a few stars classified on spectrograms taken at the Perkins Observatory on a scale of about 104 A/mm at Hγ. For RW Cep, which appears to be more luminous than such Ia standards as β Ori, δ CMa, and μ Cep, the

[3] This notation was suggested by Dr. Morgan in correspondence. It has the advantage of doing away with plus and minus signs, which have proved very confusing when applied to luminosity classes.

assigned type of K0 is necessarily rather arbitrary in the absence of a sequence
of such brilliant stars.

A calibration of the MK types in terms of effective temperature was given in
1951 as Table 1.3 of chapter 1 of *Astrophysics* (Keenan and Morgan 1951) and

TABLE 4

REVISED MK TYPES

STAR	1900		m_v	TYPE
	a	δ		
56 UMa......	11^{h}17^m	+44°02'	5.06	G8 IIb
ε Vir........	12 57	+11 30	2.95	G8 IIIab
RW Cep........	22 19	+55 27	6.8–7.5	K0 0–Ia
β Gem.......	7 39	+28 16	1.21	K0 IIIb
τ CrB........	16 05	+36 45	4.94	K0 IIIb–IVa
α UMa.......	10 57	+62 17	1.95	K0 IIIa
37 Lib........	15 28	− 9 43	4.83	K1 IVa
α Hya.......	9 22	− 8 14	2.16	K3 IIIa
63 Cyg.......	21 03	+47 15	4.88	K4 Ib–IIa

was a revision of the temperature scale set up by Kuiper (1938). Since that time,
numerous estimates of the temperatures of individual stars have been made, but
their scatter is great. For type A0, for example, we have the values in the accompanying table. In addition, at A1 the interferometric diameter of Sirius by

T_e (° K)	Method	Reference
9500.........	Model atmosphere	Hunger (1955)
10,700........	Eclipsing binary (β Aur)	Kopal (1955)
10,500........	Eclipsing binary (β Aur)	Popper (1959)
10,900........	Model atmosphere	Melbourne (1960)
9400........	Model atmosphere	Bless (1960)

Brown and Twiss (1956) was combined by Popper (1959) with a bolometric correction of −0.27 and the photoelectric $m_v = -1.47$ to give $T_e = 9350°$ K. If,
however, a larger bolometric correction, such as the value of −0.72 given by
Pearce's table (Pearce 1957), is used or if Planck's law is fitted to the photoelectric magnitudes, temperatures several hundred degrees higher than Popper's
value are obtained.

It thus appears that the 1951 estimate of 11,000° for A0 was somewhat too
high, but the choice of the "best" current value remains somewhat arbitrary.
The situation is further complicated by the fact that Kopal (1955) recommended
a lowering of the temperature scale for B stars, from a discussion of eclipsing
binaries, while McDonald and Underhill (1952) obtained much higher temperatures from their atmospheric models.

Although there have been useful general discussions of the temperature scale by Pilowski (1953), Popper (1959), and Aller (1961), it seems clear that a definitive scale of effective temperatures must await the radiometric observations of both the very red and the very blue stars, made above the absorbing layers of the earth's atmosphere. A set of provisional temperatures is given in Table 5 but should not be taken too seriously. The entry of 9170° in the Ia column at A2 is taken from the recent model by Groth (1961) and is additional evidence for the absence of a marked dependence of temperature on luminosity among the hotter stars.

TABLE 5

PROVISIONAL SCALE OF EFFECTIVE TEMPERATURES FOR MK TYPES

Types	T_e (° K)	
B0	27,000	
B1	23,000	
B2	20,000	
B3	18,000	
B5	16,000	
B6.5	14,000	
B8	12,500	
B9	11,200	
A0	10,400	
A1	9700	
A2	9100	9170
A3	8500	
A5	8200	
A7	7600	
F0	7200	

	Main-Sequence Subgiants		Giants		Supergiants	
	V	IV	III	II	Ib	Ia
F2	6900	6830	6800	6700	6600	....
F5	6700	6600	6500	6350	6200	....
F6	6500	6370	6250	6020	5800	....
F8	6200	6050	5900	5720	5450	....
G0	6000	5720	5500	5350	5050	....
G2	5740	5420	5100	4950	4750	....
G5	5520	5150	4800	4650	4500	....
G8	5320	4950	4600	4450	4300	....
K0	5120	4750	4400	4350	4100	....
K1	4920	4550	4150	4000	3850	....
K2	4760	....	3970	3860	3750	....
K3	4600	....	3820	3720	3600	....
K5	4350	....	3700	3600	3500	....
K6	4000	....	....	....	....	....
M0	3750	....	3500	3400	3300	....
M1	3600	....	3300	3150:	3050	....
M2	3350:	....	3100	2050:	....	....
M3	3100:	....	2900:	....	....	....
M4	....	....	2700:	....	....	....

The reduction of luminosity classes to absolute magnitudes has been revised considerably since 1951, particularly for the hotter stars. Photoelectric photometry in the three-color U, B, V scale has been used by Johnson and Morgan (1953) to separate intrinsic colors from interstellar reddening and thus to lead to a scale of absolute magnitudes, with the zero point tied to established moduli of galactic clusters. Figure 6 of their paper, however, shows that considerable systematic differences exist between their results and the photographic data of Petrie and his collaborators at Victoria (see § 4.3 on B stars). There has also

TABLE 6

VISUAL ABSOLUTE MAGNITUDES OF LUMINOSITY CLASSES

TYPE	MAIN SEQUENCE V	SUBGIANTS IV	GIANTS		SUPERGIANTS	
			III	II	Ib	Ia
O9	− 4.8	−5.4	−6.0	....	....	....
B0	− 4.1	−4.6	−5.0	−5.6:	−6.2	−7.0:
B1	− 3.5	−3.9	−4.4	−5.1:	−6.0	−7.0:
B2	− 2.5	−3.0	−3.6	−4.4	−5.9	−7.0:
B3	− 1.7	−2.3	−2.9	−3.9	−5.8	−7.0:
B5	− 1.1	−1.6	−2.2	−3.7	−5.7	−7.0:
B7	− 0.6	−1.0	−1.6	−3.6	−5.6	−7.0:
B8	− 0.2	−0.6	−1.2	−3.4	−5.5	−7.0:
B9	+ 0.2	−0.3	−0.8	−3.1	−5.4	−7.0:
A0	+ 0.6	0.0	−0.6	−2.8	−4.9	−7.0:
A1	+ 1.2	+0.3	−0.4	−2.6	−4.8	−7.0:
A2	+ 1.4	+0.6	−0.2	−2.4	−4.7	−7.0:
A3	+ 1.7	+0.9	0.0	−2.3	−4.6	−7.0:
A5	+ 2.1	+1.2	+0.3	−2.1	−4.5	−7.0:
A7	+ 2.4	+1.5	+0.5	−2.0	−4.5	−7.0:
F0	+ 2.6	+1.7	+0.6	−2.0	−4.5	−7.0:
F2	+ 3.0	+1.9	+0.6	−2.0	−4.5	−7.0:
F5	+ 3.4	+2.1	+0.7	−2.0	−4.5	−7.0:
F6	+ 3.7	+2.2	+0.7	−2.0	−4.5	−7.0:
F8	+ 4.0	+2.4	+0.6	−2.0	−4.5	−7.0:
G0	+ 4.4	+2.8	+0.6	−2.0	−4.5	−7.0:
G2	+ 4.7	+3.0	+0.4	−2.1	−4.5	−7.0:
G5	+ 5.2	+3.2	+0.3	−2.1	−4.5	−7.0:
G8	+ 5.6	+3.2	+0.3	−2.1	−4.5	−7.0:
K0	+ 5.9	+3.2	+0.2	−2.1	−4.5	−7.0:
K2	+ 6.3	....	−0.1	−2.2	−4.5	−7.0:
K3	+ 6.9	....	−0.2	−2.3	−4.5	−7.0:
K5	+ 8.0	....	−0.3	−2.3:	−4.5	−7.0:
M0	+ 9.2	....	−0.4	−2.4:	−4.5	−7.0:
M1	+ 9.7	....	−0.5	−2.4:	−4.5	−7.0:
M2	+10.1	....	−0.5	−2.4:	−4.5	−7.0:
M3	+10.6	....	−0.5	−2.4:	−4.5	....
M4	+11.3	....	−0.5:	−2.4:	−4.5	....
M5	+12.3	....	....	....	....	....
M6	+13.4	....	....	....	....	....

been a rediscussion by Bouigue (1959) of mean trigonometric parallaxes of near-by stars, and his means are in rather good agreement with the Lowell values. The calibrations of the various sets of measurements are not completely independent, however, and the luminosity scale for A and B stars cannot be considered as finally established. Considerable weight should be given to the estimation of $M_v = +0.5$ at A0 V by Osawa (1959), based on the motion of 99 normal stars of the main sequence. Table 6 is a rather freely smoothed modification of the 1951 table, to take account of these results, but remains only an approximation for the hotter stars.

For the Ia supergiants the earlier estimates from galactic rotation had led to a rough value of $M_v \approx -7$, but the photometric data allow this to be improved also. The Hγ intensities measured by Johnson and Iriarte (1958) gave values of from -6.6 to -7.2 for B0–A2 stars, while the discussion of color excesses by Bouigue (1959) led to a mean of -7.2 over the interval O9.5–F2. Since there are not enough Ia stars known to give clear evidence of variation of their luminosity with type, Table 6 gives merely an estimate of -7.0 for the whole range of types.

Minor changes have been entered also for late-type giants, since the improved classification discussed under type M in the next section made it possible to form new group means of the trigonometric parallaxes in the range K2–M2. The mean absolute magnitudes derived by Roman (1952) for F5–K5 stars from motions as well as trigonometric parallaxes have not been used in forming Table 6, for the reason that there are slight differences between her classes and the most accurate ones that can now be assigned. The analysis should be repeated as soon as most of the brighter stars have been reclassified.

§ 4. SPECTRAL TYPES AND CRITERIA

4.1. INTRODUCTION

In summarizing the spectral types and criteria in current use, it is clearly impossible to distinguish completely the contributions of different "systems" and to give credit to all the individuals who have shared in this collective development. We shall take up the types in order of decreasing temperatures, outlining chiefly the criteria found useful with plates of moderate dispersion for the majority of the stars in the solar neighborhood (Population I). Discussion of population differences is deferred to § 5. More detailed working rules will be found in the Yerkes *Atlas of Stellar Spectra* and in the references for each type.

4.2. TYPE O

The hottest and bluest stars were designated type O in the *Henry Draper Catalogue*. Later, those having spectra in which absorption lines predominated were given decimal subdivisions from O5 to O9 by Plaskett (1922). In 1931, Plaskett and Pearce defined the parallel sequence Of5–Of9 to indicate the stars in which the lines N III λλ 4634, 4640, 4641, and He II λ 4686 can be observed in emission on small-scale spectrograms. From examination of the lists of O stars by Morgan, Code, and Whitford (1955) and Hiltner (1956), Miss Underhill (1957) estimated that about 13 per cent of them show the Of characteristics. Although, as she pointed out, "detailed quantitative measurements . . . on moderate and high dispersion spectra indicate that some emission occurs at the N III multiplet in practically all O-stars," the distinction between the two groups has been generally retained.

Three stars with much stronger and wider emission lines were discovered with a visual spectroscope at the Paris Observatory by Wolf and Rayet (1867). Although these Wolf-Rayet stars are easily found on surveys with slitless spectrograms, their rarity is shown by the fact that only about 100 of them are known. They have been divided into two sequences, WC5–WC8 and WN5–WN8 by Beals (1930, 1934), on the basis of the relative strengths of their emission lines of carbon and nitrogen.

TABLE 7

STANDARD STARS OF TYPE O AND LINE RATIOS

Spectral Type	Stars	He II/He I	He II/Hγ, Hδ
O5........	+35°3930 N, +4°1302	2.5	3.0
O6........	+44°3639, +56°2617	1.4	1.7
O7........	9 Sge, S Mon	0.8	1.1
O8........	λ Ori, A Cyg	0.5	0.7
O9........	10 Lac, +34°980	0.25	0.4

The classification of the absorption-line O stars developed at the Dominion Astrophysical Observatory by Plaskett (1922) and revised by Pearce (Plaskett and Pearce 1931) is based chiefly on the ratios of He I λ 4471 and the mean of Hγ + Hδ to the mean of He II λ 4200 and λ 4542. Petrie (1947) measured the lines photometrically to give objective types on the same system. The mean ratios of total absorptions in the third and fourth columns of Table 7 are taken from his data. The maximum of Si IV λ 4089 at O9 is sometimes useful also.

No very sensitive spectroscopic criteria of luminosity have been found for types earlier than O9. The absence of a luminosity effect in the hydrogen lines has been explained by Underhill (1950) as the lack of Stark effect broadening in the main sequence at high temperatures. Nevertheless, there is evidence that differences exist in absolute magnitude among the O stars, for Sharpless (1952) used his modulus of 8^{m}5 for the Orion aggregate to find luminosities ranging from −5.2 to −7.4 for the O stars involved and Kopylov (1958) based a two-dimensional classification of stars later than O5 on measured line intensities.

Near O9, however, luminosity classes can be estimated from the ratios Si IV λ 4089/C III λ 4068, (Si IV + He I) λ 4119/He I λ 4144, and He II λ 4686/(C III + O III) λ 4650.

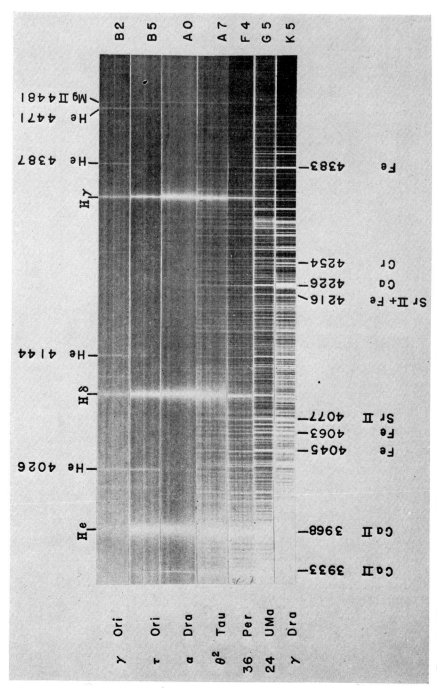

PLATE 1.—The spectral sequence of giants from B2 to K5. Prismatic dispersion of negatives: 27 A/mm. 24 UMa is probably less luminous than the other stars (note the lack of any CN break at λ 4216) and can be classified as G5 IIIb–IVa. The four top spectrograms were taken by A. Slettebak.

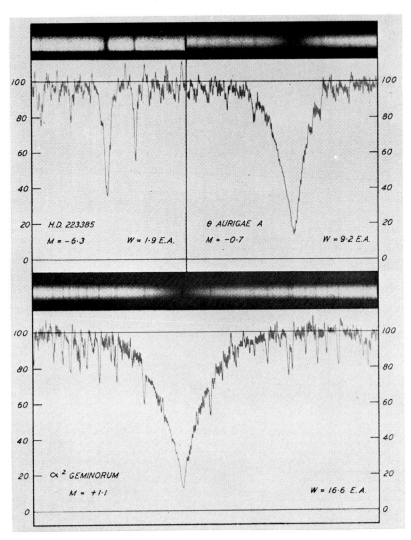

PLATE 2.—Variation of Hγ with luminosity in early A-type stars. Victoria spectrograms reproduced from Petrie and Maunsell (1950).

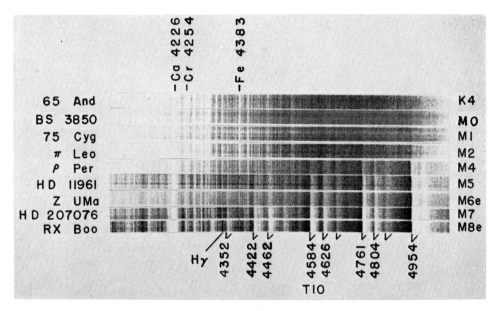

PLATE 3.—Giants from K4 to M8. Small-scale (104 A/mm at Hγ) spectrograms of the λλ 4300–4900 region. Types K5 and M3 are not shown. Z UMa had band intensities giving type M6 on the date (April 8, 1958) of the spectrogram, but it is an Me variable with a visual amplitude of about 2 mag. and is not a standard-type star.

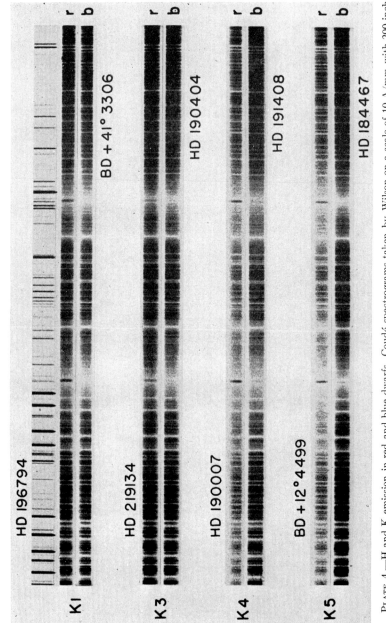

PLATE 4.—H and K emission in red and blue dwarfs. Coudé spectrograms taken by Wilson on a scale of 10 A/mm with 200-inch telescope (Wilson 1961).

4.3. Type B

The lines of He I reach their maximum near B2 and play the most prominent part in determining the subdivisions of type B. The ratio Si IV λ 4089/He I λ 4009 is useful around B0. At B1, Si IV λ 4089 becomes weaker than Si III λ 4552. Between B2 and B8, the consistent decrease in the ratio He I $\lambda\lambda$ 4144, 4121/Si II $\lambda\lambda$ 4128–4130 serves to define the type.

Luminosity effects in the ratios N II λ 3995/He I λ 4009, He I λ 4121/He I λ 4144, and Si III λ 4552/He I λ 4387 become so well marked near B2 that the discrimination of the five main luminosity classes is easily possible.

Beginning at about B3, the inverse luminosity effect in the Balmer lines become so conspicuous that their intensities are the best indicators of luminosity to about A3. The sharp and relatively weak lines in the c stars had been recognized by Miss Maury, but it was Lindblad (1922) who proposed photometric luminosity criteria involving the hydrogen lines. Measurements of several Balmer lines have since been made by a number of observers, among the first being Öhman (1927) and Anger (1930), who studied Hδ and Hγ. Among the more recent sets of measured values of the total absorption of Hγ are those obtained photographically by Petrie and Moyls (1956) and photoelectrically by Johnson and Iriarte (1958).

It is now recognized that the increased total absorptions of the Balmer lines in stars of the lower luminosities is a pressure (Stark) effect, giving rise to the wide wings characteristic of main-sequence stars of types B and A. In Plate 2, prepared at Victoria, the tracings bring out the effect clearly in early A stars, while the reproduced spectrograms show how difficult it is to estimate intensities of very broad features visually when the scale of the plates is rather large. For such features, a small scale can actually be an advantage (cf. the plates of the Yerkes *Atlas of Stellar Spectra*).

4.4. Type A

One of the obstacles to accurate classification of the A stars is the presence of several roughly parallel sequences of "peculiar" A stars and metallic-line stars. For the ordinary A stars the strength of the K line of Ca II fixes the type on spectrograms of very small scale. On such plates the line first appears near B5 in the main sequence and becomes equal to H + He near F0.

For moderate dispersions, the ratio Mg II λ 4481/Fe II λ 4385 is useful near A0, and the ratio Si II $\lambda\lambda$ 4128–4130/Mn I $\lambda\lambda$ 4030–4034 decreases steadily with type through F2. The blended Mn I lines first become noticeable near A1.

Just as in type B, the Balmer lines determine the luminosity class of the early A stars as soon as the temperature type has been fixed. For types later than A2 the ratio Fe II, Ti II λ 4417/Mg II λ 4481 is used.

From the practical standpoint it is unfortunate that one of the most sensitive luminosity criteria for types B, A, and F lies in the photographic infrared, where

these stars cannot be observed efficiently. The feature is the blended triplet
O I λλ 7771–7775. When Merrill (1925) first observed this blend in stellar
spectra, he noticed its enhancement in the supergiant α Cygni, in contrast to its
weakness in dwarfs like αCMa. Its behavior was studied in more detail by
Keenan and Hynek (1950), who found that near F0 the total absorption of
λ 7774 increased by nearly 2 mag. between class V and class Ia.

4.5. TYPE F

The swarm of metallic lines that make their appearance as the temperature
decreases become strong enough near F0 to provide a number of useful criteria.
Since the luminosity effect in the Balmer lines practically disappears near F5,
the ratios Hδ/Fe λ 4045 and Hγ/Ca I λ 4226 can be used to establish the spectral type. With dispersions of about 100 A/mm or less, the G band (mainly due
to CH) first becomes noticeable near F0 as a broad feature lying between λ 4300
and λ 4310. Up to about F5, the violet side of the band is stronger than the red
side, but in the later subdivisions the feature appears nearly symmetrical.

It is within type F that the lines of Sr II at λ 4077 and λ 4215 first become important criteria of luminosity, since the fraction of strontium atoms that are
ionized increases greatly at the low pressures that prevail in the atmospheres of
the more luminous stars. The ratios λ 4077/λ 4226, λ 4077/λ 4045, and λ 4077/
Hδ are among the most sensitive.

4.6. TYPES G AND K

It is convenient to consider the G and K stars together, since many significant
spectral features are observable throughout this range of types. The ratios of
metals to hydrogen continue to increase through type G, but Fe λ 4045 has become so strong at G5 that it is better replaced by Fe λ 4144 in the ratio λ 4144/
Hδ. The G band of CH has begun to weaken at about G8 in the giants, and
λλ 4030–4034/λ 4300 is useful around G8–K0. In the K stars, Cr λ 4289 and
Ti, Ca, and Fe λ 4300 are stronger than the blended CH features around them,
and the G band no longer appears continuous. Since association into molecules
is favored by higher pressure, it is not surprising that the G band has a negative
luminosity effect and is too weak in supergiants to be useful as a temperature
criterion.

In the later K stars the ultimate lines of the neutral metals have become
strong and continue to strengthen with decreasing temperature. Next to H and
K, the strongest line in the blue region is the resonance line of calcium at λ 4226,
and, if allowance is made for its negative luminosity effect, it is a sensitive indicator of temperature. The ratio Fe λ 4325/λ 4226 is often used. The resonance
triplet of chromium at λ 4254, λ 4274, and λ 4289 begins to be useful near K0,
particularly in the ratios λ 4300/λ 4289 and Fe λ 4250, λ 4260/λ 4254.

The Balmer lines show a positive luminosity effect in G and K stars, and, although they are used primarily as temperature criteria, the enhancement of Hδ

and Hγ is a valuable check on the luminosity of supergiants, helping to distinguish them from giants with abnormally strong CN (see below).

The primary luminosity criteria are again the relative intensities of Sr II to Fe I lines: λ 4077/λ 4063 and λ 4077/λ 4071. The line Sr II λ 4215.5 is blended with Fe I λ 4216.2 and the first head near λ 4216.0 of the strongest blue bands of CN. Except on spectrograms of relatively high dispersion (at least 20 A/mm), these individual features are not resolved, and it is the shortward-shaded CN bands that contribute most to the intensity of the blended feature. Because of the importance of these bands for classification and the complexity of their behavior, it is necessary to consider them in some detail.

The blue bands of CN comprise the $\Delta v = -1$ sequence of the $^2\Sigma$–$^2\Sigma$ system for which the lower level is the normal electronic state of the molecule and which are exceeded in strength only by the ultraviolet $\Delta v = 0$ sequence of the same system near λ 3883. On spectrograms of very small scale the band appears as a shallow depression in the continuum of the more luminous G and K stars, fading out gradually somewhat shortward of the λ 4150 Fe line. About 1921, Lindblad recognized that the absorption was due primarily to CN and showed that that the integrated absorption had a strong positive correlation with luminosity (Lindblad 1922). In the photometric classifications that grew out of this work, the integrated CN absorption is the definitive criterion of luminosity (for summaries and references see Lindblad and Stenquist 1934, and Lindblad 1946).

The λ 4216 and λ 3883 bands are scarcely noticeable in dwarfs of any type but are conspicuous in giants (G5–K3) and are even stronger in supergiants (Iwanowska 1936; Keenan 1941). They have accordingly been used generally to detect stars of high luminosity on even the shortest objective-prism spectra. With dispersions of the order of 80–200 A/mm, the "break" in the spectrum at the λ 4216 head can be taken as a measure of cyanogen strength with relatively little contamination by atomic lines if the intensity in the band is measured at about λ 4212, just far enough from the head to avoid the additional dip due to the Sr II-Fe blend. The uncertainty here comes mainly from the density fluctuations inherent in photographic emulsions; consequently, measurement of either the break or the integrated band absorption is greatly improved by direct photoelectric scanning. If the scanning slit does not have a width greater than 5 A, the intensity inside the band can be compared with the comparatively pure continuum at around λ 4219 (to about K3, where the wings of Ca λ 4226 depress this region).

Among the many investigations of the behavior of the blue CN bands as a function of temperature and luminosity, three of the more extensive photographic studies have been those of Setterberg (1947), Plassard (1950), and Yoss (1961). In addition to his measurements, Plassard also made computations of the expected profiles of the integrated band structure as the temperature dropped from 8000° to 6000° K. His diagrams are useful to observers estimating the strength of CN absorption in the spectra of giants observed with moderate dispersion.

More recently, photoelectric measurements of the λ 4216 band in 712 stars of types G8–K5 have been made by Griffin and Redman (1960) at Cambridge.[4] Their measure of CN strength was the ratio of the integrated light in the range λλ 4164–4214 within the band to that in the continua λλ 4097–4149 and λλ 4230–4283 outside the band.

The plots of CN absorption against luminosity and type made by Griffin and Redman greatly strengthen the earlier photographic evidence that (1) the CN luminosity effect is strongest in the range G8–K1, and (2) the dispersion in the amount of CN absorption at a given luminosity and temperature is too large to be explained by errors in either the photometry or the spectral classification. Thus Griffin and Redman find that the "CN absolute magnitudes" for G8–K1 stars have a r.m.s. difference from MK luminosities of about 1^m5. The relation of this dispersion to population effects will be discussed in § 5.4. As luminosity indicators, the cyanogen bands remain valuable because of their great sensitivity, but they cannot safely be used alone—other criteria should always be observed as checks. When the scale of the spectrograms is sufficient, a number of metallic lines help to define the luminosity. Thus in the work of Holliday, Hossack, and Oke at Toronto (Heard 1956), the ratio (Fe + Fe II) λ 4233/(Mn, etc.) λ 4235 proved useful at 66 A/mm, and Ca λ 4455/Fe λ 4462 could be added when the scale was increased to 33 A/mm.

The visual region of the spectrum offers few good luminosity criteria, chiefly because nearly all the lines from ionized elements lie in the blue or ultraviolet. For types K5–M2, however, Fitch and Morgan (1951) found a group of Fe I lines in the interval λλ 5175–5270 which, although blended on their scale of about 260 A/mm, were responsive enough to luminosity to allow dwarfs, giants, and supergiants to be distinguished. These green lines, like several blue multiplets that behave similarly, are intersystem lines originating in the lowest (a ^{3}D) level of the neutral Fe atom. They are valuable for work on fainter stars than can be photographed at the blue end of their spectra. Unfortunately, they cannot be used for types later than M2 because of the great λ 5165 band of TiO which hides them.

4.7. Type M

The long-standing lack of an adequate set of standard stars of type M has been due to three natural reasons.

1. The scarcity of M stars of bright apparent magnitude has hindered the calibration of the luminosities of the giant branch in terms of absolute magnitudes, especially for types M4 and later.

2. The cooler the stars, the greater is the likelihood of variability in visual and

---

[4] Photoelectric determination of CN strength by the method of filter photometry is discussed by Strömgren in the following chapter of this volume. Extensive measurements have been made by Gyldenkerne at Copenhagen and by Crawford at Kitt Peak.

photographic light—accompanied by changes in temperature and type. It has frequently been remarked that it is doubtful that any late M-type star has really constant brightness, and the stars used to define subdivisions M6 and later include several known variables of considerable amplitude. This accounts for many of the inconsistencies in types assigned by different observers at different times.

3. Absorption bands of TiO become so strong after M4 that it is increasingly difficult to find stretches of continuum where atomic lines can be compared reliably. Recognition of differences in luminosity has been handicapped particularly, and only a few of the later M stars, such as α Her, have been recognized as considerably brighter than the average.

For these reasons, Table 8 has been prepared to extend the short list of MK types originally given on pages 28 and 30 of the Yerkes *Atlas of Stellar Spectra.* Most of the spectrograms used were taken at Perkins, but some material from Yerkes, McDonald, and Mount Wilson has been included. The scale of types follows closely that of the Mount Wilson catalogue, but, in estimating average types for each star from plates taken on several different dates, it was found necessary to modify slightly some of the standards previously used.

The spectral subdivision of type M can be carried out accurately by means of estimates of band intensities (cf. section on the Mount Wilson system above). Fortunately, the estimates can usually be made well, even when the scale is as small as several hundred A/mm, provided that the definition on the plate is very good. Even a slight blurring of the edges of the band heads may lead to an underestimate of their strength and hence to a type that is too early.

The range from K4 to M1 offers most difficulty, for here the TiO bands are just becoming visible and can be confused with nearby groups of atomic lines unless the dispersion is fairly high. The bands that appear first are the 0–0 bands of the $\Delta v = 0$ sequence of the two strong triplet systems—λ 5167 of the blue α-system and λ 7054 of the red γ-system. These are both badly situated for observation; the λ 5167 band is at the long-wave limit of sensitivity of blue emulsions, and λ 7054 lies where the usual infrared emulsions (I-N) are comparatively insensitive. Consequently, observers classifying in the blue with rather low dispersion see first the 1–0 (α) band at λ 4954 at about M0 (the strongest bands can be detected as early as K4 with a scale of around 20 A/mm). The distinction between K5 and M0 is rather difficult to make, particularly since prismatic spectrograms exposed for λ 4200 are usually too dense near λ 5000. (The set of small-scale spectrograms in Pl. 2 have been exposed lightly to bring out the λ 4700 region.) Consequently, atomic lines are generally used. With a scale in the neighborhood of 100 A/mm, the ratio of Ca λ 4226 to the strongest Fe lines, such as λ 4144 and λ 4325, can be used if care is taken to allow for the sensitivity of λ 4226 to luminosity.

Beyond M2, numerous TiO bands are strong enough to serve as criteria of type. Among the best are λ 4584 and λ 4761 in the blue; λ 5446, λ 5847, and

TABLE 8

Classification of K5–M8 Giants and Supergiants

Star	α_{1900}	δ_{1900}	m_v	Type*
BS 8424	$22^{h}02^{m}$	$+44°32'$	5.32	K5+III
γ Sge	19 54	+19 13	3.71	K5+III
ν Boo	13 44	+16 18	4.28	K5+III
μ UMa	10 16	+42 00	3.21	M0 III
50 Her	16 46	+29 59	5.76	M0 IIIa
75 Leo	11 12	+ 2 34	5.44	M0 IIIb
β And	1 04	+35 05	2.37	M0 III
106 Her	18 16	+21 55	4.98	M0 III
δ Oph	16 09	− 3 26	3.03	M0.5 III
75 Cyg	21 36	+42 49	5.35	M1 III
2 Peg	21 25	+23 12	4.76	M1 III
64 Dra	20 00	+64 32	5.43	M1 III
κ Ser	15 44	+18 27	4.28	M1 III
γ Eri	3 53	−13 48	3.19	M1 III
37 Leo	10 11	+14 14	5.74	M1 III
36 Cam	12 54	+17 57	4.96	M1 III
6 BU Gem	6 06	+22 56	6.1–7.5	M2: Iab
χ Peg	0 09	+19 39	4.94	M2 III
119 Tau	5 26	+18 31	4.73	M2 Ib
α Cet	2 57	+ 3 42	2.82	M2 III (4226 weak)
BS 1155	3 40	+65 13	4.71	M2 IIa
83 UMa	13 37	+55 11	4.75	M2 IIIab
μ Cep	21 40	+58 19	4.0–4.8	M2 Ia
π Leo	9 54	+ 8 31	4.89	M2 III
HD 10465	1 37	+48 01	7.00	M2.5 II
74 Vir	13 26	− 5 47	4.83	M2+ III
β Peg	22 59	+27 32	2.61	M2+ IIb–IIIa
BS 46	0 09	− 8 20	5.36	M3 III
μ Gem	6 16	+22 34	3.19	M3 IIIa
104 Her	18 08	+31 23	5.02	M3 III
ρ UMa	8 53	+68 01	4.99	M3 IIIb
π Aur	5 52	+45 56	4.59	M3.5 II
ρ Per	2 58	+38 27	3.2–4.1	M4 IIIa
ω Vir	11 33	+ 8 41	5.47	M4–4.5 III
BS 5299	14 03	+44 20	5.44	M4–4.5 III
10 Her	16 07	+23 45	5.96	M4 III
XY Lyr	18 34	+39 35	5.8–6.8	M4–5 Ib–II
δ² Lyr	18 51	+36 46	4.52	M4 II
BS 8621	22 34	+56 17	5.47	M4 III
SU Per	2 15	+56 09	6.8–7.9	M4 Ia–Ib
HD 11961	1 52	+30 39	7.21	M5 III
56 Leo	10 50	+ 6 42	6.05	M5 III
RR UMi = BS 5589	14 56	+66 20	4.8	M5 III
HD 77443	8 57	+39 08	6.70	M5 III
17τ⁴ Ser	15 31	+15 26	6.5–7.0:	M5 IIb–IIIa
α¹ Her	17 10	+14 30	3.1–3.9	M5: Ib–II
HD 156860	17 14	+ 2 14	6.91	M5 III
BS 6702	17 54	+45 23	6.2	M5 IIb–IIIa
AC Dra = BS 7804	20 19	+68 34	6.0:	M5 IIIa
U Del	20 40	+17 44	6.4–7.9	M5–6 II
RZ Ari = 45 Ari	2 50	+17 56	5.9:	M6–III
30 g Her	16 26	+42 06	4.4–5.6	M6–III
EU Del = BS 7886	20 33	+17 55	6.2–6.9	M6 III
HD 207076	21 41	− 2 40	7.2	M7
RX Boo	14 19	+26 09	7.0–9.1	M8: (weak emission)

* Spectral types are subdivided into four steps; e.g., M0, M0+, M0.5, M1−, M1. Dashes indicate not an intermediate type but a range over which the type has been observed to vary.

λ 6159 in the yellow and red; and λ 7672 and λ 8433 in the photographic infrared. In the latest types many fainter bands appear, and the ratios of several of them make accurate classification from M5 through M8 possible. At temperatures below 3000° K, the vibrational levels (which in the case of the α-system of TiO are spaced about 0.15 ev or 1210 cm^{-1} apart) have populations appreciably influenced by the excitation temperatures. Thus the α-bands at λ 5759 (0, 2) and λ 5810 (1, 3) show little change in strength after M5 and can be compared with λ 5838 and λ 5847 of the γ-system, originating in the lowest vibrational level of the same electronic state. Similarly, the slight elevation of the lowest singlet level above the lowest triplet level is sufficient to make the triplet/singlet ratios λ 5569 + λ 5591/λ 5597 and λ 5664/λ 5661 very sensitive to temperature (Merrill, Deutsch, and Keenan 1962). These effects are less conspicuous in the blue region because the bands from the upper levels tend to be overlapped by the low-level bands but can be seen in Plate 3 in the changing ratio of λ 4422 (4, 0)/λ 4352 (7, 2) between M5 and M8.

At M7 the bands of vanadium oxide become noticeable and increase so rapidly with type that their appearance on plates of moderate scale can be taken as defining type M7. There are two strong systems of VO accessible to easy observation—the yellow-red system, with its strongest band at λ 5737 (Merrill 1940, Pl. II), and the near-infrared system with a number of conspicuous heads including $\lambda\lambda$ 7373, 7865, 7896, and 7939 (Keenan and Schroeder 1952, Fig. 1). When observed with very low dispersion, the λ 7400 and λ 7900 sequences appear as extensions proceeding longward of depressions in the continuum due to overlapping TiO bands (Nassau and van Albada 1949; Cameron and Nassau 1955).

The most sensitive luminosity criteria are ratios of lines in the blue region, especially Sr II λ 4077/Fe λ 4063, Hδ/Fe λ 4077, (Sr II + Fe λ 4216)/Fe λ 4143, Hγ/Fe, Cr λ 4337 (on small-scale spectrograms the blend of these two features is compared with Fe λ 4325), and Fe, Y II λ 4376/Fe λ 4383. With advancing type, the TiO bands at successively shorter wavelengths begin to weaken these lines and distort the ratios. The first to be affected are those in the $\lambda\lambda$ 4300–4400 region.

Several line ratios in the near infrared have been employed successfully to distinguish supergiants, giants, and dwarfs, and their sensitivity is less than that of the lines in the blue. With a scale of 48 A/mm, Keenan and Hynek (1945) found the ratios Fe II, etc., λ 7712/Ni λ 7714, Fe λ 8514/Ti λ 8435, and Fe λ 8689/Fe λ 8675 usable. On plates of much lower dispersion (200 A/mm), Sharpless (1956) was able to compare blended Fe and Ti features at λ 8308 and λ 8330 with Ti λ 8435 and Fe + Ti λ 8468. He found also that the infrared CN bands in the $\lambda\lambda$ 7800–8000 region, which persist to later types than the blue bands, can be used to separate classes Ia, Ib, II, and III.

The ultimate lines of potassium (λ 7699) and of sodium (λ 8183 and λ 8195) have a minimum in giants and are fairly strong in dwarfs and supergiants.

4.8. Type S

There is a continuous sequence of stars from pure type M, in which all the strong bands observed are due to monoxides (TiO, VO, ScO, AlO) of moderately light metals, to pure type S, in which the oxides of heavier metals (ZrO, LaO, YO) dominate. Yttrium oxide can show considerable strength in either group but tends to be stronger in type S. In the blue and visual regions it is essentially the strength of TiO or of ZrO that decides to which of the two types a star belongs. Since the S stars are much less common and thus might be regarded as variations from the normal M stars, most observers have followed the convention used by Merrill (1922) in defining the type and have assigned a star to type S only if the ZrO bands can be easily noticed on spectrograms of moderate dispersion. Thus some S stars, such as HD 22649 (HR 1105), HD 35155, and χ Cyg, actually have ZrO bands weak relative to TiO. The atomic lines of the heavy metals Zr, La, Y, Sr, and Ba help to define the type, for Merrill showed that they strengthened along with the characteristic bands. The CN bands also tend to be more intense in type S.

It was natural that the first systematic subdivision of type S should be based primarily on ZrO band strength. This was done by Davis (1934). As it became more apparent that the strength of ZrO bands depended on both temperature and the abundances of the Zr group of metals relative to the Ti group, the next obvious step was to try to separate these two variables. This was attempted (Keenan 1954) by defining the temperature type by the sum of the strengths of the two sets of ZrO and TiO bands and the abundance class by the relative strength of the two sets of bands. Most of the brighter S stars in the northern sky are included in that list of 69 stars. Examples of the notation are R Gem, S3,9e at maximum (a fairly hot, almost pure S-type star) and HD 177175, S7,3 (a cooler star in which TiO is considerably more conspicuous than ZrO). When spectrograms can be taken in the λ 7900 region, the extreme temperature sensitivity of the LaO bands makes them valuable criteria.

Although the S stars are known to be giants, no satisfactory luminosity classification within the group has been proposed. The difficulty is that all the lines of ionized elements that are present in the cool stars and are most sensitive to luminosity are due to the heavy elements Sr and Ba, which show marked abundance differences. Furthermore, there are not enough S stars known to allow other effective luminosity criteria to be detected by statistical comparison of, say, mean motions.

4.9. Carbon Stars

The red carbon stars likewise are giants differing from M stars in chemical composition, but they are more numerous than the S stars, and their spectral characteristics—the Swan bands of C_2—are so striking that they were recognized as a distinct type by Secchi and other visual observers.

In the *HD Catalogue* the carbon stars are divided into two main types, R and

N, with subdivisions R0, R3, R5, R8, Na, Nb, Nc. Shane (1920, 1928) reclassified these stars, retaining the *HD* subdivisions for the hotter group, type R, and
dividing type N into N0, N3, N5, N6, N7. His criteria of type lie in the photographic region and include the bands of C_2, CN, and the violet-degraded bands
discovered by Sanford at λ 4979 and λ 4686, which Kleman (1956) has since
identified as due to SiC_2. Shane recognized that the weakness of the violet region
of the N stars is so extreme that the gradient in the continuum of the brighter
stars cannot be seriously affected by interstellar absorption; hence he used the
increase in the gradient toward later subdivisions as a primary criterion. His
ordering of the spectra is essentially consistent with that of the *HD Catalogue*.
The Swan bands pass through a maximum between R4 and R6 and increase
again toward N6.

The subdivisions of class R form essentially a sequence of decreasing temperature, at least through R5, but it has long been known that those of type N do
not progress consistently with temperature and that the assignment of stars to
R8 or N0 is ambiguous. This conclusion follows from the realization that the
great deficiency of violet light in many N stars must be due largely to molecular
absorption and that a real temperature gradient cannot be measured in this part
of the spectrum. Recent laboratory work indicates that the triatomic molecule
C3 is responsible for much of the absorption shortward of λ 4300 (McKellar and
Richardson 1954; see also chap. 16 of Vol. **6** for discussion and references).
Nevertheless, the main division into two main types R and N, with retention of
a few of the subdivisions when they can be recognized, has remained worthwhile
for observers making objective-prism surveys with extremely low dispersion.

An effort to approach a two-parameter classification in terms of temperature
and carbon abundance was made by Keenan and Morgan (1941). The temperature class was determined by three criteria in the visual part of their spectra.

1. Absolute intensity of the D lines of Na: In the coolest carbon stars these
are much more sensitive to temperature than in M stars, where their intensity
is greatly weakened by overlying bands of TiO.

2. The relative intensity of the continuous spectra near λ 5190, λ 5670, and
λ 6150: These regions were judged to be least affected by absorption from the
numerous C_2 and CN bands in the orange, but actually no part of the observed
continuum is entirely free from such distortion.

3. The relative intensity of the λ 5685 and λ 5585 vibrational bands of the
Swan system of C_2: With decreasing temperature, absorption from the 0–1 band
of λ 5635 is favored over the λ 5585 band, which arises from absorption in the
second vibrational level. Large temperature differences produce considerable
changes, but the method is not very accurate.

Carbon abundance was measured by the absolute intensity of the Swan
bands. Since the sequence of temperature types was quite different from the
ordering of the subdivisions of type N, as discussed above (the differences are
much less in type R), the symbol "C" was suggested for the whole group, fol-

lowed by a number giving the temperature type. The types range from C0 to C9, and in the original notation a subscript was added to indicate the carbon abundance. The authors now recommend that the types be written as C1, 0; C7, 4, etc., the number following the comma being an abundance parameter, as in the notation for type S. For the range C0–C6, it is possible to observe the blue region of the spectrum, and several of the line ratios that are employed in the G and K stars have been used to relate the carbon sequence to the ordinary giant stars. Table 9 gives the C types, the corresponding subdivisions of type R, the equivalent types of G or K giants, and the approximate effective temperature, in successive columns.

TABLE 9

THE CARBON STARS, TYPES C0–C6

Carbon Sequence Type	R Type	Equivalent Oxygen Stars	Approx. T_e (° K)
C0.........	R0	G4–G6	4600
C1.........	R1	G7–G8	4450
C2.........	R2	G9–K0	4300
C3.........	R3	K1–K2	3900
C4.........	R4–R5	K3–K4	3600
C5.........	....	K5–M0	3400
C6.........	....	M1–M2:	3100:

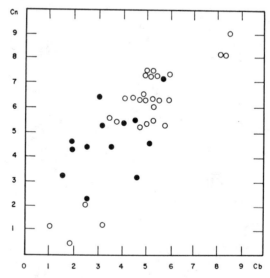

FIG. 1.—Comparison of Bouigue's types (Cb) with Yerkes type (Cn) for red carbon stars. Solid points refer to stars with the λ 6260 band strong; open circles to those with λ 6260 weak. Reproduced from Bouigue (1954).

Some checks on the temperature sequence have been furnished by intensites of ultimate atomic lines (estimated for 6 stars by Sanford 1950), vibrational temperatures derived from CN and C_2 bands (95 stars, Bouigue 1954, and 5 stars, Wyller 1957), and total absorptions of the D lines. The most extensive measurements on the D lines are those of Bouigue (1954), who preferred to define new subtypes based on the measured D-line intensities and vibrational temperature only. The relation between Bouigue and MK types is shown in Figure 1, taken from his paper. The diagram shows no definite systematic difference but a large scatter. These tests confirm the general dependence of the subdivisions of type C on temperature, but there is no doubt that there is need for improvement in the choice of criteria that will be easily accessible, as well as sensitive to temperature.

One possible improvement would be the greater use of the near infrared, where the ultimate lines of potassium and the red bands of CN can be observed. Objective-prism spectrograms on I-N plates (scale: 1700 A/mm at λ 7600), have been used at Cleveland (Nassau and Colacevich 1950) for the detection and rough classification of carbon stars.

Discussion of the several peculiar groups among the carbon stars will be found in chapter 16 of Volume 6.

§ 5. SPECTRAL CHARACTERISTICS OF POPULATION GROUPS

5.1. INTRODUCTION

The terms "Population I" and "Population II," as introduced by Baade in 1944, distinguish two groups of stars that differ in their distribution in the luminosity-spectrum (HR) diagram and in their spatial location and motions. Population I includes most of the stars in our galactic neighborhood, plus the supergiants concentrated in the plane of the Milky Way, that give the HR diagram what we have come to regard as its "normal" appearance. In Figure 2 the density of plotted points gives a rough idea of this distribution of Population I stars. The figure is affected by the usual underestimation of the stars of lowest luminosity, but this is not serious for our purpose, which is to define the regions of the diagram that are known to be occupied by stars belonging to the more extreme population groups. For the Population I stars of lower luminosities, nearby stars with parallaxes larger than 0″.075 have been selected from the catalogue of Gliese (1957), with the additions of some of the members of galactic clusters for which Arp (1958) has summarized the data. The supergiants plotted are those with the best-calibrated spectroscopic parallaxes.

As originally defined, Population II was limited to the members of globular clusters and resolved elliptical galaxies. The hatched portions of Figure 2 represent the composite distribution of members of typical halo clusters as compiled by Arp (1958), with the addition of the rather vaguely bounded zone of subdwarfs, which are generally assigned to Population II (Roman 1954; Greenstein 1956). There are, of course, some cluster stars outside the hatched areas, including the blue end of the main sequence (M3), but they are relatively few in number. It should be kept in mind, furthermore, that any one cluster, or other group of Population II stars, will usually occupy only part of the hatched area. Thus the horizontal branch extending to the blue through the RR Lyrae variables may be sparsely populated (M13), and the main upright branch will shift horizontally by several tenths of a magnitude in color index from one cluster to another.

Although the original idea of two distinct populations is now known to be much too simple and as many as five population groups, which may shade into one another, have been introduced (cf. the volume *Stellar Populations*, [1958], *Rich. Astr. Spec. Vaticana*, p. 5), it is still useful to define the spectral character-

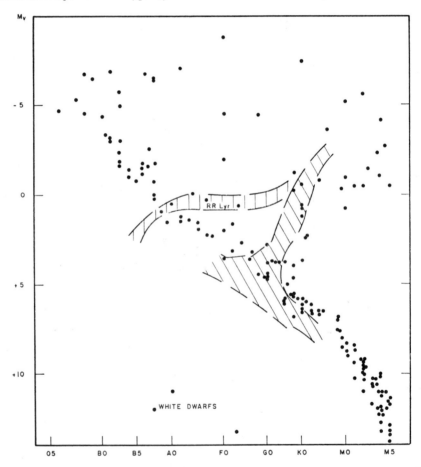

Fig. 2.—Schematic HR diagram showing regions occupied by stars of Population I (*filled circles*) and Population II (*hatched areas*). The area in which white dwarfs are found is shown also.

istics of the two main populations of Figure 2. The spectroscopic distinction between populations is rather subtle at best in most parts of the HR diagram.

Now let us use Figure 2 to pick out the areas where the two populations overlap and, for those areas, see how the spectra of Population II stars differ from the Population I stars that we have described.

5.2. TYPES B AND A

The horizontal branch of Population II crosses the ordinary main sequence near $M_v = +1$ and types B3–A0. Unfortunately, few of the blue stars in globular clusters are bright enough to have had their spectra well observed, though Münch obtained plates of several. Greenstein (1956, 1959) found a number of similar objects among the blue stars of the galactic halo, which are sometimes called "HZ stars" because the first of these high-latitude blue objects were discovered by Humason and Zwicky. The horizontal-branch stars are characterized by "strong, sharp hydrogen lines and large Balmer jump, and very weak lines of all other elements including Mg II and He I" (Greenstein 1959). Slettebak and Stock (1957) found a few of these stars on Hamburg objective-prism plates, on which they looked like supergiants because of their narrow Balmer lines; on Mount Wilson slit spectrograms with a scale of 80 A/mm the absence of metallic lines allowed the stars to be assigned to the horizontal branch (Slettebak, Bahner, and Stock 1961).

5.3. THE MAIN SEQUENCE, TYPES G–M

Because of the low intrinsic luminosity of the cooler dwarf stars, the number of those for which accurate spectral types are known remains small, and these are confined within distances of a few dozens of parsecs from the sun. This small sample volume close to the galactic plane presumably contains a preponderance of stars of Population I, at least within type M, and this selection may contribute to the observed narrowness of the lower end of the main sequence (Morgan 1938). Below and to the left of the main sequence lie the subdwarfs, which have such weak metallic lines that the first three discovered by Adams and Joy (1922) were classified by them as of type A. Miss Roman (1954) assigned 16 out of the 17 subdwarfs studied by her to type F on the basis of the strengths of their hydrogen lines. More recent work on spectrograms of sufficient scale to allow ratios of the weak metallic lines to be observed suggests that the subdwarfs belong rather in types G and K (Aller and Greenstein 1960). Their photoelectric colors are too blue for the types by factors of as much as 0.2 in $B - V$; but Sandage and Eggen (1959) have confirmed the earlier estimates by Strömgren and others that, when the effects of line absorption are removed, the subdwarfs lie on the main sequence in the luminosity-color diagram. Their membership in Population II, originally proposed by Roman on the grounds of their weak lines and large space motions, has been supported by estimates of abundances (Aller and Greenstein 1960), which show that their metals/hydrogen ratio is deficient by factors of 40–200, as compared with the sun. Thus the subdwarfs are considered as the main sequence of the more extreme groups of Population II stars.

Actually, there is no sharp boundary between the subdwarfs and the usual main sequence, and Wilson (1961) found that when Eggen's colors $(P - V)$ are plotted against spectral type, there is a considerable spread in color for ordinary dwarfs in the range G5–M5. Wilson showed that on pairs of coudé spectrograms of dwarfs having the same types but lying on the red and blue edges of the sequence, respectively, practically all the metallic lines are nearly identical, but two features show striking differences: (1) emission in the H and K lines of Ca II is much stronger in the red dwarfs (see Plate 4), and (2) absorption by the Balmer lines is stronger in blue than in red dwarfs.

The interpretation proposed by Wilson is that the redder dwarfs are deficient in metals in comparison with the blue ones by factors extending to about 1 : 100. Since, however, for types G5 and later the electrons necessary to maintain the H^- opacity are provided by the metals rather than by hydrogen, no differences in the strength of the metallic lines are observed. The observed lower temperatures of the red dwarfs are shown to account for both their weaker hydrogen absorption and their Ca II emission; the latter representing normal chromospheric emission, which will be seen more easily against the weakened violet continuum of the cooler stars.

Since the emission in H and K should be observable with dispersions considerably less than the 10 A/mm of the spectrograms reproduced in Plate 4, this feature offers a means of making direct estimates of the third dimension of classification—metal abundance—for dwarfs from G5 to at least K5.

It should be noted that, as one moves to the left of the main sequence toward the subdwarfs, an ambiguous zone will presumably be reached where the well-known ultraviolet excess of the subdwarfs roughly balances the greater temperature gradient of dwarfs of moderately low metal content. Physically, this would be the zone within which hydrogen succeeds the metals as the chief source of free electrons. The spectra of such transition stars may be expected to show very slightly weakened metal lines.

5.4. Giants and Subgiants of Types G and K

Coudé spectrograms of the brightest stars in the globular clusters M3, M13, and M92 taken by Wilson and by Deutsch (1955) have defined the two main characteristics of Population II that had been indicated earlier by examination of spectra of low dispersion. These effects are as follows: (1) General weakening of the metallic lines in relation to the hydrogen lines. The rough agreement of the temperature types estimated from the measured color indices and from the ratios of such lines as Cr λ 4254/Fe λ 4250 shows that the weakening is real. The hydrogen lines may be slightly strong for the types, but there is not a marked discrepancy. The weakening of the metallic lines is conspicuous in M92, marked in M15, and slight in M3, M5, and M13. (2) Weakening of the blue CN bands. In the giants of the globular clusters the CN break at λ 4216 is consistently weaker than in Population I stars in the solar neighborhood (Deutsch 1955, Figs. 13–15). This effect was noticed originally by Lindblad in 1922.

These two characteristics can be explained, at least in part, by the greater relative abundance of hydrogen in Population II stars postulated by Schwarzschild, Spitzer, and Wildt (1951). The effects are present in some stars of intermediate populations also, but the correlation with the other parameters that are used to distinguish populations is only weakly positive. In large part this must be due to the fact that these independent parameters, such as space motions or galactic co-ordinates, are themselves only statistical indicators of population membership. Thus the "high-velocity stars" among the giants are not all members of the disk population, although a large peculiar motion is one of the characteristics by which that population is distinguished from the arm population, which is essentially pure Population I. For example, 32 v^2 Cnc (G9 III) has a space motion of about 90 km/sec, but spectroscopically it is a good example of a Population I star, with both CN and metallic lines strong. In order to study physically homogeneous populations, we should select the members by means of spectra and colors, but, lacking sufficiently good and extensive spectroscopic data, we are obliged to fall back on the statistical indicators to provide starting points.

For the bright stars the selection can be made spectroscopically, and Miss Roman (1950, 1952) compared estimated strengths of the lines visible on small-scale spectrograms of the F5–K5 stars brighter than $m_v = 5.5$ and north of declination −20°. After setting aside the G8–K1 stars with very anomalous CN bands, she divided the remaining stars earlier than K2 into a strong-line group (designated "st-l") and a weak-line group ("wk-l"). They were distinguished "by the fact that the G band and λ 4226 of Ca I are stronger relative to the remainder of the spectrum in one group [wk-l] than they were in the other." Her spectroscopic parallaxes, based approximately on the criteria of the Yerkes *Atlas of Stellar Spectra*, allowed the computation of space motions. For the "st-l" stars Miss Roman found a mean speed of about 26 km/sec compared with 42 km/sec for the "wk-l" group.

Other observers have not been in agreement as to which K stars have strong or weak lines; the measured intensities by Thackeray (1949) and by Greenstein and Keenan (1958) of metallic lines in several stars included in Miss Roman's list show virtually no correlation with her assignments to these groups. The conclusion of Miczaika (1950) that the distinction between strong- and weak-line stars breaks down for types later than about G8 seems generally true. On the other hand, some of the stars with very weak CN (discussed below), such as HD 191046, do have very weak metallic lines and approach the appearance of the bright members of globular clusters.

In order to examine population effects in the CN bands, it is convenient to define the quantity $CN_* - \overline{CN} = \Delta CN$ as the cyanogen discrepancy[5] of a star, where CN_* refers to a particular star and $\overline{CN}$ is the measured strength of absorption for bright stars having the same type and luminosity class. The quantity ΔCN resembles a color index, in that its value for a given star depends on the method of measurement; the integrated intensity of the λ 4215 sequence, as measured by Griffin and Redman (1960), will not have the same dependence on temperature as measures of the "break" near the λ 4215 head, for the profile of the integrated vibrational and rotational structure changes rapidly with temperature (cf. Plassard 1950). This means that care must be taken in comparing different sets of measurements.

A source of systematic errors in the CN measurements is contamination by atomic lines; this has been kept to a minimum by most recent workers, who have been careful to avoid inclusion of the stronger Sr II–Fe blended line at λ 4216 in their measurements. It was shown by Greenstein and Keenan (1958) that photographic measures of the CN break from Perkins small-scale spectrograms correlated very closely with the total absorptions of a number of resolved CN-band lines from Mount Wilson coudé spectrograms for G8–K0 giants. It is only for giant stars later than about K3 that the contamination is probably serious.

Plots of CN discrepancy against space velocity for giant stars have been published by Keenan (1958) and by Griffin and Redman (1960). Both diagrams show only a weak correlation with velocity. Griffin and Redman remark: "It is quite clear that there is nothing like a one-to-one correspondence between high velocity and weak CN absorption. . . . There is indeed a small statistical difference in the CN ratio between the two groups of stars with space velocity greater or less than 80 km/sec, . . . which is little more than half the random scatter within either group." In both diagrams, however, the stars moving faster than about 100 km/sec show a marked preponderance of negative CN discrepancies. For $v > 140$ km/sec, each diagram showed only one positive discrepancy (strong CN) compared with eight to twelve negative ones.

Thus it is only the group of stars with very high velocities that consistently falls into the population of weak-CN stars; among those moving more slowly, the selection must be made spectroscopically. The fact that there is any dynamical correlation allows us to assign the weak-CN stars to the disk population, presumably shading into the halo population, which includes the typical globular clusters. The weakening of CN (and the associated line weakening) in these scattered stars approaches, but does not equal, the extreme effects observed in such globular clusters as M92 and M15. The resemblance to the members of the less extreme clusters, M2 and M3, is much closer.

It is evident that for types G and K (excepting the dwarfs) a three-dimensional classification is needed, with the strength of CN apparently providing the best criterion for the third parameter—presumably composition—observable

[5] This quantity is called the "CN anomaly" by Griffin and Redman (1960).

TABLE 10

STARS WITH ANOMALOUS INTENSITIES OF CN BANDS

STAR	α1900	δ1900	M_v	V_r	REVISED TYPE	ROMAN TYPE	CN DISCREPANCY Break (Keenan)	CN DISCREPANCY Total Abs. (Griffin and Redman)
HD 104998	12h 00.m3	+31° 46′	8.1	......	K0 III CN+3	......	......	......
HD 112127	12 49.0	+27 19	7.10	+ 2	K2+III CN+3	......	+0.15	+0.15
α Ser	15 39.3	+ 6 44	2.75	+ 3	K2 III CN+2	K2 III	+ .14	− .12
ε Dra	19 48.5	+70 01	3.99	+ 3	G8 III CN−1	G8 III wk-l	......	− .04
γ Psc	23 12.0	+ 2 44	3.85	− 14	G8 III CN−1	G8 III wk-l	......	− .11
HD 2901	0 27.2	+53 34	7.10	−107	K2 III CN−1	......	......	......
δ Lep	5 47.0	−20 53	3.90	+ 99	G8+III CN−2	......	− .11	......
BS 6853	18 13.9	+40 54	5.92	− 74	G9 III CN−2	......	− .08	− .08
48 Her	16 45.4	+30 08	6.68	− 43	K1 II-III CN−2	......	− .12	......
HD 6833	1 03.9	+54 14	7.10	−257	G8 III CN−3	......	−0.13	−0.16
BS 6152	16 26.2	+20 42	5.29	− 18	G8 II CN−3	G8p (CN very weak)	......	......

with moderate dispersion. We are faced by the problem of devising a compact notation. Miss Roman's terms of "st-l" and "wk-l" are a bit awkward and only qualitative. Since only a minority of the stars exhibit pronounced cyanogen anomalies, the simplest course is to employ the usual spectral-type–absolute-magnitude notation for most stars, adding a third symbol for any star in which a cyanogen discrepancy is noticed. One suggestion for doing this (Reports of Commission No. 29, *Trans. I.A.U.*, **9**, 404; **10**, 447) is to add the symbol CN followed by a number measuring the amount of the discrepancy. Thus a star with rather weak cyanogen might be designated by CN − 2, and the symbol CN + 1 indicates one in which the bands are only slightly stronger than normal.

The existence of stars in which the CN bands are abnormally strong appears to have been noticed first by Morgan. A number of them have been designated "4150 stars" (Roman 1952) because the heads of several adjoining bands (λ 4148 [4–5], λ 4159 [3–4]) produce a characteristic depression extending beyond λ 4150. The use of this term has not been consistent by all observers, however, and in some cases stars so described have not had exceptionally strong CN features.

Table 10 lists a few stars which have been classified as having either an excess or a deficiency of cyanogen. The finer subdivisions of their luminosity classes are not given, for the reason that a marked anomaly in CN makes the estimation of luminosity more difficult. The arrangement is in order of decreasing CN absorption. The seventh column gives Miss Roman's classification, and the eighth and ninth columns the CN discrepancy from the Perkins and Cambridge measurements, respectively. Data from other observers have not been included because of the lack of enough stars to allow $\overline{\text{CN}}$ to be computed for each type and luminosity. It is evident that the stars most anomalous in their CN absorption are easily recognized but that the separation of the larger groups (intermediate populations) requires that all three parameters of classification be carefully determined, either by measurement or by visual comparison of spectrograms.

§ 6. CLASSIFICATION OF SPECTROGRAMS OF VERY SMALL SCALE

The surveys of spectral types that have been carried out by means of plates taken through objective prisms since the preparation of the *HD Catalogue* are summarized in Table 11. Since the scales of these spectrograms are generally less than 200 A/mm, it is not usually possible to classify the stars in as many dimensions and classes as those that were described in the last section, although in a few portions of the HR diagram a surprisingly high accuracy of classification in at least one dimension has been attained. Simplified criteria must also be employed and are usually blended features, such as the whole G band.

Thorough study of the information that very short spectra can give was really initiated by Lindblad (1922) in the work that was discussed on page 97. The basic principle stated by C. Payne in *Stellar Atmospheres* (1925) is that, "in classifying a number of objects, an attempt should be made to select criteria

TABLE 11

CATALOGUES OF STARS CLASSIFIED ON SLITLESS SPECTROGRAMS

Observatory and Catalogue	Reference	Observers	Instrument	No. of Stars	Limiting Magnitude	Dispersion of Plates	Description
Uppsala-Stockholm	*Uppsala Obs. Ann.*, Vols. **1–4**; *Medd.*, Nos. 10, 11, 17, 28, 48, 107; *Stockholm Obs. Ann.*, Vols. 11–18, 1922 ——	Lindblad, Schalén, Stenquist, Ramberg, Öhman, Elvius, *et al.*	Zeiss-astrograph + prisms .... 102-cm reflector + quartz spectrograph	15,700 ±	Various (14.0:pg)	220–530 A/mm, Hε–Hγ	Spectrophotometric classification
Potsdam Spektraldurchmusterung (PSD)	*Potsdam Obs. Pub.*, Vols. **88–92**, 1931–1938	F. Becker, Bruck	Zeiss-astrograph +7°.1 or 7°.7 prism	66,700	12 pg	180 A/mm Hδ–Hγ	91 Southern Selected Areas; dwarfs (d) and giants (g) separated by CN strength for types G, K
Bergedorf Spektraldurchmusterung (BSD)	Pub. in 5 vols. by Hamburger Sternwarte, Bergedorf, 1936–1953	Schwassmann, Wachmann, Stobbe	Lippert astrographs +8°.25 prism	173,500	11.0 pg	100–400 A/mm, Hε–Hβ	115 Selected Areas; some dwarfs (d) and giants (g) separated by color and CN strength for types G, K
McCormick Proper-Motion and Faint-Stars Catalogues (McC)	*Pub. McCormick Obs. Virginia*, **7**; **10**; **11**, 1937–1958	Vyssotsky, Balz, *et al.*	Cook, 10-inch + 7° prism	75,600	11.5 pg	300 A/mm at Hγ	McCormick proper-motion stars plus AGK2 stars; some dM stars distinguished
Warner and Swasey	1. *Ap. J.*, **103**, 106, 113 2. *Ap. J.*, **120**, 1946 ——	Nassau, McCuskey, Seyfert, van Albada, Blanco, *et al.*	36/24-inch Schmidt +4° or 2° prism	50,000	1. 10.0 pg 2. 13.0 IR with 4°, 14.0 IR with 2°	1. 280 A/mm at Hγ 2. 3500 A/mm at λ 8000	1. Types and luminosity classes in Milky Way fields 2. Survey of red stars in northern Milky Way, plus high-latitude samples

TABLE 11—*Continued*

Observatory and Catalogue	Reference	Observers	Instrument	No. of Stars	Limiting Magnitude	Dispersion of Plates	Description
Tonantzintla	*Ap. J.*, Vols. **113**, **114**; *Tacubaya y Tonantzintla Bol.*, Nos. 7–11, 13–15, 1951–1956	Münch, Chavira, Gonzalez, *et al.*	30/26-inch Schmidt +4° prism	2100±	11.5 pg	250 A/mm Hγ–Hδ	Survey for discovery of OB stars in longitudes 130°–235° and 305°–360° of Milky Way; some A-type supergiants included
Crimean Ap. Obs.	*Izv. Crimean Ap. Obs.*, Vols. **14**, **20**, 1955–1958	Brodskaia, Ikhsanov, Shajn	Astrograph+6°9 prism	9150	12.5 pg	250 A/mm at Hδ	Types (and photographic magnitudes) for stars of the northern Milky Way; Cassiopeia, Cepheus, and Perseus
Hamburg–Warner and Swasey	Luminous stars in the Northern Milky Way I —— 1957	Stock, Slettebak, Hardorp, Nassau, *et al.*	Hamburg and Warner and Swasey	10,000±	13 pg	580 A/mm at Hγ	Survey through UV-prism to classify high-luminosity stars in the range O–G
Dearborn *Survey of Faint Red Stars*	*Dearborn Obs. Ann.*, Vols. **4**, **5**, 1935–1947	Lee *et al.*	10½-inch Cooke triplet+7° prism	44,076	12±vis.	630 A/mm Hβ–Hα	Red region used, blue not in focus; M,S, and C stars from −4°5 to +90° declination
Haute-Provence and Marseille	*Haute-Provence Obs. Pub.*, Vols. **3**, **4** —— 1955	Fehrenbach, Duflet	38.5-cm astrograph +normal field prism	840 (to 1960)	12 pg	110 A/mm at 4230 A	Objective-prism radial-velocity program; the fields surveyed are at low galactic latitudes

NOTES TO TABLE 11

Potsdam—Criteria were numerical ratios of the features Hδ/He 4026, K/Hδ, G/Hγ, λ 4226/G. The types were tied as closely as possible to the *HD* system by tabulating the values of the same ratios for stars in the *HD Catalogue*. For many stars of types B, A, and F the descriptive symbols n, s, and c were added.

Bergedorf—Criteria were estimated line intensities, converted to types by tabulating their values for stars from the *HD Catalogue*. According to Vyssotsky (see Table 12) the maximum correction to reduce *BSD* types to *HD* types is +2.5 near G8, but throughout type A the two systems are in good agreement.

McCormick—The dispersion of the McCormick spectrograms was less than that of most of the other programs listed. The plates were taken with the 10-inch Cooke triplet. Since the color-curve of the camera was steep, two exposures of each field were generally used, one focused near Hγ and the G band and the other at the H and K lines.

For types earlier than A2 the intensities of hydrogen lines formed the chief criteria ". . . and result in a luminosity classification rather than a temperature classification" (Vyssotsky 1941). For the later types the criteria combine those of the *HDC* and of Stockholm, the ratio of the G band to Hγ being used near G0 and for the later types the "break" at the G band (the relative intensity of the continua on each side of the band). The accuracy of classification was remarkably good in view of the small scale of the images.

A number of carbon stars and S stars were discovered in the course of the program.

Uppsala-Stockholm—Details of the Swedish classification, which is based on spectro-photometry of the blue region, are discussed by Strömgren in chap. 9. For hot stars of types B–F the intensity of hydrogen lines is the criterion. For types G and K the classification makes use of the integrated intensity of the blue CN band.

Warner and Swasey—1. The surveys carried out in the blue region, chiefly on IIa–O plates with a 4° prism, covered (a) Early-type stars within a belt 12° wide extending from longitude 333° to 202° centered on the galactic equator. Stars falling within the natural group OB were listed along with some A-type supergiants. For these objects the photographic limiting magnitude was about 10 (Nassau and Morgan 1951). (b) For the later types, F, G, K, and M, the blue plates allowed a classification to be made in both temperatures and luminosity. The luminosity criteria are the strength of the CN depression, the intensity of Ca 4226, and the G band. For type M the feature called the G band is essentially due to atomic lines, and it is the break in the spectrum at about 4308 A that is used.

2. The infrared surveys on Kodak I-N emulsions were carried out with both the 4° and the 2° prisms. Types M0 and M10 were assigned, and high-luminosity type stars in the earlier subdivisions of type M were distinguished.

Tonantzintla—The Schmidt telescope and 4° prism are similar to the Warner and Swasey equipment, and the main program was an extension to more southern parts of the Milky Way of the survey for discovery of OB stars that had been initiated at Cleveland by Nassau and Morgan.

Crimean—On objective-prism spectrograms similar to those of Cleveland and Tonantzintla, stars of types O through M were classified. Giants and dwarfs brighter than $m_{pg} = 10.5$ were distinguished.

Dearborn—The primary purpose of this survey was to provide a reasonably complete list of the red stars with banded spectra within the given limits of declination and magnitude. The catalogue is most useful as a finding list for observers. Partly because of the small scale of the spectrograms, the classification is less accurate than in most of the catalogues cited in the table, and some systematic effects are present. Thus the stars classified M7 in the Dearborn cata-logue have a mean type of about M6 in the Mount Wilson or MK systems.

Hamburg-Warner and Swasey—This survey extends by 1–2 mag. the lower limit of the earlier Cleveland and Tonantzintla programs for the discovery of early-type stars of high luminosity (Slettebak and Stock 1957). The use on both the Cleveland and the Hamburg Schmidt telescopes of prisms of Schott UBK 7 glass extends the observable spectrum short-ward to about 3400 A. The lower dispersion, about half that of similar prisms of ordinary glass, reduces the overlapping of neighboring stars and allows the fainter stars to be reached. The additional features visible in the ultraviolet permit the OB stars to be divided into four sub-groups: OB$^+$: (no Balmer lines or emission features visible); OB (no Balmer lines very weak but distinct); OB$^-$ (Balmer lines not so strong as in B1.5 V standards); and CA (sharp break at Balmer limit, but Balmer lines weak).

The group OB$^-$ contains mainly stars near B0 of luminosity classes III–V and thus repre-sents a group of lower mean luminosity than the other three. In addition to the current survey of fields within 8° of the galactic plane, a finding list of 601 stars of types F2 and earlier near the north galactic pole has been published at Hamburg (1959). The work is being extended to other latitudes, and at Cleveland Hα plates are taken also to allow classification of red stars (Nassau and Stephenson 1960).

Haute-Provence and Marseille—Because of the relatively high dispersion, most of the criteria used in the Yerkes *Atlas* could be used, and the types are approximately on the MK system. Since the 40-cm prism has been in use only since 1958, the number of stars listed in Table 11 represents only a small part of the planned program.

that will distribute the material into the most natural groups.'' In 1951, Morgan defined a natural group as made up of stars that can be placed within limited parts of the HR diagram by their common spectral characteristics. Natural groups can be thought of as the little boxes into which we sort the stellar spectra; the boxes tend to get bigger as we make the spectrograms shorter. Fig-ures 3 and 4, taken from Morgan's paper, show the natural groups that can be differentiated on plates with scales of 230 and about 1000 A/mm, respectively, in the blue region.

The techniques of classification with low dispersion have been developed

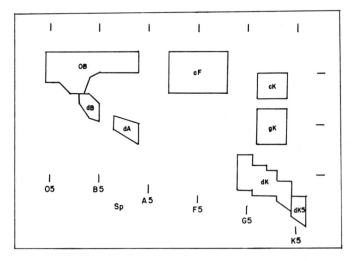

Fig. 3.—Natural groups distinguished with a dispersion of about 230 A/mm at Hδ. Repro-duced from Morgan (1951).

extensively by Nassau and his group at the Warner and Swasey Observatory (see particularly Nassau and van Albada [1947] for the blue region and [1949] for the infrared).

Intercomparisons of the types of several of these catalogues have been made, particularly by Vyssotsky (1941), and are summarized by Fehrenbach (1958) in his comprehensive article in *Handbuch der Physik*. Table 12 is a condensation

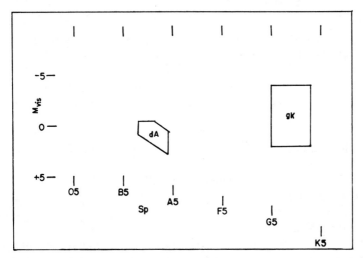

FIG. 4.—Natural groups distinguished with a dispersion of 700–1200 A/mm at Hδ. Reproduced from Morgan (1951).

TABLE 12

CORRECTIONS TO BE ADDED TO CATALOGUE TYPES
TO GIVE HD MEAN TYPES

Type	PSD	BSD	McC
B5	....	+0.1	+1.0
B8	+0.9	+0.3	+0.8
A0	0.0	+0.2	0.0
A2	+0.4	−0.3	−0.2
A5	−0.6	−0.1	−0.3
A8	+0.6	0.0	−0.4
F0	+0.6	+0.9	−0.5
F2	+1.0	+1.3	+0.5
F5	+0.8	+0.8	+0.6
F8	+0.1	+0.4	+0.8
G0	−0.3	+0.5	+1.0
G2	−1.0	+1.1	+1.2
G5	−0.4	+2.4	+1.2
G8	+0.2	+2.5	+0.2
K0	−0.1	+1.3	−0.7
K2	−0.5	+0.6	−1.0
K5	+0.6	−1.0	−1.8
K8	....	−0.5	−2.5

of Vyssotsky's tables and gives estimates of the systematic corrections for reduction of the Potsdam, Bergedorf, and McCormick catalogues to the *Henry Draper* system. There have also been published a number of shorter catalogues of spectral types in particular regions. Among these is Humason's (1932) list of 4066 stars in Kapteyn's Selected Areas.

§ 7. CONCLUSIONS—THE TECHNIQUE OF CLASSIFICATION

It should be emphasized that there is no difference in principle between classification by visual comparison of spectrograms and that by the objective methods (e.g., filter photometry) that are taken up in chapter 9. In both cases a spectral type is a measured quantity representing one or more characteristics of the spectral distribution of the star's light. The curious fact that visual methods have remained in effective use in classification of stellar spectra much longer than in other sorts of physical measurement is due to the ability of the eye accurately to select two matching patterns, even when the patterns are as complex as the absorption spectra of stars, and to detect even slight differences in one or two elements of the patterns. This partially counterbalances the far greater absolute precision of photoelectric photometry.

There is no doubt that objective methods will become steadily more important in the future, but two recent developments suggest that visual classification will remain valuable.

1. At least in certain parts of the HR diagram it seems that even three variables of classification are not enough—the abundances of several groups of elements may differ from star to star in such a way that one parameter (μ) does not completely define the composition. For example, among the red stars, there are some that must be called "peculiar" now because of anomalous intensities of certain bands (e.g., YO) that are normally quite weak. Many of these peculiarities would not be detected if the stars were classified by measurement of only the strips of spectrum containing the features that define the usual types.

2. Development of image tubes in which the final intensified image is recorded photographically means that spectrograms covering a considerable range of wavelengths can be taken of stars much fainter than have ever been accessible before. This will permit stars from more extreme population groups to be classified.

It is probable that the methods of visual and objective classification will be applied jointly in ways perhaps analogous to the simultaneous use of rapid photographic photometry and accurate photoelectric photometry to extend the magnitude and color scales to faint stars in rich fields.

REFERENCES

(See also Table 11, second column, for references to catalogues of types)

ADAMS, W. S., and
    JOY, A. H.   1932   *Ap. J.*, **56**, 242.

ADAMS, W. S., JOY, A. H.,
  and HUMASON, M. L.   1926   *Ap. J.*, **64**, 225.
ADAMS, W. S., JOY, A. H.,
  HUMASON, M. L., and
  BRAYTON, A. M.   1935   *Ap. J.*, **81**, 187.
ADAMS, W. S., and
  KOHLSCHÜTTER, A.   1914   *Ap. J.*, **40**, 385.
ALLER, L. H.   1961   *Optical Spectrometric Measurements of High Tem-
                                  peratures* (Chicago: University of Chicago
                                  Press), p. 3.
ALLER, L. H., and
  GREENSTEIN, J. L.   1960   *Ap. J. Suppl.*, Vol. **5**, No. 46.
ANGER, C. J.   1930   *Harvard Obs. Circ.*, No. 352.
ARP, H. C.   1958   *Hdb. d. Phys.*, **51**, 75.
BAADE, W.   1944   *Ap. J.*, **100**, 137.
BEALS, C. S.   1930   *Pub. Dom. Ap. Obs. Victoria*, **4**, 271.
                         1934   *Ibid.*, **6**, 95.
BIDELMAN, W. P.   1951   *Ap. J.*, **113**, 304.
BLESS, R. C.   1960   *Ap. J.*, **132**, 532.
BOUIGUE, R.   1954   *Ann. d'ap.*, **17**, 104.
                         1959   *Toulouse Obs. Ann.*, **27**, 47.
BROWN, R. H., and
  TWISS, R. Q.   1956   *Nature*, **178**, 1046.
BUSCOMBE, W.   1959   *Mt. Stromlo Obs. Mimeo.*, No. 3.
                         1962   *Ibid.*, No. 4.
CAMERON, D. M., and
  NASSAU, J. J.   1955   *Ap. J.*, **122**, 177.
CANNON, A. J., and
  PICKERING, E. C.   1918–
                         1924   *Harvard Ann.*, Vols. **91–99**.
CURTISS, R. H.   1932   *Hdb. d. Ap.*, **5**, Part 1, 1.
DAVIS, D. N.   1934   *Pub. A.S.P.*, **46**, 267.
DEUTSCH, A. J.   1955   *Principes fondamentaux de classification stellaire*
                                  (Paris: Service des Publications du C.N.R.S.),
                                  p. 32.
EVANS, D. S., MENZIES,
  A., and STOY, R. H.   1957   *M.N.*, **117**, 534.
                         1959   *Ibid.*, **119**, 638.
FAIRFIELD, P.   1924   *Harvard Obs. Circ.*, No. 264.
FEHRENBACH, C.   1958   *Hdb. d. Phys.*, **50**, 1.
FITCH, W. S., and
  MORGAN, W. W.   1951   *Ap. J.*, **114**, 548.
GLIESE, W.   1957   *Mitt. Astr. Rech.-Inst. Heidelberg (A)*, No. 8.
GREENSTEIN, J. L.   1956   *Proceedings of the Third Berkeley Symposium on
                                  Mathematical Statistics and Probability*, ed.
                                  J. NEYMAN (Berkeley, Calif.: University of
                                  California Press), **3**, 11.
                         1959   *Ann. d'ap. Suppl.*, No. 8.

GREENSTEIN, J. L., and
  KEENAN, P. C.   1958   *Ap. J.*, **127**, 172.
GRIFFIN, R. F., and
  REDMAN, R. O.   1960   *M.N.*, **120**, 287.
GROTH, H. G.   1961   *Zs. f. Ap.*, **51**, 231.
HEARD, J. F.   1956   *Vistas in Astronomy*, ed. A. BEER (London: Pergamon Press), **2**, 1357.
HERTZSPRUNG, E.   1905   *Zs. f. wiss. Phot.*, **3**, 429.
                    1907   *Ibid.*, **5**, 86.
                    1909   *A.N.*, **179**, 373.
HILTNER, W. A.   1956   *Ap. J. Suppl.*, **2**, 389.
HOFFLEIT, D.   1937   *Harvard Obs. Ann.*, **105**, 45.
HUMASON, M. L.   1932   *Ap. J.*, **76**, 274.
HUNGER, K.   1955   *Zs. f. Ap.*, **36**, 42.
HYNEK, J. A.   1936   *Ap. J.*, **83**, 476.
IWANOWSKA, W.   1936   *Ann. Stockholm Obs.*, Vol. **12**, No. 5.
JENKINS, L. F.   1952   *General Catalogue of Trigonometric Stellar Parallaxes* (New Haven: Yale University Observatory).
JOHNSON, H. L., and
  HARRIS, D. L.   1954   *Ap. J.*, **120**, 196.
JOHNSON, H. L., and
  IRIARTE, B.   1958   *Lowell Obs. Bull.*, **4**, 47 (No. 91).
JOHNSON, H. L., and
  MORGAN, W. W.   1953   *Ap. J.*, **117**, 313.
JOY, A. H.   1942   *Ap. J.*, **96**, 344.
KEENAN, P. C.   1941   *Ap. J.*, **93**, 475.
                    1954   *Ibid.*, **120**, 484.
                    1958   *Hdb. d. Phys.*, **50**, 93.
KEENAN, P. C., and
  HYNEK, J. A.   1950   *Hdb. d. Phys.*, **111**, 1.
KEENAN, P. C., and
  MORGAN, W. W.   1941   *Ap. J.*, **94**, 501.
                    1951   *Astrophysics*, ed. J. A. HYNEK (New York: McGraw-Hill Book Co., Inc.).
KEENAN, P. C., and
  SCHROEDER, L. W. 1952   *Ap. J.*, **115**, 82.
KLEMAN, B.   1956   *Ap. J.*, **123**, 162.
KOPAL, Z.   1955   *Ann. d'ap.*, **18**, 379.
KOPYLOV, I. M.   1958   *Pub. Crimean Ap. Obs.*, **20**, 156.
KUIPER, G. P.   1938   *Ap. J.*, **88**, 429.
LINDBLAD, B.   1922   *Ap. J.*, **55**, 85.
                    1924   *Ibid.*, **59**, 305.
                    1946   *Ibid.*, **104**, 325.
LINDBLAD, B., and
  STENQUIST, E.   1934   *Ann. Stockholm Obs.*, Vol. **11**, No. 12.
McDONALD, J. K., and
  UNDERHILL, A. B.   1952   *Ap. J.* **115**, 577.

McKELLAR, A., and
  RICHARDSON, E. H.   1954   *Mém. Soc. Sci. Liège*, sér. 4, **15**, 256.
MAURY, A. C., and
  PICKERING, E. C.   1897   *Harvard Ann.*, Vol. **28**, Part 1.
MELBOURNE, W. G.   1960   *Ap. J.*, **132**, 101.
MERRILL, P. W.   1922   *Ap. J.*, **56**, 457.
                         1923   *Ibid.*, **58**, 215.
                         1925   *Pub. A.S.P.*, **37**, 272.
                         1940   *Spectra of Long-Period Variable Stars* (Chicago:
                                 University of Chicago Press).
                         1941   *Ap. J.*, **94**, 171.
MERRILL, P. W.,
  DEUTSCH, A., and
  KEENAN, P. C.   1962   *Ap. J.*, **136**, 21.
MICZAIKA, G. R.   1950   *Zs. f. Ap.*, **27**, 1.
MORGAN, W. W.   1937   *Ap. J.*, **85**, 380.
                         1938   *Ibid.*, **87**, 589.
                         1951   *Pub. U. Michigan Obs.*, **10**, 33.
MORGAN, W. W., CODE,
  A. D., and WHITFORD,
  A. E.   1955   *Ap. J. Suppl.*, **2**, 41 (No. 14).
MORGAN, W. W., KEENAN,
  P. C., and KELLMAN, E. 1943   *An Atlas of Stellar Spectra* (Chicago: University of
                                 Chicago Press).
NASSAU, J. J., and
  ALBADA, G. B. VAN   1947   *Ap. J.*, **106**, 20.
                         1949   *Ibid.*, **109**, 391.
NASSAU, J. J., and
  COLACEVICH, A.   1950   *Ap. J.*, **111**, 199.
NASSAU, J. J., and
  MORGAN, W. W.   1951   *Pub. U. Michigan Obs.*, **10**, 43.
NASSAU, J. J., and
  STEPHENSON, C. B.   1960   *Ap. J.*, **132**, 130.
ÖHMAN, Y.   1927   *Uppsala Medd.*, No. 33.
ÖPIK, E.   1929   *Pub. Tartu Obs.*, Vol. **27**, No. 1.
OSAWA, K.   1959   *Ap. J.*, **130**, 159.
PAYNE, C. H.   1925   *Stellar Atmospheres*, ed. H. SHAPLEY (Cambridge,
                                 Mass.: Harvard University Press).
PEARCE, J. A.   1957   *J.R.A.S. Canada*, **51**, 59.
PETRIE, R. M.   1947   *Pub. Dom. Ap. Obs. Victoria*, **1**, 321.
PETRIE, R. M., and
  MAUNSELL, C. D.   1950   *Pub. Dom. Ap. Obs. Victoria*, **8**, 253.
PETRIE, R. M., and
  MOYLS, B. N.   1956   *Pub. Dom. Ap. Obs. Victoria*, **10**, 287 (No. 13).
PICKERING, E. C.   1890   *Harvard Ann.*, Vol. **27**.
PICKERING, E. C., and
  FLEMING, M.   1897   *Harvard Ann.*, Vol. **26**, Part 2.
PILOWSKI, K.   1953   *Zs. f. Ap.*, **33**, 120.
PLASKETT, H. H.   1922   *Pub. Dom. Ap. Obs. Victoria*, **1**, 363.

PLASKETT, H. H., and
  PEARCE, J. A.   1931   *Pub. Dom. Ap. Obs. Victoria*, **5**, 110.
PLASSARD, J.   1950   *Ann. d'ap.*, **13**, 1.
POPPER, D. M.   1959   *Ap. J.*, **129**, 647.
ROMAN, N. G.   1950   *Ap. J.*, **112**, 554.
                         1952   *Ibid.*, **116**, 122.
                         1954   *A.J.*, **59**, 307.

RUSSELL, H. N., DUGAN,
  R. S., and STEWART,
  J. Q.   1927   *Astronomy* (Boston: Ginn & Co.), Vol. **2** (new ed., 1938).

RUSSELL, H. N., and
  MOORE, C.   1938   *Ap. J.*, **87**, 389.
                         1940   *Ibid.*, **92**, 354.

SANDAGE, A. R., and
  EGGEN, O. J.   1959   *M.N.*, **119**, 278.
SANFORD, R. F.   1950   *Ap. J.*, **111**, 262.
SCHWARZSCHILD, M.,
  SPITZER, L., and
  WILDT, R.   1951   *Ap. J.*, **114**, 398.
SETTERBERG, T.   1947   *Ann. Stockholm Obs.*, Vol. **15**, No. 1.
SHANE, C. D.   1920   *Lick Obs. Bull.*, **10**, 79 (No. 329).
                         1928   *Ibid.*, **13**, 123 (No. 396).

SHAPLEY, H., and
  CANNON, A. J.   1921   *Harvard Obs. Circ.*, No. 226.
SHARPLESS, S.   1952   *Ap. J.*, **116**, 251.
                         1956   *Ibid.*, **124**, 342.

SLETTEBAK, A., and
  STOCK, J.   1957   *Zs. f. Ap.*, **42**, 61.
SLETTEBAK, A., BAHNER,
  K., and STOCK, J.   1961   *Ap. J.*, **134**, 195.
STRÖMBERG, G.   1939   *Ap. J.*, **89**, 10.
THACKERAY, A. D.   1949   *M.N.*, **109**, 436.
UNDERHILL, A. B.   1950   *Pub. Dom. Ap. Obs. Victoria*, **8**, No. 18, 385.
                         1957   *Mém. Soc. Sci. Liège*, sér. 4, **20**, 17 and 91.
VOGEL, H. C.   1895   *Ap. J.*, **2**, 333.
VYSSOTSKY, A. N.   1941   *Ap. J.*, **93**, 425; *McCormick Obs. Pub.*, Vol. **9**, Part 6.
WILSON, O. C.   1961   *Ap. J.*, **133**, 457.
WOLF, C., and RAYET, G.   1867   *C.R.*, **65**, 292.
WYLLER, A. A.   1957   *Ap. J.*, **125**, 177.
YOSS, K.   1961   *Ap. J.*, **134**, 809.
YOUNG, R. K.   1939–
                         1945   *Pub. David Dunlap Obs.*, Vol. **1**, Nos. 3 (1939), 13 (1942), and 16 (1945).

YOUNG, R. K., and
  HARPER, W. E.   1924a   *Pub. Dom. Ap. Obs. Victoria*, **3**, 1.
                         1924b   *J.R.A.S. Canada*, **18**, 9.

CHAPTER 9

Quantitative Classification Methods

BENGT STRÖMGREN

The Institute for Advanced Study, Princeton, New Jersey

§ 1. GENERAL CONSIDERATIONS

THE methods of quantitative classification of stellar spectra are in many respects similar to those of classification by inspection and comparison of spectrograms, described in chapter 8 of the present volume. Quantitative classification is usually based on measures pertaining to relatively few suitably selected features of the spectrum. However, certain procedures have been developed which are quite similar to those of the inspection method, particularly with respect to the number of spectral features utilized, but which make use of registograms instead of the spectrograms themselves. In some quantitative methods the aim is to make possible the classification of stars too faint to be classified according to the procedures described in chapter 8. In other quantitative methods the goal is higher precision.

If in some applications the use of a one-dimensional classification scheme is adequate, then the quantitative evaluation of one spectral feature is, in principle, sufficient, at least over a certain range of spectral class. For two-dimensional classification, two quantities measuring suitably selected spectral features—two spectral indices—are necessary and sufficient, again with the qualification that the selected spectral indices may be adequate for limited ranges of spectral class and luminosity only.

Historically, the development of quantitative classification methods followed that of the methods based on inspection. The fact that the latter methods had been found to be applicable to the great majority of stars in the galactic neighborhood suggested that quantitative classification based on evaluation of a few criteria should be feasible. In the actual development of the quantitative methods, use was made of samples of stars already classified by the inspection methods. In particular, peculiar stars could be eliminated from the samples in question. In this way the obvious dangers connected with classification based on a very few criteria were very much reduced.

123

After two-dimensional quantitative classification methods had been developed, further spectral indices were added for the purpose of classification in terms of three spectral parameters. In principle it is, of course, possible to add so many spectral indices to the quantitative classification scheme that all peculiarities that can be observed through inspection and comparison of spectrograms are reflected in the data. However, up until now, the quantitative methods have not been pressed far in this direction. The aim has mostly been toward two-dimensional or three-dimensional classification applicable to a very great majority of the stars. In many cases the quantitative procedure has been combined with a screening process utilizing the inspection methods. On the other hand, there are applications where the errors introduced by the presence of a small percentage of peculiar stars are of no consequence.

The first step in the development of a quantitative classification method is the choice of spectral *criteria*. Examples of criteria are the equivalent width of a given absorption line or the intensity ratio of two well-defined wavelength bands. Usually the selection of criteria is guided by the results already obtained through spectrophotometry of typical stars or in the process of development of the schemes of classification by inspection.

A method is then chosen for the photometric determination of quantities—indices—that measure, or are adequately correlated with, each of the chosen criteria. The indices are usually obtained by either *photoelectric* photometry or *photographic* photometry. The isolation of the wavelength bands to be measured can be effected with the help of glass filters or interference filters or through the use of a spectrograph.

It is possible to define spectral indices as intensity ratios of definite wavelength bands in such a way that the measures are perfectly reproducible. Nevertheless, a set of *standard stars* for which the indices in the chosen system are known according to repeated measures (in one or more series of homogeneous observations) is of considerable value. When indices are measured under circumstances that are not completely reproducible, continued repetition of observations of an adequate list of standard stars is a necessity. Photoelectric photometry with glass filters or interference filters is an example.

When a quantitative classification procedure that makes use of certain spectral indices has been set up, *calibration* in terms of more meaningful quantities must follow. Calibration in terms of, say, spectral class and luminosity class on the MK system is generally straightforward; for an adequate list of stars with known MK classification, the indices of the quantitative classification scheme must be measured. Calibration in terms of basic parameters such as effective temperature, T_e, and visual absolute magnitude, M_v, is carried out in similar fashion but, of course, requires knowledge, for a sufficient number of stars, of T_e (through discussions involving the theory of stellar atmospheres) and M_v (derived from trigonometric parallaxes and cluster parallaxes). Calibration in terms of fundamental parameters—mass, age, and chemical-composition param-

eters—is an ultimate aim. The problems of the selection of criteria and of calibration will be discussed in some detail in the following sections.

The quantitative calibration methods can be divided into groups according
to the nature of the spectral criteria they utilize. In the following we shall consider, first, methods depending on the use as criteria of intensity ratios of relatively broad bands of the spectrum (300–1000 A wide). Next, we shall describe
methods in which intensity ratios for bands of intermediate width (100–
300 A wide) are measured. Finally, methods utilizing photometry of narrow
bands (less than 100 A wide) will be discussed.

§ 2. SPECTRAL CLASSIFICATION THROUGH WIDE-BAND PHOTOMETRY

The simplest scheme of spectral classification through wide-band photometry
is based on the use of a color index for the determination of spectral class.
Application of this scheme is seriously limited through the effects of interstellar
absorption. The method can be useful, however, in investigations of areas at
high galactic latitude ($|b| > 50°$), where interstellar reddening is small.

The use of a color index yields, of course, only one-dimensional classification.
In certain cases it is known that the sample of stars investigated consists largely
of main-sequence stars, and one-dimensional classification will then permit a
very useful division of the stars into relatively homogeneous groups. As an example, consider stars at high galactic latitude in the color range $B - V < 0^m5$.
These stars are mostly main-sequence A and F stars, and photographic or photoelectric $B - V$ photometry is effective for separation of the stars into fairly
homogeneous groups. The calibration of $B - V$ in terms of MK spectral class
for main-sequence stars is well established (cf. Johnson and Morgan 1953).

Again in high galactic latitude, stars in the $B - V$ color range between 1^m0
and 1^m2 and fainter than $V = 12$ mag. are mostly main-sequence K stars (see
Malmquist 1960, regarding the giant-dwarf ratio for high galactic latitude).

Red stars of large proper motion ($B - V > 1^m5$, p.m. $> 0''3$) are main-
sequence M stars, unaffected by interstellar reddening. A red-infrared color
index as measured by Kron and Smith (1951) and Kron, White, and Gascoigne
(1953) yields very accurate quantitative classification here, as shown by Kron
(1956).

A color index represents the ratio of the integrated intensities in two wavelength bands. When another wavelength band is added, so that two independent
color indices can be derived, it becomes possible, in principle, to carry out two-
dimensional classification if the stars in question are not affected by interstellar
reddening. Also, on the basis of two color indices, one-dimensional classification
can be carried out for stars that are appreciably reddened.

The choice of wavelength regions for classification through three-color wide-
band photometry is guided by the results obtained through spectrophotometry
of stars of different spectral class and luminosity and varying degrees of inter-

stellar reddening. The intensities to be considered in this connection should be characteristic of the actual spectral intensity distribution. If the utilized spectrophotometry measures the continuous spectrum, as interpolated between the absorption lines, corrections for the effect of the lines must be applied to predict the results of wide-band photometry.

The early spectrophotometric work by Rosenberg (1914) and Wilsing, Scheiner, and Münch (1919) showed that the intensity distribution for stars of spectral classes B–M in the wavelength regions $\lambda\lambda$ 3800–4600 and $\lambda\lambda$ 4600–6000, respectively, could be well approximated by Planck curves but with different temperatures for the two regions. Brill (1923) emphasized that the numerous relatively strong absorption lines present in the spectra of F, G, K, and M stars shortward of λ 4600 strongly influence the intensity distribution and that this effect contributes to the differences in the color temperatures derived for the two wavelength regions. In the region $\lambda > 4600$, the influence of the absorption lines is considerably smaller for F–K2 stars (for K5 and M stars the situation is more complicated because of the presence of molecular bands). Spectrophotometry of stellar spectra in the ultraviolet region $\lambda\lambda$ 3300–4000 was carried out by Yü (1926), by Barbier, Chalonge, and Vassy (1935), and by Öhman (1935). These investigations demonstrated the great importance of the Balmer discontinuity at λ 3647 in stellar spectrophotometry.

Becker (1938) showed that the different character of the intensity distributions in the regions $\lambda\lambda$ 3800–4600 and $\lambda > 4600$, respectively, provided the basis for determination of both spectral class and interstellar reddening from three-color photometry, at least for late G and K stars. If the intensity measures are restricted to a wavelength region in which the intensity distribution can be well represented through a Planck curve corresponding to one temperature, then it is not possible to distinguish between the effects of the different effective temperatures of the stars and the different degrees of reddening. However, if two color indices are measured, one of which characterizes the intensity distribution shortward of λ 4600 and the other that longward of λ 4600, then the two effects can be separated, at least for stars in which the differences in color temperature between the wavelength regions in question are pronounced.

Becker utilized measures pertaining to bands with effective wavelengths of $\lambda\lambda$ 4250, 5030, 5300, and 7050. He formed color indices 4250/5030 and 5300/7050, and then plotted the *color-index difference* 4250/5030 minus 5300/7050 against the color index 4250/5030. The color-index difference in question is insensitive to interstellar reddening, while it is quite sensitive to the color index 4250/5030 and therefore to spectral type for late G and K stars. Hence for stars in this spectral range the spectral type can be determined from the color-index difference, and the amount of interstellar reddening can be found from the difference between the measured 4250/5030 color index and the value of 4250/5030 corresponding to the color-index difference in the case of an unreddened star.

However, the situation is complicated by the fact that the color-index relations depend to some extent on the absolute magnitude.

Three-color photometry has proved highly effective for determination of spectral class and interstellar reddening in the case of O and B stars of luminosity classes III, IV, and V. In this case, one wavelength region shortward and two regions longward of the Balmer discontinuity are utilized. The method was proposed by Becker (1938, 1942) and further developed by Johnson and Morgan (1953), who used photoelectric color indices $U - B$ and $B - V$ on the U, B, V system (cf. this volume, chap. 11). In describing the method, we shall follow Morgan and Harris (1956).

Call the intrinsic color indices, unaffected by interstellar reddening, $[U - B]_0$ and $[B - V]_0$ and let the color excess in $B - V$ be E_{B-V}. If the ratio of the color excess in $U - B$ and $B - V$ is a (cf. this volume, chap. 13), then the actual color indices (affected by interstellar reddening) are given by

$$[U - B]_0 = U - B - aE_{B-V},$$

$$[B - V]_0 = B - V - E_{B-V}.$$

Morgan and Harris, from a discussion of unreddened stars, showed that for B stars of luminosity class V the following linear relation is valid with an accuracy of about 0^m01 in $B - V$:

$$[B - V]_0 = 0.270 [U - B]_0.$$

The relation is presumably valid with good accuracy for O and B stars of luminosity classes III and IV also. From the relations just given, it follows that

$$E_{B-V} = \frac{(B - V) - 0.270 (U - B)}{1 - 0.270a}.$$

The value of a is close to 0.70; hence the denominator in the expression for E_{B-V} is not much smaller than 1. It follows that E_{B-V} and therefore $[U - B]_0$ and $[B - V]_0$ can be determined with very good accuracy from $U - B$ and $B - V$. This shows that the addition of an ultraviolet band has made possible satisfactory separation of temperature effects and the effects of interstellar reddening for the spectral range in question.

For strongly reddened stars, the dependence of a on E_{B-V} characteristic of the wide-band U, B, V system should be taken into account (Hiltner and Johnson 1956; Crawford 1958). Furthermore, a dependence of a on $B - V$ must be considered as shown by Lindholm (1957; see also Johnson 1958; Blanco 1957). Johnson (1958) has given a convenient nomogram for the determination of $[B - V]_0$ from $U - B$ and $B - V$.

The combination of MK classification and U, B, V photometry has proved very effective for B stars. For the stars found by the MK classification to be luminosity class III, IV, or V, the method of quantitative classification from $U - B$ and $B - V$ determines the spectral class and the color excess with higher accuracy than could be obtained from MK classification and $B - V$ photometry alone.

Kron (1958) has shown that a procedure similar to that just discussed can be used for quantitative determinations of spectral class and color excess for supergiants of classes F0–K0. The color indices $(V - B)$ and $(R - I)$ of the Stebbins-Whitford photoelectric six-color photometry (cf. Stebbins and Whitford 1945; Stebbins and Kron 1956) were utilized for the purpose.

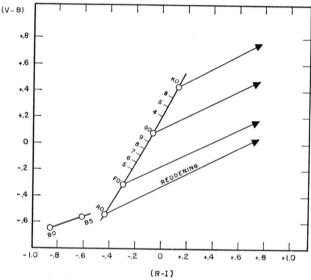

Fig. 1.—Locus of unreddened supergiant stars and reddening lines in the $(V - B)$-$(R - I)$ diagram (Kron 1958).

Figure 1 shows the locus of unreddened supergiant stars in the $(V - B)$-$(R - I)$ diagram according to Kron. The direction of displacement in this diagram through interstellar reddening is also indicated. It is seen that, for the spectral range A0–K0, the angle between the locus of unreddened supergiant stars and the reddening line is sufficiently great for reliable determination of the points of intersection. In other words, when the location of a supergiant star in the $(V - B)$-$(R - I)$ diagram is known, accurate projection back onto the locus of unreddened stars is possible, so that the intrinsic color indices and the color excess can be determined. The calibration of the intrinsic colors in terms of spectral classes is shown in the diagram.

The method is similar to that described above for the O and B stars of luminosity classes III, IV, and V based on U, B, V photometry. The fact that accurate projection back onto the line of unreddened stars is possible corresponds precisely with the fact that the denominator in the equation for E_{B-V} is not much smaller than 1. However, here the discrimination between the effects of change in effective temperature and change in the amount of interstellar reddening is made possible through the inclusion of an infrared band with a correspondingly wide wavelength base line of the photometry. Kron determined the locus of unreddened stars as the limit (to the left) of the distribution of the reddened stars in the diagram, allowing, by estimate, for the small reddening presumably present even for the bluest supergiants of each spectral class.

Having discussed quantitative one-dimensional classification with the help of wide-band photometry, for the case both of unreddened stars and of stars affected by interstellar reddening, we shall now consider two-dimensional classification, first for unreddened stars. Öpik (1925) pioneered the use of three-color photometry for classification purposes. The effective wavelengths in this work were approximately λλ 3650, 4300, and 5300. An investigation of the possibilities of two-dimensional classification was carried out by Öpik. A two-color index diagram (3650/4300 against 4300/5300) is of particular interest. It suggests a separation of giants and dwarfs for F stars, although the photometric accuracy was not very high and the number of stars observed relatively small.

We have already referred to the fact that the results of stellar spectrophotometry suggest that wide-band photometry for classification purposes should include bands in three regions: (1) the region longward of λ 4600, where the influence of absorption lines is relatively small; (2) the region shortward of λ 4600 but above the Balmer discontinuity, which is relatively strongly influenced by absorption lines for spectral classes F–M; and (3) the region shortward of the Balmer discontinuity. It should be noted that the effect of the higher members of the Balmer series of absorption lines extends the region of Balmer absorption to wavelengths somewhat greater than λ 3647.

In view of this situation, Becker (1946) advocated the use of four bands for the purpose of quantitative spectral classification: two bands above λ 4600 that would yield a color index relatively free of the influence of absorption lines; one band in the region of crowding of absorption lines but above the Balmer discontinuity; and one band below the Balmer discontinuity, or at least below the effective limit of crowding of the Balmer absorption lines. With a view to applications in photographic photometry, Becker chose the following effective wavelengths for the four bands: approximately λλ 3700, 4200, 4800, and 6400. The half-widths of the bands were between 300 and 600 A.

The results of photometry in these four bands might be expected to contain nearly all the information that could be obtained from wide-band photometry for the purpose of quantitative classification. This appears to be the case, except for the following qualifications. In certain cases, particularly when interstellar reddening is strong, an extension of the wavelength base into the infrared is advantageous. Also for the purpose of the two-dimensional classification of reddened stars, the addition of a second wavelength below the Balmer discontinuity is of importance.

An infrared band is included in the photoelectric six-color photometry of Stebbins and Whitford (1945). The effective wavelengths are $\lambda\lambda$ 3500 (U), 4200 (V), 4900 (B), 5700 (G), 7200 (R), and 10,300 (I), while the half-widths range from 500 to 1500 A.

A band at approximately λ 3200 is an important part of the intermediate band-width schemes of T. and J. H. Walraven (1960) and Borgman (1960), which will be discussed in the following section.

Extensive work has been carried out by Becker with a modification of the original four-color scheme into three-color photometry with bands at $\lambda\lambda$ 3700 (U), 4700 (G), and 6400 (R). The application of the method to stars that are members of galactic clusters has proved particularly fruitful. This work is described in chapter 13 of the present volume. We shall limit ourselves here to a brief discussion of two-dimensional classification for unreddened stars from measures in the three bands just mentioned.

Becker and Steinlin (1956) plotted the results of photographic wide-band U, G, R photometry for a number of stars of known spectral class and absolute magnitude in a two-color index diagram, $U - G$ versus $G - R$. They found a clear separation of giants and dwarfs for the spectral classes G and K, the separation amounting to about $0\overset{m}{.}2$–$0\overset{m}{.}4$, in $U - G$ for equal $G - R$, in the sense of an ultraviolet deficiency of the giants (luminosity class III) in comparison with the dwarfs (luminosity class V). In the $(U - G)$-$(G - R)$ diagram the shift due to interstellar reddening is not quite, but is approximately, parallel to the main-sequence line for the G and K stars. Therefore, a moderate amount of interstellar reddening does not interfere with the separation of giants and dwarfs.

For B stars the $(U - G)$-$(G - R)$ diagram is essentially equivalent to the $(U - B)$-$(B - V)$ diagram of U, B, V photometry. In particular, determination of spectral class and color excess can be carried out in a way quite similar to that described above for the case of U, B, V photometry. However, for G and early K stars the U, G, R photometry leads to a separation of giants and dwarfs, which is not the case for the U, B, V photometry. The difference is due to the fact that the wavelength region G is above the crowding of absorption lines, while the region of B extends to wavelengths strongly affected by the lines. The K5 giants can be segregated from the main-sequence stars in both systems.

Argue (1961) has investigated the question of the feasibility of giant-dwarf separation through photographic U, G, R photometry for G and K stars. The results obtained by Becker and Steinlin for K stars were confirmed, but for G stars Argue found no clear separation in the $(U - G)$-$(G - R)$ diagram between giants and dwarfs. The different result could possibly be explained by a difference in the stellar samples with respect to the content of ultraviolet-excess giants.

For A and F stars there is an indication in the $(U - B)$-$(B - V)$ diagram of Johnson and Morgan (1953) that absolute magnitudes could be determined from U, B, V photometry for unreddened stars. For equal $B - V$, the value of

$U - B$ appears to increase with increasing luminosity. Johnson (1953), through an investigation of members of NGC 752, established this correlation for F stars, and Bidelman (1956), through a study of members of the Praesepe Cluster, found that it held for A stars. Strömgren (1958a) derived the variation of $U - B$ with M_v for equal $B - V$ for F stars from an investigation of field stars within 50 pc.

In the following section we shall discuss a method of two-dimensional classification for unreddened stars of spectral classes A2–G0 which is based on a similar principle. The previous discussion has referred to the Population I stars of luminosity classes I–V. We shall now briefly discuss two applications of wide-band photometry to classification of stars beyond this limitation.

Harris (1956b) has measured photoelectric color indices $U - B$ and $B - V$ for a number of white dwarfs. In the $(U - B)$-$(B - V)$ diagram the white dwarfs in the $B - V$ range -0^m1 to $+0^m4$ are located more than half a magnitude above the standard curve for luminosity class V stars. The stars of luminosity classes I–IV are nearly on, or below, the standard curve. The white dwarfs are low-luminosity objects, and the interstellar reddening is small for those that are brighter than $V = 17$ mag. Hence, in the $B - V$ range mentioned, white dwarfs can be identified with a high degree of certainty from photoelectric U, B, V photometry. However, a reddened O or early B star might be mistaken for a white dwarf on the basis of U, B, V photometry only, and, as pointed out by Greenstein (1958), unresolved double stars containing a blue and a red component might fall in the same region of the $(U - B)$-$(B - V)$ diagram as the white dwarfs. However, if the U, B, V photometry is followed up by even low-dispersion spectrography, then the ambiguity can be resolved.

Roman (1954) obtained photoelectric U, B, V photometry for a number of F-type subdwarfs of extreme Population II and found that they had an ultraviolet excess of about 0.2 mag., in comparison with Population I stars of luminosity class V of the same $B - V$. The effect is so large that the stars of this category can easily be segregated from Population I of luminosity classes I–V stars through U, B, V photometry, at least in high galactic latitudes where no strongly reddened O and B stars are present. However, on the basis of U, B, V photometry alone, they cannot be distinguished from late-type white dwarfs.

§ 3. SPECTRAL CLASSIFICATION THROUGH PHOTOMETRY IN BANDS OF INTERMEDIATE WIDTH

In photometric work on very faint stars it is desirable that the wavelength bands be as wide as possible. In work on brighter stars, narrower bands may be chosen, and certain advantages gained thereby.

The results of photometry in bands of intermediate width (100–300 A half-width, *ib* photometry) are more readily connected with those of spectrophotometry and with predictions from model-atmosphere calculations. In particular, an intermediate-width band that is wholly below λ 3647 is more suitable in this respect than the standard U band of wide-band photometry (*wb* photometry), which contains regions on both sides of the discontinuity. An inconvenient feature of *wb* photometry—namely, the dependence of the effective wavelength on the extent of interstellar reddening—is practically eliminated in *ib* photometry.

Most single absorption-line features are too weak to influence *ib* intensities significantly. However, the hydrogen absorption lines just above λ 3647 do influence the intensity of a suitably chosen band of intermediate width strongly enough for a valuable index of this absorption to be obtained, as will be seen in the following discussion of a classification method due to T. and J. H. Walraven. Generally, however, narrow-band photometry (*nb* photometry) is necessary to obtain indices that measure the strengths of individual absorption-line features.

T. and J. H. Walraven (1960) have developed two systems of two-dimensional classification for O and B stars based on photoelectric *ib* photometry. One system utilizes four bands of intermediate width which are separated through

TABLE 1

CENTRAL WAVELENGTHS AND BAND WIDTHS
IN THE W, U, B, V SYSTEM

Band Designation	λ (A)	Half-Width (A)	Band Designation	λ (A)	Half-Width (A)
V........	5450	850	U.......	3670	260
B........	4295	420	W.......	3270	150

the use of a quartz-prism spectrograph and are accurately defined with the help of a specially designed filter of quartz and Iceland spar. The central wavelengths and the half-widths of the bands are shown in Table 1. For each star the intensities in the bands were observed simultaneously. It may be noted that the chosen half-widths of the bands increase with wavelength, which tends to equalize intensities for early-type stars. In describing the method as one of intermediate band width, we go by the width of the narrowest band utilized. In comparison with U, B, V photometry, there is some loss in intensity because the W, U, and B bands are relatively narrow, but for early-type stars the loss in sensitivity is small.

The W, U, B, V method makes possible two-dimensional classification of B stars even in the case that the stars are appreciably affected by interstellar reddening. Consider, first, the case that reddening is negligible. It is known that the supergiant B I and B II stars are well separated from the B V stars in a $(U - B)$-$(B - V)$ diagram, showing an ultraviolet deficiency (cf. Johnson and Morgan 1953). However, for appreciably reddened stars, segregation is not possible on the sole basis of U, B, V photometry. Following a suggestion by Divan (1954), T. and J. H. Walraven added the band W at λ 3270, in order to

obtain two color-index combinations that were practically insensitive to interstellar reddening and which would yield two-dimensional classification.

For regions in our Galaxy or in other galaxies, where the standard wavelength
dependence of interstellar reddening, as derived by Divan (1954) and Whitford
(1958), is valid to a sufficient degree of approximation, the following relations
between the color excesses E_{B-V}, E_{U-B}, and E_{W-U} can be utilized:

$$E_{U-B} = 0.66 \, E_{B-V} , \qquad E_{W-U} = 0.55 \, E_{B-V} .$$

The first relation corresponds to that given in § 2, with a small difference in
the coefficient due to a difference in U, B, and V wavelengths in the Walraven

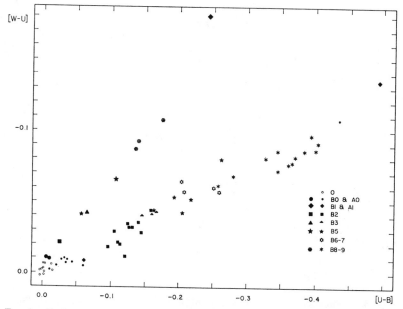

FIG. 2.—Early-type stars in the $[U - B]$-$[W - U]$ diagram (T. and J. H. Walraven 1960).
The larger symbols represent supergiant stars; the smaller symbols, main-sequence stars.

and the standard U, B, V systems, respectively. The color-index combinations,
defined by

$$[U - B] = U - B - 0.66 \, (B - V) , \qquad [W - U] = W - U - 0.55 \, (B - V)$$

are therefore insensitive to interstellar reddening.

Figure 2 shows the result when main-sequence and supergiant B stars are
plotted in a $[U - B]$-$[W - U]$ diagram. In view of the fact that the photoelectrically determined color indices are accurate to better than 0.01 mag., there is
excellent separation of supergiants and main-sequence stars for the spectral
range B2–B9. Supergiant A stars are also very well segregated. O–B1 stars can

be separated from the rest of the stars, but here the W, U, B, V method does not give good luminosity classification.

Further investigation by T. and J. H. Walraven led to the result that the absolute magnitude could be determined with good accuracy from the location in the $[U - B]$-$[W - U]$ diagram for the whole range between the lower envelope of the main-sequence stars and the supergiants, again for stars of spectral class B2 or later. This investigation was based on a comparison with absolute magnitudes of members of the Scorpio-Centaurus association as determined by Bertiau

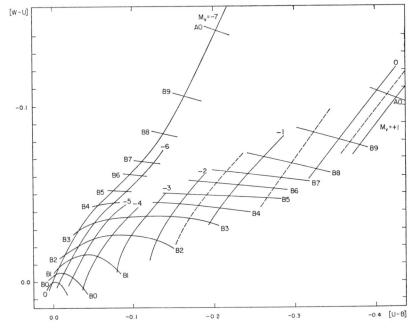

Fig. 3.—Calibration-curves in the $[U - B]$-$[W - U]$ diagram (T. and J. H. Walraven 1960).

(1958) from a discussion of proper motions and radial velocities. Figure 3 shows a calibration of the $[U - B]$-$[W - U]$ diagram in terms of spectral class and absolute magnitude. The authors emphasize, however, that, while the separation of supergiants and main-sequence stars is very well established, the detailed features of the calibration network are still uncertain because the B stars with accurately known absolute magnitudes are relatively few and not adequately distributed over the whole diagram. We shall return in § 5 to the question of the accuracy of the absolute magnitudes determined by the W, U, B, V method.

The second system of T. and J. H. Walraven utilizes a combination of the wavelength bands U, B, V with a wavelength band L centered on λ 3900 and having a half-width of 300 A. The latter band was isolated through the use of a composite glass filter (Schott UG2, 2 mm, plus Schott WG2, 2 mm) and was observed simultaneously with the other bands. The band L includes the Balmer lines $H\epsilon$, $H\zeta$, $H\eta$, and $H\theta$. The intensity ratio L/B is a measure of Balmer line absorption, since the band B, which is wider and contains only two Balmer lines, is considerably less influenced by this effect. As in the W, U, B, V method, the influence of interstellar reddening is eliminated through the use of a color-index combination, in this case

$$[L - B] = L - B - 0.40 \, (B - V) \,,$$

where the coefficient of $(B - V)$ is again computed according to the standard reddening law.

It was found that supergiants and luminosity class V B stars are very well separated in a $[U - B]$-$[B - L]$ diagram. Furthermore, it was found that the index $[L - B]$ correlates very well with indices measuring the strength of $H\beta$ and $H\gamma$,

TABLE 2

CENTRAL WAVELENGTHS AND BAND WIDTHS
USED BY BORGMAN

Band	λ (A)	Half-Width (A)	Band	λ (A)	Half-Width (A)
K.........	5880	215	P......	3750	110
L.	5420	220	Q........	3560	90
M........	4550	200	R......	3295	80
N.........	4055	200			

respectively, as measured through photoelectric narrow-band (nb) photometry (cf. § 4.5) by Crawford (1958) and Johnson (1959). The comparison was made for stars of the Scorpio-Centaurus association. Since it had previously been found by Crawford and Johnson that the $H\beta$ and $H\gamma$ indices were well correlated with absolute magnitude for B stars, the conclusion was that $[L - B]$ is a very useful absolute magnitude index here. In § 4 we shall return to this question.

In comparison with nb photometry, the ib photometry is considerably more economical of light, which is a definite advantage for work on faint stars. On the other hand, the results obtained by ib photometry are more sensitive to changes in the reddening law, which, under certain circumstances, is a disadvantage.

Borgman (1960) has carried out photoelectric ib photometry of O, B, and A stars with the help of interference filters for similar purposes. A catalogue of intensities in seven bands for 356 O, B, and A stars is given, but the discussion of the material has not yet been published. The peak transmission wavelengths and the half-widths of the filters are listed in Table 2.

We shall consider next a method for two-dimensional classification in the spectral range A2–G0 based on photoelectric ib photometry which was developed by Strömgren (1962). The method in question is useful only in the case of stars for which the interstellar reddening is negligible. For A2–G0 stars, there is, however, a considerable field of application, even with this limitation. Within a sphere of radius 100 pc, interstellar reddening is practically negligible, and the number of A2–G0 stars in this volume is somewhat over 10,000. Two-dimensional classification of relatively high accuracy is desirable for these stars in connection with discussions of their space motions.

Two-dimensional classification is obtained through photoelectric ib photometry in four bands with the central wavelengths and half-widths shown in Table 3.

The bands v, b, and y are isolated with the help of interference filters, the u band with a composite glass filter. It is seen that the wavelengths of these bands correspond closely to the four shortest wavelengths of the Stebbins-Whitford six-color photometry and to the wavelengths of Becker's four-color photometry

TABLE 3

CENTRAL WAVELENGTHS AND BAND WIDTHS
USED BY STRÖMGREN

Band	λ (A)	Half-Width (A)	Band	λ (A)	Half-Width (A)
u.........	3500	300	b........	4670	180
v..........	4110	190	y........	5470	230

(cf. § 2). However, the bands are narrower, and, in particular, the transmission region of the u band is completely below the Balmer discontinuity. The four bands represent, in fact, the four wavelength regions described in § 2.

We have (§ 2) referred to the fact that the luminosity of an unreddened A or F star can be inferred from its location in the $(U - B)$-$(B - V)$ diagram. The method to be discussed depends on a further development of this approach.

The color index $b - y$ has properties very similar to those of $B - V$; however, $b - y$ is less influenced by line absorption, a fact that is of importance in connection with the effect of the variable chemical composition of the stellar atmospheres in question. A color-index difference $c_1 = (u - v) - (v - b)$, where u, v, and b are magnitudes corresponding to the intensities observed in the bands just defined, is clearly an index of the Balmer discontinuity.

From the results already referred to of Johnson and Morgan (1953), Johnson (1953), Bidelman (1956), and Strömgren (1958b) pertaining to the variation of $U - B$ with M_v for equal $B - V$ in the case of A and F stars, one would expect a $c_1 - (b - y)$ diagram to yield satisfactory two-dimensional classification for A and F stars and presumably also for early G stars. It would also be expected that the sensitivity of c_1 to absolute magnitude, for equal $b - y$, would be greater than that of $U - B$ for equal $B - V$. Both expectations have been confirmed through the application of the method to unreddened stars in the spectral range A2–G0.

In this connection, reference is made to the results of Chalonge (1955; cf. also Chalonge 1958), who investigated the distribution of B, A, and F stars in a D-ϕ_b diagram, D being the Balmer discontinuity and ϕ_b the gradient in the wavelength region $\lambda\lambda$ 3800–4600 according to spectrophotometric measures. It was found that there was an appreciable spread of the D values for equal ϕ_b

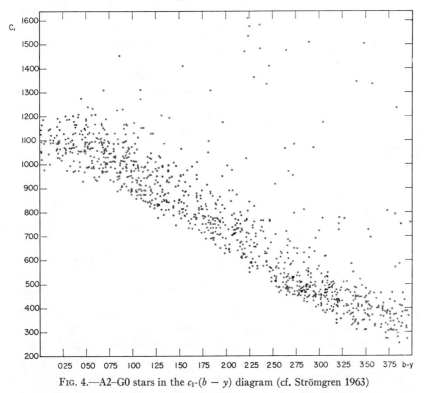

FIG. 4.—A2–G0 stars in the c_1-$(b-y)$ diagram (cf. Strömgren 1963)

for A and F stars. In § 4.2 we shall return to this question in connection with the discussion of Chalonge's method of three-dimensional classification on the basis of measures of D, ϕ_b, and λ_1 (cf. § 4.2).

The c_1-$(b-y)$ method of two-dimensional classification has been applied by Strömgren (1962) to A2–G0 stars brighter than apparent magnitude 6.5 and north of declination $-10°$. Figure 4 shows the distribution of about 1100 A2–G0 stars in the c_1-$(b-y)$ diagram. The lower limit to the distribution in the c_1-$(b-y)$ diagram corresponds to the lower limit of the distribution of main-sequence Population I stars in the Hertzsprung-Russell diagram. This limiting curve is referred to as the "initial main-sequence line" or the "zero-age line" (cf. Johnson and Hiltner 1956; Johnson 1957; Sandage 1957). It is the locus of

Population I stars in the stage of evolution where equilibrium between radiation into space and thermonuclear energy generation has been reached and the fraction of hydrogen transmuted into helium is still negligible. The stars above the zero-age line in the c_1-$(b-y)$ diagram are more luminous than the stars on the line which have the same $b-y$, and they are further advanced in their evolution.

The calibration of the c_1-$(b-y)$ diagram in terms of spectral class (or the color index $B-V$) and visual absolute magnitude M_v has been carried out on the basis of results obtained from stars with trigonometric parallaxes and cluster parallaxes, particularly members of the Hyades Cluster (cf. van Bueren 1952; Heckmann and Johnson 1956). Table 4 summarizes the results.

The values of c_1, M_v, and $B-V$ are given as functions of $b-y$ for a standard line, the zero-age line. When $b-y$ and c_1 are known for a star, the difference

TABLE 4

CALIBRATION DATA FOR THE c_1-$(b-y)$ DIAGRAM

$b-y$ (Mag.)	c_1 (Mag.)	M_v	$B-V$	Sp. Class	Factor $\Delta M_v/\Delta c_1$
+0.05	+0.97	2.0	+0.09	A3	8
+ .10	+ .89	2.3	+ .17	A6	8
+ .15	+ .79	2.7	+ .24	A8	8
+ .20	+ .66	3.1	+ .31	F0	8
+ .25	+ .53	3.4	+ .38	F2	9
+ .30	+ .43	3.8	+ .46	F6	10
+ .35	+ .35	4.4	+ .54	F8	13
+0.40	+0.31	5.0	+0.63	G1	16

Δc_1 between c_1 and the value on the standard line corresponding to $b-y$ is found. The last column of Table 4 gives the factor $\Delta M_v/\Delta c_1$, by which Δc_1 should be multiplied to give the difference between M_v for the star and M_v on the standard line for the same $b-y$. For a star above the standard line, Δc_1 is positive and ΔM_v negative, i.e., the star is more luminous than a star on the standard line of the same $b-y$.

It is seen from Figure 4 that the great majority of the stars fall in a band above the standard line with a width Δc_1 equal to $0^m.1$–$0^m.2$ ($0^m.1$ at G0; $0^m.2$ at A5). From the values of $\Delta M_v/\Delta c_1$ given in Table 4 it is found that the corresponding range in absolute magnitude is a little less than 2. The band in question therefore contains the stars of luminosity classes V, IV, and III for the A and early F stars and stars of luminosity classes V and IV for the late F and early G stars (cf. chap. 8 of this volume).

Above the band a relatively small number of stars is found, practically all supergiants of luminosity classes II and I. It may be noted that stars of luminosity class III and spectral type G0 or later have $b-y > 0^m.40$, i.e., they are beyond the range of the calibration summarized in the table and mostly outside the limits of the diagram in Figure 4. This reflects the well-known fact that the color of G stars of luminosity class III is more advanced than that of luminosity class V stars of the same spectral class.

Since most of the supergiants in question are appreciably affected by interstellar reddening, they cannot be accurately classified by the method being discussed. However, the supergiants can be segregated without any difficulty. Using the standard reddening law (Divan 1954; Whitford 1958), one finds

$$E_{b-y} = 0.70\, E_{B-V}, \qquad E_c = -0.12\, E_{B-V}.$$

Interstellar reddening thus moves points in the c_1-$(b - y)$ diagram to the right and downward along lines the slope of which is somewhat smaller than the average slope of the standard zero-age line.

The points plotted in the diagram of Figure 4 correspond to observed values of $b - y$ and c_1 which have an accuracy of $\pm 0^m004$ (p.e.) and $\pm 0^m006$ (p.e.), respectively (mean of two observations). The observational uncertainty in the location of a point in the c_1-$(b - y)$ diagram is therefore much smaller than the width of the band above the zero-age line just discussed.

From the probable errors of $b - y$ and c_1 and the calibration data summarized in Table 4, it follows that the probable error of an absolute magnitude M_v determined from $b - y$ and c_1 is between $\pm 0^m1$ and $\pm 0^m2$. This estimate of the accuracy takes into account only the effects of errors in the photometry. The effect of the limitation to two-dimensional classification will be discussed in § 5 on the basis of comparison with the absolute magnitudes derived from trigonometric and cluster parallaxes. As we shall see, the accuracy obtained corresponds to a probable error of about $\pm 0^m2$ for one observation.

In § 2 we referred to the use of U, B, V photometry for the segregation from Population I stars of F-type subdwarfs of extreme Population II. The latter have an ultraviolet excess of 0^m2-0^m3 in $U - B$ in comparison with Population I main-sequence stars of the same $B - V$. As was first shown by Chamberlain and Aller (1951), the stars in question have a relatively very low atmospheric abundance of metals. The ultraviolet excess is due mostly, if not entirely, to a corresponding great reduction in the influence of metal absorption lines on the intensity distribution measured by wb photometry (cf. Schwarzschild, Searle, and Howard 1955; also Reiz 1954; Code 1959; Sandage and Eggen 1959; Burbidge, Burbidge, Sandage, and Wildey 1959; Melbourne 1960).

In view of the results just referred to, one would expect the ultraviolet excess for late F and early G stars to be an index of atmospheric metal content over the range from young Population I to extreme Population II. This expectation has been confirmed by Wallerstein and Carlson (1960) and Wallerstein (1962). Comparison of the ultraviolet excess according to U, B, V photometry and the iron-hydrogen abundance ratio derived from quantitative analysis based on high-dispersion coudé spectra for 31 nearby G dwarfs and 3 F subdwarfs indicated a very good correlation.

We have previously discussed the variation of $U - B$ with absolute magnitude for equal $B - V$. This effect does not seriously complicate the discussion in the investigation just referred to. Sufficiently accurate absolute magnitudes derived from trigonometric parallaxes are available for the stars in question, and it is found that they are generally within 1 mag. of the Population I zero-age line.

Arp (1959) has investigated ultraviolet excesses for main-sequence F stars in three globular clusters (M5, M13, and M2) and found values quite similar to those determined for extreme Population II F subdwarfs, i.e., $0^{m}2$–$0^{m}3$. Again the absolute magnitude was known, and the absolute magnitude effect did not cause any difficulty (cf. also Baum, Hiltner, Johnson, and Sandage 1959).

It is clear, however, that the dependence of the ultraviolet excess on absolute magnitude leads to complications in the determination of the metal content of field stars if independent information regarding absolute magnitudes is not available. It is also evident that the influence of variable metal content on absolute magnitudes determined by the c_1-$(b - y)$ procedure discussed above must be looked into unless it is known that the sample of stars investigated is chemically homogeneous to a sufficient degree.

Such considerations suggest that a three-dimensional classification scheme based on ib photometry in the four bands u, v, b, and y defined in Table 3 might be useful. In addition to spectral class and absolute magnitude, a metal-content index would be determined from the photometry. A scheme of this kind would be similar in some respects to the MK classification scheme when extended through the addition of the weak-line–strong-line characterization (cf. Roman 1950 and this volume, chap. 8).

We have already discussed the fact that the two bands b and y are relatively much less affected by the metal absorption lines than are the bands u and v. It would therefore be expected that $b - y$ as an indicator of effective temperature would not be very much disturbed by changes in metal content from star to star and, furthermore, that a color-index difference m_1, defined by

$$m_1 = (v - b) - (b - y),$$

is a good indicator of metal content.

Strömgren (1958a) has measured a metal-content index m very similar to m_1, through photoelectric photometry in three bands approximately 100 A wide centered on $\lambda\lambda$ 4030 (e), 4500 (d), and 5000 (a),

$$m = (e - d) - (d - a).$$

It was found that the deviations of m from the average value for a given color index are fairly well correlated with the ultraviolet excess. For F subdwarfs of extreme Population II, m was found to be $0^{m}1$–$0^{m}2$ smaller than for average Population I stars of the same color index $B - V$. The index m, which was measured with a probable error of $\pm 0^{m}006$ (two observations), therefore gives a clear separation of the extreme Population II stars. For the F stars of Population I an analysis of the scatter in m considered as a function of $B - V$ for stars close to the zero-age line strongly suggested that at least one further parameter beyond effective temperatures and absolute magnitude was of importance in determining the properties of the spectrum, the scatter in m being considerably bigger than the observational scatter corresponding to the probable error of the photometric observations. In § 4.2 we shall discuss a similar conclusion reached by Chalonge (1958) through photographic spectrophotometry.

Borgman (1959) measured the metal-content index m, using the same filters as Strömgren, and extended the work to late G stars. Borgman investigated a few high-velocity stars characterized by a considerable ultraviolet excess, yet somewhat smaller than that of the extreme Population II subdwarfs. It was found that these stars stood out very clearly in a diagram of m versus spectral type. Regarding late G and K stars, Borgman suggested that the combination of the index m and criteria used by Strömgren and Gyldenkerne (1955) for two-dimensional classification through photoelectric nb photometry might yield useful three-dimensional classification. As we shall see in § 4.5, Gyldenkerne (1961) has found that this is indeed the case.

We shall now return to the discussion of the use in the framework of u, v, b, y photometry of the index m_1 defined above. Through observations of Hyades stars, a standard relation between the metal-content index m_1 and the color index $b - y$ was established for the $B - V$ range 0^m40–0^m65. This procedure is similar to the one adopted in determining ultraviolet excesses relative to the Hyades stars from U, B, V photometry. The dependence of m_1 on absolute magnitude was investigated over a range of 0–1.5 mag. above the zero-age line. For the range $B - V$ 0^m35–0^m50, it was found that, to a high degree of accuracy, m_1 was independent of the absolute magnitude and only a function of $b - y$. For $B - V$ 0^m50–0^m65, the variation of m_1 with absolute magnitude is small but not quite so well determined. For $B - V$ 0^m05–0^m35, it was found that m decreased with increasing luminosity, for equal $b - y$. This variation of m_1 with luminosity is connected with the fact that the band v contains the hydrogen absorption line $H\delta$, which decreases in strength with increasing luminosity, thus causing the v magnitude and hence m_1 to decrease. For $B - V > 0^m35$, this effect is very small because $H\delta$ is relatively weak and it is partly compensated for by other small effects. It was found that for $B - V$ 0^m05–0^m35, the effect can be allowed for and m_1 reduced to the value for the zero-age line through the addition of $0.10 \, \Delta c_1$, where Δc_1 is the excess of the Balmer discontinuity index c_1 over the standard value for the zero-age line (cf. Table 4).

With the correction $0.10 \, \Delta c_1$, the values of m_1 obtained from the observations of Hyades stars with $B - V < 0^m35$ were reduced to the zero-age values. The resulting standard relation between m_1 and $b - y$ valid for the zero-age line is shown in Table 5. The scatter of the m_1 values for members of the Hyades cluster around the standard relation is quite small, measured by a probable error of $\pm 0^m004$ (metallic-line stars excluded, cf. below).

When the values of the indices $b - y$, c_1, and m_1 for a star have been determined from u, v, b, y photometry, then the value of the metal-content index which would correspond to Hyades atmospheric composition can be computed from $b - y$ and c according to the procedure just outlined. The difference Δm_1 between this value and the m_1 value actually measured for the star is now an indicator of the difference in metal content between the star and Hyades members. We count Δm_1 positive when the m_1 index for the star is smaller than the Hyades value; hence positive Δm_1 indicates a metal-content deficiency, as does an ultraviolet excess.

TABLE 5

THE STANDARD RELATION BETWEEN COLOR-INDEX
DIFFERENCE m_1 AND COLOR INDEX $b-y$
FOR THE ZERO-AGE LINE

$b-y$ (Mag.)	m_1 (Mag.)	$B-V$ (Mag.)	Sp. Class
+0.10	+0.210	+0.17	A6
+ .15	+ .201	+ .24	A8
+ .20	+ .185	+ .31	F0
+ .25	+ .171	+ .38	F2
+ .30	+ .171	+ .46	F6
+ .35	+ .189	+ .54	F8
+0.40	+0.234	+0.63	G1

TABLE 6

THE CORRELATION BETWEEN THE ABUNDANCE RATIO Fe/H
AND THE METAL-CONTENT INDICATOR Δm_1

Group	Range of [Fe/H]	No. of Stars	Average [Fe/H]	Average $U-B$ Excess (Mag.)	Average Δm_1 (Mag.)	Average $b-y$ (Mag.)
1	+0.4 to +0.1	7	+0.22	+0.00	+0.010	+0.39
2	−0.2 to −0.6	5	−0.39	+ .10	+ .062	+ .40
3	−1.7 to −2.0	2	−1.88	+0.28	+0.172	+0.37

On the basis of results obtained for 14 late F and early G stars in common with the list of stars for which Wallerstein (1962) has given atmospheric metal abundances relative to hydrogen, the metal-content indicator Δm_1 was calibrated in terms of the abundance ratio Fe/H. The procedure is similar to that used by Wallerstein and Carlson (1960) for calibrating the ultraviolet excess in terms of the Fe/H ratio. The results are summarized in Table 6. The stars in question have been divided into three groups according to the Fe/H ratio as determined by Wallerstein. The second column indicates the range of [Fe/H], where

$$\left[\frac{Fe}{H}\right] = \log \left(\frac{\text{abundance of Fe}}{\text{abundance of H}}\right)_{\text{star}} - \log \left(\frac{\text{abundance of Fe}}{\text{abundance of H}}\right)_{\text{sun}} .$$

Table 5 further gives the average values for each group of [Fe/H] and $U - B$ excess according to Wallerstein (1962) and of Δm_1 according to the photoelectric u, v, b, y photometry (Strömgren 1963).

Since the photometric probable error of Δm_1 for one star is ± 0.004 (mean of three observations), the three groups are clearly separated both in $U - B$ excess and in m_1. The individual [Fe/H] values are well represented by a linear relation

$$\left[\frac{Fe}{H}\right] = 0.3 - 12\Delta m_1.$$

The photometric probable error of a value of [Fe/H] predicted from this relation is ± 0.04. The actual scatter in the [Fe/H] $- \Delta m_1$ relation is considerably larger, reflecting the additional uncertainty in the determination of the abundance from the high-dispersion spectra and presumably some intrinsic scatter. For the Hyades the residual in [Fe/H] is 0.2 or 0.3, depending on which abundance determination is preferred (cf. Wallerstein 1962). However, the material indicates that [Fe/H] can be predicted from Δm_1 with an accuracy of about 0.1 (p.e.) for the category of stars considered (F8–G2 stars within 1.5 mag. of the zero-age line). Since the number of stars on which the conclusion is based is rather small, the indicated degree of accuracy is, of course, subject to some uncertainty. It would be desirable to carry out calibration of Δm_1 in terms of metal content for early G stars 1.5–3 mag. above the zero-age line (G IV stars such as ζ Her and η Boo). However, abundance determinations from high-dispersion spectra are not yet available here. It is already clear, though, that Δc_1 and Δm_1 will satisfactorily determine absolute magnitude, as well as metal content, for this category of stars also.

In the further discussion of the results Δm_1 determinations for the 1200 A2–G0 stars brighter than 6^m5 (apparent visual magnitude) for which photoelectric u, v, b, y photometry has been carried out by Strömgren and Perry (1963), we shall divide the stars into three groups according to $b - y$, namely, $0^m05–0^m21$, $0^m22–0^m27$, and $0^m28–0^m40$. The corresponding $B - V$ ranges are approximately $0^m05–0^m33$, $0^m34–0^m39$, and $0^m40–0^m63$.

For the group with $b - y$ $0^m28–0.40$ (F5–G stars), the range of variation of Δm_1 is $0^m00–0^m06$. The calibration in terms of Fe/H is at least approximately valid for this spectral range, and it is therefore concluded that the atmospheric metal content of the stars in question varies from that of the Hyades Cluster members to a value down by a factor of about 4–5. A third classification parameter representing the atmospheric metal content is clearly of importance in this range. In § 4.5 we shall discuss a similar result pertaining to K giants. For these stars the so-called cyanogen discrepancies indicate the importance of a third classification parameter connected with atmospheric heavy-element content (cf. this volume, chap. 8).

We note that the sample of stars brighter than apparent visual magnitude 6.5 is too small to contain any stars of extreme Population II, with large Δm_1.

The two stars in group 3 in Table 6 (HD 19445 and HD 140283) are fainter than 6^m5.

The group with $b - y$ 0^m22–0^m27 (F1–F4 stars) is found to have a very small range of variation of Δm_1, measured by a dispersion (p.e.) of less than $\pm 0^m005$ when allowance is made for the influence of observational scatter. The sensitivity of the Δm_1 indicator to metal content is smaller here because the level of absorption-line strengths is lower. As yet, no adequate material of atmospheric abundances determined from high-dispersion spectra is available for this spectral range, so that calibration of the Δm_1 indicator in terms of metal content cannot be carried out. However, on the basis of an estimate of the reduction in sensitivity, it is concluded that the variations in metal content are considerably smaller for this group than for the previous one. Among the 60 stars in the group, there are a few with appreciable positive Δm_1, among them the well-known ultraviolet-excess star 28 σ Boo (cf., e.g., Strömgren 1958a; Melbourne 1960).

Near $b - y = 0^m22$, the dispersion in Δm_1 changes rather abruptly, and for the group with $b - y$ 0^m05–0^m21 the range of variation in Δm_1 is about 0^m06, with a considerable number of negative m_1 values indicating a metal-content excess. The known metallic-line stars in the sample of stars under consideration are all in the 0^m05–0^m21 group, and their first appearance as one goes to smaller $b - y$ is at 0^m21; they have generally negative Δm_1 values. The known metallic-line stars in the Hyades Cluster stand out clearly from the other cluster members with negative Δm_1 values. Of the stars with appreciably negative Δm_1, about half have not been classified as metallic-line stars.

Whereas the variations in atmospheric metal content found in late F and early G stars are generally attributed to differences in the chemical composition of the interstellar matter out of which the stars were originally formed, the variations in the metal-content index for the group with $b - y$ 0^m05–0^m21 (A3–F0 stars) can hardly be accounted for in this way, since the stars in question are all relatively young and slow-moving. The variations in Δm_1 observed within the Hyades group are of significance in this connection.

Since visual inspection of spectra taken for classification purposes reveals considerable differences between metallic-line stars and normal stars, it is not surprising that the metallic-line stars stand out from normal stars in quantitative photometric investigations. Considerable photometric differences were found by Chalonge (1958), by Berger, Fringant, and Menneret (1956), and by Strömgren (1955, 1956a, b). At the present time it is not clear whether the negative Δm_1 values of metallic-line stars are due solely to the effect of the metal absorption lines or to differences in the intensity distribution in the continuum (cf. Chalonge 1958; Oetken 1960; Unsöld 1960) or to both effects.

The necessity of introducing a third parameter—a metallicity index—in photometric classification through wb photometry of A and early F stars has been emphasized by Kron (1960) in connection with a discussion of the distribution of stars in the $(V - B)$-$(R - I)$ diagram (cf. § 2). In view of the importance of a third classification parameter, for A3–F0 stars, as well as for F5–G1 stars, it is necessary to return to the question of the determination of the absolute magnitude M_v from the location in the $c_1 - (b - y)$ diagram. For the stars in the group with $b - y$ 0^m05–0^m21, it is found, from a discussion based on cluster parallaxes and trigonometric parallaxes, that the absolute magnitudes M_v determined from $(b - y)$ and c_1 as described before show no appreciable systematic errors depending on the value of Δm_1. In particular, the absolute magnitudes of metallic-line stars are predicted correctly. Both the u and the v bands are, of course, affected by variations in metallicity, but in this color-index group the effects cancel out very nearly in the color difference c_1. For the group $b - y$ 0^m22–0^m27, the dispersion in m_1 is so small that the effect on M_v can be neglected. For the third group, with $b - y$ 0^m28–0^m40, an analysis of the differences in absolute magnitudes determined from trigonometric parallaxes and c_1 and $b - y$, respectively, in terms of Δm_1 values indicated that here $c_1 + 0.7$ Δm_1 should be used together with $b - y$ for the determination of the absolute magnitude. In other words, the effect of the chemical composition on the intensity of the u band influences c_1, but the influence of the effect on the v-band intensity on c_1 goes in the opposite direction; however, complete cancellation is not obtained, and a correction of c_1 equal to $0.7\Delta m_1$ is required.

The chemical-composition effect on $b - y$ as an indicator of effective temperature is quite small, less than 0^m01 for all A2–G0 stars except extreme Population II stars, and even for these stars the effect is presumably less than 0^m02. If desirable, a correction in terms of Δm_1 can be applied.

In a general way it is clear that the wavelength dependence of the influence of a change in metal content on intensities measured in ib photometry is a function of effective temperature. Consider two stars, with Hyades metal content and, say, one-fourth of this content, respectively. First, the effect of the absorption lines on the intensities measured in bands of intermediate width will cause appreciable differences between the two stars that depend on the band wavelength, and the nature of this wavelength dependence is a function of effective temperature. Second, the continuous absorption produced by metals and its effects on the intensities will be different for the two stars. For A and early F stars this effect is probably quite small, but for late F and early G stars it may be noticeable in the ultraviolet (cf., e.g., Vitense 1951; Swihart 1956).

In the discussion of the W, U, B, V method of T. and J. H. Walraven we referred to the fact that a relatively wide band is used in the yellow (the V band). This is an advantage for early-type stars. For the A2–G0 stars the lowest intensity in u, v, b, y photometry is nearly always that of the u band, and, since this band cannot be made broader than 200–300 A without loss of efficiency of the method, there would be no advantage here in choosing greater widths for the other bands, although this could be done without materially changing the properties of the indices derived from the photometry.

When we compare the results obtained through four-color photometry such as the W, U, B, V photometry and the u, v, b, y photometry discussed in this section with those of three-color U, B, V photometry, we note the following advantages gained through the addition of one band and the choice of somewhat narrower bands: for reddened early-type stars, W, U, B, V photometry gives two-dimensional classification (effective temperature and absolute magnitude) as compared with one-dimensional classification from U, B, V photometry. For unreddened A2–G0 stars, u, v, b, y photometry yields three-dimensional classification (effective temperature, absolute magnitude, and metal-content index), while two parameters can be determined from U, B, V photometry, notably effective temperature and a metal-content index when the absolute magnitude is approximately known from other sources of information. These advantages of four-color ib photometry are, of course, gained at the expense of some loss in terms of limiting magnitude.

§ 4. SPECTRAL CLASSIFICATION THROUGH NARROW-BAND PHOTOMETRY

4.1. QUANTITATIVE PHOTOGRAPHIC METHODS UTILIZING THE LINDBLAD CRITERIA

Lindblad has developed methods of two-dimensional classification based on spectrophotometric measures in objective-prism spectra of low dispersion (cf. Lindblad 1922, 1925, 1926, 1927; Lindblad and Stenquist 1934). Relatively strong features were selected as classification criteria. The spectrophotometric measures pertained to average intensities in bands having widths of 20–40 A.

The Lindblad criteria have been utilized in much subsequent work on quantitative stellar classification. Figure 5 indicates the location of the bands measured by Lindblad for spectral classes B–F8, namely, bands containing $H\gamma$ and $H\delta$ and comparison bands relatively unaffected by Balmer line absorption, the latter also yielding a color equivalent. Figure 6 shows the bands defining the Lindblad criteria used for spectral classes F8–M. They are (1) the intensity ratio between bands at λ 4360 and λ 4260, g, the break at the G band, and (2) the intensity ratio between bands at λ 4260 and λ 4180, c, measuring the strength of cyanogen absorption in the region shortward of the cyanogen band head at λ 4216. The wavelength λ 4180 is chosen to get maximum sensitivity to cyanogen absorption. The intensities at $\lambda\lambda$ 4360, 4260, 4180, 4140, and 4095 define a color equivalent, k; the magnitude at these points is plotted against reciprocal wavelength, and the slope of the best line through these points (obtained through a least-squares solution) is determined.

For early-type stars, the measured $H\gamma$ and $H\delta$ strengths are used as a luminosity criterion; for the late-type stars the cyanogen index c serves this purpose. The measured indices are combined with spectral classes determined by inspection methods. In this way, two-dimensional classification is obtained. For late-type stars, quantitative two-dimensional classification is possible on the basis of the measured indices c and g or c and k. The latter method gives results that are affected by interstellar reddening, but not strongly so, since c and k are very sensitive indicators of effective temperature, in spite of the relatively narrow wavelength base.

The method has been successfully used by Lindblad with unwidened objective-prism spectra of a dispersion of 1.7 mm between $H\gamma$ and $H\epsilon$. For late-type stars, giants and dwarfs were clearly separated. Such separation can generally not be achieved with inspection methods when unwidened spectra of this relatively low dispersion are used. The method is particularly useful for work on faint stars.

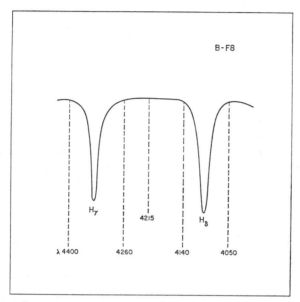

FIG. 5.—Location of the wavelength bands of the Lindblad criteria for B–F8 stars (Lindblad and Stenquist 1934).

In § 1 we referred to the fact that quantitative spectral classification is naturally developed in such a way that only a minimum of suitably chosen indices are measured. Öhman (1927) developed a version of the Lindblad method for quantitative two-dimensional classification of late-type stars which is of this category. Widened spectra were used, and with a Schilt photometer average intensities in three bands were measured, namely, $\lambda\lambda$ 4138–4173, $\lambda\lambda$ 4232–4272, and $\lambda\lambda$ 4326–4368. The first two give the Lindblad index g, the last two the index c, and these two indices yield two-dimensional classification for G and K stars.

Öhman (1930) used the same photographic-spectrophotometric method for the determination of an index indicating the strength of the K line of Ca II, as well as an index of the strength of $H\gamma$, and demonstrated that these two indices would yield quantitative two-dimensional classification for A stars, the K line being a good measure of the temperature and the Hγ line a good indicator of luminosity.

Lindblad and Stenquist (1934) have shown that the spectrophotometry of unwidened spectra gives values of the indices in question that are independent of the photographic density level of the spectra, as long as the relevant photographic densities are on the straight portion of the characteristic curve of the

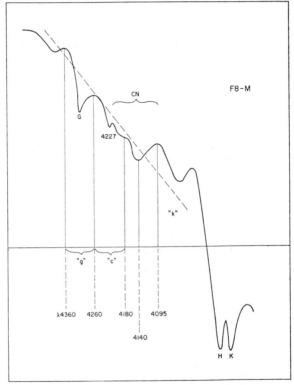

Fɪɢ. 6.—Location of the wavelength bands of the Lindblad criteria for F8–M stars (Lindblad and Stenquist 1934).

photographic plate. Öhman (1927), through a detailed analysis, has shown that a similar result holds for spectrophotometry with widened spectra; the strength of an absorption feature is measured with very good accuracy through the mean photographic density in one fixed band of suitable width that contains the feature.

The method of determining absolute magnitudes for early-type stars from measured strengths of Balmer lines was used by Anger (1931, 1932a, b), particularly in investigations of members of galactic clusters.

The Lindblad methods of quantitative two-dimensional classification from low-dispersion objective-prism spectra have been extensively used (cf., e.g., Schalén 1928; Elvius 1951; Ramberg 1957; Malmquist 1960). They have been further developed by Westerlund (1951, 1953a, b), who included additional criteria and utilized combinations of indices that are insensitive to interstellar absorption.

Petrie and Maunsell (1950) and Petrie (1952, 1956) used spectrophotometrically measured equivalent widths of the Balmer line Hγ for quantitative determination of absolute magnitudes of B and early A stars. In most of the work, widened spectra obtained with a one-prism spectrograph (dispersion 30 A/mm, or 51 A/mm) were used, and two or more plates were evaluated for each star.

The measured equivalent widths $W\gamma$ of Hγ were used, together with spectral types found by standard inspection methods for determinations of absolute magnitudes. The method of Petrie is therefore one of two-dimensional classification. It was expected from the earlier work that the absolute magnitude of B and early A stars would depend mainly on $W\gamma$ and only to a smaller extent on the spectral class. This expectation was confirmed, and the accuracy of spectral classes found by the inspection method is therefore quite satisfactory for the purpose.

The method was calibrated with the help of absolute magnitudes independently known for members of galactic clusters and associations and for components of visual binaries (cf. the references given above). The calibration was checked through the use of trigonometric parallaxes, proper motions, and radial velocities. In carrying out the calibration, Petrie assumed the validity of one calibration-curve $M_v - W\gamma$ for all spectral classes considered, with a correction for spectral type that is the same for all absolute magnitudes, i.e.,

$$M_v = \text{A function of } W\gamma + \text{a function of Sp. cl.},$$

rather than making the general assumption of two-dimensional classification, $M_v = M_v (W\gamma, \text{Sp. cl.})$.

A high degree of accuracy is obtained with Petrie's method. The probable error in M_v corresponding to the observational uncertainty of $W\gamma$ as determined from two widened one-prism slit spectrograms is about $\pm 0^m2$. Comparison with the absolute magnitudes used in the calibration indicates that the accuracy obtained corresponds to a probable error about equal to $\pm 0^m3$. We shall discuss the question further in § 5.

Kopylov (1958) based two-dimensional classification of O5–B7 stars on measured equivalent widths of all Balmer lines between λ 3700 and λ 5000, as well as of lines of He, O, Si, N, C, and Mg and Ca in the same wavelength region. The equivalent widths were measured on widened spectra with a dispersion of 75 A/mm at Hγ, and absolute magnitude and spectral class were determined for O5–B7 stars. The absolute magnitudes depend mainly on the equivalent widths of the Balmer lines. The internal accuracy obtained by Kopylov is very high, ± 0.014–0.028 of a spectral class and ± 0.10 in absolute magnitude, respectively.

Sinnerstad (1954, 1961) developed two schemes of two-dimensional classification of B and early A stars. Both schemes utilize the mean equivalent width of Hγ and Hδ, $W(\gamma\delta)$, as an indicator of luminosity. In the first scheme the mean of the measured central depths for Hγ and Hδ, $d(\gamma\delta)$, is used as a temperature indicator, and two-dimensional classification is obtained from the indices $W(\gamma\delta)$ and $d(\gamma\delta)$. In the second scheme, $W(\gamma\delta)$ is combined with a measured spectral class. The spectral-class determination depends on measurements of a considerable number of ratios of line intensities (lines due to He, C, N, O, Mg, and Si). The measures were made on slit spectrograms with a dispersion of 75 A/mm at Hγ.

The second procedure gives the highest accuracy. The measured central depth of Hγ and Hδ is an indicator of temperature for the stars in question, but Sinnerstad points out that the results are affected by axial rotation and by incipient emission of the stars, and reliable measures are possible only with fairly high spectrographic resolving power.

The two procedures are calibrated in terms of absolute magnitude M_v with the help of M_v values for cluster and association stars. For the early A stars, trigonometric parallaxes are also used. The scheme is truly two-dimensional, M_v being determined as a function of two indices, $W(\gamma\delta)$ and $d(\gamma\delta)$, and $W(\gamma\delta)$ and Sp. cl., respectively. The photometric uncertainty of the absolute magnitudes is about $\pm 0^m.15$ (p.e.). The calibration residuals indicate probable errors of $\pm 0^m.18$ and $\pm 0^m.15$ for the W-Sp. cl. and the W-d methods, respectively.

Sinnerstad (1954) in the first application of the W-d method to a relatively small number of stars found a division of the B stars later than about B1 and early A stars into two separated sequences—main-sequence stars and supergiants. This is confirmed by a more extensive investigation (Sinnerstad 1961). The separation is also indicated in results obtained by Crawford (1958), Kopylov (1958), Strömgren (1958b), and T. and J. H. Walraven (1960).

Sinnerstad showed that when the supergiant-branch stars are left out and the sample of stars restricted to the main-sequence branch, a one-dimensional classification based on $W(\gamma\delta)$ yields very satisfactory absolute magnitudes, the dependence on the second classification index within the main-sequence branch being small. The absolute magnitudes derived in this way have probable errors of $\pm 0^m.21$. A similar procedure was used by Crawford (1958) for late B stars.

In applying such a procedure, some caution is, of course, necessary because the age distribution of the stars may vary according to the sample. The average absolute magnitude corresponding to a given Balmer line strength is somewhat different for a sample of zero-age stars in a very young cluster or association and for a field-star mixture of all ages represented in the main-sequence band.

The problem of absolute magnitude calibration for B stars is admittedly a difficult one (cf. chap. 8, this volume). A comparison by Sinnerstad (1961) with results obtained by Petrie (1953, 1956), Petrie and Maunsell (1950), and Petrie and Moyls (1956) indicates differences of about three-quarters of a magnitude. Comparison with M_v values of Johnson and Iriarte (1958) gives differences up to $0^m_.7$ for the supergiants. In view of the high internal accuracy of the M_v determination, it can be expected that further work on cluster and association stars will considerably reduce the calibration uncertainties.

The early work of Lindblad has been further developed for late-type stars also, the aim being greater accuracy in bright-star classification from spectra of higher dispersion. Setterberg (1947) carried out a spectrophotometric investigation of molecular bands of CN and CH in late-type stars, using slit spectra with a dispersion of 22 A/mm. At this dispersion it was possible to measure the intensities in narrow wavelength bands where the influence of metallic-line blends was small, so that measures of the molecular absorption could be obtained and studied as a function of effective temperature and absolute magnitude.

Plassard (1950) investigated the CN band strengths in G and K stars with slit spectra with a dispersion of 63 A/mm. Intensities in narrow bands around λλ 4163, 4193, and 4213 were measured as indicators of the CN absorption. These regions are nearly free of blends. The λ 4163 region was found to be the most suitable. The relation between absolute magnitude and spectral class was investigated, and the results of previous investigations regarding the possibility of giant-dwarf separation were confirmed. For G7–K5 stars of luminosity class III, an accuracy of the absolute magnitude of $\pm 0^m_.3$ is indicated. However, the disturbing effect of the cyanogen discrepancy (cf. chap. 8) is referred to.

Yoss (1958) for G5–K5 giants combined determination of MK spectral class and luminosity class by the inspection method, with spectrophotometric measures of a CN index defined according to Lindblad by the intensity ratio of bands approximately 30 A wide at λ 4180 and λ 4260. Widened objective-prism spectra with a dispersion of approximately 300 A/mm at Hγ were used. Since the cyanogen strength is not employed in the determination of MK luminosity class, this procedure yields a three-dimensional classification (spectral class, luminosity class, and cyanogen discrepancy) similar to that obtained by Keenan and Keller (1953) within the framework of the inspection methods (cf. chap. 8).

In the further development of quantitative classification methods for late-type stars, the question of the cyanogen discrepancy has proved important. We shall return to this question in § 4.5 (photoelectric methods).

4.2. Quantitative Methods Based on the Use of the Ultraviolet Criteria of Barbier and Chalonge

In § 2 we referred to the work of Yü (1926), Barbier, Chalonge, and Vassy (1935), and Öhman (1935) which showed the importance of the Balmer discontinuity at λ 3647 in stellar spectra. Barbier and Chalonge (1939) have developed a method of two-dimensional classification for B, A, and F stars which utilizes measures of the magnitude of the Balmer discontinuity and, in addition, a wavelength λ_1 that indicates the effective location of the Balmer discontinuity in the spectrum.

While the lower members of the Balmer series of absorption lines are well separated in stellar spectra with the exception of those of white dwarfs, the higher numbers gradually merge and form a continuation of the Balmer absorption continuum extending longward of λ 3647. This effect is pressure-dependent and therefore a function of the absolute magnitude for stars of equal effective temperature.

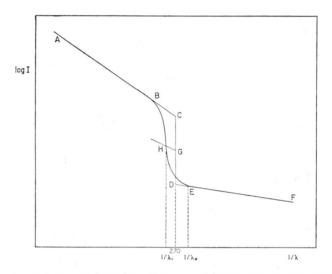

Fig. 7.—Definition of the Barbier-Chalonge criteria D and λ_1 (Barbier 1955)

Barbier and Chalonge (1939, 1941) utilized widened slitless spectra with a dispersion of 80 A/mm at Hγ covering the wavelength region $\lambda\lambda$ 3100–4500 and derived the intensity as a function of wavelength. In drawing the intensity-curve of the continuous spectra, they avoided the absorption lines as far as possible, and, in particular, the intensity-curve through the wavelength region longward of λ 3647 was drawn through the intensity maxima between the Balmer lines.

Barbier and Chalonge succeeded in deriving two well-defined quantities from the intensity-curve for the continuous spectrum, namely, D, indicating the magnitude of the Balmer discontinuity, and λ_1, which shows its effective location. We shall follow Barbier (1955) in describing the procedure through which D and λ_1 are obtained. Figure 7 shows schematically the variation with the reciprocal wavelength $1/\lambda$ of log I, where I is the intensity (per unit wavelength) in the continuous spectrum, measured as far as possible between the absorption lines. The straight portion AB of the curve longward of λ 3647 is extrapolated to its intersection at C with the line representing $1/\lambda = 2.70$ (λ 3700). Similarly, the straight portion EF of the curve shortward of λ3647 is extrapolated to D on the line $1/\lambda = 2.70$. The value of D is then given by the distance CD. A line GH parallel to AB drawn through the mid-point G of CD defines the point H, the wavelength of which is λ_1.

Both the Balmer discontinuity index D and the wavelength λ_1 depend on the effective temperature T_e, as will the absolute visual magnitude M_v; however, Barbier and Chalonge showed that the functional dependences on T_e and M_v are sufficiently different for D and λ_1 for satisfactory two-dimensional classification to be obtained.

For main-sequence stars, D increases with T_e through the spectral classes G and F, reaches a maximum at a T_e corresponding to a spectral type about A4, and then decreases with T_e through the range of the B stars. For higher luminosity, the variation of D with T_e is similar; however, the maximum of D occurs at a lower value of T_e. The range of variation of D is about 0.5, corresponding to a magnitude range well over 1 mag.

For constant T_e, the wavelength λ_1 increases with decreasing luminosity. Decreasing luminosity means higher atmospheric pressure and broader hydrogen lines, the merging of which is more pronounced, thus producing a shift of the intensity-curve around H (Fig. 7) to the left and hence a larger value of λ_1. The range of variation of λ_1 from luminosity class V to luminosity class I is about 100 A.

The fact that D considered as a function of T_e has a maximum means that there is an ambiguity in the values of T_e and M_v determined from D and λ_1. However, if the spectral class is already known approximately, this ambiguity does not give rise to any difficulty except for a narrow range of spectral class around the value of T_e for which D is a maximum. In applications of the $\lambda_1 D$ method to bright stars, sufficiently accurate spectral classes are known in advance for the ambiguity to be resolved, except for a very small fraction of the stars considered. For samples of stars for which interstellar reddening is known to be small, a color index such as $B - V$ can serve the same purpose as the spectral class.

Barbier and Chalonge found that for B, A, and F stars the values of D and λ_1 could be determined through their photographic spectrophotometry with probable errors of 0.01–0.02 and about 3 A, respectively (from four spectrograms). Hence, in view of the ranges of variation just referred to, two-dimensional classification of high accuracy appeared possible with the $\lambda_1 D$ method. This expectation has been fully confirmed. The $\lambda_1 D$ method of Barbier and Chalonge has been extensively applied to precision classification of relatively bright stars by Chalonge and Divan (1952). In the latter investigation, spectra obtained with a slitless spectrograph and having a dispersion of 225 A/mm at Hγ were used.

Chalonge and Divan (1952) determined a calibration of the $\lambda_1 D$ method in terms of MK spectral classes and luminosity classes (cf. also Chalonge 1955). They utilized spectral classes and luminosity classes on the MK system determined by the inspection method, largely by Johnson and Morgan (1953). With a view to the ambiguity referred to above, the calibration was carried out separately for spectral classes O6–A4 and A5–F8. Figure 8 shows the result for the O6–A4 stars. In a $\lambda_1 D$ diagram, compartments of nearly equal spectral class and luminosity class are indicated by limiting curves.

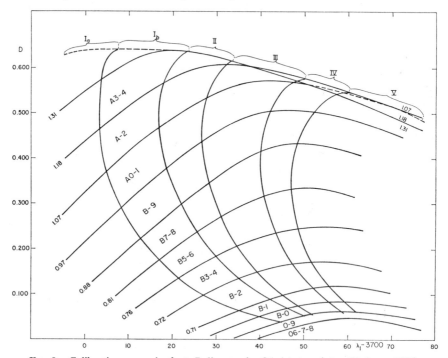

Fig. 8.—Calibration-curves in the $\lambda_1 D$ diagram for O6–A4 stars (after Chalonge 1956)

For each of the limiting curves that separate successive spectral classes, the corresponding value of the spectrophotometric gradient in the blue region of the spectrum ($\lambda\lambda$ 3800–4800) is indicated:

$$\phi_b = -\frac{1}{\log e}\,\frac{d\,\log(I\lambda^5)}{d(1/\lambda)}.$$

The connection with the color temperature T_b for the blue region is given by the well-known relation

$$\phi_b = \frac{c_2}{T_b}(1 - e^{-c_2/\lambda\,T_b})^{-1}.$$

Figure 9 similarly shows the result of the calibration for A5–F8 stars. The widths of the compartments of equal type as shown in Figures 8 and 9 in the λ_1

and D directions are seen to be considerably larger than the photometric probable errors of λ_1 and D, respectively, so that classification to an accuracy considerably better than one-tenth of a spectral class and one luminosity class is
possible by the $\lambda_1 D$ method. The agreement with the results of the MK classification determined by visual inspection was very satisfactory.

As one goes from early to late F stars, the hydrogen criteria become weaker,
and, for this reason and also because the influence of the metal absorption lines

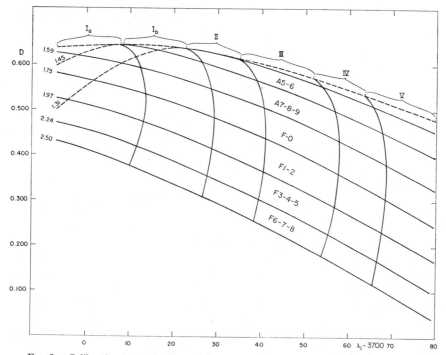

FIG. 9.—Calibration-curves in the $\lambda_1 D$ diagram for A5–F8 stars (after Chalonge 1956)

grows stronger, the measures of λ_1 and D become less accurate. The method
cannot be used beyond about G0, and for late F stars the influence of the metal
absorption lines on the values obtained for λ_1 and D according to the procedure
described above is considerable.

Barbier and Chalonge have emphasized that the two criteria of the $\lambda_1 D$
method reflect the variations of hydrogen features with T_e and M_v and that,
since hydrogen is the most abundant element, it may be expected to be less
sensitive to variations in chemical abundance from star to star than criteria such
as individual metal-line strengths, which also reflect variations in relative abundance of a particular element.

Since the $\lambda_1 D$ method has only two criteria, it is of the general type described
in § 1 which utilizes the minimum number of criteria necessary for two-dimen-

sional classification. Barbier, Chalonge, and Morguleff (1941) tackled the problem of determining whether or not the spectra of two stars with equal λ_1 and D are equal (when the effects of the ambiguity referred to above are removed) with respect to other criteria, i.e., whether two-dimensional classification is sufficient or whether further classification parameters must be introduced. The H and K lines of Ca II and the Balmer lines were investigated. For the sample of stars investigated and to the accuracy of the investigation, two-dimensional classification was found to be sufficient without exception. In particular, Barbier, Chalonge, and Morguleff found that the equivalent widths of the Balmer lines Hγ and Hδ are functions of and well predictable from λ_1 and D. We shall return to this point in § 4.3.

The investigation of the question of whether or not two-dimensional classification is sufficient for very accurate classification was continued by Chalonge (1955, 1958), in collaboration with Divan (1956) and Berger, Fringant, and Menneret (1956). In this work a third index measured through photographic spectrophotometry—namely, the blue gradient ϕ_b referred to above—was added to the indices λ_1 and D. The discussion was limited to relatively nearby stars for which the effects of interstellar reddening on ϕ_b could be safely neglected and was therefore largely concerned with stars of the spectral range A4–G0 and with luminosity classes IV and V. Accordingly, the ambiguity referred to previously does not enter into the picture, and the question that is investigated is the following: Do λ_1 and D uniquely predict ϕ_b, or is a significant scatter of the ϕ_b values for equal λ_1 and D indicated by the spectrophotometric observations? If the latter is the case, two-dimensional classification is inadequate, and a third parameter has to be added to the effective temperature T_e and the absolute visual magnitude M_v.

It should be noted in passing that the effects of interstellar reddening can be largely eliminated, if that is desirable, through the choice, instead of ϕ_b, of a combination of a blue and an ultraviolet spectrophotometric gradient, following the suggestion of Divan (cf. § 3).

Figure 10 shows a $\lambda_1 D$ diagram similar to that in Figure 9, with a number of relatively bright, mostly nearby, stars plotted (for the identification of individual stars we refer to the original publication, Chalonge 1958). The signatures allow distinction between normal stars (classified on the MK system by Morgan), metallic-line stars, and subdwarfs of Population II. For the normal stars of luminosity classes IV and V it is found that a certain linear combination of λ_1 and D predicts values of ϕ_b in good agreement with the measured ϕ_b values.

Figure 11 shows a comparison of the linear combination of λ_1 and D with the measured values of ϕ_b. The normal stars occupy a region of relatively small dispersion around a mean curve. The metallic-line stars (investigated by Berger, Fringant, and Menneret 1956), however, are located above the region of normal stars, i.e., their ϕ_b is higher (indicating lower color temperature) than predicted from λ_1 and D according to the mean curve found for normal stars.

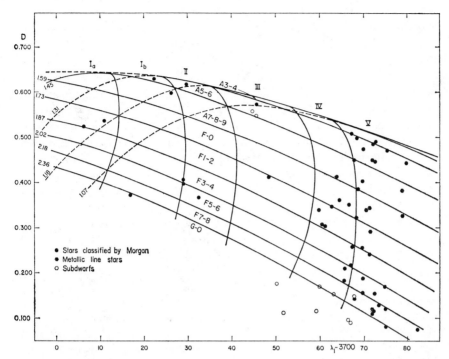

FIG. 10.—A2–G0 stars in the $\lambda_1 D$ diagram (after Chalonge 1958; the identifications of the stars are given in this publication).

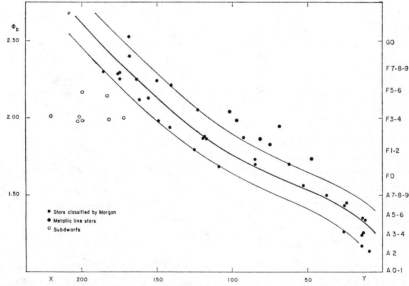

FIG. 11.—A2–G0 stars in the xy–φ_b diagram (cf. Fig. 10) (after Chalonge 1958; the identifications of the stars are given in this publication).

The subdwarfs of Population II (investigated by Divan 1956) are also clearly separated from the normal stars, being located below the region occupied by the latter.

The results of the spectrophotometric investigation thus show that, for a sample of stars which contains metallic-line stars or subdwarfs of Population II in addition to stars classified as normal on the MK system, three-dimensional classification is necessary, as was already clear from the investigations of Morgan and Keenan by the method of visual inspection described in chapter 8; they further indicate that the combination of the indices λ_1, D, and ϕ_b yields quantitative three-dimensional classification (for unreddened stars). At this point we refer to the investigations based on photoelectric determinations of the metal indices m and m_1 discussed in § 3, which gave an analogous result.

If metallic-line stars and the subdwarfs of Population II are excluded from the sample of stars, there still remains a certain scatter around the mean curve in Figure 11. Chalonge (1958) has investigated the nature of this scatter further for late F and G0 stars through a comparison with the strong-line–weak-line classification of Roman (1952). It might be expected that the weak-line stars would fall below the mean curve in Figure 11, like the Population II stars but closer to the mean curve than the latter, and that the strong-line stars would fall above the mean curve, i.e., have positive $\Delta\phi_b$. For six stars that are common to both investigations, there is agreement with this expectation in five cases, disagreement in one. In another discussion Chalonge (1959) has given data for ten late F and G0 main-sequence stars which are also classified by Roman as strong-line or weak-line stars. There is agreement for seven stars and disagreement for three. The average value of $\Delta\phi_b$ is found to be larger for strong-line than for weak-line stars, as expected.

Combined with the result obtained for the Population II stars, this would suggest that the third parameter needed in the description of the spectrophotometric material of observations of λ_1, D, and ϕ_b is a chemical-composition parameter, more specifically a metal-content parameter. The available material is not sufficient for a comparison of $\Delta\phi_b$ values with the results of the determination of chemical composition from high-dispersion spectra by Wallerstein (1962) similar to the comparison carried out for the metal index m_1 (cf. § 3).

Since the importance of a third parameter was indicated, Chalonge (1958, 1959) investigated the question of the determination of absolute visual magnitudes M_v from observations of the three indices λ_1, D, and ϕ_b. For the spectral range of the A and F stars, a linear relation between M_v and the indices is assumed:

$$M_v = a_1 + a_2(\lambda_1 - 3700) + a_3 D + a_4 \phi_b .$$

The constant coefficients a_2, a_3, and a_4 have been determined from measures of visual double stars for which the angular separation is large enough for separate spectra to be obtained (cf. Berger 1958; Chalonge 1958, 1959). When the difference between the absolute visual magnitudes of the two components is known from measures of the apparent magnitudes and the differences $\Delta\lambda_1$, ΔD, and $\Delta\phi_b$ have been measured, the star pair in question yields one equation for the determination of a_2, a_3, and a_4:

$$\Delta M_v = a_2\Delta\lambda_1 + a_3\Delta D + a_4\Delta\phi_b\,.$$

Chalonge (1959) discusses results obtained from seven pairs and gives the following values of a_2, a_3, and a_4:

$$a_2 = +0.094\,,\qquad a_3 = -15.18\,,\qquad a_4 = -3.88\,.$$

The residuals in the seven equations are very small, all less than 0^m2. It would be desirable to subdivide the material further instead of assuming constant values of a_2, a_3, and a_4 for the whole range of the A and F stars. Calibration work in this direction based on observations of a larger number of visual double stars is in progress (cf. Chalonge 1960).

From the known probable errors of the photometric determinations of λ_1, D, and ϕ_b and the values of the coefficients a_2, a_3, and a_4 the probable error of one determination (from six spectrograms) of M_v is found to be $\pm 0^m2$–0^m3 for A and F stars. Chalonge has compared the photometrically determined values of M_v with values obtained from trigonometric parallaxes as well as cluster parallaxes (for Hyades stars) for 40 stars. From the scatter, a probable error of the photometrically determined M_v of $\pm 0^m3$ is found when allowance is made for the scatter due to the errors of the parallaxes.

It may be noted that for A and F stars two-dimensional classification on the basis of D and ϕ_b is analogous to two-dimensional classification from $U - B$ and $B - V$, or c_1 and $b - y$ (cf. § 3).

Three-dimensional classification is achieved through the addition of the index λ_1 to D and ϕ_b, while, in the scheme of u, v, b, y photometry discussed in § 3, this is done through the addition of the index m_1.

In the determination of λ_1, D, and ϕ_b the effect of metal absorption lines is avoided as far as possible. However, it is likely that these lines do have an influence, at least for the late F and G0 stars (cf. § 5). This, of course, does not detract from the value of λ_1, D, and ϕ_b as classification indices.

4.3. PHOTOGRAPHIC METHODS UTILIZING MEASURES OF THE BALMER DISCONTINUITY AND BALMER LINE STRENGTHS

In § 4.1 we discussed the method of using Balmer line strengths as luminosity indicators for B, A, and F stars as developed by Lindblad (1922). We also referred to the fact that the Balmer discontinuity is a good indicator of effective temperature T_e (except for the ambiguity connected with the fact that the Balmer discontinuity has a maximum in the range of the A stars; cf. § 4.2).

Öhman (1935) investigated the relation between T_e and M_v, on the one hand, the Balmer discontinuity D and the Balmer line strengths, on the other. He emphasized that for late B and early A stars the Balmer discontinuity is fairly independent of the luminosity and records mainly the effective temperature, while, according to Lindblad, the Balmer line strengths are indicators of the luminosity, nearly independent of spectral class.

Strömgren (1951, 1952, 1956a, b, 1958b) has developed a method of photoelectric narrow-band photometry for two-dimensional classification of B, A, and F stars in which two indices of the kind just referred to are used, one measuring the Balmer discontinuity and one the strength of the Hβ absorption line. This method will be discussed in § 4.5.

Hack (1953) utilized the Balmer discontinuity D (cf. § 4.2) and the strength of the Hδ absorption line measured through photographic spectrophotometry for the purpose of two-dimensional classification in the spectral range O9–F8. The choice of these indices was suggested through the successful applications of the $\lambda_1 D$ method described in § 4.2, on the one hand, and, on the other, the result obtained by Barbier, Chalonge, and Morguleff (1941) that the strength of Hγ (or Hδ) can be well predicted from λ_1 and D.

Hack utilized widened spectra with a dispersion of 225 A/mm at Hγ. The index D was determined through the spectrophotometric procedure described in § 4.2. The apparent central intensity given by the spectrophotometric tracings of the Hδ profile was adopted as an index of the Hδ strength. At the relatively low dispersion used (188 A/mm at Hδ), this quantity represents the equivalent width with sufficient accuracy.

Including plate material (with a dispersion of 80 A/mm at Hγ) previously obtained by Barbier and Chalonge (1941), Hack obtained two-dimensional classification by the $DH\delta$ method for 243 O, B, A, and F stars. As in the case of the $\lambda_1 D$ method (cf. § 4.2), the discussion is carried out separately for the two categories of stars with effective temperatures in the ranges above and below that of the Balmer maximum, respectively, i.e., on the main sequence separately for O–A0 and A2–F8 stars. The stars are plotted in the $DH\delta$ diagrams similar to the $\lambda_1 D$ diagrams in Figures 8 and 9. Comparison with the results of previous classification on the MK system, obtained through the method of visual inspection and the $\lambda_1 D$ method, respectively, yields a division of the $DH\delta$ plane into compartments of equal spectral class and luminosity class similar to that shown in Figures 8 and 9. The agreement between the results obtained by the $DH\delta$ method and those of the visual inspection method and the $\lambda_1 D$ method is very satisfactory.

Hack investigated the relative merits of Hγ, Hδ, and H8 strengths for combination with D to yield two-dimensional classification; Hδ was preferred over Hγ and H8 because this line is less influenced by blends, and in particular over Hγ because it is less sensitive to the disturbances by Balmer line emission.

4.4. Photographic Methods Based on Quantitative Determination of Line
Ratios for a Considerable Number of Absorption-Line Pairs

In § 4.1 we referred to the work of Kopylov (1958) and Sinnerstad (1961) on two-dimensional classification of O and B stars. In this work, spectral-class determination is carried out on the basis of quantitative measures of equivalent widths on spectrograms of fairly high dispersion of a considerable number of absorption lines. The approach is similar to that of the methods of visual inspection discussed in chapter 8; however, measures of equivalent widths take the place of eye-estimates of line ratios.

Oke (1957) developed a method of two-dimensional classification for F5–K1 stars on the basis of measures of line-strength ratios in the wavelength region $\lambda\lambda$ 4040–4480 made on microphotometer tracings of widened slit spectrograms having a dispersion of 33 A/mm at $H\gamma$. In selecting the classification criteria, Oke included only line ratios of relatively sharp and unblended lines. The strength of a line was represented by the logarithm of its central depth on the microphotometer tracing. The classification criteria were line ratios measured by the ratios of the logarithms of the central depths. These ratios (when measured on well-exposed plates) are insensitive to errors in the adopted calibration-curve of the photographic plate.

The luminosity and spectral-class criteria were selected on the basis of previous experience gained in the application of the visual inspection method of classification to spectra of similar dispersion (Adams, Joy, Humason, and Brayton 1935; Young and Harper 1924; cf. chap. 8). For G5–K1 stars, ten ratios of metal lines (of neutral atoms or ions) were measured as luminosity criteria; for F5–G2 stars, six line ratios. For the determination of spectral class, five line ratios were used. Weighted means of the ratios obtained for the line pairs were formed to yield spectral indices for the determination of absolute magnitude and spectral class. Trigonometric and cluster parallaxes were used for the calibration.

The accuracy of the absolute visual magnitudes determined in this way is high. Oke evaluated the precision from the scatter in the relation between the luminosity index and the values of M_v determined from trigonometric and cluster parallaxes and found a probable error of $\pm 0^m.2$. For the stars of luminosity class III the number of stars with good determinations of M_v from the parallax is quite small, and the group is homogeneous with respect to the cyanogen discrepancy (cf. §§ 4.1, 4.5), so that the estimate of the precision obtainable for luminosity class III stars is somewhat uncertain here.

The spectral-class index is calibrated in terms of the color index $B - V$. The latter can be converted into spectral class, if this is desirable, with the help of the standard relations given by Johnson and Morgan (1953). The stars in question are within 100 pc and hardly affected by interstellar reddening. The accuracy with which $B - V$ can be predicted from the spectral index is found to be given by a probable error of $\pm 0^m.02$–$0^m.03$.

Hossack (1954) has developed a technique of two-dimensional classification of G8–K5 stars that utilizes an oscilloscopic microphotometer (cf. Hossack 1953). Widened spectra with a dispersion of 33 A/mm were used. The oscilloscopic microphotometer presents on an oscilloscope screen spectrophotometric traces of two spectra—that of the star to be classified and a standard comparison spectrum. The trace amplitude in the vertical direction can be adjusted through electronic amplification controls, separately for either trace. Line depths in the oscilloscope traces can also be varied by accurately measurable changes in the intensity of the analyzing light of the microphotometer. With these facilities, it is possible to get a quantitative measure of the line ratio of a chosen line pair in the spectrum to be classified in terms of the ratio in the standard spectrum. With this technique, two-dimensional classification was carried out on the basis of measured line ratios; four line ratios were used as luminosity criteria, five as spectral-class criteria. The line ratios were calibrated individually in terms of luminosity classes and spectral classes on the MK system on the basis of observations of stars for which standard MK classification was available.

The luminosity class and spectral class are found as averages of the results obtained for the individual line ratios. The internal accuracy obtainable with Hossack's method is very high. From a comparison of results derived from different plates, the probable error of a luminosity class (1 spectrogram) was found to be ± 0.15 of a luminosity class, corresponding to about $\pm 0^m4$ in absolute visual magnitude. The probable error of a spectral class was ± 0.02 of a spectral class, corresponding to about $\pm 0^m015$ in $B - V$.

The method of Hossack has been used by Halliday (1955) for determinations of absolute visual magnitudes, distances, and space velocities for 227 G8–K1 stars, mostly brighter than visual magnitude 7.0, and for a derivation of luminosity functions for G8–G9 and K0–K1 stars.

4.5. Methods Based on Photoelectric Narrow-Band Photometry

In § 3 we discussed methods of quantitative classification through photoelectric photometry in bands of intermediate width. It is clear that in photoelectric narrow-band photometry—nb photometry—there will be a wider choice of criteria. In some quantitative classification problems the choice of nb photometry is necessary or advantageous, and the loss in terms of limiting magnitude for a given length of collecting time is accepted.

In § 4.3 we saw that the early work of Lindblad (1922) and Öhman (1935; cf. also Yü 1926; Barbier, Chalonge, and Vassy 1935) suggested the combination of a Balmer discontinuity index and a Balmer line index of two-dimensional classification of early-type stars. Strömgren (1951, 1952, 1956a, b, 1958b) has developed a method of this category. For B, A, and F stars, two-dimensional classification is obtained through photoelectric narrow-band photometry.

The Balmer discontinuity index is measured through determination of the intensities in three bands, two above and one below the Balmer discontinuity, while an index of the strength of Hβ is derived from intensity measures in one band centered on Hβ and two comparison bands on either side of Hβ. Five of the wavelength bands in question are isolated through the use of interference filters, the sixth (in the ultraviolet) with a glass filter. Table 7 shows the wavelengths of peak transmission and the half-widths of the filters. The filters were used in a photoelectric photometer in standard fashion, i.e., they were placed in the diverging beam, between the diaphragm in the Cassegrain focal plane of the telescope and the cathode of the photomultiplier. The aperture ratio, 1:13, was small enough for the corresponding increase in the half-widths of the interference to be negligible. The intensities through the six filters were measured in succession.

Since Hβ is a strong feature, the chosen half-width is adequate. For work on high-luminosity stars with faint Balmer lines, a narrower filter, e.g., with a half-width of 10–15 A, can be used to advantage, while for main-sequence A stars a

TABLE 7

CENTRAL WAVELENGTHS AND BAND WIDTHS
USED IN THE STRÖMGREN NARROW-
BAND PHOTOMETRY

Filter	λ_{max} (A)	Half-Width (A)
a Interference filter........	5030	90
b Interference filter........	4861	35
c Interference filter........	4700	100
d Interference filter........	4520	90
e Interference filter........	4030	90
f Glass filter............	3650	350

slightly wider filter might be preferred. A half-width of 30–35 A has, however, generally proved satisfactory. It is narrow enough for the transmitted light to be a sufficiently sensitive indicator of the variations in Hβ strength when the intensities are measured with the accuracy obtainable through photoelectric photometry, and it is wide enough for the Hβ index to be insensitive to the effect of rotational broadening of the Hβ profile.

An Hβ index was here preferred to an Hγ or Hδ index because the Hβ wavelength band is less disturbed by metal absorption lines, a feature which is important, particularly in the application to late F stars. On the other hand, the Hβ index is more sensitive to the effect of hydrogen-line emission; the method was applied to samples of stars from which emission-line stars had been eliminated on the basis of previous spectroscopic investigations of Hα. For classification work that is restricted to B stars, the choice of Hγ or Hδ is better if hydrogen-line emission stars have not already been eliminated.

The Balmer discontinuity index c is defined as the color-index difference,

$$c = [m(f) - m(e)] - [m(e) - m(d)],$$

where $m(d)$, $m(e)$, and $m(f)$ denote magnitudes corresponding to the intensities measured through the filters d, e, and f described above. The index c corresponds closely to the Balmer discontinuity index c_1 discussed in § 3. It differs, however, from the latter in two respects. Since the measures through the filters d and e are to be combined with measures through the narrow-band filter b, there is no great advantage in choosing them to be as wide (200 A) as those used for measuring c_1. If half-widths of about 100 A are chosen for d and e, then the peak transmission wavelengths of d, e, and f can be selected relatively close together and yet in such a way that there are no Balmer lines within bands d and e. With the choice of the band-wave lengths at $\lambda\lambda$ 3650, 4030, and 4520, the influence of interstellar reddening on the Balmer discontinuity index is almost negligible if the standard reddening law is valid (cf. Divan 1954; Whitford 1958). Even in the case of considerable deviations from the standard spacing law, the interstellar reddening effect would presumably be small for the wavelength spacing in question. The ultraviolet filter f of the c combination is not so suitable as that used in the later u, v, b, y photometry described in § 3, in that its transmission band extends longward to about λ 3900. The sensitivity of the index c to changes in the Balmer discontinuity is thereby somewhat reduced. In this respect the filter f is intermediate between the ultraviolet filter of U, B, V photometry and the filter u of u, v, b, y photometry.

An Hβ index l is defined as follows:

$$l = m(b) - \tfrac{1}{2}[m(a) + m(c)],$$

where $m(a)$, $m(b)$, and $m(c)$ are magnitudes measured through the filters a, b, and c described in Table 7. The index l is insensitive to the influence of interstellar reddening.

Since the lc method of two-dimensional classification utilizes hydrogen criteria that reach a maximum for early A stars, the stars to be classified must be divided into two groups—B stars and A3–F8 stars—for ambiguities to be avoided, and in a narrow range of spectral type (around A1 for main-sequence stars) the method is unsuitable for precision classification. In this respect the method is similar to the $\lambda_1 D$ method of Barbier and Chalonge discussed in § 4.2 and to that of Hack described in § 4.3. Previous relatively crude spectral classification is sufficient for the division into the two groups. For samples of stars for which interstellar reddening is known to be small, the color index $B - V$ may serve the purpose.

Figure 12 shows an lc diagram for B stars, mostly brighter than apparent visual magnitude 5.5. The abscissa and ordinate are c and l in units of $0^{m}001$. The curve indicates the location in the lc diagram of stars that have just reached the hydrogen-burning phase, the zero-age line (cf. § 3). It was constructed on the basis of lc measures for stars in the associations I Ori and II Sco. The member stars of these associations are so young that the evolutionary change since the beginning of the hydrogen-burning phase is very small over the range of spectral classes in question.

It would have been desirable to derive the zero-age line through a statistical analysis, as the lower envelope of the point distribution in the c diagram (Fig. 12). However, the number of stars represented in Figure 12 is too small for a very reliable determination of the line.

It is seen from Figure 12 that the stars of MK luminosity class III are located in the upper part of the main-sequence band and that the supergiants of luminosity class I are above the main-sequence band and well separated from it.

A calibration in terms of visual absolute magnitude M_v has been carried out for stars close to the zero-age line with the help of distances and M_v values determined for II Sco stars by Bertiau (1958). The photoelectric narrow-band photometry of these stars is largely due to Crawford (1958). The relation between l and M_v in Table 8, valid near the zero-age line, was derived by Strömgren (1958b). The table shows that the Hβ index l changes about 0^m04 per magnitude

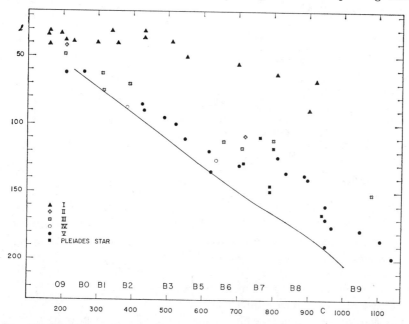

Fig. 12.—O9–B9 stars of luminosity classes I–V in the lc diagram (Strömgren 1958b). The curve indicates the location of the zero-age line.

TABLE 8

THE RELATION BETWEEN THE Hβ INDEX l AND
ABSOLUTE MAGNITUDE M_v

l (Mag.)	M_v (Mag.)	Sp. Class	l (Mag.)	M_v (Mag.)	Sp. Class
0.100......	−1.7	B2.5	0.160.......	−0.1	B7
.120......	−1.0	B4	.180.......	+ .3	B8
0.140......	−0.5	B6	0.200.......	+0.6	B9

change in M_v in the spectral range B3–B9. The probable error of one observation of l was about $\pm 0^m004$, and the corresponding photometric probable error in M_v is therefore about $\pm 0^m1$ for the stars considered.

From the scatter in the relation between l and M_v for the calibration star, the actual accuracy in the determination of M_v from l was found to be given by a probable error of about $\pm 0^m2$ (one observation). This question will be discussed further in § 5.

For the B stars of luminosity classes III–V of the main-sequence band, there is a practically unique relation between the Balmer index c and the color index $[U - B]_0$, i.e., the color index $U - B$ corrected for the influence of interstellar reddening according to U, B, V photometry (cf. § 2). The relation given in Table 9 was derived by Strömgren (1958b). The table also gives $(B - V)_0$ and the spectral class according to the relations with $(U - B)_0$ derived by Morgan and Harris (1956). The probable error of one observation of c was $\pm 0^m008$. It is

TABLE 9

THE RELATION BETWEEN THE BALMER INDEX c AND $[U-B]_0$

c (Mag.)	$[U-B]_0$ (Mag.)	$[B-V]_0$ (Mag.)	Sp. Class	c (Mag.)	$[U-B]_0$ (Mag.)	$[B-V]_0$ (Mag.)	Sp. Class
1.00....	−0.19	−0.05	B9	0.50....	−0.73	−0.20	B3
0.90....	− .29	− .07	B8	.40....	−0.85	− .23	B2
0.80....	− .39	− .10	B7	.30....	−0.99	− .27	B1
0.70....	− .50	− .13	B6	0.20....	−1.14	−0.31	O9
0.60.....	−0.61	−0.16	B5				

seen from the table that this corresponds to a probable error of $\pm 0^m009$ on the $[U - B]_0$ scale, $\pm 0^m003$ on the $[B - V]_0$ scale, and ± 0.010 of a spectral class.

Strömgren (1958b) developed an alternative method of deriving an Hβ index through simultaneous observation with two photomultipliers in one narrow- and one intermediate-width band, both centered on Hβ. The method has been described in detail by Crawford (1958) and has been used by him for two-dimensional classification of B stars in clusters and associations.

Crawford used a narrow interference filter with a half-width of about 15 A and a comparison interference filter of half-width 150 A. The peak transmissions were at Hβ for both filters. A photoelectric photometer with a beam-splitter and two photomultipliers was used for simultaneous observation through the 15 A and the 150 A bands. A filter-slide arrangement made it possible to alternate between the 15 A Hβ filter and another 150 A Hβ filter, so that the relative sensitivity of the two photomultipliers could be determined for each star observed.

The color index,

$$\beta = m(15 \text{ A}) - m(150 \text{ A}),$$

is a measure of the Hβ strength. Because of the narrower filter, the index is a more sensitive measure than the Hβ index l. On the other hand, there is some loss of sensitivity because the 150 A is also affected by the Hβ absorption. Table 10, valid for O and B stars, shows the relationship between the Hβ indices l and β as determined from a number of stars measured by both procedures. The relation is practically linear, and the β scale is about 1.9 times wider than the l scale. It may be noticed that, for late A and F stars, the relation between l and β was found to be slightly different. This is to be expected, since a B star and an F star for which the equivalent width of Hβ is the same have Hβ lines with somewhat different profiles. Quite generally it has been found (cf. Crawford 1960) that Hβ indices measured for B stars with different interference filters with half-widths between 15 and 40 A are linearly related to a high degree of accuracy. This is true even when Hβ filters with transmission peaks a few angstroms off from λ 4861 are used. When the deviations from λ 4861 are larger, more complicated relations must be used for reduction to l or β. For 33 standard stars in the spectral range O9–A0, Crawford (1960) has given β values on the basis of observations on many nights (between 10 and 50 for most of the stars). Observations of Hβ strengths with interference filters can thus be reduced to the β

TABLE 10

THE RELATION BETWEEN THE Hβ INDEX l AND
COLOR INDEX β FOR O AND B STARS

l (Mag.)	β (Mag.)	l (Mag.)	β (Mag.)
0.040........	2.548	0.160........	2.778
.080........	2.624	0.200........	2.854
0.120........	2.700		

scale, and any particular filter scale can be tested for linearity. Referring to the general remark in § 1, it should be emphasized that, with the interference-filter technique, it is necessary to observe a number of standard stars on each night in order to achieve high photoelectric accuracy.

Crawford (1958) determined the probable error of β to be $\pm 0^m004$ (one observation) when the stars were bright enough for the effect of the statistical fluctuations of the photoelectric signal to be negligible. It was also found that the measures of β through simultaneous observations, as described above, were practically independent of variations in the terrestrial atmosphere. In other words, a photometric sky is not required for this type of work.

The index β was combined by Crawford (1958) with $(U - B)_0$ to yield two-dimensional classification of B stars. From what has already been stated concerning the relation between c and $(U - B)_0$, on the one hand, and l and β, on the other, it is clear that β-$(U - B)_0$ classification is very nearly equivalent to cl classification. The β-$(U - B)_0$ scheme has the advantage that β photometry can be combined with separately performed, or already existing, U, B, V photometry.

Figure 13 shows a β-$(U - B)_0$ diagram in which a number of stars with

known MK classification have been plotted. Filled circles indicate main-sequence stars. The open circles represent stars for which the β-$(U - B)_0$ spectral
type derived from the location of the representative point relative to the dividing line shown differs from that of the MK classification, usually by 0.1 of a
spectral class. The agreement is seen to be quite satisfactory. Triangles indicate
luminosity class III stars. They are all located in the upper part of the main-
sequence band of the β-$(U - B)_0$ diagram. The crosses represent supergiants.
These are situated above the main-sequence band, as expected. It is seen that

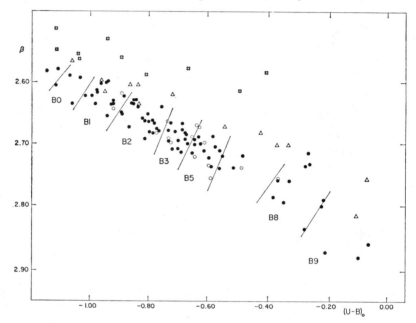

Fig. 13.—B stars in the β-$(U - B)_0$ diagram. The lines indicate ranges of MK spectral
class of the main-sequence band (Crawford 1958). The symbols are explained in the text.

the properties of the star distribution in the diagram of Figure 13 are very
similar to those shown in Figure 12.

The β-$(U - B)_0$ method was applied by Crawford (1958) to stars of the
northern section of the Scorpio-Centaurus association, the Orion association, the
ζ Per association, the α Per cluster, and the Pleiades. For the member stars of
the Orion association, β photometry was combined with U, B, V photometry by
Sharpless (1952, 1954); for the α Per cluster, U, B, V photometry by Harris
(1956a) was utilized. The location of the member stars in the β-$(U - B)_0$ diagram is markedly different for the various groups. Differences in age have a
similar effect in the β-$(U - B)_0$ diagram as in the H-R diagram. The representative points of the member stars of the youngest groups (ζ Per, Sco-Cen, Orion)
are very close to the zero-age line for $(U - B)_0$ values corresponding to B0 or

later, while members of the Pleiades Cluster deviate from the zero-age line at B7–B9.

The same effect of evolution is clearly shown by results of two-dimensional MK classification by the inspection method (cf., in particular, the location of class III stars in the diagrams of Figs. 12 and 13); however, the quantitative methods achieve somewhat higher accuracy in measuring it. The $\lambda_1 D$ method of photographic spectrophotometry discussed in § 4.2 as applied to association and cluster B stars shows the evolution effect very clearly (cf. Chalonge 1959). The question of age determination will be briefly discussed in § 6.

We have already commented on the question of M_v calibration of the lc diagram near the zero-age line, where l-M_v relation can be used with satisfactory accuracy. For the β-$(U - B)_0$ diagram the situation is quite similar. It is clearly desirable to calibrate the lc diagram and the β-$(U - B)_0$ diagram quite generally (i.e., according to a two-dimensional scheme) in terms of absolute visual magnitude M_v, but the problem has not yet been solved in a completely satisfactory way. An analogous problem has already been considered in § 4.1 in connection with the discussion of a quantitative two-dimensional classification of B stars through photographic narrow-band photometry. The difficulties caused by the limitations of the available material of fundamental distances for the B stars were referred to there, and the progress achieved by the work of Petrie, Kopylov, and Sinnerstad, as well as remaining discrepancies, was mentioned.

Since relatively faint stars can be reached by the method of photoelectric narrow-band photometry (cf. § 5) member stars of a rather large number of clusters and associations can, in principle, be used in the calibration work. Individual cluster and association distances can be determined from U, B, V photometry of the unevolved section of the main sequence (cf. Johnson 1957; also this volume, chap. 13), and it is then possible to carry out the calibration of the lc diagram and the β-$(U - B)_0$ diagram in terms of M_v for those parts of the diagram that are populated by member stars which have evolved away from the zero-age line.

Johnson and Iriarte (1958) have used Hγ strength determined through photoelectric narrow-band photometry in combination with U, B, V photometry for two-dimensional classification of early-type stars. The method is analogous to the β-$(U - B)_0$ method just described. The Hγ photometry was carried out with a spectrograph-photometer, the spectrograph serving to isolate the wavelength bands in question. In addition to Hγ strengths measured photoelectrically, Johnson and Iriarte also used equivalent widths of Hγ as determined through photographic spectrophotometry by Petrie (1953, 1956) and Petrie and Maunsell (1950) (cf. § 4.1).

The calibration in terms of M_v on the zero-age line was carried out by Johnson and Iriarte on the basis of Hγ measures for stars on the unevolved part of the main sequence for nine clusters and associations. Stars in the Pleiades and in M34 were used for calibration in the B7–B9 part of the main-sequence band above the age-zero line. The main-sequence band earlier than B7 is not adequately covered. The calibration for supergiants depended on stars in the cluster h and χ Per and the I Ori association. Johnson and Iriarte give a calibration table of M_v as a function of the equivalent width of Hγ and $(B - V)_0$ as determined from U, B, V photometry.

Johnson and Iriarte found that the absolute visual magnitudes derived from their calibration differed systematically from those determined by Petrie (cf. § 4.1), the average difference being about $0^m.7$ in the sense that the luminosities assigned by Petrie are lower. Sinnerstad (1961) compared results following from

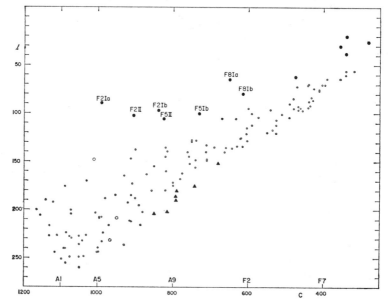

FIG. 14.—A2–F8 stars in the lc diagram (Strömgren 1958b). The symbols are explained in the text.

his calibration (cf. § 4.1) with those of Johnson and Iriarte and found the agreement to be generally good. However, for luminosity class I supergiants, the two calibrations differ, M_v (J. and I.) $- M_v$(S.) $= +0^m.6$.

The Johnson-Iriarte M_v calibration on the zero-age line agrees closely with that given above according to Crawford and Strömgren, except that the Johnson-Iriarte M_v values are larger by $0^m.3$–$0^m.4$ for B7–B9 stars.

We shall now return to the lc method of two-dimensional classification and discuss its application to stars in the spectral range A3–F8. Figure 14 shows the representative points in an lc diagram of a number of A3–F8 stars, mostly brighter than apparent visual magnitude 5.5. The small open circles correspond to stars of luminosity class III–V, the filled circles to luminosity classes I and II, the triangles to metallic-line stars, and the larger open circles to spectrum variables.

The distribution of stars in the lc diagram is similar in many respects to that found for the $c_1 - (b - y)$ diagram discussed in § 3 (cf. Fig. 4). The lower boundary of the distribution corresponds to the zero-age line. For equal c_1, the luminosity increases with decreasing l through the main-sequence band and to the supergiants.

The calibration of the lc diagram in terms of absolute visual magnitude M_v has been carried out on the basis of trigonometric parallaxes and cluster parallaxes (mostly for Hyades stars).

A calibration in terms of intrinsic color index $(B - V)_0$ was performed, using color indices of nearby stars practically unaffected by interstellar reddening. Table 11 (Strömgren 1958b) shows the result of the calibration for the spectral range A9–F7, valid for the main-sequence band (luminosity classes III, IV, and

TABLE 11

THE RELATION BETWEEN BALMER INDEX c AND Hβ INDEX l, INTRINSIC
COLOR $(B-V)_0$, AND ABSOLUTE VISUAL MAGNITUDE M_v FOR THE
ZERO-AGE LINE IN THE lc DIAGRAM

c (Mag.)	l Zero-Age Line (Mag.)	Sp. Class	$(B-V)_0$ Zero-Age Line (Mag.)	$d(B-V)_0/dl$	M_v Zero-Age Line (Mag.)	dM_v/dl
0.400....	0.086	F7	0.487	1.8	4.2	89
.500....	.108	F3	.404	2.0	3.8	76
.600....	.130	F2	.342	2.2	3.4	62
.700....	.153	F0	.302	1.7	3.1	49
0.800....	0.175	A9	0.268	0.8	2.7	35

V). The values of l, $(B - V)_0$, and M_v are given as functions of c for a standard line in the lc diagram chosen to correspond to the zero-age line. When l and c are known from observation, the difference Δl between the zero-age value of l corresponding to c and the observed value l is found, and the corrections to the zero-age values of $(B - V)_0$ and M_v corresponding to c are computed, using the factors $d(B - V)_0/dl$ and dM_v/dl given in the calibration table.

The probable error of one determination of the Hβ index was about $\pm 0^m004$, the p.e. for c was $\pm 0^m008$ (one observation). From the calibration data it follows that the photometric p.e. (one observation) of $(B - V)_0$ and M_v as derived from l and c are as given here: for A9, $(B - V)_0 = \pm 0^m005$, $M_v = \pm 0^m15$; for F7, $(B - V)_0 = \pm 0.010$, $M_v = \pm 0.3$.

The photometric classification accuracy is thus high around F0 but decreases with advancing spectral type. Beyond F8 the index l is no longer suitable for precision classification; the Hβ absorption line is too weak, and the metal-line absorption in the band used is too strong.

The calibration residuals (metallic-line stars excluded, cf. below) indicate that the actual probable errors of $(B - V)_0$ and M_v determined by the lc method are about as given above, the average values for the group of A9–F7 being $\pm 0^{m}008$ in $(B - V)_0$ and $\pm 0^{m}2$ in M_v.

In comparison with the lc method, the $c_1 - (b - y)$ method of ib photometry has the advantage of better light-economy and of being useful up to, or somewhat beyond, G0. On the other hand, the lc method has the great advantage that it yields accurate two-dimensional classification independent of interstellar absorption, the indices l and c being insensitive to interstellar reddening. In particular, the lc method lends itself to precision determination of color excess for F stars. If l, c, and $B - V$ have been measured, then l and c give the intrinsic color $(B - V)_0$, and the color excess follows.

The lc method is applicable to A3–A8 stars and here gives $(B - V)_0$ and M_v with a precision about equal to that obtained for early F stars. Detailed calibration has not yet been carried out here, but the following linear expressions for $(B - V)_0$ and M_v give quite good accuracy (Strömgren 1956a): $(B - V)_0 = 0^{m}626 - 0.564l - 0.347c$, valid for A3–A8 stars; $M_v = 2^{m}84 + 26.4l - 7.2c$, $(B - V)_0$ $0^{m}10$–$0^{m}20$, luminosity classes III, IV, and V.

Referring to the discussion in §§ 3 and 4.2, we ask the question: Is it necessary to consider a third parameter? In particular, do the variations in the metallicity for A and early F stars that are indicated by the metal index m or m_1 influence the relations between l and c, on the one hand, and $(B - V)_0$ and M_v, on the other?

It has been found that the lc method predicts luminosities that are too low for the metallic-line stars. In extreme cases the predicted M_v is about 1 mag. too large. A correction in terms of m or m_1 would presumably remove the discrepancy. Detailed investigations have not been carried out, but the correction term appears to be about equal to $15\Delta m_1$. In the calibration referred to above, metallic-line stars were excluded from the discussion.

In this respect the lc method differs from the $c_1 - (b - y)$ method, which gives M_v practically independent of m_1 for A and early F stars (cf. § 3). For the color-index range $(B - V)_0$ $0^{m}34$–$0^{m}40$ (F2–F3 stars), i.e., the c range $0^{m}50$–$0^{m}60$, the scatter in m is so small that the lc method is applicable without any correction.

We shall turn next to spectral classification through photoelectric nb photometry for late G and K stars. In § 4.1 we discussed methods of quantitative two-dimensional classification of late G and K stars through photographic narrow-band photometry, utilizing the Lindblad criteria. A corresponding method of photoelectric narrow-band photometry has been developed by Strömgren and Gyldenkerne (1955), who used interference filters to isolate the bands in question. Since the Lindblad criteria measure relatively strong features, it was possible to use fairly wide bands with half-widths averaging about 90 A (a detailed description of the filters is given by Gyldenkerne 1958). In comparison with U, B, V photometry, the filters used give a light-loss of 3–4 mag.

Strömgren and Gyldenkerne utilized three classification indices, defined as color indices as follows: $g = m(\lambda\ 4240) - m(\lambda\ 4360)$; $n = m(\lambda\ 4170) - m(\lambda\ 4240)$; $k = m(\lambda\ 4030) - m(\lambda\ 3910)$.

The Lindblad indices g and n measure the discontinuity at the G band and the strength of the cyanogen absorption in the band with its head at $\lambda\ 4216$, respectively, while the index k is a measure of the strength of K-line absorption. The $\lambda\ 3910$ filter had a half-width of 120 A, and the transmitted intensity was therefore strongly influenced by the K line. A peak transmission longward of $\lambda\ 3868$ was chosen with a view to the use of the index for work on earlier types where the Hϵ absorption should be avoided. However, a filter centered at $\lambda\ 3850$ would presumably give a better index for K-star work.

Photoelectric measures of the classification indices g, n, and k were carried out by Gyldenkerne (1955) for 234 G and K stars, mostly brighter than apparent visual magnitude 5.5. These and additional similar measures have been reduced to one system by Gyldenkerne (1958), who gives values of g, n, and k for 258 G and K stars. The results were discussed by Strömgren and Gyldenkerne (1955) and by Gyldenkerne (1958). It was found that g and k gave accurate spectral classes for G8–K5 stars, the best range for k being G8–K3 and for g, K1–K5. The photoelectric probable error (one observation) of a classification index (g, k, or n) was about $\pm 0^{m}006$. The corresponding accuracy of a spectral class derived from g or k, for luminosity class III stars, was found to be about ± 0.015 of a spectral class (p.e., one observation).

For stars of luminosity class III in the spectral range G8–K3, it was found (Strömgren and Gyldenkerne 1955; Gyldenkerne 1958) that intrinsic color indices $(B - V)_0$ could be predicted with very satisfactory accuracy from measures of the index k. From a discussion based on measures of 38 nearby, unreddened G8–K3 III stars for which $(B - V)$ values were available, Gyldenkerne (1958) derived the following linear relation between $(B - V)_0$ and k:

$$(B - V)_0 = 1^{m}509 - 1.660k.$$

The residuals indicate that $(B - V)_0$ can be predicted from k with a probable error of about $\pm 0^{m}012$ (two stars with quite large deviations were omitted in the determination of the scatter). This is very nearly the value corresponding to the photometric probable error of k. The result shows that the method can be used for color-excess determinations of very satisfactory accuracy for the group of G8–K3 III stars.

Since k is defined as a color index corresponding to bands at $\lambda\ 3910$ and $\lambda\ 4030$, interstellar reddening influences k. However, the effect is small, and when measures of k are combined with measures of $B - V$ for determination of color excesses, it can easily be allowed for.

From the results obtained by photographic spectrophotometry, one would expect the index n to be a good indicator of luminosity (cf. § 4.1) and therefore that the combinations of k and n or g and n would yield two-dimensional classification. If the results of the measures by Gyldenkerne are plotted in a *gn* diagram, then there is indeed a separation of the luminosity classes; for equal *g*, the index *n* is largest for the supergiants and smallest for stars of luminosity class V. The distribution in a *kn* diagram has similar properties.

However, the range of variation of the index *n* for the same *g* or *k* for luminosity class III stars is fairly large, about $0^{m}08$, and the question arises whether this variation in *n* is largely due to the scatter of the luminosity for class III stars, for the same *g*, or whether scatter in the amount of the cyanogen discrepancy (cf. § 4.1) is more important. The contribution of the photometric scatter is quite small.

It is difficult to resolve the question because the material of independently known absolute visual magnitudes (derived from cluster parallaxes and trigonometric parallaxes) is quite limited. For G8–K0 III stars or a corresponding area of the *gn* diagram, the available material does suggest that *n* is a relatively sensitive indicator of absolute visual magnitude M_v $(dM/dn \simeq 15)$ and that the scatter in *n* for equal *g* is due to variations in M_v rather than to scatter in the amount of the cyanogen discrepancy. The probable error of M_v as determined from *g* and *n* is found to be $\pm 0^{m}5$ or smaller for the limited range of spectral class and luminosity considered. It should be emphasized, however, that this estimate of the accuracy depends on a discussion of a relatively small number of stars.

When stars in the whole range of luminosity from I to V are considered, the average sensitivity of the index *n* is found to be considerably smaller $(dM_v/dn \simeq 50)$. The effects of the cyanogen discrepancy on M_v, as determined from *g* and *n* or *k* and *n*, are relatively large and prevent a sure distinction between stars of luminosity classes III, IV, and V. For the late spectral classes (K3–K5), however, the separation of giants and dwarfs is so pronounced that a clear separation can be made, and, since luminosity class IV stars are absent here, a relatively homogeneous group can be segregated with the help of the *gn* method.

Griffin and Redman (1960) have investigated questions connected with the use of a cyanogen index for spectral classification on the basis of measures of the CN band at λ 4216 for 712 late-type stars. The cyanogen strength was measured through photoelectric narrow-band photometry.

Griffin and Redman used a spectrometer for the isolation of the wavelength bands and measured the intensities photoelectrically. The spectrometer was mounted at the coudé focus of a 36-inch reflector. The dispersion of the grating spectrometer was 18 A/mm. The width of the entrance slit was 2″.

Three separate photomultipliers were used for simultaneous intensity measures in three wavelength bands, defined through diaphragms in the focal plane of the spectrometer. The relative sensitivities of the three photomultipliers were determined at suitable intervals with the help of a tungsten-filament lamp.

In the work on the cyanogen strength the following three bands were selected: (A) λλ 4097–4149, comparison; (B) λλ 4164–4214, cyanogen; (C) λλ 4230–

4283, comparison. The band limits were defined by the spectrometer with an accuracy of about 1 A. Since the bands were chosen in such a way that stronger absorption features near the band edges were avoided, the variations in the measured intensity ratios corresponding to wavelength shifts of the order of 1 A were practically negligible. The ratio

$$r(CN) = \frac{I(A) + I(C)}{I(B)},$$

where $I(A)$, $I(B)$, and $I(C)$ are the measured intensities for the three bands, was chosen as an index of cyanogen strength. The observed values of $r(CN)$ are practically independent of variations in the transparency of the earth's atmosphere. The probable error of one observation (consisting of two consecutive measures) of $r(CN)$ was found to be ± 0.022. Since the average value of r is about 2.2, this corresponds to $\pm 0^m010$. For most stars three observations of r were obtained.

For most of the 712 program stars, MK classification obtained through the method of visual inspection was available. The measured values of the index $r(CN)$ were analyzed in terms of MK spectral class and luminosity class. For each luminosity class, $r(CN)$ was plotted against spectral class, and a mean curve was derived. The mean curves had the properties expected from the previous work on cyanogen indices. In particular, it was found that the cyanogen strength increased with luminosity.

The mean curves were then used for determinations of the cyanogen discrepancy (or cyanogen anomaly). For each star the difference $\Delta r(CN)$ between the observed value $r(CN)$ and that derived from the MK spectral class and luminosity class using the mean curves was obtained. A positive $\Delta r(CN)$ means that the cyanogen feature is stronger than the average for the MK type.

Griffin and Redman found the root-mean-square variation of $\Delta r(CN)$ to be about 0.07, corresponding to about 0^m03. The contribution of the errors of the photometry to this scatter is practically negligible. Also, from the known slope of the mean curves $r(CN)$ versus spectral class and the estimated precision of the MK spectral classes, it is found that inaccuracies in the spectral class contribute very little to the scatter. An estimate of the range of variation of M_v for the stars belonging to the same luminosity class, combined with the value of $dM_v/dr(CN)$ from the mean curves, led Griffin and Redman to the conclusion that most of the observed scatter in $r(CN)$ for a given MK spectral class and luminosity class was actually due to the variations in the cyanogen discrepancy. It then follows that apparent visual magnitudes M_v derived from the cyanogen index $r(CN)$ and the MK spectral class do not have high precision, the probable error being about $\pm 1^m0$.

The result of Griffin and Redman confirms the conclusion (cf. chap. 8 and § 4.6) that a three-dimensional scheme is necessary for the adequate classification of late G and K stars. The combination of MK spectral class, MK luminos-

ity class, and the cyanogen index r(CN) clearly yields three-dimensional classification.

Employing the same technique, Griffin and Redman (1960) measured an
index of the strength of the G band. In this case the following wavelength
regions were selected: (A) $\lambda\lambda$ 4230–4270, comparison; (B) $\lambda\lambda$ 4285–4315, G
band; (C) $\lambda\lambda$ 4342–4380, comparison. An index

$$r\,(\text{G band}) = \frac{I\,(A) + I\,(C)}{I\,(B)}$$

was measured for 212 late-type stars. It was found that the index r (G band) is
well correlated with the spectral type and a good indicator of MK spectral type
for the spectral range G8–K1. The index r (G band) considered as a function of
spectral type reaches a maximum near K3, and it is therefore not useful for
determining spectral class for K2–K5 stars.

Deeming (1960) used the Redman spectrometer-photometer technique for
measures of an index of the strength of the magnesium b triplet at $\lambda\lambda$ 5167,
5173, and 5184. According to photographic-spectrophotometric investigations
by Thackeray (1939, 1949), the equivalent width of the magnesium line at
λ 5184 decreases with increasing luminosity for late-type stars. Deeming investigated the possibility of using an Mg b index for determination of luminosities of G0–K5 stars. The intensities of the following bands were measured:
(A) $\lambda\lambda$ 5110–5140, comparison; (B) $\lambda\lambda$ 5160–5189, Mgb; (C) $\lambda\lambda$ 5214–5243,
comparison. An index

$$r\,(\text{Mg }b) = \frac{I\,(A) + I\,(C)}{I\,(B)}$$

was determined from the photoelectric narrow-band photometry for 539 G0–K5
stars. The probable error of one observation (consisting of two consecutive
measures) was ± 0.024, corresponding to about $\pm 0\overset{m}{.}010$. Three observations
were obtained for most of the stars.

Figure 15 shows an r(Mg b)-$(B - V)$ diagram for a number of stars for which
MK classification was available. The crosses denote supergiants, the small dots
stars of luminosity class III, the filled circles class IV, and the open circles class
V stars. It is seen that in the color-index range $B - V$ $0\overset{m}{.}9$–$1\overset{m}{.}5$ there is an almost perfect separation of the luminosity classes in the r(Mg b)-$(B - V)$ dia-
gram.

Since $B - V$ is sensitive to interstellar absorption, the method is limited to
stars for which interstellar reddening is negligible. Such limitation is undesir-
able, particularly for stars of luminosity class III and brighter. However, Deeming points out that, since the index r (G band) predicts the spectral class with
very good accuracy for G8–K1 stars, an r(Mg b)-r (G band) diagram would give
quite satisfactory two-dimensional classification for this spectral range, and now
both indices are insensitive to interstellar reddening.

Furthermore, as we have seen, the index k utilized by Strömgren and Gylden-kerne (1955) predicts $(B - V)_0$ with high accuracy for G8–K3 III stars, and the combination of $r(\text{Mg }b)$ and k should therefore give two-dimensional classification for this more extended spectral range. In fact, if the data of Deeming (1960) and Gyldenkerne (1958) are combined and plotted in an $r(\text{Mg }b)$-k diagram, then again an almost perfect separation of the luminosity classes is found for stars of the color range $0\overset{m}{.}9$–$1\overset{m}{.}5$.

Griffin (1961) has studied the usefulness for G5–K5 star classification of an index of the strength of the Fe I triplet near $\lambda\,5250$ measured through the Redman

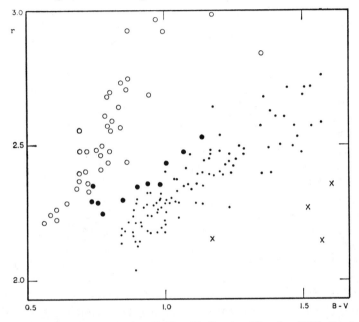

Fig. 15.—G5–K5 stars in the $r(\text{Mg }b)$-$(B - V)$ diagram (Deeming 1960). See text for explanation of symbols.

technique of photoelectric narrow-band photometry. In this case the selected wavelength bands were (A) $\lambda\lambda$ 5190–5224, comparison; (B) $\lambda\lambda$ 5245–5256, Fe I; (C) $\lambda\lambda$ 5278–5312, comparison. The Fe I band is somewhat narrower than those utilized in the CN, G-band, and Mg b work, but the spectrometer accuracy was improved, and errors in the selection of the wavelength band were found to have a negligible effect on the measured intensity ratio even here. Griffin found that the combination of MK spectral class with the index $r(5250)$ yielded practically perfect separation of the MK luminosity classes for G5–K5 stars. The actual accuracy with which the apparent visual magnitude M_v can be determined from $r(\text{Mg }b)$ or $r(5250)$ has not been evaluated because of the difficulties due to the limitations of the distance material (cluster and trigonometric parallaxes), which we have already commented on. It is already clear, however, that quantitative three-dimensional classification of G8–K5 stars is possible through the combination of such indices as k, $r(\mathrm{Mg}\,b)$, and r (CN).

In § 4.1 we referred to the suggestion of Borgman (1959) that the metal index m (cf. § 3) might be combined with the indices k and n of Strömgren and Gyldenkerne (1955) to give three-dimensional classification. This possibility has been investigated by Gyldenkerne (1961) on the basis of measures of m, k, and n for 250 G and K stars. Gyldenkerne has found that if the three indices are combined to yield indices L and C, defined as follows: $L = m - n - \frac{1}{4}k$, $C = m + n + \frac{5}{4}k$, then L will indicate the luminosity, irrespective of the degree of the cyanogen discrepancy, while C is an index of chemical composition.

A plot of L against apparent visual magnitudes M_v determined partly from trigonometric parallaxes and cluster parallaxes and partly according to M_v determinations by Wilson's method (Wilson and Bappu 1957; cf. the following § 4.6) indicates a linear relation with a scatter equal to a probable error of about $\pm 0^m.3$ in M_v as determined from L. It is possible, although not very probable, that the scatter appears somewhat reduced through a correlation of errors in the M_v values derived from L and by Wilson's method, respectively.

Gyldenkerne compared the C values with mean equivalent widths of weak Fe I lines, the latter being indicators of metal content. Data were available for five stars according to high-dispersion spectrophotometry by M. and B. Schwarzschild, Searle, and Meltzer (1957). The material is small, but it suggests a good correlation between the index C as defined above and relative iron content.

Crawford (1961) investigated the use of the metal index m_1 (cf. § 3) in connection with indices similar to g and n. He utilized interference filters with smaller half-widths (40–70 A) than those previously employed for the measures of g and n and thereby obtained somewhat better sensitivity to the variations in the spectral features measured by the indices in question.

Kraft (1960) has used photoelectric narrow-band photometry for classification of F4–G2 supergiants of luminosity class Ib, including cepheids. From an inspection of the Yerkes *Atlas of Stellar Spectra* (Morgan, Keenan, and Kellman 1943), Kraft concluded that the strength of the G band measured through photoelectric nb photometry should be a good criterion of spectral class and intrinsic color index for the stars in question. A G-band index Γ was measured, using two interference filters centered at λ 4305 and λ 4290 and with half-width of 10 A (G-band filter) and 200 A (comparison filter), respectively. Consecutive measures as well as simultaneous measures with the help of the beam-splitter photometer described by Crawford (1958) were utilized for the measures of Γ. Kraft found that Γ is a very satisfactory indicator of spectral class and of $(B - V)_0$ for the category of supergiant stars considered and has used measures of Γ and $(B - V)$ for determinations of color excess (Kraft 1960, 1961a, b).

From the discussion in this section it is clear that the choice of criteria for spectral classification through photoelectric nb photometry has been guided largely by previous experience gained in the development of the classification methods of visual inspection and those of photographic spectrophotometry. The whole range of spectral classes and luminosity classes of the MK system is not covered by the methods of photoelectric nb photometry that have been developed so far, and the important role played by MK classification in providing a general framework and in aiding the selection of stars to be measured by photoelectric nb photometry has been emphasized.

Meinel tackled the problem of selecting criteria suitable for classification by photoelectric nb photometry, using a scanning-ratio spectrometer (Meinel and Golson 1959). The spectrum of a star is scanned simultaneously in two bands, one narrow (60 A) and one wide (comparison band of 250 A), the centers of which approximately coincide. The ratio of the intensities of the two bands is recorded. The spectrum is scanned from λ 3300 to λ 6000. A systematic comparison of ratio scans of stars of the various MK classes, and with different metal indices and cyanogen discrepancies, should suggest the most useful criteria to be used in subsequent photoelectric nb photometry.

4.6. O. C. WILSON's METHOD OF DETERMINING ABSOLUTE MAGNITUDES FROM MEASURES OF THE WIDTHS OF H AND K EMISSION LINES

Wilson and Bappu (1957) studied the H and K emission lines of 185 stars of spectral classes G, K, and M on slit spectrograms with a dispersion of 10 A/mm. Emission-line widths of the H and K lines were measured, and the values obtained were corrected for instrumental width. The average of the widths of H and K was taken, except when there was an indication that H was disturbed by other lines, in which case the K-line width was adopted. The widths W_0 were compared with the absolute visual magnitude M_v obtained from available trigonometric or spectroscopic determinations. It was found that the relation between $\log W_0$ and M_v could be represented by a straight line over a range of 15 mag., valid for stars of spectral classes G, K, and M. The width varied from about 2 A for supergiant stars to about 0.2 A for M dwarfs. Since the available M_v values generally are not of very high accuracy, it is difficult to estimate the precision with which M_v can be determined from W_0. However, a discussion of the more accurate M_v values suggests that M_v is found from W_0 with a probable error of about $\pm 0^m.4$. Comparison with the L-index method of Gyldenkerne (1961), discussed in § 4.5, also leads to the conclusion that the W_0 method gives absolute magnitudes of high accuracy.

The W_0 method is not economical of light, since it requires high dispersion, and the H and K emission lines are observed at the bottom of absorption lines, where the intensity is reduced by a factor of about 6 in comparison with the surrounding continuum. However, it is a very valuable method for brighter stars. Wilson (1959) applied the W_0 method in an investigation of the distribution of G, K, and M stars in the solar neighborhood in the Hertzsprung-Russell diagram.

§ 5. ACCURACY AND LIMITING MAGNITUDE OBTAINABLE IN QUANTITATIVE SPECTRAL CLASSIFICATION

In § 1 we referred to the fact that certain quantitative classification methods have been developed for the purpose of obtaining high classification accuracy, while in others the aim has been to reach very faint stars. Among those using the procedure of photographic spectrophotometry, the Barbier-Chalonge method (§ 4.2) and those of Petrie, Kopylov, and Sinnerstad (§ 4.1) are high-precision methods, while that of Lindblad (§ 4.1) reaches faint stars. The photoelectric methods of wide-band photometry (§ 2) have the most favorable limiting magnitudes; photoelectric narrow-band photometry (§ 4.5), on the other hand, yields high precision. The method of T. and J. H. Walraven (§ 3), based on photometry of bands of intermediate width, combines for early-type stars the advantages of good accuracy and very favorable limiting magnitude.

High precision in spectral classification is desirable in the solution of a variety of problems. The following are typical examples: (1) accurate absolute magnitudes and corresponding spectroscopic distances of stars are needed in galactic fine-structure investigations pertaining to the distribution of stars, as well as interstellar matter, and in work on stellar space velocities; (2) accurate intrinsic color indices and color excesses are essential for studies of the distribution of interstellar matter; (3) accurate intrinsic color indices and absolute magnitudes are required for investigations of the distribution of stars in the Hertzsprung-Russell diagram aiming at studies of the effects of stellar evolution and determinations of stellar ages; (4) accurate determinations of chemical-composition parameters of classification form part of discussions of problems of the evolution of the Galaxy.

In the discussion of the various methods of quantitative spectral classification, the contribution of the photometric errors to the probable errors of the classification parameters derived was generally given. This contribution is found in a straightforward way from the photometric probable errors of the measured classification criteria and the properties of the relation between classification criteria and classification parameters as determined through the calibration of the method in question. Contributions due to other sources of error were also referred to. We shall discuss this problem somewhat further here.

A number of the classification schemes described in the previous sections yield two-dimensional classification, like the method of MK classification through visual inspection. Consider a sample of stars of identical chemical composition, all non-rotating and of a structure uninfluenced by magnetic fields. The properties of a star of such a sample are completely determined by the mass and the age of the star; in other words, it is possible to describe the stars and, in particular, also their emitted spectra accurately in terms of two basic parameters—mass and age. Two-dimensional classification in terms of mass and age would then be possible on the basis of photometric measures pertaining to two suitably selected spectral features. It might happen that two stars of different mass and different age had the same effective temperature T_e and the same surface gravity g and therefore identical spectra; but, apart from this ambiguity, which is not generally important, the two-dimensional classification scheme would yield the values of the classification parameters with no other errors than those corresponding to the errors of photometry.

However, in the case that the structure and the spectrum of a star depend on a parameter, or parameters, in addition to the basic ones of mass and age, there will no longer be a unique correspondence between the measured values of two chosen classification indices, on the one hand, and the mass and age of the star, on the other. In particular, the effective temperatures and luminosities of a group of stars with identical values of the two classification indices would show a scatter even when the effects of observational errors were negligible. We shall refer to such scatter as "cosmic scatter," emphasizing that it always relates to a chosen classification scheme.

Suppose, for instance, that the stars of the sample considered differed in three respects: mass, age, and metal-hydrogen ratio. In a scheme of two-dimensional classification, there would then generally be cosmic scatter in the effective temperatures and luminosities determined from two measured indices. With a three-dimensional scheme based on the use of three suitably chosen indices, cosmic scatter would vanish in this case. But if the same three-dimensional scheme were applied to a sample of stars influenced by further chemical-composition parameters or by an axial-rotation parameter, then there would again be cosmic scatter.

We may note that the absence of observable effects of cosmic scatter in, say, absolute magnitude as determined by a given two-dimensional classification scheme for stars of a certain spectral range does not necessarily mean that the properties of the stars of the sample considered are governed by two parameters only. The absence of scatter may be due to compensation by different effects, and the influence of further parameters in the sample may be revealed if other indices are chosen. From the point of view of application (e.g., determination of absolute magnitude), this is welcome, and the particular choice of classification indices is advantageous.

Let us consider problems of cosmic scatter for the main-sequence band first. For B stars we have seen in § 2 that U, B, V photometry yields a satisfactory determination of spectral class or effective temperature. There is little indication that cosmic scatter is important here, but the test is not a very sharp one because there are only relatively few practically unreddened stars available for a test. As far as the material goes, however, it suggests that for luminosity class V stars the relation between $(U - B)_0$ and $(B - V)_0$ is almost unique, being insensitive to luminosity and evidently nearly uninfluenced by further parameters (cosmic scatter). With regard to absolute visual magnitude M_v, however, the situation is different. As we have seen in §§ 3, 4.1, and 4.5, comparison between values of M_v derived from cluster and association distances and quantitative two-dimensional classification, respectively, reveals the effect of cosmic scatter. The corresponding probable error in M_v was found to be $\pm 0^m.2$–$0^m.3$.

T. and J. H. Walraven (1960) have carried out an instructive comparison between visual absolute magnitudes M_v determined by various methods of quantitative spectral classification, on the one hand, and M_v from cluster parallaxes (for 23 Sco-Cen stars, Bertiau 1958), on the other. Whereas there is close agreement between the M_v values determined through photoelectric photometry by Crawford (1958), Johnson (1959), and T. and J. H. Walraven (1960), discrepancies between these values and the cluster-parallax value of over 1 mag. occur (cf. also Hardie and Crawford 1961; Crawford and Golson 1961).

Two points should be noticed in connection with a comparison of this kind: (1) in individual cases there may be doubt about the membership of a star in a cluster or association, and a large deviation may be spurious because the star in question is actually a non-member; (2) a considerable fraction of the stars are undoubtedly binary stars that have not been recognized as such because of observational limitations. If one component is several magnitudes fainter than the other, the effect in comparisons of the kind considered is not large. In the case that the components are equal, the spectroscopic analysis is unaffected, but the absolute magnitude derived refers to that of one component and differs from that corresponding to the combined light by $0^m.7$. For intermediate cases the effect can be computed as a function of the magnitude difference for the particular classification scheme in question, and allowance for the effect can be made in a statistical way if the distribution function of the magnitude difference is known. Quite generally, the presence of binaries in the samples of stars which are considered affects, to some extent, all applications of spectroscopically determined M_v values to distance determination.

The M_v discrepancies for main-sequence B stars are presumably due to the two effects just considered, as well as to the cosmic scatter caused by the influence of parameters beyond mass and age, such as axial-rotation and magnetic-field parameters.

For main-sequence A and early F stars, observations have revealed the importance of a metallicity parameter (cf. §§ 3, 4.2, and 4.5). Absolute magnitudes determined from the two-dimensional schemes $\lambda_1 D$ and lc, respectively, must be corrected for the metallicity effect as measured by a third index, m_1 or m, while M_v values found by the $c_1 - (b - y)$ procedure are practically uninfluenced by the degree of metallicity.

For a relatively narrow spectral range around F2, there is hardly any evidence of cosmic scatter in the values of $(B - V)_0$ and M_v determined through photoelectric $c_1 - (b - y)$ or lc photometry. The probable errors (one observation) are practically those given by the errors of photometry, about $\pm 0^m.006$ and $\pm 0^m.2$.

In the main-sequence spectral range F5–G0, three-dimensional classification is in order because of the variations in chemical composition as measured by, say, the metal index m_1 (cf. the $\lambda_1 D\phi_b$ method, § 4.2, and the $c_1 - (b - y) - m_1$ method, § 3). These methods according to the tests with the help of cluster and trigonometric parallaxes give M_v with probable errors $\pm 0^m2-0^m3$.

For stars outside the main-sequence band the situation is more complicated. We shall consider luminosity class III stars of the spectral range G8–K3 as an example. From investigations of H-R diagrams of galactic clusters, it is known that this group of stars is a mixture of stars of the mass range 1–3 solar masses (cf. Johnson 1956; Sandage 1957; Burbidge and Sandage 1958; Sarma and Walker 1962). The massive stars are relatively young stars (age about 5×10^8 years), as found in the Hyades and Praesepe clusters, those of about solar mass have ages of $5-10 \times 10^9$ years (like M67 and NGC 188 stars), while stars like those in NGC 752 have intermediate masses. The massive stars are probably fairly homogeneous with respect to chemical composition; there is, however, a considerable range of variation in the metal-hydrogen ratio for the smaller masses.

In § 4.1 and particularly in § 4.5 the methods of two-dimensional and three-dimensional classification applicable to the G8–K3 III stars were discussed. While it is not certain that a complete segregation into subgroups that are nearly homogeneous with respect to age, mass, and chemical composition is possible with these or similar methods, it has been found that intrinsic color indices $(B - V)_0$ and absolute visual magnitudes M_v of considerable accuracy can be determined, the probable errors being about $\pm 0^m012$ and $\pm 0^m3$.

The role of exceptional stars with peculiar spectra has already been referred to, and the advantage in quantitative classification of dealing with samples from which such stars have been eliminated on the basis of visual inspection of spectrograms has been emphasized. In many cases stars of this category will stand out very clearly as peculiar even when information is restricted to that contained in two or three indices. As an example, we refer to the strikingly peculiar star investigated by Kron and Gordon (1961), which has the intensity distribution of a normal late F main-sequence star for the wavelength included in the B, G, R, and I bands of the six-color photometry, while there is a deficiency of over a quarter-magnitude in the V band, and of about half a magnitude in the U band. A star like this stands out as an isolated case, e.g., in classification on the basis of the indices $(b - y)$, c_1, and m_1.

The limiting magnitudes of the various methods of quantitative spectral classification depend, of course, on the size of the telescope used and the exposure times. Except in the methods of classification that utilize wide-band photometry or objective-prism spectra, the sky background is generally not important as a factor determining the limiting magnitude. In the following illustrative examples we shall assume that a 36-inch reflector is being used except when a different aperture is indicated. The limiting magnitudes given are approximate, the actual value varying with the details of the instrumentation.

Widened slit spectra with a dispersion of 120 A/mm suitable for MK classification by the visual inspection method are obtained for stars of photographic magnitude 11 with an exposure time of 1 hour. Slit spectra, with a dispersion of about 30 A/mm such as are used in several of the methods discussed in § 4.1, reach about 9 mag. with 1-hour exposure, while 10-minute spectra of the kind utilized in the Barbier-Chalonge method (§ 4.2) reach about 9 mag.

The Lindblad methods, utilizing short, objective-prism spectra (§ 4.1), reach 13–14 mag. with an astrograph of 16-inch aperture and 80-inch focal length. The sky background and, in the Milky Way, the crowding of the spectra are the limiting factors here.

Wide-band photoelectric photometry, such as U, B, V photometry has been pushed to magnitude 20 with an 82-inch telescope and photometer integration times of hours (cf. Johnson 1958).

The Walraven methods of photoelectric ib photometry (§ 3) reach about 15 mag. with integration times of 10 minutes or 17 mag. with 1-hour integration time. Photoelectric narrow-band photometry, such as that used in the lc method, goes to about 14 mag. in 1 hour. If the accuracy requirements are relaxed, the limits for both methods may be pushed 1–2 mag.

The Redman technique of photoelectric narrow-band photometry (§ 4.5) reaches 9–10 photographic magnitude with a photometer integration time of 1 minute.

It is seen that the limiting magnitudes of the photoelectric classification methods are several magnitudes more favorable than those of the photographic methods that yield comparable accuracy. This is a consequence of the fact that the quantum efficiency of the photocathodes used is much higher than that of the most sensitive photographic emulsions. The advantage of higher sensitivity is purchased at the cost of limitation of the information obtained to a relatively small number of spectral features. It is to be expected that the combination of a spectrograph and image-amplification devices will give the advantages of photoelectric-cathode sensitivity, as well as that of recording a large number of spectral features.

§ 6. APPLICATIONS OF THE THEORY OF MODEL STELLAR ATMOSPHERES TO RESULTS OBTAINED THROUGH QUANTITATIVE SPECTRAL CLASSIFICATION

Questions of the interpretation of the results obtained in qualitative spectral classification work through application of the theory of stellar atmospheres have been discussed in chapter 8. It is clear that the results of quantitative classification work lend themselves particularly well to interpretation in terms of model-atmosphere theory: they pertain to quantitative measures on well-defined spectral features, and, furthermore, the number of spectral features under discussion is generally small. General discussions of the subject have been presented by Pecker (1955) and de Jager (1955). A number of questions in this field have been investigated by van Regemorter (1959).

We shall restrict ourselves here to general remarks and a brief discussion of a few typical examples of model-atmosphere calculations aimed particularly at evaluation of results of quantitative spectral classification.

The connection between parameters of stellar structure, parameters of stellar atmospheres, and observable spectral features is schematically indicated thus:

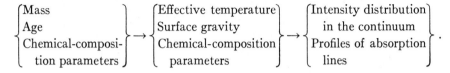

For a star of specified mass M and chemical composition, the radius R and the luminosity L can, in principle, be computed as functions of the stellar age, t, from the theory of stellar structure. The effective temperature T_e and the surface gravity g can then be found directly from M, L, and R, again as functions of t. Application of the theory of model atmospheres leads to quantitative knowledge of the emitted spectrum as a function of the chemical-composition parameters, the effective temperature T_e, and the gravity g. From this knowledge the numerical value of any well-defined classification index can be derived, as a function of the atmospheric parameters or as a function of the basic parameters that define the structure of the star. In this way any classification diagram can be calibrated in terms of the atmospheric parameters or in terms of the basic parameters.

Consider the lc diagram in which a star is represented according to the measured value of the Hβ index l and the Balmer discontinuity index c. Through the kind of computational process just outlined, tables of l and c as functions of T_e, g, and the chemical-composition parameters can be calculated, and, for any specified chemical composition, curves of constant T_e and constant g in the lc diagram can be constructed. Similarly, it is possible to construct curves of constant mass and constant age in the lc diagram.

It should be noted in this context that a classification index such as c is defined as a color-index difference, and therefore the values determined from the photometric observations on a given system contain an arbitrary additive constant. The constant can, however, be determined if absolute intensity measures for the continuous spectrum are available for at least one of the stars observed in the photometric system in question.

For diagrams such as the $c_1 - (b - y)$ diagram the situation is quite similar. In the case of the k-r(Mg b) diagram discussed in § 4.5, the calibration involves the calculation of two line strengths as a function of the atmospheric parameters. An accurate calibration would be somewhat complicated here because the wavelength bands defining the two classification indices contain, besides the two main spectral features (K and Mg b), a number of fainter absorption lines, but, in principle, it could be carried out rigorously.

Baschek (1960) utilized model-atmosphere and curve-of-growth results for a theoretical calculation of the variation of the metal index m (cf. § 3) with metal content. The calculations were carried out for models with the effective temperature and the surface gravity equal to the solar values. Baschek found a nearly linear relation between m and log A, where A is the ratio number of hydrogen atoms and ions to the number of atoms and ions of all metals.

The extension of work of this kind to the G8–K3 III stars is difficult because of the pronounced line blending. However, the results of such calculations when supplemented with theoretical calculations on the strength of the cyanogen features along the lines of the investigations of Schwarzschild, Spitzer, and Wildt (1951) would contribute to the solution of the problem of the G8–K3 III stars discussed in § 5.

REFERENCES

ADAMS, W. S., JOY, A. H., HUMASON, M. L., and BRAYTON, A. M.	1935	*Ap. J.*, **81**, 187.
ANGER, C. J.	1931	*Harvard Circ.*, No. 362.
	1932a	*Ibid.*, No. 372.
	1932b	*Ibid.*, No. 373.
ARP, H.	1959	*A.J.*, **64**, 441.
ARGUE, A. N.	1961	*M.N.*, **122**, 197.
BARBIER, D.	1955	*Principes fondamentaux de classification stellaire* (Paris: Coll. Int. Centre Nat. Rech. Sc., Vol. **55**), p. 47.
BARBIER, D., and CHALONGE, D.	1939	*Ann. d'ap.*, **2**, 254.
	1941	*Ibid.*, **4**, 30.
BARBIER, D., CHALONGE, D., and MORGULEFF, N.	1941	*Ann. d'ap.*, **4**, 137.
BARBIER, D., CHALONGE, D., and VASSY, E.	1935	*J. de phys. et rad.*, **6**, 137
BASCHEK, B.	1960	*Zs. f. Ap.*, **50**, 296.
BAUM, W. A., HILTNER, W. A., JOHNSON, H. L., and SANDAGE, A. R.	1959	*Ap. J.*, **130**, 749.
BECKER, W.	1938	*Zs. f. Ap.*, **15**, 225.
	1942	*A.N.*, **272**, 179.
	1946	*Veröff. U.-Sternw. Göttingen*, Nos. 79–82.
BECKER, W., and STEINLIN, U.	1956	*Zs. f. Ap.*, **39**, 188.
BERGER, J.	1958	*J. d. Obs.*, **41**, 105.
BERGER, J., FRINGANT, A.M., and MENNERET, C.	1956	*Ann d'ap.*, **19**, 294.
BERTIAU, F. C.	1958	*Ap. J.*, **128**, 533.
BIDELMAN, W. P.	1956	*Pub. A.S.P.*, **68**, 318.
BLANCO, V. M.	1957	*Ap. J.*, **125**, 209.

BORGMAN, J.	1959	*Ap. J.*, **129**, 362.
	1960	*B.A.N.*, **15**, 255.
BRILL, A.	1923	*A.N.*, **219**, 21 and 353; cf. also *Hdb. d. Ap.*, Vol. **5**, chap. 3, p. 1, 1932.
BUEREN, H. G. VAN	1952	*B.A.N.*, **11**, 385.
BURBIDGE, E. M., BUR-BIDGE, G. R., SANDAGE, A. R., and WILDEY, R.	1959	*Modèles d'étoiles et évolution stellaires* (Rept. 9th Liège Symposium), p. 427.
BURBIDGE, E. M., and SANDAGE, A.	1958	*Ap. J.*, **128**, 174.
CHALONGE, D.	1955	*Principes fondamentaux de classification stellaire* (Paris: Coll. Int. Centre Nat. Rech. Sc., Vol. **55**), p. 55.
	1956	*Ann. d'ap.*, **19**, 258.
	1958	*Stellar Populations*, ed. D. J. K. O'CONNELL (Amsterdam: North-Holland Pub. Co.; New York: Interscience Publishers), p. 345.
	1959	*I.A.U. Symposium No. 10: The Hertzsprung-Russell Diagram*, ed. J. L. GREENSTEIN, pp. 61 and 71, *Ann. d'ap. Suppl.*, No. 8; also (Cambridge: Cambridge University Press).
	1960	NUFFIC Int. Summer Course in Science (unpub.).
CHALONGE, D., and DIVAN, L.	1952	*Ann. d'ap.*, **15**, 201.
CHAMBERLAIN, J. W., and ALLER, L. H.	1951	*Ap. J.*, **114**, 52.
CODE, A. D.	1959	*Ap. J.*, **130**, 473.
CRAWFORD, D. L.	1958	*Ap. J.*, **128**, 185.
	1960	*Ibid.*, **132**, 66.
	1961	*A.J.*, **66**, 281.
CRAWFORD, D. L., and GOLSON, J. C.	1961	*A.J.*, **66**, 42.
DEEMING, T. J.	1960	*M.N.*, **121**, 52.
DIVAN, L.	1954	*Ann. d'ap.*, **17**, 456.
	1956	*Ibid.*, **19**, 287.
ELVIUS, T.	1951	*Stockholm Obs. Ann.*, Vol. **16**, No. 5.
GREENSTEIN, J. L.	1958	*Hdb. d. Phys.* (Berlin: Springer), **50**, 161.
GRIFFIN, R. F.	1961	*M.N.*, **122**, 181.
GRIFFIN, R. F., and REDMAN, R. O.	1960	*M.N.*, **120**, 287.
GYLDENKERNE, K.	1955	*Ap. J.*, **121**, 38.
	1958	*Ann. d'ap.*, **21**, 26 and 77.
	1961	*Ap. J.*, **134**, 657.
HACK, M.	1953	*Ann. d'ap.*, **16**, 417.
HALLIDAY, I.	1955	*Ap. J.*, **122**, 222.

HARDIE, R. H., and
  CRAWFORD, D. L.   1961   *Ap. J.*, **133**, 843.
HARRIS, D. L.   1956*a*   *Ap. J.*, **123**, 371.
                    1956*b*   *Ibid.*, **124**, 665.

HECKMANN, O., and
  JOHNSON, H. L.   1956   *Ap. J.*, **124**, 477.
HILTNER, W. A., and
  JOHNSON, H. L.   1956   *Ap. J.*, **124**, 367.
HOSSACK, W. R.   1953   *J.R.A.S. Canada*, **47**, 195.
                    1954   *Ap. J.*, **119**, 613.

JAGER, C. DE   1955   *Principes fondamentaux de classification stellaire*
                                 (Paris: Coll. Int. Centre Nat. Rech. Sc., Vol.
                                 55), p. 141.

JOHNSON, H. L.   1953   *Ap. J.*, **117**, 356.
                    1956   *Proceedings of the Third Berkeley Symposium*, ed.
                                 J. NEYMAN (Berkeley, Calif.: University of Cal-
                                 ifornia Press), **3**, 31.
                    1957   *Ap. J.*, **126**, 121.
                    1958   *Lowell Obs. Bull.*, No. 90.
                    1959   *Ibid.*, No. 94.

JOHNSON, H. L., and
  HILTNER, W. A.   1956   *Ap. J.*, **123**, 267.
JOHNSON, H. L., and
  IRIARTE, B.   1958   *Lowell Obs. Bull.*, No. 91.
JOHNSON, H. L., and
  MORGAN, W. W.   1953   *Ap. J.*, **117**, 313.
KEENAN, P. C., and
  KELLER, G.   1953   *Ap. J.*, **117**, 241.
KOPYLOV, I. M.   1958   *Izv. Ap. Obs. Crimea*, **20**, 156.
KRAFT, R. P.   1960   *Ap. J.*, **131**, 330.
                    1961*a*   *Ibid.*, **133**, 39 and 57.
                    1961*b*   *Ibid.*, **134**, 616.
KRON, G. E.   1956   *Proceedings of the Third Berkeley Symposium*, ed.
                                 J. NEYMAN (Berkeley, Calif.: University of
                                 California Press), **3**, 39.
                    1958   *Pub. A.S.P.*, **70**, 561.
                    1960   *Vistas in Astronomy*, ed. A. BEER (London: Per-
                                 gamon Press), **3**, 171.

KRON, G. E., and
  GORDON, K. C.   1961   *Pub. A.S.P.*, **73**, 267.
KRON, G. E., and
  SMITH, J. L.   1951   *Ap. J.*, **113**, 324.
KRON, G. E., WHITE,
  H. S., and GASCOIGNE,
  S. C. B.   1953   *Ap. J.*, **118**, 502.

LINDBLAD, B. 1922 *Ap. J.*, **55**, 85.
1925 *Nova Acta Reg. Soc. Sci. Upsala*, Ser. IV, Vol. **6**, No. 5.
1926 *Medd. Astr. Obs. Uppsala*, No. 11.
1927 *Ibid.*, No. 28.

LINDBLAD, B., and
STENQUIST, E. 1934 *Stockholm Obs. Ann.*, Vol. **11**, No. 12.
LINDHOLM, E. H. 1957 *Ap. J.*, **126**, 588.
MALMQUIST, K. G. 1960 *Uppsala Obs. Ann.*, Vol. **4**, No. 9.
MEINEL, A. B., and
GOLSON, J. C. 1959 *Pub. A.S.P.*, **71**, 445.
MELBOURNE, W. G. 1960 *Ap. J.*, **132**, 101.
MORGAN, W. W., and
HARRIS, D. L. 1956 *Vistas in Astronomy*, ed. A. BEER (London: Pergamon Press), **2**, 1124.

MORGAN, W. W.,
KEENAN, P. C., and
KELLMAN, E. 1943 *An Atlas of Stellar Spectra* (Chicago: University of Chicago Press).

ÖHMAN, Y. 1927 *Medd. Astr. Obs. Uppsala*, No. 33.
1930 *Ibid.*, No. 48.
1935 *Stockholm Obs. Ann.*, Vol. **12**, No. 1.
ÖPIK, E. 1925 *Pub. Obs. Tartu*, Vol. **26**, No. 4.
OETKEN, L. 1960 *A.N.*, **286**, 1 and 9.
OKE, J. B. 1957 *Ap. J.*, **126**, 509.
PECKER, J. C. 1955 *Principes fondamentaux de classification stellaire* (Paris: Coll. Int. Centre Nat. Rech. Sc., Vol. **55**), p. 85.
PETRIE, R. M. 1953 *Pub. Dom. Ap. Obs. Victoria*, **9**, 251.
1956 *Vistas in Astronomy*, ed. A. BEER (London: Pergamon Press), **2**, 1346.

PETRIE, R. M., and
MAUNSELL, C. D. 1950 *Pub. Dom. Ap. Obs. Victoria*, **8**, 253.
PETRIE, R. M., and
MOYLS, B. N. 1956 *Pub. Dom. Ap. Obs. Victoria*, **10**, 287.
PLASSARD, J. 1950 *Ann. d'ap.*, **13**, 1.
RAMBERG, J. 1957 *Stockholm Obs. Ann.*, Vol. **20**, No. 1.
REGEMORTER, H. VAN 1959 *Ann. d'ap.*, **22**, 249, 341, 363, and 681.
REIZ, A. 1954 *Ap. J.*, **120**, 342.
ROMAN, N. G. 1950 *Ap. J.*, **112**, 554.
1952 *Ibid.*, **116**, 122.
1954 *A.J.*, **59**, 307.
ROSENBERG, H. 1914 *Abh. d. Kais. Leop.-Carol. Deutsch. Akad. d. Naturforsch. Nova Acta*, Vol. **101**, No. 2.
SANDAGE, A. R. 1957 *Ap. J.*, **125**, 435.
SANDAGE, A. R., and
EGGEN, O. J. 1959 *M.N.*, **119**, 278.

SARMA, M.B.K., and
  WALKER, M. F.   1962   *Ap. J.*, **135**, 11.
SCHALÉN, C.   1928   *Medd. Astr. Obs. Uppsala*, No. 37.
SCHWARZSCHILD, M.,
  SEARLE, L., and
  HOWARD, R.   1955   *Ap. J.*, **122**, 353.
SCHWARZSCHILD, M.,
  SCHWARZSCHILD, B.,
  SEARLE, L., and
  MELTZER, A.   1957   *Ap. J.*, **125**, 123.
SCHWARZSCHILD, M.,
  SPITZER, L., and
  WILDT, R.   1951   *Ap. J.*, **114**, 398.
SETTERBERG, T.   1947   *Stockholm Obs. Ann.*, Vol. **15**, No. 1.
SHARPLESS, S.   1952   *Ap. J.*, **116**, 251.
                          1954   *Ibid.*, **119**, 200.
SINNERSTAD, U.   1954   *Stockholm Obs. Medd.*, No. 82.
                          1961   *Stockholm Obs. Ann.*, Vol. **21**, No. 6, and Vol. **22**, No. 2.
STEBBINS, J., and KRON,
  G. E.   1956   *Ap. J.*, **123**, 440.
STEBBINS, J., and
  WHITFORD, A. E.   1945   *Ap. J.*, **102**, 318.
STRÖMGREN, B.   1951   *A.J.*, **56**, 142.
                          1952   *Ibid.*, **57**, 200.
                          1955   *Principes fondamentaux de classification stellaire* (Paris: Coll. Int. Centre Nat. Rech. Sci., Vol. **55**), p. 65.
                          1956*a*   *Proceedings of the Third Berkeley Symposium*, ed. J. NEYMAN (Berkeley, Calif.: University of California Press), **3**, 49.
                          1956*b*   *Vistas in Astronomy*, ed. A. BEER (London: Pergamon Press), **2**, 1336.
                          1958*a*   *Stellar Populations*, ed. D. J. K. O'Connell (Amsterdam: North-Holland Pub. Co.; New York: Interscience Publishers), p. 245.
                          1958*b*   *Ibid.*, p. 385.
                          1959   *I.A.U. Symposium No. 10: The Hertzsprung-Russell Diagram*, ed. J. L. GREENSTEIN, p. 59, *Ann. d'ap. Suppl.*, No. 8.
                          1963   *Quarterly J.R.A.S.*, unpublished.
STRÖMGREN, B., and
  GYLDENKERNE, K.   1955   *Ap. J.*, **121**, 43.
STRÖMGREN, B., and
  PERRY, C.   1963   *Ap. J.*, unpublished.
SWIHART, T. L.   1956   *Ap. J.*, **123**, 143.

THACKERAY, A. O.	1939	*M.N.*, **99**, 492.
	1949	*Ibid.*, **109**, 436.
UNSÖLD, A.	1960	*Zs. f. Ap.*, **49**, 1.
VITENSE, E.	1951	*Zs. f. Ap.*, **28**, 81.
WALLERSTEIN, G.	1962	*Ap. J.*, **135**, 310.
WALLERSTEIN, G., and CARLSON, M.	1960	*Ap. J.*, **132**, 276.
WALRAVEN, T., and WALRAVEN, J. H.	1960	*B.A.N.*, **15**, 67.
WESTERLUND, B.	1951	*Uppsala Obs. Ann.*, Vol. **3**, No. 6.
	1953*a*	*Ibid.*, No. 8.
	1953*b*	*Ibid.*, No. 10.
WHITFORD, A. E.	1958	*A.J.*, **63**, 201.
WILSING, J., SCHEINER, J., and MÜNCH, W.	1919	*Pub. Ap. Obs. Potsdam*, No. 74.
WILSON, O. C.	1959	*I.A.U. Symposium No. 10: The Hertzsprung-Russell Diagram*, ed. J. L. GREENSTEIN, p. 39, *Ann. d'ap. Suppl.*, No. 8.
WILSON, O. C., and BAPPU, M. K. V.	1957	*Ap. J.*, **125**, 661.
YOSS, K. M.	1958	*A.J.*, **63**, 61.
YOUNG, R. K., and HARPER, W. E.	1924	*Pub. Dom. Ap. Obs. Victoria*, Vol. **3**, No. 1.
YÜ, C.-S.	1926	*Lick Obs. Bull.*, **12**, 104.

CHAPTER **10**

Spectral Surveys of K and M Dwarfs

A. N. VYSSOTSKY

Leander McCormick Observatory

§ 1. DISCOVERY OF RED DWARF STARS

Until fairly recently, the only known method of finding red dwarfs was a search among stars with fairly large proper motions. Many published lists of stars with proper motions larger than a given amount, say $0''2$ or $0''5$ per year, are a rich source for the discovery of red dwarfs, especially among stars of faint apparent magnitude. As subsequent observations of parallaxes, spectra, and colors have indicated, a considerable portion of these stars are red dwarfs. Thus Eggen (1956) finds that 45 per cent of the 391 proper-motion stars that he has taken from Luyten's catalogue (1955) are red dwarfs. There is, however, one great disadvantage in using proper motions for the discovery of red dwarfs, in that it invalidates any discussion of their motions, even a discussion of their radial velocities. We shall return to this subject in § 5.

Some thirty years ago Lindblad (1925) developed a method of determining absolute magnitudes by a spectrophotometric technique applicable to spectra of small dispersion obtained with a prismatic camera. This method opened the way for a systematic survey of faint stars, irrespective of their proper motions. It consists of estimating, or measuring with a registering microphotometer, the intensities of several points in the continuous spectrum and of a few stronger absorption lines. Lindblad's method has been used by various Swedish observers (Stenquist 1937; Schalén 1948; Elvius 1951; Ramberg 1957); however, since their actual surveys have been mostly limited to small selected areas of the sky, the number of red dwarfs in their catalogues is relatively small. For example, Elvius (1951) in his survey of twelve selected areas lists 81 red dwarfs with spectral classes K0, K2, K4, and K8 and only one dM star out of the 2550 stars included in his catalogue. Moreover, there is some reason to suspect that, since dwarfs of types K0 and K2 are distinguished from giants of the same class mainly by the strength of the cyanogen absorption, some giants may have been classified as dwarfs (Vyssotsky 1950).

192

A different criterion for discovering dwarf M stars and estimating their absolute magnitudes was also found by Lindblad (1935). He noticed that in the spectra of these stars the portion of the spectrum immediately to the red of the line λ 4227 Ca I was much weakened or depressed; this depression diminishes gradually as it extends toward, or even beyond, the G band. Vyssotsky discovered this criterion independently, and he and Wirtanen (1942) applied it in a systematic search for dwarf M stars; subsequently, Vyssotsky (1946) described and used three additional characteristics for estimating spectral subclass and absolute magnitude. These were the break at the G band, the intensity of λ 4227, and the intensity of TiO bands in the blue portion of the spectrum. Vyssotsky and his collaborators (1943, 1946, 1952, 1956) surveyed the collection of McCormick prismatic camera plates which cover the sky north of −15° and found 875 stars with spectral types ranging from dK5 to dM5; most of these are brighter than twelfth apparent photographic magnitude. Estimated spectrophotometric intensities were correlated with the known absolute magnitudes of 330 stars as derived from trigonometric parallaxes. Thus it was possible to assign both spectral class and absolute magnitude to practically all the 875 McCormick dM stars. Finally, Keenan and Nassau (1946) adopted a set of criteria similar to those described above.

A third unbiased derivation of absolute magnitudes of red dwarfs was made by Edmondson and his collaborators (1949). Edmondson obtained low-dispersion slit spectrograms of 681 K0 and K2 stars between 10.0 and 11.0 photovisual magnitudes taken from the McCormick proper-motion catalogues (van de Kamp and Vyssotsky 1937; Vyssotsky and Williams 1948). Absolute magnitudes of these stars were estimated following the criteria of Morgan, Keenan, and Kellman (1943). Some 6 per cent in low latitudes (0°–30°) and 12 per cent in higher latitudes (30°–90°) were found to belong to the Yerkes luminosity class V; in all, some 60 K dwarfs were found. The catalogue of radial velocities of these stars has not yet been published.

§ 2. ABSOLUTE MAGNITUDES

Determinations of the absolute magnitudes of red dwarfs obtained by various methods are not in complete agreement. As has been described in chapter 8, absolute magnitudes have been derived by the observers at Mount Wilson (Adams, Joy, Humason, and Brayton 1935) and Yerkes (Kuiper 1938; Morgan 1938; Kuiper 1942; Keenan and Morgan 1951) by estimating intensity ratios of pairs of lines on slit spectra. In these catalogues the dwarf stars were selected by their large proper motions. The Mount Wilson observers used the blue portion of the spectrum, while those at Yerkes utilized only the yellow and red portions.

As we see in Table 1, for a given spectral class there are fairly large differences between the absolute magnitudes derived at Mount Wilson and those at Yerkes. These are probably attributable to differences in estimating spectral subclasses, since different portions of the spectrum were used by the two observatories; however, this does not explain the difference between the two sets obtained at Mount Wilson Observatory (second and third columns of Table 1). In the 1935 catalogue (Adams *et al.* 1935) the absolute magnitudes were spectroscopic and depended on a fairly large number of annual and secular parallaxes, whereas the absolute magnitudes appearing in the two later lists (Joy 1947; Joy and Mitchell 1948) were simply computed from trigonometric parallaxes and apparent magnitudes. Since the spectral subclasses of individual stars do not show any variation from the first catalogue to the other two, the reasons for the systematic differences in absolute magnitudes remain obscure. The last

TABLE 1

VISUAL ABSOLUTE MAGNITUDES OF RED DWARFS

Sp. Cl.	Mt. W. 1	Mt. W. 2	Yerkes	McC.	Stock.
K0.........	5.5	....	6.0	....	5.7
K2.........	5.8	....	6.4	....	6.4
K4.........	6.5	7.0	7.5	....	6.7
K5.........	6.7	7.6	7.9	7.0	....
K6.........	7.3	8.0	8.5	....	....
K8.........	....	....	....	7.4	8.1
M0.........	8.3	8.2	9.1	8.4	....
M0.5.......	....	8.5	9.3	....	....
M1.........	8.8	9.0	9.6	....	....
M1.5.......	....	9.2	9.9	....	....
M2.........	9.4	9.6	10.2	9.7	....
M2.5.......	....	10.0	10.5	....	....
M3.........	10.0	10.4	10.7	....	....
M3.5.......	....	10.8	11.2	....	....
M4.........	10.6	11.5	11.4	....	....
M4.5.......	....	12.4	11.9	....	....
M5.........	11.9	13.6	12.3	....	....
M5.5.......	....	14.7	12.8	....	....
M6.........	....	....	13.4	....	....

two columns were derived from the absolute magnitude determinations of Vyssotsky (1946, 1956) and of Elvius (1951). We see from Table 1 that if we wish to find the absolute magnitude of a red dwarf from its spectral subclass, we must know at which observatory and at what time the spectrum of the star was classified. Because of this, it appears (see § 4) that a well-determined color yields a more objective determination of absolute magnitude.

§ 3. DISTRIBUTION BY SPECTRAL CLASS AND APPARENT MAGNITUDE; LUMINOSITY FUNCTION

It is of some interest to study statistically the dwarfs found at McCormick and Indiana by spectroscopic methods. The McCormick lists include many red dwarfs with small proper motions which would not have been detected otherwise; and some conclusion as to the frequencies of the dK stars may be obtained from the Indiana material, where the dwarfs were also discovered without knowledge of their motions. The Indiana observations (Edmondson *et al.* 1949) of K0 and K2 stars between visual magnitudes 10.0 and 11.0 contain 94 stars of luminosity class IV, 20 of class IV+, and 58 of class V. However, because of accidental errors in the luminosity classification, the number of stars in class V is probably closer to 65. This leads to 4.5 K0 and K2 dwarfs per 10 square degrees. Now, assuming for the average absolute magnitude of K0 and K2 dwarfs the value of 5.7 derived from Mount Wilson data (Adams *et al.* 1935), we compute the number of K0 and K2 dwarfs in 1000 cubic parsecs as 3.3. The luminosity-curve of van Rhijn (1936) gives 2.75 stars per 1000 cubic parsecs, which,

TABLE 2

COUNTS OF MCCORMICK DWARF M STARS BY APPARENT
MAGNITUDE AND SPECTRAL CLASS

Vis. mag.	K5	K8	M0	M2	M5	M	Total
6.0– 6.9......	....	1	....	....	....	....	1
7.0– 7.4......	....	1	1	....	....	....	2
7.5– 7.9.... .	1	2	3	2	....	....	8
8.0– 8.4......	1	11	6	1	....	....	19
8.5– 8.9......	2	19	15	13	....	....	49
9.0– 9.4......	5	54	39	11	2	....	111
9.5– 9.9......	6	73	63	21	1	1	165
10.0–10.4......	9	70	128	26	4	2	239
10.5–10.9......	5	41	118	18	1	5	188
11.0–11.4......	....	11	66	3	2	5	87
11.5–12.0......	....	....	4	....	....	2	6
Total......	29	283	443	95	10	15	875

TABLE 3

LUMINOSITY FUNCTION OF DWARF STARS
(No. of Stars per 1000 Cubic Parsecs)

M_{vis}	Mumford	van Rhijn	Luyten	M_{vis}	Mumford	van Rhijn	Luyten
7.50.......	(2.1)	2.9	5.6	8.75.......	5.9	5.1	6.9
7.75.......	2.9	3.1	5.9	9.00.......	6.0	5.6	7.2
8.00.......	3.8	3.5	6.2	9.25.......	6.2	6.0	7.4
8.25.......	4.8	4.0	6.4	9.50.......	(6.2)	6.4	7.7
8.50.......	5.5	4.5	6.7				

taking into account the uncertainties in both values, is in very satisfactory agreement.

Table 2 gives the distribution of dwarf M stars by spectral class and apparent magnitude from the McCormick material (Vyssotsky 1956). It is seen that incompleteness appears to begin after magnitude 9.9 for subclasses K8 and M2 and after magnitude 10.4 for subclass M0, while only a few M5 stars are included. Although this material is limited to a small range of absolute magnitudes, since very few stars earlier than K8 or later than M2 have been listed, the comparison in Table 3 of the luminosity function as derived from the McCormick material (Mumford 1956) with van Rhijn's luminosity-curve (1936) is of interest.

It is seen that van Rhijn's luminosity-curve is deficient in the interval between absolute magnitudes 7.75 and 8.75, which may be explained by the fact that investigations based on proper motions miss the red dwarfs with small motions in this interval of absolute magnitudes. In the last column of the table we have added the luminosity function of Luyten as given by Trumpler and Weaver (1953). Luyten's numbers are considerably larger.

§ 4. COLORS OF RED DWARFS

The colors of red giant stars change little as we move along the spectral sequence from K5 to M2 (Johnson and Morgan 1953), but for the red dwarfs the

TABLE 4

MEAN COLORS OF RED DWARF STARS

ABSOLUTE MAGNITUDE	COLOR $(B-V)$	
	Johnson and Morgan	Mumford
6.1	+0.86 (K1)	
6.4	+1.01 (K3)	
7.4		+1.16 (K8)
7.5	+1.18 (K5)	
8.3	+1.37 (K7)	
8.4		+1.36 (M0)
9.6	+1.48 (M1)	
9.7		+1.49 (M2)
10.7	+1.49 (M3)	
11.5:		+1.55: (M5)
12.3	+1.69 (M5)	

color depends very strongly on the spectral subclass, as may be seen in Table 4. This table has been arranged with absolute magnitude as the principal argument, since the Yerkes spectral subclasses differ systematically from those assigned at McCormick (Table 1). It is seen that the agreement between the mean Yerkes and McCormick colors for a given absolute magnitude is very good indeed.

Additional material comes from Lick Observatory, where Kron (1956) measured red and infrared colors of dwarf M stars. These data are presented in his Figure 1, which is reproduced here. Again the dependence of color on absolute magnitude is well pronounced. This leads us to the conclusion that for red dwarf stars the photoelectric color is a more objective determination of the absolute magnitude than the spectral subclass, especially when red and infrared magnitudes are measured (Kron et al. 1957). Moreover, the individual accuracy of such a determination is higher than that derived from a trigonometric parallax except for the very nearest stars.

Both Kron and Mumford noticed that some stars deviate conspicuously from the average run of the color with spectral class or absolute magnitude. These exceptional stars are mostly too blue for their spectral class, and some of them show emission lines in their spectra; at least one is a flare star. We shall return to these stars in § 6.

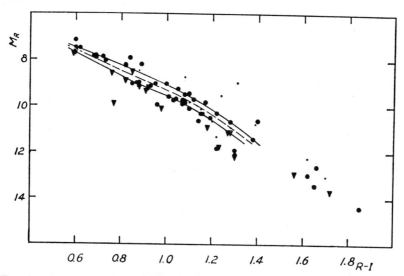

Fig. 1.—The relation between the red-infrared color (*abscissae*) and the red absolute magnitude (*ordinates*) for dwarf M stars according to Kron (1956). Large dots and triangles are, respectively, low- and high-velocity stars; small dots are known doubles.

§ 5. KINEMATIC CHARACTERISTICS

The danger of attempting to determine the general characteristics of the motions of any group of stars which were originally selected because of their large proper motions has been pointed out on several occasions; even the radial velocities of such stars fail to yield a representative picture (e.g., Vyssotsky and Williams 1944; Dyer 1954). Consequently, we shall be concerned here with the space motions of red dwarfs discovered in the spectroscopic searches of Edmondson, Vyssotsky, and their collaborators.

The solar motion with respect to the red dwarfs is of special interest because these stars form a relatively homogeneous nearby group, i.e., a definitely local group. Unfortunately, the observational material at present is limited. Edmondson (private letter) discussed the radial velocities of 58 dK stars, which he secured at the McDonald Observatory. Assuming the apex at $l = 24°5$, $b = +21°5$ (R.A. = 270°, decl. = +30°), he obtained the value $V_\odot = 14.9 \pm 4.6$ km/sec for the velocity of the sun with respect to this group of stars, with the K term equal to $+4.0 \pm 2.6$ km/sec. Combining both proper motions and radial velocities and assuming for the absolute magnitudes of his stars the values by Keenan and Morgan (1951), he obtained for the velocity of the sun a somewhat higher value, namely,

$$V_\odot = 17.2 \pm 4.9 \text{ km/sec}, \qquad K = +5.1 \pm 2.7 \text{ km/sec}.$$

Edmondson also finds dispersions of the velocities along the three axes of the ellipsoid for dK stars as follows (expressed in km/sec):

$$\sigma_1 = 30.2, \qquad \sigma_2 = 21.5, \qquad \sigma_3 = 17.8.$$

A much larger material is available for dM stars. Dyer (1954) observed and collected the radial velocities of the first 305 M dwarfs found at McCormick. His discussion of this material (1956) gave the following values for the solar motion with respect to dM stars:

$$A = 278° \pm 7°, \qquad D = +33° \pm 8°, \qquad V_\odot = 16.6 \pm 2.1 \text{ km/sec},$$
$$K = +3.0 \pm 1.4 \text{ km/sec}$$

from radial velocities and

$$A = 282° \pm 4°, \qquad D = +42° \pm 4°, \qquad V_\odot = 20.0 \pm 1.1 \text{ km/sec}$$

from space motions.

Since the observations of dK stars by Edmondson and of dM stars by Dyer are distributed mostly to the north of $-20°$ declination, the solutions are sensitive to the introduction in the solution of the K term, which essentially reflects some sort of systematic error in observed radial velocities.

Dyer obtained the following dispersions of peculiar velocities of dM stars along the axes of the velocity ellipsoid (expressed in km/sec):

$$\sigma_1 = 34.5 \pm 1.0, \qquad \sigma_2 = 26.3 \pm 0.7, \qquad \sigma_3 = 20.7 \pm 0.6.$$

As would be expected, these are somewhat higher than those obtained by Edmondson from dK stars.

Finally, Mumford (1956), discussing the proper motions and absolute magnitudes of 825 dM stars from McCormick lists, obtained the following results:

$$A = 273°.5 \pm 3°.5, \qquad D = +41°.6 \pm 2°.5, \qquad V_\odot = 19.7 \pm 0.8 \text{ km/sec},$$
$$\sigma_1 = 31.4 \pm 0.7 \text{ km/sec}, \qquad \sigma_2 = 25.1 \pm 0.6 \text{ km/sec},$$
$$\sigma_3 = 18.0 \pm 0.4 \text{ km/sec}.$$

These dispersions are somewhat smaller than those found by Dyer; this is partly because relatively more of Mumford's stars were earlier than M0.

A word should be said about values of dispersions based on stars discovered by their large proper motions. Parenago (1950) has published a table of dispersions based on such material in which the effects of selection are supposedly allowed for. However, a comparison of his values with those derived from the Indiana and McCormick unbiased material indicates that Parenago's corrections have been inadequate. His dispersions are about 50 per cent too large for the dK stars and 20 per cent too large for the dM's. Similarly, Nordström's (1936) discussion of radial velocities shows the effects of selection (Vyssotsky and Williams 1948).

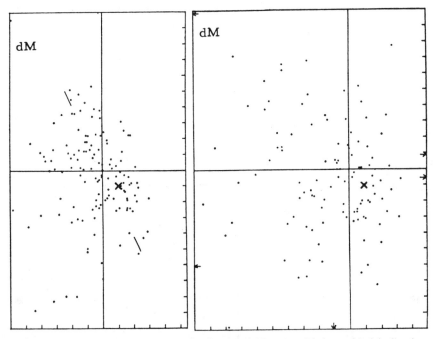

Fig. 2.—The velocity-vector diagrams for dwarf M stars with low orbital inclinations (*left*) and high inclinations (*right*). The origin corresponds to the circular velocity around the galactic center; the direction to the center is down, and the direction of rotation to the right; the large cross represents the sun's velocity. The smallest subdivision on the scale is 10 km/sec (Vyssotsky 1957).

Finally, it is illuminating to examine the detailed distribution of velocity vectors among the M dwarfs. For this purpose, the stars have been grouped according to the inclination of their orbits around the galactic center. It is seen from Figure 2 that, in general, stars of high orbital inclinations have much larger peculiar motions than do stars of low orbital inclinations. Interpreted by the Haas-Bottlinger diagram (Bottlinger 1933), this means that large values of orbital inclination are strongly correlated with large values of orbital eccentricity, as is the case with the orbits of the asteroids in the solar system (Russell, Dugan, and Stewart 1945). Again, the distribution of the velocity-vector points for stars of low orbital inclination shows a definite deviation of the vertex that is not present in the distribution for the stars of high orbital inclination. This is interpreted to mean (Vyssotsky 1957) that some of the dM stars of low orbital inclination are associated with the local spiral arm.

§ 6. POPULATION GROUPS AMONG RED DWARF STARS

It is well established that, in general, stars which belong to Population II have larger group motions and larger velocity dispersions than those of stars of

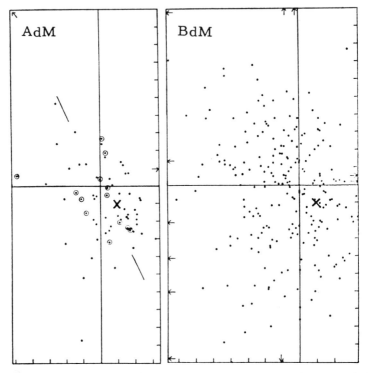

Fig. 3.—The velocity-vector diagrams for dwarf M stars with emission lines (*left*) and without emission lines (*right*). Origin, directions, etc., as in Fig. 2 (Vyssotsky 1957).

Population I. However, just as in the case of red dwarfs, it is necessary to establish criteria independent of motions for distinguishing various population groups before any discussion of their kinematic characteristics, since some stars with relatively small space velocities are to be expected among stars of Population II and, conversely, some rather large motions may be found among stars of Population I. When the question arises as to the further subdivision into population subgroups, spectroscopic criteria become even more important.

A search for spectroscopic criteria related to population groupings has been made by Miss Roman (1952) and by Vyssotsky and Skumanich (1953), among others. These investigations were concerned mainly with stars of spectral types F, dG, and gK.

The first spectroscopic criterion related to population groups among dM stars was pointed out by Delhaye (1953), who discussed the space motions of these stars found within 5 parsecs. He found that the average velocity component in the direction perpendicular to the galactic plane of 12 dwarf M stars with emission lines was only 6 km/sec, while the same component for 15 M dwarfs without emission amounted to 17 km/sec. He concluded that this was an indication that dwarf M stars with emission lines form a very flat subgroup and are probably very young. Much more material became available when Dyer (1954) published his observations of the radial velocities of dwarf M stars from the McCormick lists; among these, spectra of 65 stars showed emission in Ca II lines, and 13 of these had emission in hydrogen lines as well. Vyssotsky and Dyer (1957) discussed the space motions of these, as well as those of the 240 stars with no emission lines detected. They found that the solar velocity and the velocity dispersion for the 65 dMe stars amounted to 11 ± 2 and 18 ± 1 km/ sec, respectively, while similar figures for non-emission stars were 22 ± 1 and 30 ± 1 km/sec. For the 13 stars with emission in both Ca II and H, the average dispersion amounted to only 15 km/sec. These results confirmed those of Delhaye.

Figure 3 (Vyssotsky 1957) presents the distribution of velocity-vector points on the galactic plane for the two groups of dM stars: those with emission lines in their spectra (designated AdM) and those without emission (BdM). It is seen that dwarf Me stars behave kinematically very much like A stars of population I (Vyssotsky 1957, Fig. 4), while the distribution of velocities among the non-emission M dwarfs is similar to that of the stars with larger orbital inclinations to the galactic plane (Vyssotsky 1957, Fig. 5). This tends to confirm Delhaye's opinion concerning the relative youth of dwarf M stars with emission lines. A similar opinion was expressed by Baade (1958).

§ 7. CONCLUDING REMARKS

The chief importance of the spectral surveys for red dwarfs is that, for the first time, they provide unbiased material upon which studies of group motion, dispersions, and velocity distribution may be based and from which more detailed studies of population differences among these stars will be possible. It is clear now that, since large orbital eccentricities are associated with large orbital inclinations, we cannot hope to obtain representative values of solar motion, velocity dispersions, etc., from discussions of the radial velocities of stars originally selected because of their large proper motions.

REFERENCES

ADAMS, W. S., JOY, A. H.,
  HUMASON, M. L., and
  BRAYTON, A. M.   1935   *Ap. J.*, **81**, 187.
BAADE, W.   1958   *A.J.*, **63**, 207.
BOTTLINGER, K. F.   1933   *Veröff. Sternw. Berlin-Babelsberg*, Vol. **10**, No. 2;
                                see also J. HAAS, *A.N.*, **239**, 97, 1930.

DELHAYE, J. 1953 *C.R.*, **237**, 294.
DYER, E. R., JR. 1954 *A.J.*, **59**, 218, 221.
 1956 *Ibid.*, **61**, 228.
EDMONDSON, F. K.,
 VYSSOTSKY, A. N., and
 JANSSEN, E. M. 1949 *Ap. J.*, **110**, 182.
EGGEN, O. J. 1956 *A.J.*, **61**, 462.
ELVIUS, T. 1951 *Ann. Stockholm Obs.*, Vol. **16**, No. 4.
JOHNSON, H. L., and
 MORGAN, W. W. 1953 *Ap. J.*, **117**, 313, Table IV.
JOY, A. H. 1947 *Ap. J.*, **105**, 96.
JOY, A. H., and
 MITCHELL, S. A. 1948 *Ap. J.*, **108**, 234.
KAMP, P. VAN DE, and
 VYSSOTSKY, A. N. 1937 *Pub. McCormick Obs.*, Vol. **7**.
KEENAN, P. C., and
 MORGAN, W. W. 1951 *Astrophysics*, ed. J. A. HYNEK (New York: McGraw-Hill Book Co., Inc.), p. 23.
KEENAN, P. C., and
 NASSAU, J. J. 1946 *Ap. J.*, **104**, 458.
KRON, G. E. 1956 *Proceedings of the Third Berkeley Symposium on Mathematical Statistics and Probability*, ed. J. NEYMAN (Berkeley, Calif.: University of California Press), **3**, 39.
KRON, G. E.,
 GASCOIGNE, S. C. B.,
 and WHITE, H. S. 1957 *A.J.*, **62**, 205.
KUIPER, G. P. 1938 *Ap. J.*, **87**, 592.
 1942 *Ibid.*, **95**, 201.
LINDBLAD, B. 1927 *Uppsala Medd.*, No. 28.
 1935 *Ann. Stockholm Obs.*, Vol. **12**, No. 2.
LUYTEN, W. J. 1955 *A Catalogue of 1849 Stars with Proper Motions Exceeding 0".5 Annually* (Minneapolis, Minn.: Lund Press).
MORGAN, W. W. 1938 *Ap. J.*, **87**, 589.
MORGAN, W. W.,
 KEENAN, P. C., and
 KELLMAN, E. 1943 *An Atlas of Stellar Spectra* (Chicago: University of Chicago Press).
MUMFORD, G. S., III 1956 *A.J.*, **61**, 213, 224.
NORDSTRÖM, H. 1936 *Lund Medd.*, Ser. II, No. 79, Table 38.
PARENAGO, P. P. 1950 *A.J. U.S.S.R.*, **27**, 152.
RAMBERG, J. M. 1957 *Ann. Stockholm Obs.*, Vol. **20**, No. 1.
RHIJN, P. J. VAN 1936 *Pub. Kapteyn Astr. Lab., Groningen*, No. 47.
ROMAN, NANCY G. 1952 *Ap. J.*, **116**, 122.
RUSSELL, H. N.,
 DUGAN, R. S., and
 STEWART, J. Q. 1945 *Astronomy* (Boston: Ginn & Co.), **1**, 351.

SCHALÉN, C. 1948 *Ann. Uppsala Obs.*, Vol. **2**, No. 4.
STENQUIST, E. 1937 *Uppsala Medd.*, No. 72.
TRUMPLER, R. J., and
  WEAVER, H. F. 1953 *Statistical Astronomy* (Berkeley, Calif.: University of California Press), p. 389.
VYSSOTSKY, A. N. 1943 *Ap. J.*, **97**, 381.
  1946 *Ibid.*, **104**, 239.
  1950 *Trans. I.A.U.*, **7**, 448.
  1956 *A.J.*, **61**, 201.
  1957 *Pub. A.S.P.*, **69**, 109.
VYSSOTSKY, A. N., and
  DYER, E. R., JR. 1957 *Ap. J.*, **125**, 297.
VYSSOTSKY, A. N.,
  JANSSEN, E. M.,
  MILLER, W. J., and
  WALTHER, M. E. 1946 *Ap. J.*, **104**, 234.
VYSSOTSKY, A. N., and
  MATEER, B. A. 1952 *Ap. J.*, **116**, 117.
VYSSOTSKY, A. N., and
  SKUMANICH, A. 1953 *A.J.*, **58**, 96.
VYSSOTSKY, A. N., and
  WILLIAMS, E. T. R. 1944 *A.J.*, **51**, 4.
  1948 *Pub. McCormick Obs.*, Vol. **10**.
VYSSOTSKY, A. N., and
  WIRTANEN, C. A. 1941 *Pub. A.A.S.*, **10**, 176.
WILLIAMS, E. T. R., and
  VYSSOTSKY, A. N. 1948 *Pub. McCormick Obs.*, **10**, 29.

CHAPTER 11

Photometric Systems

H. L. JOHNSON
*Lowell Observatory**

§ 1. INTRODUCTION

THE history of astronomical photometry is a long one, and a discussion of "photometric systems" could properly include an account of older photometric work. In order to emphasize the modern methods and applications, however, we shall not enter into this matter but, instead, shall refer the reader to the series of articles by H. F. Weaver in *Popular Astronomy* (1946). No attempt will be made here to relate or transform the earlier photographic and visual photometric work to a modern standard system. Our principal aim will be to discuss photometric systems as defined and observed by photoelectric techniques. Photographic techniques in photometry will be regarded as secondary and useful for accurate astronomical photometry only in conjunction with photoelectric work. The one great advantage of photographic plates—the ability to record simultaneously data for many stars—requires us, however, to consider the photographic method as still important.

§ 2. GENERAL CONSIDERATIONS

The use to which a photometric system is to be put determines to a considerable extent the procedures of measurement and reduction, as well as the spectral regions and the width of the spectral bands that are to be employed. Furthermore, significant restrictions on the choice of the spectral regions and the width of the bands are imposed by the limitations of the available receivers; in practice, these limitations have been important (and, indeed, decisive) in the choice of spectral regions and in the definitions of photometric systems. For example, the choice of the yellow region (actually green, but often called yellow because of the appearance of the filters that are used to isolate the region) was dictated long ago by the color response of the human eye. The choice of the blue region was due to the fact that early photographic plates were sensitive primarily to

* Now at the University of Arizona, Tucson.

the blue and ultraviolet light. Thus the basis for the International System was provided.

There have been many attempts to define blue-yellow photometric systems by visual and photographic means (Weaver 1946), but, because of difficulties with the calibration and standardization of visual and photographic receivers, they have not achieved the precision and reproducibility that are required for present-day astronomical research. The appearance of photoelectric techniques upon the scene, particularly the development and mass production of good photomultipliers, such as the RCA 1P21, has, however, made possible the definition of standard systems of sufficient precision for the purposes of modern astronomy.

It is legitimate to question the need for an accurate standard photometric system. After all, the ultimate goal of photometric measures is to provide data upon which physical interpretations about the stars can be based, and this goal can be attained without a generally accepted standard system. Without such a system, it is necessary for each observer to make enough observations according to his own methods and in his own system to provide the necessary data for his interpretations. The principal objection to this procedure is that it leads to a superabundance of almost identical observations on many bright standard stars; it is to avoid this redundance that a standard system is considered to be desirable. The proposal of a single standard system is not made as an attempt to enforce conformity but as a service to observers, so that they may save the time that otherwise would be spent making routine observations on standard stars. The existence of such a system does not, of course, preclude the making of observations in other manners for specific purposes. We can, however, hope to define a system that is sufficiently general that it can be of use in a great many different investigations.

A standard photometric system should probably include the usual blue and yellow spectral regions that have in the past been regarded as the International System. If the system is to be applied to faint stars as well as to bright ones, relatively broad spectral regions (to include more energy) are needed. Also, it would be advantageous to add at least one other wavelength to the usual blue and yellow ones; as Becker (1938, 1948) has shown, the addition of an ultraviolet band makes it possible to discriminate, from the results of the three-color photometry, between certain attributes of stars.

These considerations lead to the choice of wavelength bands about 1000 A wide centered at about λ 5500 and λ 4300 and, because the blue-sensitive photocathodes permit, a third band at about λ 3500. The exact specifications of the wavelengths of the edges of the bands and even the shapes of the pass bands are important if the maximum precision and convenience of transformation to the standard system are to be attained (Johnson 1952). It is important, therefore, that certain specified filters, photomultipliers, etc., be used. It should be emphasized that this condition is made as a matter of convenience for the observer in his transformations to the standard system.

A system defined in this manner—specified filters, photomultipliers, etc.—is an instrumental system. This is an essential requirement if a single homogeneous system is to be obtained. It is particularly important in this respect that the standard values that were obtained from the standard instrument must not be combined with other data taken by other observers using different instruments and methods. While many astronomers might feel that a procedure of combining data from several observers would lead to a more precisely defined standard system, this will actually be true only if the several instruments involved are carefully standardized in terms of the original one. If data from heterogeneous sources are combined, the homogeneity of the original instrumental system will be destroyed, and, if these combinations are made over a period of time, the "system" could even be an evolving one. An example of an evolving photoelectric system is that of Eggen (1950a, b, c, d, 1951a, b, c, d, 1955). Also, it should be noted that the proposals of Commission 25 of the I.A.U., made at the Moscow meeting (Stoy and Becker 1960), imply a further evolution of existing photometric systems. Clearly, one should be as careful as possible in the original definition of the system and then use the original values unchanged for future work, even though more data become available for the standard stars.

One might hope that the physical characteristics of the original standard apparatus would be so thoroughly specified that anyone could construct another one that would duplicate its performance. In principle, this can be done, but, in practice, it may not always be possible or convenient to specify adequately the performance of the standard apparatus. Because of this problem, it has universally been the practice to attempt to follow the next-best procedure: to give sufficient data concerning the performance of the standard apparatus, when it is used to measure stars, to permit other observers to make adequate transformations to the system. The use of this procedure means that it is necessary to give a long list of the observed standard values for all kinds of stars, of all spectral types and luminosity classes, including representative peculiar stars. Actually, experience has now shown that it is possible to give in fairly simple form sufficient physical specifications for a *photoelectric* photometer, so that, while a photometer constructed according to these specifications will not exactly duplicate the performance of the standard apparatus, it will be near enough that linear, single-valued transformations will provide satisfactory precision.

It is my opinion that a standard photometric system should be defined and used photoelectrically only. The calibration of the photometer in terms of magnitudes should be made in the laboratory and should not in any way depend on actual measures of stars. If this procedure is followed, it does not matter at all whether the standard stars are bright or faint; all that is necessary is that the range of colors of these stars be sufficient to provide an adequate check on the transformations to the standard system. Photographic photometry (except for work of a survey nature) should be used *only* as a method of *interpolation* between photoelectrically measured sequence stars in the immediate region that is being investigated. Methods of using photographic photometry as an interpolation device have been discussed by Hoag (1959).

§ 3. THE *U, B, V* SYSTEM

With these points in mind, the *U, B, V* system (Johnson and Morgan 1953) has been devised. This system is intended for use with blue-sensitive photomultipliers, such as the RCA 1P21. The blue filter was chosen to reduce the effects of the Balmer continuum on the blue magnitudes (Johnson 1952), and the blue band is not exactly the same as that which has in the past been considered to be "International Photographic" (Seares and Joyner 1943). The visual magnitudes, *V*, have no significant color term with respect to the visual magnitudes of the International System, and their zero point has been adjusted to agree with the values for North Polar Sequence stars given by Stebbins, Whitford, and Johnson (1950). An ultraviolet magnitude, *U*, has been included. The zero point of the blue-yellow color indices, $B - V$, has been set at A0, in accord with the original definition (Seares 1922) of the International System, and it is found that the scale of $B - V$ also agrees with this original definition. The zero point of $U - B$ is also set at A0. It should be emphasized that, except for the precisely stated zero-point shifts, the published standard values for the *U, B, V* system (Johnson and Morgan 1953; Johnson and Harris 1954; Johnson 1955) are exactly the quantities (in terms of magnitudes) that were observed. In other words, the *U, B, V* system is the "natural" system of the original apparatus.

In previous expositions of the *U, B, V* system (Johnson and Morgan 1953; Johnson 1955), emphasis has been placed, in the time-honored manner, on the need for a large number of stars of all kinds, in order to allow proper transformations to the system to be made. However, my experience with the *U, B, V* system during the last 12 years has shown that the transformations from the observed natural system to the *U, B, V* system will be linear and single-valued, provided that (1) the photomultiplier is an RCA type 1P21; (2) the yellow filter is Corning No. 3384, standard optical thickness; (3) the blue filter is Corning No. 5030, standard optical thickness, cemented to 2-mm Schott GG 13; (4) the ultraviolet filter is Corning No. 9863, standard optical thickness; (5) the telescope is a reflector and the mirrors are aluminized; (6) the reduction procedures of Johnson and Morgan (1951, 1953) are followed; and (7) the altitude at which the observations are made is approximately 7000 feet above sea level. The systematic errors will be less than ± 0.02 mag. (generally less than ± 0.01 mag.) for the most extreme cases; this statement also holds for globular clusters (Johnson 1959) and galaxies (de Vaucouleurs 1959). If all seven of these conditions are met, the ten primary standard stars listed in Table 1 are sufficient for the standardization of the photometry. Experience has shown that these ten stars are really quite constant in light; α Ari seems to have become about 0.03 mag.

fainter since 1951, and HR 8832 has been reported by Hiltner (1954) to be slightly variable (I have not been able to confirm this variation). Some of the other primary standard stars may be slightly variable (Johnson and Iriarte 1959), but this possible variation is significant only in the magnitudes, not in the colors. Although the results obtained by using the ten primary standard stars of Table 1 have so far been satisfactory, it is, of course, not advisable for the definition of a photometric system to depend on such a small number of stars. Furthermore, not all these stars are available to Southern Hemisphere observers. An additional list of well-observed standard stars, thoroughly tied in with the ten primary standards, is given in Table 2. According to Johnson and Morgan (1953), the closure errors in the primary standard stars are less than 0.01 mag.; according to Harris (Strömgren 1956), the right ascension errors (systematic errors correlated with right ascension) in the fundamental standards of the

TABLE 1

THE TEN PRIMARY STANDARD STARS OF THE U, B, V SYSTEM

HD No.	Name	V	$B-V$	$U-B$	Sp. Type
12929.........	α Ari	2.00	+1.151	+1.12	K2 III
18331.........	HR 875	5.17	+0.084	+0.05	A1 V
69267.........	β Cnc	3.52	+1.480	+1.78	K4 III
74280.........	η Hya	4.30	−0.195	−0.74	B3 V
135742.........	β Lib	2.61	−0.108	−0.37	B8 V
140573.........	α Ser	2.65	+1.168	+1.24	K2 III
143107.........	ε CrB	4.15	+1.230	+1.28	K3 III
147394.........	τ Her	3.89	−0.152	−0.56	B5 IV
214680.........	10 Lac	4.88	−0.203	−1.04	O9 V
219134.........	HR 8832	5.57	+1.010	+0.89	K3 V

U, B, V system are less than 0.005 mag. Hogg (1958) has recently published a list of U, B, V observations on 244 bright stars that were observed from Mount Stromlo Observatory. A comparison of data for stars that are common to his list and those of the U, B, V system (Johnson and Morgan 1953; Johnson and Harris 1954; Johnson 1955) permits an evaluation of the declination errors (systematic errors correlated with declination) in both series of observations. This comparison appears in Figure 1, which shows that the declination errors in both series are small, except for V.

Many of the standard stars in Tables 1 and 2 are quite bright ($V \sim 2$), and some astronomers have, for this reason, been critical of the lists. Apparently, their photometers are not capable of measuring such bright stars. In my opinion, this criticism is not valid because it is entirely possible to design and construct a photoelectric photometer that will accurately measure such stars, even with telescopes with apertures as large as 82 or 100 inches. In the original work on the U, B, V system (Johnson and Morgan 1953) stars as bright as $B \sim 1.5$ were measured regularly with the 82-inch telescope, and the standard values depend

TABLE 2

The Photometric Standards of the U, B, V System

HD No.	Name	V	$B-V$	$U-B$	n	Sp. Type
886......	γ Peg	2.83	-0.23	-0.87	6	B2 IV
1280......	θ And	4.61	$+0.06$	$+0.04$	6	A2 V
4727......	ν And	4.53	-0.15	-0.58	5	B5 V
6961......	θ Cas	4.33	$+0.17$	$+0.11$	5	A7 V
8538......	δ Cas	2.68	$+0.13$	$+0.12$	5	A5 V
9270......	η Psc	3.62	$+0.97$	$+0.76$	5	G8 III
10476......	107 Psc	5.23	$+0.83$	$+0.50$	5	K1 V
10700......	τ Cet	3.50	$+0.72$	$+0.20$	5	G8 Vp
11636......	β Ari	2.65	$+0.13$	$+0.10$	5	A5 V
....	$-18°359$	10.18	$+1.53$	$+1.16$	3	....
....	$+2°348$	10.03	$+1.44$	$+1.08$	3	
15318......	ξ^2 Cet	4.28	-0.06	-0.13	5	B9 III
....	HR 753 B	11.65	$+1.61$	$+1.12$	3	....
20630......	κ Cet	4.82	$+0.68$	$+0.18$	7	G5 V
21120......	o Tau	3.59	$+0.89$	$+0.62$	5	G8 III
21447......	HR 1046	5.08	$+0.05$	$+0.03$	5	A1 V
22049......	ϵ Eri	3.73	$+0.89$	$+0.57$	6	K2 V
28305......	ϵ Tau	3.54	$+1.02$	$+0.88$	6	K0 III
30652......	π^3 Ori	3.19	$+0.45$	-0.01	11	F6 V
30836......	π^4 Ori	3.69	-0.17	-0.80	9	B2 III
32630......	η Aur	3.17	-0.18	-0.67	6	B3 V
33111......	β Eri	2.80	$+0.13$	$+0.10$	8	A3 III
35299......	....	5.70	-0.22	-0.87	15	B2 V
35468......	γ Ori	1.64	-0.23	-0.87	5	B2 III
35497......	β Tau	1.65	-0.13	-0.49	5	B7 III
36395......	$-3°1123$	7.97	$+1.47$	$+1.21$	17	
36512......	ν Ori	4.63	-0.26	-1.07	11	B0 V
36591......	....	5.35	-0.20	-0.94	9	B1 V
37043......	ι Ori	2.77	-0.25	-1.08	5	O9 III
37128......	ϵ Ori	1.70	-0.19	-1.04	6	B0 Ia
38678......	ζ Lep	3.55	$+0.10$	$+0.06$	5	....
38899......	134 Tau	4.90	-0.07	-0.18	5	B9 IV
....	$+17°1320$	9.63	$+1.50$	$+1.18$	4	....
47105......	γ Gem	1.93	0.00	$+0.03$	5	A0 IV
....	$+5°1668$	9.82	$+1.56$	$+1.12$	3	....
56537......	λ Gem	3.58	$+0.11$	$+0.10$	6	A3 V
58946......	ρ Gem	4.16	$+0.32$	-0.03	6	F0 V
62345......	κ Gem	3.57	$+0.93$	$+0.68$	5	G8 III
71155......	HR 3314	3.90	-0.02	-0.02	5	A0 V
76644......	ι UMa	3.14	$+0.18$	$+0.07$	6	A7 V
79469......	θ Hya	3.88	-0.06	-0.13	6	B9.5 V
....	$-12°2918$	10.06	$+1.53$	$+1.15$	2	....
82885......	11 LMi	5.41	$+0.77$	$+0.45$	14	G8 IV–V
87696......	21 LMi	4.48	$+0.18$	$+0.08$	7	A7 V
87901......	α Leo	1.36	-0.11	-0.36	7	B7 V
89021......	λ UMa	3.45	$+0.03$	$+0.06$	6	A2 IV
....	$+1°2447$	9.63	$+1.52$	$+1.19$	3	....
91316......	ρ Leo	3.85	-0.14	-0.95	6	B1 Ib
100600......	90 Leo AB	5.95	-0.16	-0.64	23	....
102647......	β Leo	2.14	$+0.09$	$+0.07$	8	A3 V
102870......	β Vir	3.61	$+0.55$	$+0.10$	9	F8 V
103095......	HR 4550	6.45	$+0.75$	$+0.17$	25	G8 Vp
103287......	γ UMa	2.44	0.00	$+0.01$	6	A0 V
106591......	δ UMa	3.31	$+0.08$	$+0.07$	9	A3 V
106625......	γ Crv	2.60	-0.11	-0.35	5	B8 III
....	$+0°2989$	8.49	$+1.41$	$+1.26$	3	M0.5 V
113139......	78 UMa	4.93	$+0.36$	$+0.01$	16	F2 V
114710......	β Com	4.28	$+0.57$	$+0.07$	11	G0 V

TABLE 2—*Continued*

HD No.	Name	V	B−V	U−B	n	Sp. Type
115617.....	61 Vir	4.75	+0.71	+0.25	5	G6 V
116658.....	α Vir	0.96	−0.23	−0.94	7	B1 V
116842.....	80 UMa	4.01	+0.16	+0.08	15	A5 V
117176.....	70 Vir	4.98	+0.71	+0.26	8	G5 V
121370.....	η Boo	2.69	+0.58	+0.19	8	G0 IV
130109.....	109 Vir	3.74	0.00	−0.03	7	A0 V
130819.....	α¹ Lib	5.16	+0.41	−0.04	7	....
130841.....	α² Lib	2.75	+0.15	+0.08	8	....
....	−7°4003	10.56	+1.61	+1.20	6	....
141003.....	β Ser A	3.67	+0.06	+0.07	8	A2 IV
141004.....	λ Ser	4.43	+0.60	+0.10	7	G0 V
142860.....	γ Ser	3.85	+0.48	−0.03	6	F6 V
....	−12°4523	10.13	+1.60	+1.18	5	....
149757.....	ζ Oph	2.56	+0.02	−0.86	10	O9.5 V
154363.....	−4°4225	7.73	+1.16	+1.05	5	K5 V
....	−4°4226	10.07	+1.43	+1.09	5	M3.5: V
157881.....	+2°3312	7.54	+1.36	+1.26	5	K7 V
159561.....	α Oph	2.08	+0.15	+0.10	11	A5 III
161096.....	β Oph	2.77	+1.16	+1.24	10	K2 III
161868.....	γ Oph	3.75	+0.04	+0.04	9	A0 V
....	+4°3561*	9.54	+1.74	+1.29	9	M5 V
....	−3°4233	9.38	+1.52	+1.21	5	....
176437.....	γ Lyr	3.25	−0.05	−0.09	10	B9 III
177724.....	ζ Aql	2.99	0.00	−0.01	6	....
....	+4°4048	9.13	+1.49	+1.16	6	M3.5 V
184279.....	+3°4065	6.82	+0.02	−0.83	5	....
184915.....	κ Aql	4.96	−0.01	−0.87	6	B0.5 III
187642.....	α Aql	0.77	+0.22	+0.08	14	A7 IV-V
188512.....	β Aql	3.71	+0.86	+0.48	16	G8 IV
196867.....	α Del	3.77	−0.06	−0.22	6	B9 V
198001.....	ε Aqr	3.77	+0.01	+0.04	5	A1 V
....	−15°6290	10.17	+1.60	+1.15	4	....
216494.....	74 Aqr	5.81	−0.08	−0.32	6	....
218045.....	α Peg	2.49	−0.05	−0.06	7	B9 V
222368.....	ι Psc	4.13	+0.51	0.00	8	F7 V
....	+1°4774	8.98	+1.48	+1.09	5	M2 V

* Barnard's proper-motion star.

on these observations. I have, on one or two occasions, compared stars of the second magnitude directly, using one photometer and amplifier on the 82-inch telescope, with stars of the twentieth magnitude and fainter. It is necessary to use a standard light-source to calibrate out the fatigue of the photomultiplier that results from its exposure to the light of bright stars. In my experience, only RCA 1P21 photomultiplier tubes exhibit sufficiently low fatigue effects for such operation, but this restriction is of no consequence, since I have also found these tubes to be the most sensitive and, in general, the most satisfactory tubes for astronomical photometry in the blue spectral region.

If not all the conditions specified above are met (if a 1P21 is not used, other filters than those specified are used, etc.), significant systematic deviations from linear, single-valued transformations may be found for some kinds of stars. In this case, the observer can make use of the extensive lists of observations defining the U, B, V system (Johnson and Morgan 1953; Johnson 1955). Further observations made on the U, B, V system with the original apparatus may be found in the lists of Johnson and Knuckles (1955, 1957). One should keep in mind, however, that these lists do not contain all possible kinds of objects and that, if one is observing objects of a kind not included in the standard lists, proper transformations may not be possible.

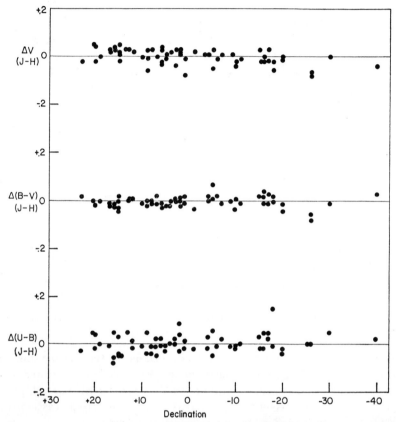

Fig. 1.—The comparison of Northern Hemisphere U, B, V photometry with the Southern Hemisphere photometry of Hogg (1958), for stars in common.

It is important that the reduction procedures outlined by Johnson and Morgan (1951, 1953) be followed. Arp (1958a) has shown that deviations of certain kinds from the method of extinction correction for $B - V$ can lead to small, but significant, systematic differences from the standard U, B, V system. It is also important that the $U - B$ extinction coefficient be assumed to be independent of the colors of the stars. Johnson and Morgan (1953) used no color term in this coefficient, although some other observers have found one to be necessary. Actually, Johnson and Morgan used a zero color term as a matter of definition, not as a matter of observation. The actual observed relationship, as determined (in 1950–1951) from extinction measures on a large number of stars of all types, between the $U - B$ extinction coefficient, K_u, and the spectral types of the stars, is shown in Figure 2. The dip at A0 is caused by the shift in effective wavelength of the U filter for differing values of the Balmer jump. Because of the large amount of absorption in the Balmer continuum in A0 V stars, the weight of the U filter is shifted to longer wavelengths for these stars than for earlier- and later-type stars. This shift results in a smaller extinction coefficient for A0 V stars than for most of the other types. Supergiants and white dwarfs show a smaller dip. It is evident from Figure 2 that if a linear color term in K_u is assumed and if the slope is determined from only a red and a blue star, the

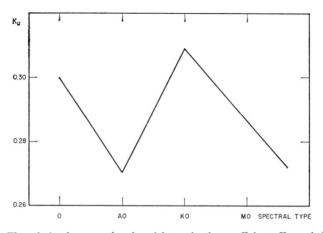

Fig. 2.—The relation between the ultraviolet extinction coefficient, K_u, and the spectral types of the stars.

size (and even the sign) of this color term depend on the types of the stars that are used in the extinction determinations. For example, an O star and an M star will yield a positive color term; an A0 V star and a K0 star will yield a negative color term. It is for this reason that Johnson and Morgan assumed the color term in the $U - B$ extinction coefficient to be zero.

The error that is caused by this approximation in the $U - B$ extinction coefficient is not large (of the order of 0.03 mag.) at moderate zenith distances. It is not usually important, since the standard stars will be observed at about the same zenith distances as the other stars and the errors will largely cancel out. Small systematic deviations of the U system from that which would have been observed outside the atmosphere will, of course, be present (Blanco 1957). It is important, however, to consider the effect of this approximation on the observations of southern stars that are made from northern sites and vice versa, since such observations are often made at systematically greater zenith distances than are those of the standard stars of the same types. My published observations of southern stars contain some approximate compensation for this error, but other observers may not have recognized the existence of the problem (Walker 1957; Shane 1958).

It may be difficult or impossible adequately to transform ultraviolet observations that are made at or near sea level to the U system. The relatively large amount of extinction at sea level for wavelengths around λ 3300 shifts the weight of the U filter toward longer wavelengths, compared with the same apparatus used at 7000-foot altitude. This shift may result in the observations being taken in a filter band that is sufficiently different from that of the standard U system to cause significant transformation difficulties (Borgman 1959).

If a standard photometric system is to be of the maximum use to photometric observers, the standard colors of normal (unreddened) stars must be known on the system. It is for this reason that Johnson and Morgan (1953) thoroughly tied in their photometry with the revised Yerkes (MK) system of spectral classification. The relationship between intrinsic color and spectral type has been established on a firm basis (Johnson and Morgan 1953; Morgan, Harris, and Johnson 1953; Mendoza 1956) for stars of the main sequence. Since there are many nearby, probably unreddened, main-sequence stars of almost all types, there are no special problems and little uncertainty in the determination of the intrinsic color–spectral-type relationship for luminosity class V, except for the earliest-type stars. For the O and early B stars, recourse must be had to several galactic clusters that contain O and early B stars and also stars around A0 V. The differences in color index between the early-type and the later-type stars in the clusters permit a determination of the intrinsic colors of the early-type stars. It should be mentioned that Schmidt (1958) feels that a correction of -0.02 mag. may be necessary to the zero points of $B - V$ and $U - B$. He finds that some of the A0 V stars that were used by Johnson and Morgan to set the zero points of their color indices may be slightly reddened.

There have been several investigations of the intrinsic color–spectral-type relationship for the higher-luminosity stars (Johnson 1958; Mawridis 1958; Schmidt 1958; Serkowski 1958; Arp 1958c; Feinstein 1959). While the results of these investigations are not in as good agreement as one might like, the consensus appears to be that the B-type supergiants are somewhat redder and that the A-type supergiants are somewhat bluer than main-sequence stars of the same spectral types. A compilation of the best available values for the intrinsic colors of stars of the various spectral types and luminosity classes is given in Table 3. This table has been constructed without use of the -0.02-mag. correction advocated by Schmidt (1958); if this correction is valid, all these intrinsic colors should be reduced by 0.02 mag.

Several authors (Becker 1938, 1948; Johnson and Morgan 1953; Morgan, Harris, and Johnson 1953; Becker and Stock 1954; Morgan and Harris 1956) have pointed out that three-color photometry which includes ultraviolet measures makes possible (with certain restrictions) the determination of the intrinsic

TABLE 3

INTRINSIC COLORS

$B-V$

Sp. Type	V	III	II	Ib	Ia
O5	−0.32	−0.32	−0.32	−0.32	−0.32
O6	− .32	− .32	− .32	− .32	− .32
O7	− .32	− .32	− .32	− .31	− .31
O8	− .31	− .31	− .31	− .29	− .29
O9	− .31	− .31	− .31	− .28	− .28
O9.5	− .30	− .30	− .30	− .27	− .27
B0	− .30	− .30	− .29	− .24	− .24
B0.5	− .28	− .28	− .26	− .22	− .22
B1	− .26	− .26	− .24	− .19	− .19
B2	− .24	− .24	− .22	− .17	− .17
B3	− .20	− .20	− .18	− .13	− .13
B5	− .16	− .16	− .14	− .09	− .09
B6	− .14	− .14	− .12	− .07	− .07
B7	− .12	− .12	− .10	− .05	− .05
B8	− .09	− .09	− .07	− .02	− .02
B9	− .06	− .06	− .04	.00	.00
B9.5	− .03	− .03	− .01	+ .01	+ .01
A0	.00	.00	+0.01	+ .01	+ .01
A1	+ .03	+ .03	....	+ .01	+ .01
A2	+ .06	+ .06	....	.00	.00
A3	+ .09	....	....	.00	.00
A5	+ .15	+0.15	....	+ .07	+ .07
A7	+ .20	....	....	+ .13	+ .13
F0	+ .30	....	....	+ .24	+ .24
F2	+ .38	....	....	+ .34	+ .34
F5	+0.45	....	....	+0.45	+0.45

$U-B$

Sp. Type	V	III	II	Ib	Ia
O5	−1.15	−1.15	−1.15	−1.15	−1.15
O6	−1.14	−1.14	−1.14	−1.14	−1.14
O7	−1.14	−1.14	−1.14	−1.14	−1.14
O8	−1.13	−1.13	−1.13	−1.13	−1.13
O9	−1.12	−1.12	−1.12	−1.12	−1.12
O9.5	−1.10	−1.11	−1.12	−1.09	−1.10
B0	−1.08	−1.09	−1.10	−1.05	−1.07
B0.5	−1.01	−1.03	−1.05	−1.01	−1.04
B1	−0.93	−0.96	−1.00	−0.96	−1.00
B2	−0.86	−0.89	−0.95	−0.91	−0.96
B3	−0.71	−0.74	−0.83	−0.82	−0.87
B5	−0.56	....	−0.69	−0.72	−0.78
B6	−0.49	....	−0.62	−0.67	−0.73
B7	−0.42	....	....	−0.62	−0.68
B8	−0.30	....	....	−0.53	−0.60
B9	−0.19	....	....	−0.48	−0.56
B9.5	−0.10	....	....	....	....
A0	0.00	....	....	....	....

colors of stars and, therefore, the amount of interstellar reddening. This determination from three-color photometry depends on the fact that interstellar reddening and "temperature reddening" do not produce the same effects in all
three wavelength bands. These differences are particularly striking in the B and
A stars, as is shown in Figure 3, where the dotted line represents the positions
of unreddened main-sequence stars in the $U - B$ versus $B - V$ diagram. The
solid line represents the positions of main-sequence stars that are reddened by
0.60 mag.; it therefore represents the positions in the diagram where we expect
to find the main-sequence stars of a cluster that is reddened by 0.60 mag. Reddening of a cluster main sequence shifts the two-color index plot along the

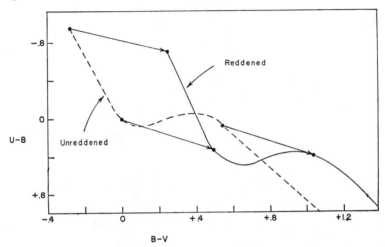

Fig. 3.—The relation between $U - B$ and $B - V$ for main-sequence stars. The dotted line
represents the positions of unreddened stars; the solid line, stars reddened by 0.60 mag.

"reddening line," and the reddening can be estimated from the amount of this
shift. This is the procedure that was used by Becker and Stock (1954) for their
reddening calculations for clusters.

A modification of this "sliding-fit" procedure (called the "Q-method"), valid
for main-sequence O and B stars has been proposed by Johnson and Morgan
(1953). This modification allows numerical computation of the intrinsic colors
and reddening of individual O and B stars, provided that it can be established
by some independent means that they are main-sequence stars; when we are
dealing with a star cluster, such stars may be selected from the cluster main sequence as exhibited by the color-magnitude diagram. More complete discussions
of the Q-method of intrinsic color and interstellar reddening determination and
its limitations have been published by Johnson (1957, 1958) and Morgan and
Harris (1956).

The relationship between intrinsic color and absolute magnitude, on the
U, B, V system, for the "zero-age" main sequence is also of interest to users of

the system. The evolutionary ideas behind this sequence and examples of its use have been given by Johnson and Knuckles (1955), Johnson and Hiltner (1956), Sandage (1957), and Johnson (1957). An example of the zero-age sequence is given in each of the last three of these papers, but probably the best such sequence is that of Johnson and Iriarte (1958), which is given in Table 4. Every user of this zero-age main sequence should be aware of the assumptions and

TABLE 4

THE STANDARD ZERO-AGE MAIN SEQUENCE

$B-V$	M_v	$U-B$	M_v
−0.25.......	−2.10	−0.90......	−1.98
−0.20.......	−1.10	− .80......	−1.50
−0.15.......	−0.30	− .70......	−1.03
−0.10.......	+0.50	− .60......	−0.59
−0.05.......	+1.10	− .50......	−0.13
0.00	+1.50	− .40......	+0.27
+0.05.......	+1.74	− .30......	+0.66
+0.10.......	+2.00	− .20......	+1.02
+0.20.......	+2.45	− .10......	+1.30
+0.30.......	+2.95	0.00......	+1.50
+0.40.......	+3.56		
+0.50.......	+4.23		
+0.60.......	+4.79		
+0.70.......	+5.38		
+0.80.......	+5.88		
+0.90.......	+6.32		
+1.00.......	+6.78		
+1.10.......	+7.20		
+1.20.......	+7.66		
+1.30.......	+8.11		

uncertainties that are inherent in its derivation. Johnson and Iriarte (1958) remark:

The procedure by which the zero-age main sequence is derived and the method by which the photometric distances of galactic clusters are determined assumes that all clusters have a common unique zero-age main sequence. This assumption implies the additional assumption that all clusters have identical chemical compositions. Our stated probable error of ±0.1 mag. for the position of the zero-age main sequence in the color-magnitude diagram does not include any allowance for possible non-validity of our assumptions.

These uncertainties in the method of derivation of the zero-age main sequence have been emphasized by Henyey, LeLevier, and Levee (1959).

§ 4. THE P, V SYSTEM

Another photometric system which has been proposed for a standard system is the P, V system. The most recent exposition of this system is that of Eggen (1955), who has proposed a two-color approximation to the International System, which he calls the $(P, V)_E$ system. Eggen has published a list of 833 stars in both Northern and Southern Hemispheres which can be considered to define the system. Unfortunately, the $(P, V)_E$ system cannot be considered to be a homogeneous instrumental system in the sense in which the U, B, V system can be so considered. Eggen made a significant change in the blue filter (to reduce the sensitivity to the ultraviolet) partway through the observing program; also, he transformed the "natural" system into an approximation to the International System of the North Polar Sequence.

Another serious disadvantage of Eggen's $(P, V)_E$ system is the fact that it is not by any means the only P, V system upon which there are published data. Even Eggen himself (1951b) has an earlier P, V system on which he has published a number of magnitudes and colors in Harvard Region C 12, SA 61, and the North Polar Sequence. A different P, V system is the one used by Johnson and Morgan (1951) and by Baum in his work on M13 (1954) and several selected areas (see, for example, H. M. Johnson 1959). A fourth P, V system has been used by Weaver (1953) in the Coma Berenices star cluster; a system similar to Weaver's was used by Cuffey and McCuskey (1956) in NGC 2169. This system cannot be considered to be an unambiguous one; in fact, the various P, V systems differ as much in color system among themselves as they do from the B, V part of the U, B, V system (Johnson 1955).

The transformation equations from the $(P, V)_E$ system to the B, V system are (Eggen 1955)

$$V = V_E, \qquad B - V = 0.964 \, (P - V)_E + 0.120 \,,$$

except that for dwarf stars, for which $+1.0 < B - V < +1.5$, the transformation is (Eggen 1955)

$$B - V = 1.19 \, (P - V)_E - 0.10 \,.$$

The double-valued transformation for red stars demonstrates very effectively the necessity for using the standard filters of the U, B, V system if one expects to obtain satisfactory precision from linear, single-valued transformations.

§ 5. THE CAPE SYSTEMS

The magnitudes and colors of 880 southern bright stars have been published by the Royal Observatory, Cape of Good Hope (Royal Obs. 1953a). The magnitudes were determined photographically by a "Fabry" method (Cousins 1950). The scale of these blue magnitudes, BPg, has been checked photoelectrically (at the Cape) and has been found not to be in error by as much as 0.01 mag. over the range from $BPg = 0.0$ to 6.5. The colors, Cpe, have been measured photoelectrically, but the observations are not homogeneous because of changes in apparatus during the course of the observing program. From all the available data, the best linear transformations of this system to the B, V system are

$$V = BPg - 1.312 \, Cpe - 0.042 \,, \qquad B - V = 1.025 \, Cpe + 0.195 \,.$$

The Cape blue magnitudes, BPg, contain more ultraviolet light than do the B magnitudes, and the best transformation is not the linear one, above, but a non-linear one. *Cape Mimeogram* No. 1 gives as the best transformation the following:

$$BPg = +0.205\ (B - V) + 0.05\ (U - B) - 0.190\ .$$

Unfortunately, $U - B$ colors are not known for most of the southern stars, and this transformation cannot be used.

The second Cape System is "The 1953 S System" (Royal Obs. 1953b), which applies to the magnitudes and colors of stars in a number of the Harvard E-regions. The transformation equations from the 1953 S system to the B, V system are (mean of those in *Cape Mimeogram* No. 3 and Arp 1958b):

$$V = SPv + 0.08\ SCI - 0.04\ ,\qquad B - V = 0.85\ SCI + 0.26\ ,$$

where SPv is the "yellow" magnitude and SCI the blue-yellow color index on the 1953 S system. As in the case of the first Cape system, there is evidence of non-linearity in the transformations, due to a greater amount of ultraviolet light in the Cape blue observations than in the B observations.

§ 6. THE C_1 SYSTEM

The C_1 color system of Stebbins and Huffer (1934) and Stebbins, Huffer, and Whitford (1940) is the fourth and last of the photoelectrically observed systems more or less comparable with the International System that we shall discuss here. The C_1 system was observed with a photoelectric cell, not a photomultiplier, and the base line of the color indices is about half that of the other blue-yellow systems we have been discussing. Nevertheless, this system has seen considerable use, and, indeed, data for many stars of interest are still available only on this system of Stebbins, Huffer, and Whitford. No new observations are now being made on this system.

The relations between the C_1 system and $B - V$ are

$$B - V = +0.30 + 2.06\ C_1, \text{ for reddened and unreddened}$$
$$\text{O and B0 I}a\text{–B2 I}a \text{ stars;}$$

$$B - V = +0.18 + 1.76\ C_1, \text{ for unreddened B1–A7 main-}$$
$$\text{sequence stars;}$$

$$B - V = +0.27 + 1.37\ C_1, \text{ for yellow giant stars.}$$

These relations are derived from those given by Morgan, Harris, and Johnson (1953).

§ 7. THE R, I SYSTEM

We now turn our attention to photometric systems which, because of their special applications, make no pretense of transformation to any other system. The first of these systems that we shall discuss is that of Kron and Smith (1951),

TABLE 5
THE PHOTOMETRIC STANDARDS OF THE R, I SYSTEM

HD No.	Star	R	$R-I$	n	Sp. Type
886..........	γ Peg	3.06	−0.22	4	B2 IV
9270..........	η Psc	3.23	+0.32	5	G8 III
10700..........	τ Cet	3.16	+0.26	5	G8 V
....	−18°359	9.00	+1.02	4	....
....	+2°348	9.02	+0.86	4	....
15318..........	ζ Cet	4.45	−0.13	3	B9 III
....	HR 753 B	10.26	+1.28	6	....
18331..........	HR 875	5.26	−0.04	3	A1 V
20630..........	κ Cet	4.57	+0.22	8	G5 V
21120..........	o Tau	3.28	+0.32	4	G8 III
22049..........	ϵ Eri	3.33	+0.30	4	K2 V
....	o^2 Eri A	4.07	+0.31	3	....
27371..........	γ Tau	3.30	+0.34	4	K0 III
27697..........	δ Tau	3.41	+0.34	4	K0 III
30652..........	π^3 Ori	3.05	+0.16	5	F6 V
30836..........	π^4 Ori	3.86	−0.19	4	B2 III
33111..........	β Eri	2.82	−0.01	5	A3 III
35299..........	....	5.91	−0.23	4	B2 V
35468..........	γ Ori	1.84	−0.25	4	B2 III
36395..........	−3°1123	6.87	+0.84	5	....
36512..........	υ Ori	4.84	−0.25	5	B0 V
36591..........	....	5.53	−0.20	4	B1 V
37043..........	ι Ori	2.95	−0.24	4	O9 III
37128..........	ϵ Ori	1.88	−0.20	4	B0 Ia
38678..........	ζ Lep	3.61	−0.05	4	A3 V
38899..........	134 Tau	5.04	−0.14	4	B9 IV
....	Ross 614 AB	9.42	+1.38	5	....
....	+17°1320	8.64	+0.74	4	....
47105..........	γ Gem	2.02	−0.09	4	A1 IV
....	γ CMa	4.24	−0.16	3	B8 II
56537..........	λ Gem	3.64	−0.05	5	A3 V
....	Luyten's Star	8.40	+1.19	6	....
....	Ross 882	9.76	+1.40	6	....
69267..........	β Cnc	2.77	+0.52	4	K4 III
71155..........	HR 3314	4.03	−0.14	4	A0 V
74280..........	η Hya	4.47	−0.21	4	B3 V
79469..........	θ Hya	4.01	−0.15	6	A0p
....	−12°2918	8.84	+1.04	3	....
87901..........	α Leo	1.48	−0.17	3	B7 V
91316..........	ρ Leo	4.01	−0.19	7	B1 I
....	Wolf 359	11.28	+1.85	3	....
....	Ross 128	9.55	+1.30	5	....
102647..........	β Leo	2.18	−0.06	4	A3 V
102870..........	β Vir	3.39	+0.16	8	F8 V
106625..........	γ Crv	2.72	−0.16	3	B8 III
....	Wolf 424 AB	10.50	+1.62	3	....
....	0°2989	7.58	+0.66	2	M0.5 V
116658..........	α Vir	1.19	−0.26	1	B1 V
117176..........	70 Vir	4.68	+0.24	2	G5 IV–V
121370..........	η Boo	2.45	+0.20	1	G0 IV
130109..........	109 Vir	3.86	−0.10	2	A0 V
130841..........	α^2 Lib	2.82	−0.03	2	A3 V
135742..........	β Lib	2.72	−0.14	2	B8 V
....	−7°4003	9.26	+1.10	1	....
140573..........	α Ser A	2.10	+0.37	2	K2 III
141003..........	β Ser A	3.74	−0.06	2	A2 IV
141004..........	λ Ser	4.20	+0.20	1	G0 V
142860..........	γ Ser	3.67	+0.14	3	F6 IV

TABLE 5—*Continued*

HD No.	Star	R	$R-I$	n	Sp. Type
....	$-12°4523$	8.71	$+1.20$	1	....
149757..........	ζ Oph	2.64	-0.07	1	O9.5 V
....	$-4°4626$	8.99	$+0.91$	2	M3.5: V
157881..........	$+2°3312$	6.67	$+0.60$	2	K7 V
159561..........	α Oph	2.10	0.00	2	A5 III
161096..........	β Oph	2.24	$+0.39$	1	K2 III
161868..........	γ Oph	3.84	-0.09	1	A0 V
....	$+4°3561$	8.09	$+1.23$	2	M5 V
....	$-3°4233$	8.34	$+0.88$	1	....
177724..........	ζ Aql	3.10	-0.07	2	B9.5 V
....	$+4°4048$	7.90	$+1.00$	2	M3.5 V
184279..........	$+3°4065$	6.99	-0.06	2	....
184915..........	κ Aql	5.02	-0.09	2	....
187642..........	α Aql	0.76	$+0.02$	1	A7 IV-V
188512..........	β Aql	3.35	$+0.31$	1	G8 IV
196867..........	α Del	3.91	-0.11	2	B9 V
198001..........	ε Aqr	3.86	-0.11	2	A1 V
....	Wolf 922	10.43	$+1.36$	2	....
....	LPM 837	10.26	$+1.66$	2	....
....	$-15°6290$	8.76	$+1.22$	2	....
216494..........	74 Aqr	5.95	-0.14	1	....
218045..........	α Peg	2.63	-0.08	1	B9 V
222368..........	ι Psc	3.94	$+0.19$	1	F7 V
....	$+1°4774$	7.95	$+0.87$	1	M2 V

Kron, White, and Gascoigne (1953), and Kron and Gascoigne (1953). The system is defined by the observations that are given by Kron and Smith, while the later data were transformed to the original R, I system from a slightly different one. The change in the system was caused by a change in filters.

This R, I photometric system consists of the photoelectric observations at λ 6800 (R) and λ 8250 (I) on a total of 227 bright stars, stars in Harvard C-regions, and those in Kapteyn Selected Areas. The system stands by itself, and comparisons of these data with those of the systems discussed above are of interest with respect to the intrinsic properties of the stars. Relatively broad-band filters were used, and the faintest star that has been observed on the system is of magnitude $R = 15.17$; it should, however, be possible to observe fainter stars on this system, especially with improved techniques and apparatus. All the work so far published on the R, I system has been done by Kron and his collaborators.

Kron, White, and Gascoigne (1953) have published a list of R, I observations on 82 stars, which they consider to represent the system. These data are reprinted in Table 5. The declinations of the stars range from $+18°$ to $-18°$, and all of them may be observed from both Northern and Southern Hemispheres. Seventy-two of the R, I standards of Table 5 are common to the list of standards of the U, B, V system (Tables 1 and 2), and it should be emphasized that, between these two systems, U, B, V and R, I, we have a well-defined five-color photometric system.

§ 8. THE SIX-COLOR PHOTOMETRY

The six-color photometry of Stebbins, Whitford, and Kron is another example of a photometric system that exists independently of any standard system. This work consists of observations in six broad-band spectral regions ranging in wavelength from λ 3500 to λ 9000. The latest revised list of data on the six-color system is that of Stebbins and Kron (1956), who have published data for 409 stars of different spectral types. This photometry is especially valuable because the sun has been measured on the system (Stebbins and Kron 1957). The six-color photometry deals with the colors of the stars; only for a few stars (including the sun) were photoelectric magnitudes measured by the authors of the system. It is an instrumental system in the same sense as is the U, B, V system; the system is not homogeneous, however, since several changes of filters and other apparatus were made during the course of the observations.

The six-color photometry covers a much larger range of wavelengths than do the other systems we have discussed here, and it is, in this respect, not comparable with them. Transformations between some of the six-color data and other systems are discussed by Morgan, Harris, and Johnson (1953) and by Kron (1958), but the six-color system has applications sufficiently different from those of the other systems that intercomparisons are of relatively small interest. The photometry has been applied only to bright stars; practically no stars fainter than the seventh magnitude have been observed on the system.

Kron (1958) has shown that it is possible to use the data that are obtained from the $V, B, R,$ and I filters of the six-color photometry to calculate the intrinsic colors and interstellar reddening of later-type supergiant stars, in a manner similar to that employed by Becker (1938, 1948), Becker and Stock (1954), and Johnson and Morgan (1953) for the early-type stars. He gives a list of six-color observations of 139 supergiant stars, many of which are not contained in the other lists of the system. He has carried out the analysis of these observations and has derived intrinsic colors and reddening values for later-type supergiant stars.

We note that if we combine the U, B, V system of Johnson and Morgan with the R, I system of Kron, White, and Gascoigne, a five-color photometric system is formed that is directly competitive with the six-color photometry. Unfortunately, the same symbols are used to name the magnitudes of the two systems—a situation that may, in time, lead to some confusion.

§ 9. CONCLUSION

We have discussed here the principal photometric systems that have been established by photoelectric techniques. Of these systems, it seems probable that four—the U, B, V system of Johnson and Morgan; the $(P, V)_E$ system of Eggen; the R, I system of Kron and his collaborators; and the six-color photometry—will be used for virtually all the broad-band photometry of the future.

Among these four, we have two competitive blue-yellow systems and two competitive multicolor systems.

During the last decade, the engineering problems of astronomical photometry have been carried to acceptable solutions. Satisfactory photometric systems of the required precision have been set up and tested. Photoelectric photometers of great sensitivity, efficiency, and convenience have been designed and constructed. Good methods of using photographic photometry in conjunction with photoelectric observations have been worked out. We are now ready, from these standpoints, to go ahead on large-scale photometric programs that will provide us with a great deal of information about the universe. It seems probable that the next decade will see our present photometric methods and systems combined with modern computational methods, resulting in a veritable flood of accurate photometric data. The methods and procedures are available—they will be used.

REFERENCES

Arp, H. C.	1958a	*A.J.*, **63**, 58.
	1958b	*Ibid.*, p. 118.
	1958c	*Hdb. d. Phys.* (Berlin: Springer-Verlag), **51**, 75.
Baum, W. A.	1954	*A.J.*, **59**, 422.
Becker, W.	1938	*Zs. f. Ap.*, **15**, 225.
	1948	*Ap. J.*, **107**, 278.
Becker, W., and Stock, J.	1954	*Zs. f. Ap.*, **34**, 1.
Blanco, V. M.	1957	*Ap. J.*, **125**, 209.
Borgman, J.	1959	*Ap. J.*, **129**, 362.
Cousins, A. W. J.	1950	*M.N.*, **110**, 531.
Cuffey, J., and McCuskey, S. W.	1956	*Ap. J.*, **123**, 59.
Eggen, O. J.	1950a	*Ap. J.*, **111**, 65.
	1950b	*Ibid.*, p. 81.
	1950c	*Ibid.*, p. 414.
	1950d	*Ibid.*, **112**, 141.
	1951a	*Ibid.*, **113**, 367.
	1951b	*Ibid.*, p. 657.
	1951c	*Ibid.*, p. 663.
	1951d	*Ibid.*, **114**, 141.
	1955	*A.J.*, **60**, 65.
Feinstein, A.	1959	*Zs. f. Ap.*, **47**, 218.
Henyey, L. G., LeLevier, R., and Levee, R. D.	1959	*Ap. J.*, **129**, 2.
Hiltner, W. A.	1954	*Ap. J.*, **120**, 41.
Hoag, A. A.	1959	*A.J.*, **64**, 410.
Hogg, A. R.	1958	*Mt. Stromlo Obs. Mimeo.*, No. 2.

Johnson, H. L.   1952   *Ap. J.*, **116**, 272.
                                  1955   *Ann. d'ap.*, **18**, 292.
                                  1957   *Ap. J.*, **126**, 121.
                                  1958   *Lowell Obs. Bull.*, **4**, 37.
                                  1959   *Ibid.*, p. 117.

Johnson, H. L., and
    Harris, D. L., III   1954   *Ap. J.*, **120**, 196.

Johnson, H. L., and
    Hiltner, W. A.   1956   *Ap. J.*, **123**, 267.

Johnson, H. L., and
    Iriarte, B.   1958   *Lowell Obs. Bull.*, **4**, 47
                                  1959   *Ibid.*, p. 99.

Johnson, H. L., and
    Knuckles, C. F.   1955   *Ap. J.*, **122**, 209.
                                  1957   *Ibid.*, **126**, 113.

Johnson, H. L., and
    Morgan, W. W.   1951   *Ap. J.*, **114**, 522.
                                  1953   *Ibid.*, **117**, 313.

Johnson, H. M.   1959   *Pub. A.S.P.*, **71**, 226.

Kron, G. E.   1958   *Pub. A.S.P.*, **70**, 561.

Kron, G. E., and
    Gascoigne, S. C. B.   1953   *Ap. J.*, **118**, 511.

Kron, G. E., and
    Smith, J. L.   1951   *Ap. J.*, **113**, 324.

Kron, G. E.,
    White, H. S., and
    Gascoigne, S. C. B.   1953   *Ap. J.*, **118**, 502.

Mawridis, L.   1958   *Zs. f. Ap.*, **45**, 98.

Mendoza, E. E.   1956   *Ap. J.*, **123**, 54.

Morgan, W. W., and
    Harris, D. L., III   1956   *Vistas in Astronomy*, ed. A. Beer (London and
                                          New York: Pergamon Press), **2**, 1124.

Morgan, W. W.,
    Harris, D. L., III, and
    Johnson, H. L.   1953   *Ap. J.*, **118**, 92.

Royal Obs., Cape of
    Good Hope, South
    Africa   1953a   *Cape Mimeo.*, No. 1.
                                  1953b   *Ibid.*, No. 3.

Sandage, A.   1957   *Ap. J.*, **125**, 435.

Schmidt, T.   1958   *Zs. f. Ap.*, **46**, 145.

Seares, F. H.   1922   *Trans. I.A.U.*, **1**, 79.

Seares, F. H., and
    Joyner, M. C.   1943   *Ap. J.*, **98**, 302.

Serkowski, K.   1958   *Acta Astr.*, **8**, 135.

Shane, C. D.   1958   *A.J.*, **63**, 364.

STEBBINS, J., and
  HUFFER, C. M.   1934   *Pub. Washburn Obs.*, Vol. **15**, Part 5, p. 217.

STEBBINS, J.,
  HUFFER, C. M., and
  WHITFORD, A. E.   1940   *Ap. J.*, **91**, 20.

STEBBINS, J., and
  KRON, G. E.   1956   *Ap. J.*, **123**, 440.
                           1957   *Ibid.*, **126**, 266.

STEBBINS, J.,
  WHITFORD, A. E., and
  JOHNSON, H. L.   1950   *Ap. J.*, **112**, 469.

STOY, R. H., and
  BECKER, W.   1960   *Trans. I.A.U.*, **10**, 384.

STRÖMGREN, B.   1956   *A.J.*, **61**, 45.

VAUCOULEURS, G. DE   1959   *Lowell Obs. Bull.*, **4**, 105.

WALKER, M. F.   1957   *Ap. J.*, **125**, 636.

WEAVER, H. F.   1946   *Pop. Astr.*, **54**, 211, 287, 339, 389, 451, 504.
                           1953   *Ap. J.*, **117**, 366.

CHAPTER 12

Interstellar Reddening

STEWART SHARPLESS

U.S. Naval Observatory, Washington, D.C.

§ 1. THE LAW OF INTERSTELLAR REDDENING

1.1. THE REDDENING-CURVE

ONE of the most puzzling problems in astronomy during the late 1920's was the existence of stars whose color temperatures were apparently much lower than the temperatures indicated by the degree of ionization in their spectra. Since, in a very rough approximation, interstellar reddening follows a law similar to that of temperature reddening, the resolution of this paradox was not immediately available through spectrophotometric studies. The definitive demonstration of the existence of interstellar material came, rather, through a comparison of the distances of galactic clusters obtained geometrically, on the one hand, and photometrically, on the other (Trumpler 1930a, b). The latter type of distance measurement is affected by interstellar absorption, whereas the former is not. Through a study of color indices and spectral types of stars in distant clusters, Trumpler further concluded that interstellar absorption is selective with respect to wavelength, amounting to an increase in the observed color index of about 0.31 mag/kpc. A spectrophotometric comparison of reddened and unreddened stars of early type (Trumpler 1930c) led to the conclusion that interstellar absorption does not follow Rayleigh's law in being proportional to $1/\lambda^4$ but, in the limited spectral region studied by Trumpler, varies more nearly as $1/\lambda$. This suggested the existence of interstellar particles having sizes comparable with a wavelength of visible light.

Following the recognition of the existence of interstellar absorption, the two observational problems were (1) to establish the "reddening-curve," i.e., the relation between interstellar absorption and wavelength, and (2) to study possible variations in the reddening-curve in different parts of the sky that might result from regional variations in the optical properties of the interstellar medium. These two problems are discussed in the following sections of this chapter.

225

A schematic reddening-curve is shown in Figure 1, where absorption in magnitudes, A, is plotted as a function of inverse wavelength for a certain standard total absorption. Since neutral absorption is negligible (Dufay 1957), the reddening-curve tends to zero as the wavelength tends to infinity. The dashed portion of the curve represents an extrapolation beyond the last observed point in the infrared. If the magnitude of a star is observed at two effective wavelengths,

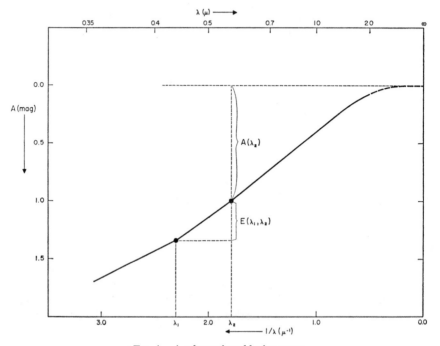

Fig. 1.—A schematic reddening-curve

λ_1 and λ_2, then the contribution to the corresponding color index resulting from interstellar reddening is

$$A(\lambda_1) - A(\lambda_2) = E(\lambda_1, \lambda_2) ,$$

where E is the color excess. The corresponding ratio of total to selective absorption, R, then is

$$R(\lambda_1, \lambda_2) = \frac{A(\lambda_1)}{E(\lambda_1, \lambda_2)} = \frac{A(\lambda_1)}{A(\lambda_1) - A(\lambda_2)} .$$

Once R is established from the reddening-curve, the total absorption at wavelength λ_1 can be found from the measured color excess. The magnitude of a star measured at effective wavelength λ_1 can thus be corrected for the effect of interstellar absorption.

The reddening-curve can be established through a spectrophotometric comparison of a pair of stars, one highly reddened and one little reddened. In principle, any intrinsic differences in the spectral energy distribution of the two stars can be taken into account on the basis of their spectra, and the remaining difference in magnitude, as a function of wavelength, can be attributed to the effects of interstellar absorption. In practice, it is more convenient to select pairs of stars having the same spectral type. In this case the two stars are assumed to have the same intrinsic spectral energy distribution, and the differences in magnitude as a function of wavelength are due entirely to interstellar absorption except for a constant difference depending on the relative distances and absolute magnitudes of the two stars. In practice, this constant is evaluated by extrapolating the observed reddening-curve to $1/\lambda = 0$ beyond the last observed point in the infrared.

Following the work of Trumpler, spectrophotometric studies of this type were made by Rudnick (1936), Greenstein (1938), and others. These confirmed Trumpler's conclusion that, in the range of wavelength accessible with photographic emulsions, interstellar absorption was approximately a linear function of reciprocal wavelength, although a slight curvature in the relation was suggested by these observations. The study of the interstellar absorption-curve was first extended into the infrared by J. S. Hall (1937) in his photoelectric investigation of ζ and ε Persei. This pair of stars has proved useful in studies of interstellar absorption on account of their brightness, their similarity in spectral type, and their differing amounts of reddening. Hall's observations of ζ and ε Persei extended our knowledge of the absorption-curve to a wavelength of approximately 1 μ. A relation of the form

$$\Delta m(\lambda) \propto \lambda^{-a}$$

was fitted to the observations. Although a coefficient of $a = 1$ provided an adequate fit, a literal interpretation of the data suggested that a increases from a value of 1.2 in the visual to 1.6 in the infrared.

Once the law of interstellar absorption had been established over a wide spectral range, the uniformity of the law in different parts of the sky became a problem of considerable interest. This was investigated in great detail by Stebbins and Whitford (1943, 1945). Photoelectric observations were made in six rather broad spectral regions between λ 3530 and λ 10,300 for a number of reddened and unreddened early-type stars. Comparisons were then made of pairs of stars, one reddened and one unreddened, in order to obtain curves of Δm versus $1/\lambda$. These curves were normalized to the same total reddening, and deviations from a linear $1/\lambda$ relation ($1/\lambda$ law) between λ 3530 and λ 10,300 were computed for each pair. Several important conclusions were reached. First, in all cases the deviations from the $1/\lambda$ law are in the same direction, so that the absorption in the intermediate spectral regions is greater than the $1/\lambda$ law would indicate. Second, the amount of deviation from the $1/\lambda$ law is, within the errors of observation, the same for stars in different parts of the sky. A single exception, θ^1

Orionis, will be discussed in § 2.2 below. These results suggested a considerable uniformity in the optical properties of the interstellar medium. A number of curves, resulting from the work of Stebbins and Whitford, which show the observed deviations from the 1/λ law for various pairs of stars are shown in Figure 2.

More recently, Whitford (1958) has compared pairs of reddened and unreddened stars by means of a photoelectric spectrum scanner developed by Code (1954). The wavelength range is approximately the same as that of the six-color photometry, and the agreement between the two types of observations is excellent. The scanner observations are superior to the six-color results, in the sense

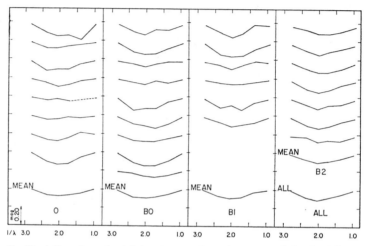

Fɪɢ. 2.—Deviations from the 1/λ law for stars in various parts of the sky (after Stebbins and Whitford 1943).

that a greater number of points along the reddening-curve can be measured with the scanner and their respective effective inverse wavelengths can be more precisely determined.

The extension of the observed reddening-curve into the infrared beyond the 1 μ region was accomplished by Whitford (1948, 1958), using a lead sulfide photoconductive cell. Observations of reddened and unreddened stars at inverse wavelengths of 1.11, 0.84, and 0.48 μ^{-1} were made, and the segment of the reddening-curve that was established in this way was fitted to the previously determined reddening-curve based on the spectrum-scanner observations.

The definitive reddening-curve of Whitford is shown in Figure 3. The solid circles represent means of spectrum-scanner observations of three pairs of stars, while the open circles represent means of the lead sulfide observations of five pairs of stars. For each pair, the observations were normalized to a standard color excess. The reddening-curve, as shown in Figure 3, appears to consist of three distinct sections: a linear portion between $1/\lambda = 2.2\ \mu^{-1}$ and $0.8\ \mu^{-1}$; another linear portion between 3.0 μ^{-1} and 2.2 μ^{-1}, which has a smaller slope; and a curved portion in the infrared between 0.8 μ^{-1} and 0.0 μ^{-1}. The dotted segment is extrapolated. The fact that the two linear sections of the curve have different slopes accounts for the observed deviations from the linear $1/\lambda$ law in the spectral range covered by the six-color photometry. The inverse curvature in the infrared corresponds more nearly to the limiting case of scattering by dielectric particles much smaller than the wavelength, i.e., extinction proportional to $1/\lambda^4$.

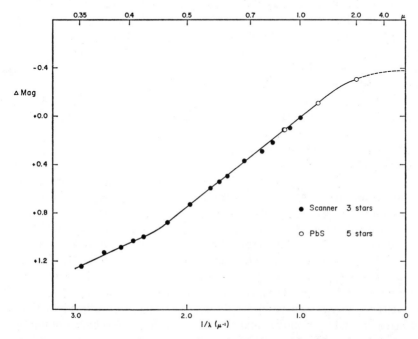

FIG. 3.—The reddening-curve derived from observations with a photoelectric spectrum scanner and a lead sulfide photoconductive cell (after Whitford 1958).

1.2. THE RATIO OF TOTAL TO SELECTIVE ABSORPTION

The ratio, R, of total to selective absorption for any two-color system for which the effective inverse wavelengths are known can be obtained directly from the observed reddening-curve. Three sources of error are inherent in this method of determining R. The first of these arises from errors in the observed reddening-curve itself. These, in turn, can arise primarily from errors in the determination of the effective inverse wavelengths at which the individual observations were made (Whitford 1958) and errors arising from differences in the intrinsic spectral energy distributions of the two stars being compared. Errors of the first type can be minimized by making the individual observations with a relatively narrow-band receiver such as the spectrum scanner used by Whitford.

Errors of the second type will be small, provided that the two stars being compared have the same effective temperature. However, if the two stars differ in luminosity, an intrinsic difference will exist between their respective Balmer discontinuities. This difference must be taken into account in deriving the ultraviolet portion of the reddening-curve (Divan 1954).

The second source of error in the determination of R arises from whatever error is committed in the extrapolation of the reddening-curve from the last observed point in the infrared to $1/\lambda = 0$. The important theoretical work of van de Hulst (1949) can serve here as a guide. Theoretical extinction-curves have been tabulated by van de Hulst under various assumptions regarding the refractive index and size-distribution function of the interstellar particles. Those theoretical curves which provide the best fit to the observed portion of the reddening-curve can provide reasonable extrapolations to $1/\lambda = 0$ that interagree satisfactorily.

The third source of error in R arises from errors in the determination of the effective inverse wavelengths corresponding to the color system for which R is being determined. These depend on the spectral response-curves of the equipment and, to some extent, on the spectral energy distribution of the stars being observed (Blanco 1956).

One of the objections to the determination of the ratio of total to selective absorption from the reddening-curve lies, as mentioned above, in the fact that it is based on an extrapolation of the curve to $1/\lambda = 0$. This is necessary in order to evaluate the constant difference in magnitude between the reddened and unreddened stars which arises from differences in luminosity and in distance. If a pair of stars, one reddened and one unreddened, could be found which have the same spectral type and luminosity and which are at the same distance, then this constant would be zero. The measured differences in magnitude as a function of wavelength would then be identical with the absorption suffered by the reddened star, and the ratio of total to selective absorption could be obtained directly by a comparison of the measured absorption at the appropriate wavelength with the color excess. The extrapolation of the reddening-curve in this case would be unnecessary. Pairs of stars having the same temperature and luminosity, the same distance, and different degrees of reddening can indeed be found in distant clusters and associations. In practice, a group of stars having the same spectral type and luminosity class can be segregated from the membership of a large association. Then, for these stars,

$$m = m_0 + RE,$$

where m is the apparent magnitude and m_0 is the apparent magnitude corrected for absorption. Since m_0 is essentially the same for all stars of this group, R can be read directly as the slope of the relation between the apparent magnitudes and the color excesses. If the absolute magnitudes of the stars in the association can be accurately estimated, then all the members can be treated together by means of the relation

$$m - M = R E + 5 \log D - 5,$$

where M is the absolute magnitude and D is the distance. In this case, R can be read as the slope of the relation between the apparent distance moduli and the color excesses, since D is the same for all members. Determinations of R have been made in this way by Sharpless (1952), Whitford (1958), and Houck (1956). This method of obtaining R has the additional advantage that precise knowledge of the effective inverse wavelengths of the photometric system for which R is being determined is not necessary. By far the largest source of error in this method is the large scatter introduced into the relation between $m - M$ and E which arises from uncertainties in the absolute magnitude determinations.

1.3. Reddening Measured in Two- and Three-Color Systems

The first extensive study of the distribution of observed color excesses was made by Stebbins, Huffer, and Whitford (1940). The colors of 1332 O- and B-type stars were observed photoelectrically at effective wavelengths of $\lambda\lambda$ 4260 and 4770. These colors define the C_1 system. A comparison of these colors with normal colors derived from observations of nearby stars yielded color excesses denoted by E_1. The ratio of total visual absorption to E_1 was taken to be $R = 7$ on the basis of the above effective wavelengths and the simple assumption that the absorption is a linear function of $1/\lambda$. Fortuitously, the effective wavelengths of the C_1 system are such that the value of R so obtained is close to the value that results from Whitford's reddening-curve. The currently accepted value of R on the C_1 system (Morgan et al. 1953) is

$$\frac{A_v}{E_1} = 6.1 \pm 0.4.$$

On the basis of mean absolute magnitudes and the C_1 photometry, Stebbins, Huffer, and Whitford determined approximate distances for the 1332 O- and B-type stars in their list. The very important conclusion reached in this investigation is that the absorption in our Galaxy is so irregular that a mean absorption coefficient has little significance. It is evident that the concept of a uniform absorbing layer in our Galaxy is not valid and that photometric distance determinations of individual stars require individual absorption corrections.

The application of a three-color photometric system to the study of interstellar reddening was first discussed by Becker (1938, 1942, 1948). The "color difference" (CD) proposed by Becker consists of the difference between two color indices: a short-wavelength index ($\lambda\lambda$ 3700–4800) and a long-wavelength index ($\lambda\lambda$ 4800–6300). These wavelengths were chosen so that the color excesses were identical for the two colors. Consequently, the effects of interstellar absorption cancel in the color difference, and the latter is independent of inter-

stellar reddening. The color difference thus makes it possible to distinguish between reddened B-type stars and unreddened late-type stars without knowledge
of their spectral types.

The three-color method of Becker has been extended by Johnson and Morgan
(1953), Hiltner and Johnson (1956), and Johnson (1958) in connection with the
U, B, V system. The effective wavelengths in this system are approximately
$\lambda\lambda$ 3500, 4350, and 5550. If E_u and E_y are the ultraviolet and blue-yellow color
excesses, respectively, a quantity Q can be constructed such that

$$Q = (U - B) - \frac{E_u}{E_y}(B - V).$$

Thus Q is independent of interstellar reddening and is related to the intrinsic
color. For the B-type stars, Q has been calibrated in terms of spectral type and
luminosity class (Johnson 1958); thus, if the luminosity class of a B-type star is
known, as in the case of a star on the main sequence of a cluster, then Q can be
used directly to determine the spectral type.

In order for Q to be determined, the coefficient E_u/E_y must be known. Blanco
(1956) suggests that this coefficient is not constant over a wide range of color,
on account of small shifts in the effective wavelengths of the filters dependent
on the color of the star being observed. Hiltner and Johnson (1956) found this
to be the case, and for O-type stars they obtained the relation

$$\frac{E_u}{E_y} = 0.72 + 0.05E_y.$$

For B-type stars, Johnson (1958) has given the coefficient in the form

$$\frac{E_u}{E_y} = X + 0.05E_y,$$

where $X = 0.72$, as before, for O-type stars and has slightly different values for
the B-type subclasses. The fact that E_u/E_y depends slightly on spectral type was
first pointed out by Lindholm (1957).

Since, for a given luminosity class, Q is a function of spectral type, then Q can
be related to intrinsic color. Johnson (1958) has found that, for B-type stars of
luminosity class V,

$$(B - V)_0 = 0.332 \, Q.$$

A comparison of $(B - V)_0$ determined in this way with the observed value of
$B - V$ immediately yields the color excess, E_y. Some knowledge of spectral type
and luminosity class is necessary, however, for the determination of color excesses in this way.

The ratio of total to selective absorption on the $B - V$ system has been
discussed by Blanco (1956), who finds a value of

$$R = \frac{A_v}{E_y} = 3.0$$

on the basis of Whitford's reddening-curve. Hiltner and Johnson (1956) have studied variations in the absorption within the region of h–χ Persei by the method discussed above and find

$$R = 3.0 \pm 0.3 \text{ (p.e.)} .$$

These values suggest a mean of

$$R = 3.0 \pm 0.2 \text{ (p.e.)}$$

for the ratio of total to selective absorption on the $B - V$ system.

§ 2. VARIATIONS IN THE LAW OF INTERSTELLAR REDDENING

2.1. PHOTOMETRIC STUDIES

The problem of possible variations in the reddening-curve in different parts of the sky has been a matter of interest as long as the reddening-curve has been known. If such variations exist, they reflect, on the one hand, variations in the quality of the interstellar medium in different regions of the Galaxy and, on the other hand, quantitative variations in the total interstellar extinction as compared with a given color excess. The latter would result in errors in photometric parallaxes derived on the basis of a mean ratio of total to selective absorption. An understanding of the degree of constancy of R throughout the Galaxy is important, therefore, in studies of the space distribution of distant stars.

Spectrophotometric studies of the reddening-curve for pairs of stars in various parts of the sky have suggested that the absorbing properties of the interstellar medium are extremely uniform. Figure 2 shows curves of deviation from the $1/\lambda$ law for a variety of pairs of stars throughout the sky. Probably no discrepancies between individual curves exist that cannot be ascribed to accidental errors of observation. The only exception is θ^1 Orionis, for which the deviations from the $1/\lambda$ law (not shown in Fig. 2) are approximately twice as large as for other stars. In a more restricted spectral range, Mlle Divan (1954) has studied the reddening-curve between λ 3130 and λ 6100 by means of photographic spectrophotometry. In the region of overlap, the agreement with the results of the six-color photometry is excellent (Whitford 1958). Mlle Divan found, for the spectral range in which she worked, a uniform law of reddening in various parts of the sky. This is in disagreement, however, with the results of Schalén (1952, 1957), which suggest small real variations in the reddening-curve among various stars in the regions of Cygnus and Cepheus.

Possible variations in the law of interstellar reddening have also been investigated by means of three-color photometry. Johnson and Morgan (1955) and Hiltner and Johnson (1956) have investigated the possibility of variations in the ratio of the color excesses, E_u/E_y, for several hundred O-type stars. Since these stars all have essentially the same intrinsic color, the ratio of the color excesses can be read directly as the slope of the relation between $U - B$ and $B - V$ for these stars. An anomalous slope has been found for those O-type stars located behind the Great Rift in Cygnus. This is illustrated in Figure 4, in which the open circles correspond to stars behind the Cygnus Rift, while the solid circles represent stars elsewhere in the Milky Way. The curve has been drawn to represent the "reddening line,"

$$\frac{E_u}{E_y} = 0.72 + 0.05\, E_y,$$

which has been adopted as standard by Hiltner and Johnson. A further anomaly appearing in Figure 4 is that the Rift stars lie along a straight line, whereas the

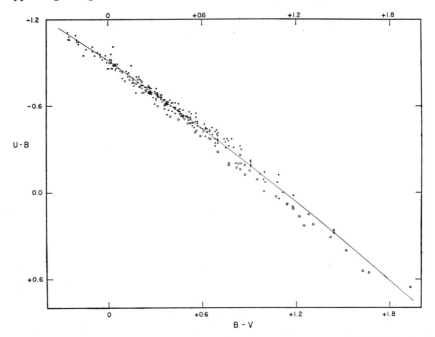

Fig. 4.—The reddening line for O-type stars. Open circles represent stars behind the Great Rift in Cygnus; solid circles represent stars elsewhere in the Milky Way (after Hiltner and Johnson 1956).

other stars lie along a line curved in accordance with the above expression. The possibility that the apparent difference in the reddening lines for the two groups of stars is caused by intrinsic differences in the stars themselves cannot be entirely ruled out on the basis of the data at hand. It seems probable, however, that the difference between the two reddening lines results from an anomalous reddening law for the Cygnus stars. More detailed spectrophotometric studies will be necessary, however, to determine the exact nature of the anomaly.

Another method of employing broad-band photometry in the study of variations in the law of reddening is through the study of variations in the ratio of total to selective absorption as determined from differences in the amount of reddening among the members of distant clusters and associations (see § 1.2 above). An example of this method is shown in Figure 5, which illustrates the determination of R for the I Crucis association (Houck 1956). In this case, the apparent distance moduli for members of the I Crucis association are plotted against the observed color excesses on the E_1 system. Crosses represent background stars, while open and solid circles represent, respectively, points of half and full weight. The value of R so obtained is

$$R = \frac{A_v}{E_1} = 6.3 \pm 0.2 .$$

This agrees well with the currently adopted value of 6.1 $\pm$ 0.4 and thus suggests that there is no peculiarity in the reddening of the I Crucis association.

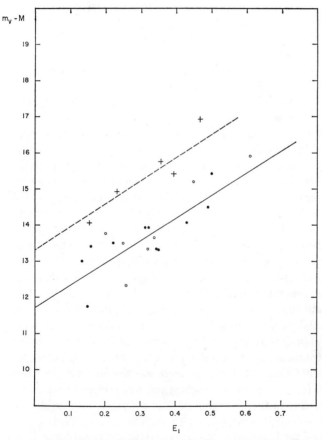

FIG. 5.—Apparent distance moduli for stars in the association I Crucis plotted against color excess. Open and solid circles carry half and full weight, respectively. Crosses represent distant background stars (after Houck 1956).

It should be emphasized that, in the search for variations in the law of inter-stellar reddening, the study of possible variations in R is a more powerful approach than the study of possible variations in the ratio of color excesses, such as E_u/E_y. Variations in E_u/E_y depend only on changes in the curvature of the reddening law in the wavelength interval between λ 3500 and λ 5500. Variations in R, however, are related to the inverse curvature of the reddening law in the infrared and, in effect, indicate peculiarities in the reddening law between λ 4500 and infinite wavelength. Thus an anomalous value of E_u/E_y does not necessarily indicate an anomalous ratio of total to selective absorption, and vice versa, since the peculiarity in E_u/E_y may reside in the ultraviolet. In either case, spectrophotometric studies over a wide wavelength range are of considerable value in tracing the peculiarity.

2.2. The Orion Nebula Region

The stars immersed in the Orion Nebula have been the subject of a number of investigations since the early spectrophotometric work of Baade and Minkowski (1937), which indicated that the reddening-curves for stars in this region are peculiar. Subsequent six-color observations of the Trapezium stars by Stebbins and Whitford (1945) tended to confirm this conclusion, since the deviations from the $1/\lambda$ law for these stars exceeded the normal values by a factor of about 2. Photometric observations of the Trapezium stars are complicated by their proximity to one another and by the brightness of the surrounding nebula. In the case of the six-color observations, all four components were measured simultaneously through a diaphragm 41″ in diameter. The spectral types of the components range from O6 to B3; consequently, no completely satisfactory comparison star was available. Stebbins and Whitford compared the integrated light of the Trapezium stars with an unreddened star of type B0.

In the more limited wavelength range of $\lambda\lambda$ 3900–6100, Mlle Divan (1954) studied the reddening-curves of stars in the Orion Nebula by means of photo-graphic spectrophotometry. She concluded that within this wavelength interval there is no difference between the reddening-curves for the Orion stars and those for stars in general. Sharpless (1954) arrived at essentially the same conclusion, pointing out that the ratio of color excesses, E_u/E_y, is normal in Orion and that therefore the curvature in the reddening law in the wavelength range $\lambda\lambda$ 3500–5500 does not deviate appreciably from that of other stars. The six-color observations of stars in the Orion Nebula were extended by Stebbins and Kron (1956) to include θ^2 Orionis. In this case, there was also evidence for abnormally large deviations from the $1/\lambda$ law. Stebbins and Kron suggest that the peculiarities in the observed reddening-curves for θ^1 and θ^2 Orionis may be due to the presence of unseen red companions, since these stars are known spectroscopic binaries. It was shown that a normal reddening-curve would result for θ^2 Orionis if it were assumed to have an unseen companion of spectral type K0. No satisfactory representation of this kind could be found for θ^1 Orionis, however. Infrared spectrograms of θ^1 (A, B, C, and D) Orionis and θ^2 Orionis have been obtained by Sharpless (1956) and of θ^1 (C) Orionis by Hallam (1959). No evidence of late-type companions was found up to the red limit of the spectra, i.e., about λ 9000. Although no direct evidence has been found to support the conclusion that the peculiar reddening-curves found for stars in the Orion Nebula are caused by unseen red companions, this is nevertheless a possibility that should be considered in studies of the infrared portion of the reddening-curve.

The ratio of total to selective absorption in the Orion Nebula region was studied by Sharpless (1952). Plots of color excess versus visual apparent magnitude for groups of Orion stars having the same spectral type and luminosity class yielded a value of R approximately twice the normal value. This is in keeping with the large deviations from the $1/\lambda$ law found for these stars on the basis of the six-color photometry. Sharpless' assumption that the high value of R applies to the entire Orion aggregate may not be justified, although the reddening in the regions outside the immediate surroundings of the nebula is generally too small for a definite conclusion to be reached on this point.

A search for variations in the law of interstellar reddening was made by Hallam (1959) by means of a seven-color photometry extending from λ 2950 to λ 11,000. Fifty-four reddened early-type stars in various parts of the sky were observed, as well as a number of slightly reddened stars for comparison. A $1/\lambda$ law was fitted to each set of observations at the red ($1/\lambda = 1.39\ \mu^{-1}$) and blue ($1/\lambda = 2.41\ \mu^{-1}$) points, and all curves were normalized to the same total amount of reddening. Deviations from the $1/\lambda$ law were then presented as a plot of the deviation $\Delta Y(1/\lambda = 1.68)$ versus the deviation $\Delta G(1/\lambda = 2.02)$. These results are shown in Figure 6. The three brightest Trapezium stars were observed and plotted individually. In the observation of these stars a small enough diaphragm was used that the deflection due to the nebular background was never more than a few per cent that of the star. Figure 6 indicates large deviations from the $1/\lambda$ law for stars associated with the Orion Nebula, as well as deviations of moderate size for stars associated with NGC 2244. Hallam points out that two distinct regions in Figure 6 can be isolated when it is recognized that almost all the stars located below the dashed line are associated with regions of bright emission nebulosity. Those associated with the brightest nebulosity show the largest deviations. The Cygnus Rift stars, on the other hand, exhibit yellow deviations which are somewhat smaller than average.

2.3. Conclusions

On the basis of the extensive spectrophotometric work which has been done in connection with the study of the law of reddening in different parts of the sky, one can conclude that the accuracy of photometric parallaxes is not generally limited by the use of a mean ratio of total to selective absorption. Small variations in color excess amounting to several hundredths of a magnitude per magnitude of total absorption may occur, however, from star to star. Stars in two regions exhibit anomalous reddening: those in the Great Rift in Cygnus, which indicate a value of E_u/E_y higher than average, and those in the Orion Nebula, which indicate a value of R about twice the average value. Spectrophotometric data extending beyond 1 μ are in agreement with these results: the small deviations from the $1/\lambda$ law found by Hallam for stars in the Cygnus Rift are in accord with the large value of E_u/E_y in this region; similarly, the large deviations

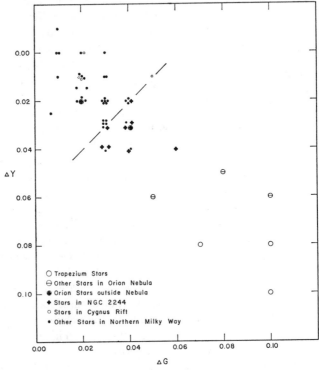

FIG. 6.—Deviations from the $1/\lambda$ law in the yellow plotted against corresponding deviations in the green (after Hallam 1959). The dotted line is explained in text.

from the $1/\lambda$ law found for the Orion stars are in accord with the large value of R found there. Apparently, the reddening-curve for the Orion region has a smaller slope than normal in the blue and visual as compared with the red region. The reddening-curve for the Cygnus Rift, on the other hand, has a larger slope than normal in the blue and ultraviolet, indicative of a relatively greater amount of absorption in this spectral region.

It has been suggested by Johnson and Morgan (1955) that the absorbing characteristics of a dust cloud can be modified by the proximity of an O-type star. If the effect of the radiation of the star is to shift the maximum of the particle size distribution toward larger sizes, then the relatively small absorbing

power in the ultraviolet observed in the Orion Nebula can be explained. The
dust which forms the Great Rift, on the other hand, is situated in the foreground
relative to the reddened stars in Cygnus, and the particle size distribution is thus
probably unmodified by radiation from O-type stars. The reddening-curves observed for the majority of early-type stars in the Galaxy may represent cases
which are intermediate between these two extremes. This additional dimension
in the study of interstellar reddening, i.e., the relative placement of star and
absorbing clouds, is an important matter for future consideration.

REFERENCES

BAADE, W., and		
MINKOWSKI, R.	1937	*Ap. J.*, **86**, 123.
BECKER, W.	1938	*Zs. f. Ap.*, **15**, 225.
	1942	*A.N.*, **272**, 179.
	1948	*Ap. J.*, **107**, 278.
BLANCO, V. M.	1956	*Ap. J.*, **123**, 64.
CODE, A. D.	1954	*Proceedings N.S.F. Conference on Stellar Atmos-pheres*, ed. M. H. WRUBEL (Bloomington: Indi-ana University Press).
DIVAN, L.	1954	*Ann. d'ap.*, **17**, 456.
DUFAY, J.	1957	*Galactic Nebulae and Interstellar Matter* (London: Hutchinson), p. 177.
GREENSTEIN, J. L.	1938	*Ap. J.*, **87**, 151.
HALL, J. S.	1937	*Ap. J.*, **85**, 145.
HALLAM, K. L.	1959	*Ph.D. thesis, University of Wisconsin.*
HILTNER, W. A., and		
JOHNSON, H. L.	1956	*Ap. J.*, **124**, 367.
HOUCK, T. E.	1956	*Ph.D. thesis, University of Wisconsin.*
HULST, H. C. VAN DE	1949	*Pub. Utrecht Obs.*, Vol. **11**, Part 2.
JOHNSON, H. L.	1958	*Lowell Obs. Bull.*, **4**, 37.
JOHNSON, H. L., and		
MORGAN, W. W.	1953	*Ap. J.*, **117**, 313.
	1955	*Ibid.*, **122**, 142.
LINDHOLM, E. H.	1957	*Ap. J.*, **126**, 588.
MORGAN, W. W.,		
HARRIS, D. L., and		
JOHNSON, H. L.	1953	*Ap. J.*, **118**, 92.
RUDNICK, J.	1936	*Ap. J.*, **83**, 394.
SCHALÉN, C.	1952	*Ann. Uppsala Obs.*, Vol. **3**, No. 5.
	1957	*Lund Obs. Medd.*, Ser. II, No. 135.
SHARPLESS, S.	1952	*Ap. J.*, **116**, 251.
	1954	*Ibid.*, **119**, 200.
	1956	Unpublished.
STEBBINS, J.,		
HUFFER, C. M., and		
WHITFORD, A. E.	1940	*Ap. J.*, **91**, 20.

STEBBINS, J., and
   KRON, G. E.   1956   *Ap. J.*, **123**, 440.

STEBBINS, J., and
   WHITFORD, A. E.   1943   *Ap. J.*, **98**, 20.
                           1945   *Ibid.*, **102**, 318.

TRUMPLER, R. J.   1930a *Lick Obs. Bull.* **14**, 154.
                           1930b *Pub. A.S.P.*, **42**, 214.
                           1930c *Ibid.*, p. 267.

WHITFORD, A. E.   1948   *Ap. J.*, **107**, 102.
                           1958   *A.J.*, **63**, 201.

CHAPTER 13

Applications of Multicolor Photometry

W. BECKER

University of Basel, Switzerland

§ 1. GENERAL REMARKS

THE classical wavelength bands used in visual and photographic integrated photometry are instrumentally conditioned by the color sensitivity of the eye and by the early photographic plates. The same is true of the first photoelectric observations by Guthnick and Stebbins, in which the photocell prescribed the spectral region. It still holds for most photoelectric and photographic photometry being done at present because the color sensitivity of modern multipliers and photographic emulsions favors the classical spectral bands, which are adequate for most photometric problems at the present time.

Since the spectral bands of integrated photometry are based on instrumental conditions, it is natural to add new ones according to instrumental possibilities and to test their use empirically. Öpik and Livländer (1925) and Livländer, Öpik, and Silde (1935) used for the first time an ultraviolet band and defined an ultraviolet color index. The two-color index diagram appears for the first time in their work, but only to show the complicated relation between the classical color index and their new one. King and Ingalls (1930) determined red magnitudes for the first time, and Hall (1934) introduced an infrared band. However, the potentialities of multicolor photometry were still not realized. New bands were often used only to enlarge the scale of color indices and thus make them relatively more accurate.

For an unbiased evaluation of the various spectral bands used, the objectives of integrated stellar photometry must be kept in mind and chief emphasis given to observational, rather than instrumental, requirements. Only then can photometry develop successfully (Becker 1946, 1948; Greenstein 1946).

The radiation of a star differs significantly from the radiation of a black body. The most pronounced deviations are the Balmer discontinuity in early spectral types and the over-all depression of the intensity toward the shorter wavelengths in later-type stars, which becomes greater for the shorter wavelengths and for the later spectral types (Brill 1923). Both deviations depend on spectral type and luminosity, as shown schematically in Figure 1 (Becker and Hartwig 1937).

It is clear from the foregoing that it is necessary to consider the various problems to be solved by multicolor photometry when deciding upon the spectral

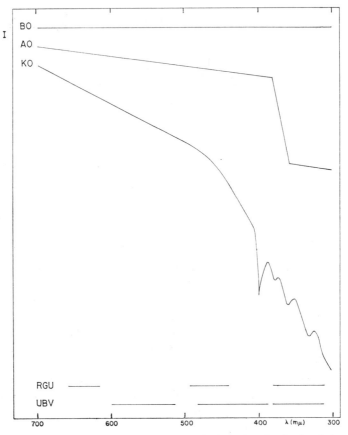

FIG. 1.—The relation between wavelength and the intensity distribution (schematic) in stellar spectra and the half-widths of the spectral bands in the R, G, U and the U, B, V systems.

bands to be used. Each problem has its special requirements. There are problems in which only a single magnitude is needed for as many stars as possible. Other problems, however, require the determination of certain peculiarities of the intensity distribution with the help of integrated photometry, because monochromatic spectrophotometry may not be possible or economical. In this case broad-band multicolor photometry is used. However it should be borne in mind that the amount of information obtained from multicolor photometry does not necessarily increase with the number of spectral bands used, because the magnitudes referring to the different sections are not independent of each other.

Multicolor photometry is of relatively recent origin, and it is not yet possible to make definite statements about its potentialities. The method is still being tested in various ways, and the establishment of one or several photometric systems will be the end result rather than the beginning of these tests. The tests are made more difficult because there is at present no comprehensive system of photoelectrically measured monochromatic intensity distributions in stellar spectra that may serve as a guide and a test of a multicolor photometric system. Only in the cases where intensities of lines or bands are to be measured with the help of multicolor photometry are the facts and the instrumental needs clear. The bands must have a certain position and a certain width, which can be obtained only by means of interference filters. Strömgren (1950, 1951) has established this kind of multicolor photometry and has used it for a two-dimensional classification based on the Lindblad criteria (see also R. v. d. R. Woolley 1956). More about this method will be found in chapter 9.

If the color sensitivity of the photometric system has to be defined by the combination of a receiver and a color filter, as is generally the case in multicolor photometry, the situation becomes complicated, in that the reproducibility suffers because of compromises which must be made between what is specified by the system and what is available to the observer. It is helpful if the system can be closely related to a monochromatic spectral photometry, especially when photometry in only three spectral bands is involved.

The number of spectral bands in a multicolor photometry, their position, and, to a certain degree, their width should be determined by the aims pursued with this photometry. These aims vary, and one has to consider at the outset the possibility that each different problem may require a different photometric system. Only when photometric work has reached a more advanced state of development will it be possible to decide whether there exists a single, especially economical, system that satisfies all requirements, although perhaps not in the most efficient way.

The chief aims of multicolor photometry at present are the measurements of the Balmer discontinuity, the general depression in the range of shorter wavelengths in late-type stars, color excesses caused by interstellar absorption, and the determination of population type. We shall see that multicolor photometry must fulfil different requirements for each of these cases. It appears at the present time that all four problems can be solved satisfactorily by three-color photometry, but the optimum positions of the bands differ. The Balmer jump is best measured when two colors are entirely on the longer-wavelength side, but not too close together, and the third color completely on the shorter-wavelength side. The determination of the ultraviolet depression is most successful when two colors are on the red side of λ 4700, where the depression is still small. The third should again be as far as possible in the ultraviolet, where the depression is the greatest. The determination of interstellar reddening ideally requires a position of the colors such that the color excess amounts to the same for both color indices.

In this case the width of the spectral bands is important. If they are too broad, then the effective wavelength of each regional band is shifted according to increasing reddening by interstellar absorption. This means that, within the same photometric system, large and small color excesses correspond to different effective wavelengths. As far as the determination of population type is concerned, this requires the measurement of an ultraviolet magnitude, but the most favorable positions of the two other wave bands are as yet not too well known. In regard to the other problems of three-color photometry mentioned above, it has been found that the smaller the spectral bands, the better the results. However, the fact that multicolor photometry has its principal application in work on faint stars puts limitations to this rule.

If we summarize the essential purpose of multicolor photometry, we find that it has to give the best possible representation of certain peculiarities in the intensity distribution of celestial bodies by means of well-defined color indices in those cases in which a monochromatic spectral photometry is impossible or uneconomical. The choice of spectral bands is a compromise between the demand for the greatest efficiency and what can be technically realized. Conservative viewpoints or the demand for convertibility between the different systems is, in the long run, not essential in this type of photometry.

§ 2. MULTICOLOR SYSTEMS IN USE AT PRESENT

There are at present four systems of multicolor photometry being used, not counting photometry with interference filters. They are the six-color photometry of Stebbins and Whitford (1943) and three different systems of three-color photometry, namely, the U, B, V system of Johnson and Morgan (1953), the U_c, B, V system of the Cape Observatory (*Cape Mimeo.*, No. 5, 1958) and the R, G, U system of Becker (1938, 1946). The first three systems are defined photoelectrically, the last one photographically. Details of these systems are discussed in chapter 11.

The six-color photometry was designed as a method for high-precision measurement of intensity distributions, principally for application to fainter objects. Peculiarities in the spectra were not considered at first, and the spectral bands were so chosen that the instrumental requirements could be easily realized. It is important to fix the effective wavelengths exactly for different intensity distributions, to avoid systematic errors in the application of this method. The effective wavelengths defined by Brill (1923) seem to be the best system. So far, the method has been used mainly to measure intensity distributions and color temperatures in non-variable and variable stars and to determine the dependence of interstellar absorption on the wavelength. A six- or more color photometry of this kind may also be used for testing the efficiency of different spectral bands for certain purposes. Photographic photometry is not practical in this type of work.

The three different systems of three-color photometry were defined to give an expression for certain peculiarities in stellar spectra by means of color indices. These measurements should give essential data about the observed objects which could not be obtained with two-color photometry.

The U, B, V system and the U_c, B, V system are mainly designed to measure the Balmer discontinuity by adding a third spectral band in the ultraviolet to the two classical bands. The R, G, U system, on the other hand, has its spectral bands in such a position that, in addition to the Balmer jump, the depression of the spectra toward shorter wavelengths can be measured in a very efficient way. When the R, G, U system was established, it was intended to have the spectral bands so located that the two color excesses caused by interstellar reddening

TABLE 1

EFFECTIVE WAVELENGTHS λ_i AND HALF-WIDTH $\Delta\lambda$ OF THE SPECTRAL BANDS

Band	λ_i	$\Delta\lambda$	Band	λ_i	$\Delta\lambda$	Band	λ_i	$\Delta\lambda$
U......	3500*	700	U_c......	3700†	....	U......	3690†	540
B......	4350*	970	B......	4350	970	G......	4680‡	490
V......	5550*	850	V......	5550	850	R......	6380‡	400

* After K. H. Schmidt (1956). These wavelengths should be $\lambda\lambda$ 3660, 4400, and 5530.
† Approximate value.
‡ Including the filtering effect of the atmosphere at the zenith.

should be of the same size. However, with the revised law of absorption, this is no longer the case. The effective wavelengths of the three systems of three-color photometry and the half-widths of the spectral ranges are given in Table 1 (Becker and Stock 1954; Johnson 1955).

In three-color photometry the photometric data of an object are given by the magnitude in one of the three colors (V in the U, B, V system, G in the R, G, U system) and two color indices, one for the shorter and one for the longer wavelengths. The definition of the color indices for the longer wavelengths is

$$CI_l = G - R \ (0.56)$$

or

$$B - V \ (0.51) ,$$

and, for the shorter wavelengths,

$$CI_s = U - G \ (0.58)$$

or

$$U - B \ (0.56)$$

or

$$U_c - B \ (0.40) .$$

In the parentheses are given the differences in the reciprocal effective wave-lengths.

Both color indices may contain, besides the stellar color index, a part which is caused by interstellar absorption. Using the two color indices, one can define a quantity, called the "color difference," ΔCI, which is free of the interstellar effect (Becker 1938), where

$$\Delta CI = CI_s - x\, CI_l \,.$$

In this equation x is a numerical factor so chosen that the color excess is the same for both color indices and therefore disappears in ΔCI.

The value of x is derived for the different systems from the sensitivity-curves and the law of interstellar absorption. As long as this law was assumed to be of the form $1/\lambda$, the following definition for x was justified:

$$x = \frac{1/\lambda_U - 1/\lambda_G}{1/\lambda_G - 1/\lambda_R} \quad (\text{Becker})\,.$$

Since the $1/\lambda$ law does not hold, it is preferable to use one of the following empirical relations (Johnson and Morgan 1953):

$$x = \frac{E(U-B)}{E(B-V)}$$

or

$$x = \frac{E(U_c-B)}{E(B-V)}$$

or

$$x = \frac{E(U-G)}{E(G-R)}\,.$$

Johnson and Morgan give the following designation of the color difference obtained with the factor x: $Q = \Delta CI$. The numerical values of x are as follows: $x = 0.72 + 0.05\, E(B-V)$ in the U, B, V system (Hiltner and Johnson 1956); 0.38 in the U_c, B, V system (Stoy 1959); and 0.70 in the R, G, U system (Kruspan 1957). It is seen that the value of x depends on the color excess itself in the U, B, V system and, of course, also in the U_c, B, V system. This is caused by the great width of the classical spectral bands B and V. The effective wavelength of these bands shifts according to the intensity distribution and consequently also according to the color excess (Golay 1959). In the R, G, U system the value of x is practically constant. Three-color photometry can be done either photoelectrically or by the photographic method. This depends upon whether high accuracy is desired or whether extensive work is required, as in the case of photometry of rich clusters or star fields.

§ 3. DIAGRAMS OF THREE-COLOR PHOTOMETRY AND THEIR APPLICATION

3.1. GENERAL

The purpose of three-color photometry is to derive other data from the two color indices or from the color differences, ΔCI. It is therefore necessary, for calibration purposes, to know the relation between the data of three-color photometry and the desired data for a representative number of stars. These relations are best known for the photoelectrically defined U, B, V system and the least for the R, G, U system, which has been used so far only photographically. For this reason, the relations which follow refer chiefly to the U, B, V system.

3.2. COLOR DIFFERENCE, BALMER DISCONTINUITY, AND SPECTRAL TYPE

The relation between these data is given by Becker (1951) for the R, G, U system (see also Golay 1955); Barbier (1952) gives it for a three-color system (U, V, G), which is adopted from the six-color photometry by Stebbins and Whitford. Figure 2 shows the relation for the U, B, V system. The D-values for the Balmer discontinuity are taken from a paper by Chalonge and Divan (1952).

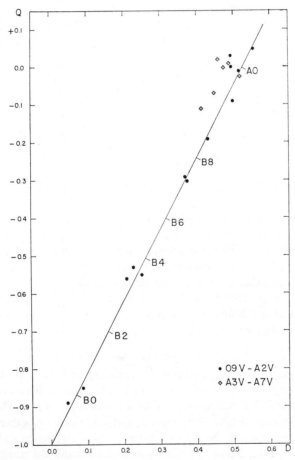

FIG. 2.—The relation between the Balmer jump, D, and color differences, Q, in the U, B, V system (Chalonge and Divan 1952).

For the spectral types from O to A2 of luminosity class V, the data can be represented by the linear equation

$$D = +0.525 + 0.525\ Q\ .$$

This equation can be used for the determination of the Balmer jump for stars earlier than A2 by measuring the color difference Q. The essential points are that it is a simple and precise method, that it also applies to faint stars which are beyond the range of any monochromatic spectral photometry, and that the determination is not affected by interstellar absorption. According to Johnson and Morgan (1953) and Johnson (1958), the relation between Q and the intrinsic color index $(B - V)_0$ is also linear for these stars, and we have

$$(B - V)_0 = 0.332\ Q\ .$$

For those stars for which this relation holds, it is possible to determine the interstellar absorption. Johnson and Morgan (1953) have used it to correct the distance moduli of galactic clusters for interstellar reddening. The relation between

TABLE 2

SPECTRAL TYPE AND COLOR DIFFERENCE, Q

Spectral Type	Q (Mag.)	Spectral Type	Q (Mag.)	Spectral Type	Q (Mag.)
B0 V.......	0.86	B4.........	0.51	B8.........	0.24
B2.........	0.69	B6.........	0.39	A0 V......	0.00

color difference, Q, and spectral type for classes B0 V–A0 V is given in Table 2 (Johnson 1958).

The Balmer jump depends on the spectral type, which means the color temperature (color index). For this reason, the color temperature can also be derived from the color difference, always under the assumption that the stars involved are of type A2 or earlier and of luminosity class V. The Q-values for other luminosity classes are given by Johnson (1958).

The U, B, V system and R, G, U system show the same efficiency for the determination of the Balmer discontinuity, but the U_c, B, V system is, by its nature, somewhat less efficient.

3.3. COLOR DIFFERENCE AND COLOR INDEX

The relation between the Balmer discontinuity and the color difference was considered only for stars earlier than A2 V. The relation between color difference and color index includes stars of all spectral types. So far, the situation is clear only for stars of luminosity class V, and only this class is therefore considered here. In Figure 3 the relation between color difference and color index (Becker 1938, 1942, 1951a, b, 1952a) is given for unreddened stars for the U, B, V system; Q is taken as abscissa and the color index $(B - V)_0$ as ordinate. The curve in the diagram consists of three parts, each of which is nearly linear. The first part expresses the equation between $(B - V)_0$ and Q given above. The inclination of the second part is due to the decreasing Balmer jump with increasing color index. The third part shows the further decrease in color temperature with increasing color index and, above all, the depression toward shorter wavelengths in late-type spectra. The stars between B0 and about K5 are lined up along this curve according to their spectral types and therefore according to

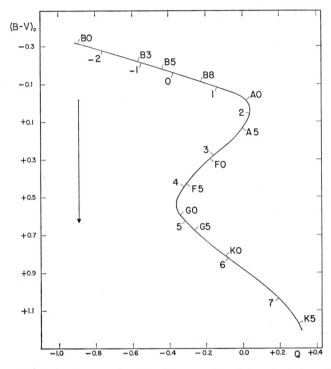

Fig. 3.—The relation between the color difference, Q, and the color index, $(B - V)_0$, in the U, B, V system. The arrow indicates the direction of shift due to interstellar reddening.

their absolute magnitudes. By means of this diagram, it is possible to determine the spectral type or absolute magnitude of a star of class V from three-color photometry, if there is no interstellar absorption involved. This is a very efficient method for stellar statistics that has seldom been used. If there is any interstellar absorption, the stars are shifted vertically downward in the diagram proportional to the absorption, since interstellar reddening changes the ordinate in that direction. The translation due to interstellar reddening for stars of a given apparent magnitude naturally depends in these diagrams on the absolute magnitude or spectral type and is largest at the beginning of the curve for the early-type stars. However, it is only possible to decide in each special case

whether all the available information can lead to a determination of the luminosities, interstellar absorption, and distance modulus.

As far as stars of luminosity class V are concerned, the U, B, V and the
R, G, U systems are probably equally good. For the behavior of stars of other
luminosity classes see § 3.6.

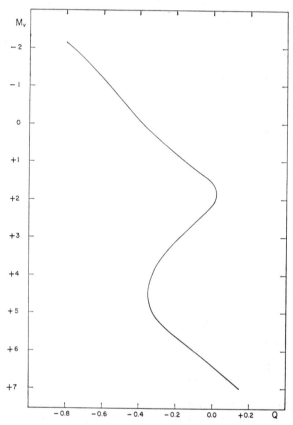

Fig. 4.—The relation between the color difference, Q, and absolute magnitude, M_v, in the
U, B, V system for main-sequence stars (Johnson and Morgan 1953; Johnson 1958).

3.4. Color Differences and Absolute Magnitude

The relation between color differences and absolute magnitude follows from
what has been discussed in §§ 3.2 and 3.3. The diagram in Figure 4 is taken
from data by Johnson and Morgan (1953) and Johnson (1958) for stars of
luminosity class V not affected by interstellar absorption. It is similar to the
diagram in Figure 3 but is used in a different way for the purpose of obtaining a
photometric determination of the absolute magnitudes of stars which are all at
the same distance, as in a star cluster. Becker (1951a, b, 1952b) used this dia-

gram for the first determinations of distances of galactic clusters with the help of the three-color photometry method. For this purpose the diagram of a cluster with apparent magnitudes as the ordinate is superposed over a standard diagram with absolute magnitudes as the ordinate. The difference of the ordinates gives the distance modulus $m - M$, which has to be corrected for interstellar absorption. The color excess which gives this correction is found by comparing the observed color indices of the cluster stars with the intrinsic color index of stars

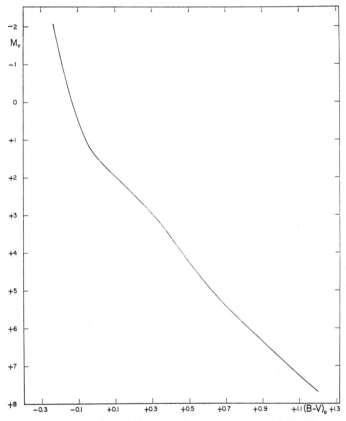

FIG. 5.—The relation between the absolute magnitude, M_v, and a standard main sequence for the color system $(B - V)_0$ (Johnson and Morgan 1953; Johnson 1958).

with the same absolute magnitude (see § 3.5). Whereas the Q-method by Johnson and Morgan (§ 3.2) uses only stars earlier than A2 for the distance determination, this method makes use of all the stars in a cluster. The method is to be recommended especially when there is differential absorption within a cluster.

The U, B, V and R, G, U systems are equally efficient in this case, but the U_c, B, V system is somewhat less favorable because of the smaller influence of the U_c band.

3.5. Color Index and Absolute Magnitude

The relation between color index and absolute magnitude is well known from two-color photometry. The same relation is very useful in three-color photometry because of the significant difference between the two color indices. The Balmer jump and the depression in the ultraviolet part of the spectra for the late-type stars give different shapes to the curves for the two colors, as shown in Figures 5 and 6 (Johnson and Morgan 1953; Johnson 1958).

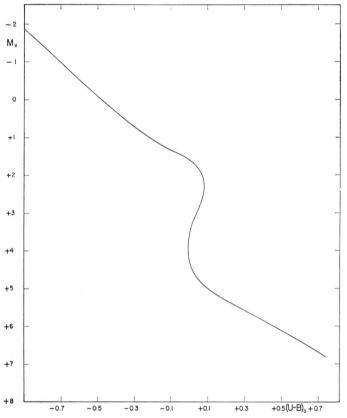

Fig. 6.—The relation between the absolute magnitude, M_v, and the standard main sequence for the color system $(U - B)_0$ (Johnson and Morgan 1953; Johnson 1958).

Becker and Stock (1954) have used the two diagrams for the determination of the distance modulus and color excess of galactic clusters. In general, the method is the same as explained above in § 3.4, but it is more efficient and lucid. One has to superpose the two color-magnitude diagrams of a cluster on the diagrams of Figures 5 and 6. Three conditions have to be met in this case: (1) both diagrams have to coincide as completely as possible, which means that stars with evolutionary effects have to be excluded; (2) the distance modulus has to be the same for both diagrams; (3) the two color excesses have to show the relation that characterizes the photometric system. The method works with the understanding that the "standard zero-age main sequence" is realized at least partly in all clusters and that the law of interstellar absorption can be used uniformly. The authors estimate that the results obtained are correct within 10 per cent.

In some cases, only the $(U - B)$ diagram of a cluster is sufficient for the application of the method. This is the case when the stars of the cluster cover both the flat part and the almost vertical part of the curve. The first part determines the distance modulus and the second part the color excess. The R, G, U and U, B, V systems are equally efficient when applied to this method, but the U_c, B, V system is somewhat less efficient.

3.6. The Relation between the Two-Color Indices

The relation between the two-color indices is given in the two-color diagram. This diagram does not give anything fundamentally new compared with the above-mentioned color difference–color index diagram, but it is clearer and more convenient. The two-color diagram for stars of luminosity class V in the U, B, V system is shown in Figure 7 (Johnson and Morgan 1953; Johnson 1958). The curve deviates from a straight line similar to that in Figure 3 on account of the deviations in the radiation of a star from that of a black body. This difference shows itself most clearly in the color index for the short wavelengths. For a discussion of the outlines of the diagram based on the theory of stellar atmospheres see Bonsack *et al.* (1957). If the stars radiated like black bodies, they would line up along the broken straight line in Figure 7. The Balmer jump causes the first nearly straight part of the curve. The curved part results from the combination of the decreasing Balmer jump, temperature, and the increasing depression in the ultraviolet. The second, nearly straight, part shows the influence of the increasing depression with decreasing temperature.

Unreddened stars of luminosity class V are arrayed along the curve in the diagram according to spectral types or, what is more important, according to decreasing luminosity and is similar to the alignment in Figure 3. In case of interstellar reddening, the stars move away from the curve in a direction given by the properties of the photometric system and the law of interstellar absorption. Assuming that this law generally holds, the reddening line of the U, B, V system is given by the expression

$$\frac{CE(U - B)}{CE(B - V)} = 0.72 + 0.05 \, CE \, (B - V)$$

(Hiltner and Johnson 1956). It is difficult to determine the first part of the curve because most O and B stars show some interstellar reddening. Further contributions to this question have been given by Lindholm (1957), Mawridis (1958), and Th. Schmidt (1958).

The use of the two-color diagram varies. If there is no reddening present, it gives a determination of the absolute magnitude or the spectral type in a manner similar to the color difference–color index diagram. The assumption is that the stars are of luminosity class V. It can be used to characterize the intensity distribution of objects in relation to class V stars and yield characteristics for the identification and classification of such objects, as shown in Figures 8–12. Supergiants of early spectral classes are arranged above the class V stars (Fig. 8) because of their smaller Balmer absorption (Arp 1958*b*). The same holds in general (Fig. 9) for white dwarfs (Johnson and Morgan 1953; Harris 1956), while the late-type supergiants are placed below. Stars of Population II in globular clus-

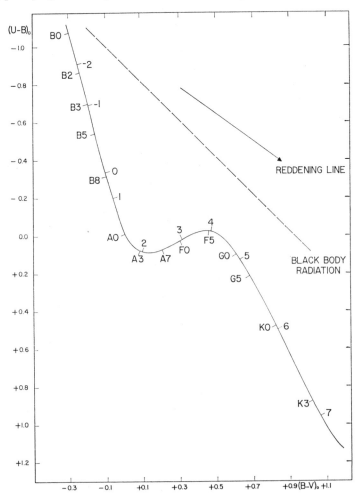

Fig. 7.—The relation between $(U - B)_0$ and $(B - V)_0$ for the main sequence (Johnson and Morgan 1953; Johnson 1958). The broken line represents black-body radiation. The arrow indicates the reddening path for the O stars.

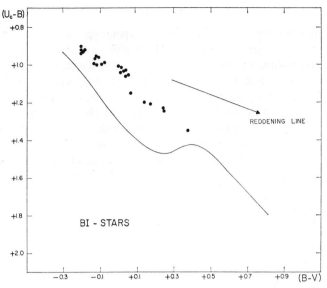

Fɪɢ. 8.—The position of the supergiant B stars in the $(U_c - B)$, $(B - V)$ diagram (Arp 1958). The arrow indicates the reddening path for the O stars.

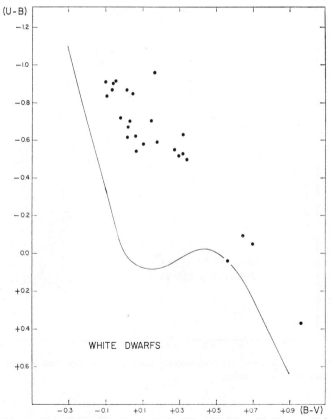

Fɪɢ. 9.—The position of the white dwarfs in the $(U - B)$, $(B - V)$ diagram (Johnson and Morgan 1953; Harris 1956).

ters may deviate systematically from corresponding stars of Population I in some parts of the diagram (Arp and Johnson 1955; Johnson and Sandage 1956). Among other points, the "wave" in the two-color diagram may be more pronounced than for Population I stars as in M13. It is not yet known whether the same holds for field stars of Population II and whether it may be used as a means of identification. High-velocity stars of spectral classes F and G (Fig. 10), however, show an ultraviolet excess compared with main-sequence stars that is caused by the lower intensity of metallic lines in these stars (Roman 1956). This is shown in Figure 12. Investigations of the position and the "path" of variable stars in the diagram have been made by Hardie (1955) and Fitch (1957) for

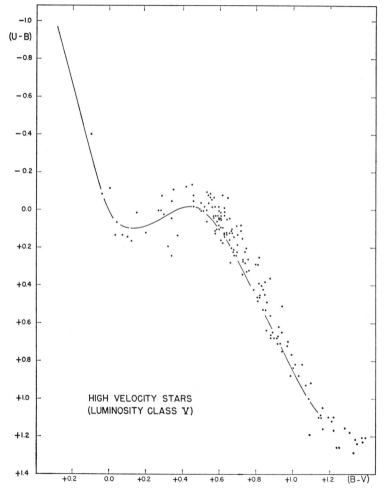

FIG. 10.—The position of the high-velocity stars of luminosity class V in the $(U - B)$, $(B - V)$ diagram (Roman 1956).

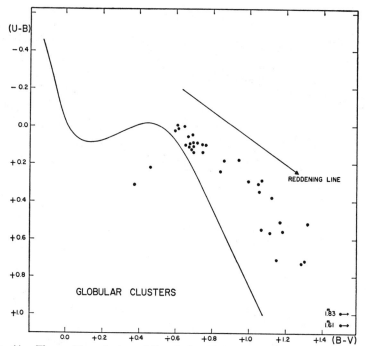

FIG. 11.—The position of stars of Population II in globular clusters in the $(U - B)$, $(B - V)$ diagram (Arp and Johnson 1955; Johnson and Sandage 1956).

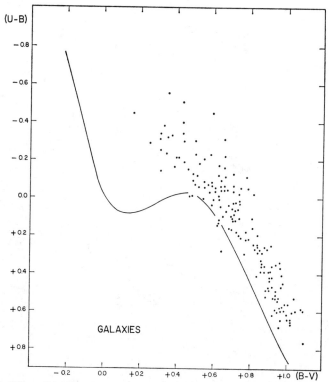

FIG. 12.—The position of galaxies in the $(U - B)$, $(B - V)$ diagram (Johnson and Morgan 1953; de Vaucouleurs 1959).

RR Lyrae stars and by Arp (1957, 1958a) and Sandage (1958) for δ Cephei stars. Physical and especially visual binaries may occupy a large area of the diagram that is not on the curve of the main-sequence stars (Steinlin 1956).

According to Johnson (1959), globular clusters are either on the same curve or to the right of it (Fig. 11). Galaxies of different types (Fig. 12) are placed exclusively to the right of the curve, according to Hiltner and Iriarte (1958) and de Vaucouleurs (1959; see also Morgan and Mayall 1958).

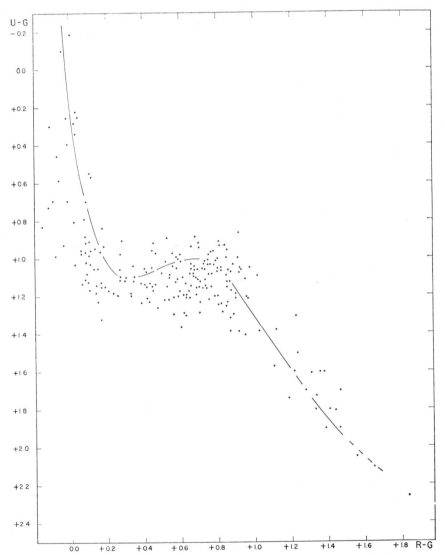

Fig. 13.—$U - G$, $R - G$ diagram of main-sequence stars between 11 and 17 mag. in a star field (Cassiopeia) in the galactic equator (Becker and Steinlin 1956).

The two-color diagram, as well as the color difference–color index diagram, plays an important role in stellar statistics (Becker 1942; Becker and Steinlin 1956; H. Schmidt 1958) because they make possible statistical studies according to luminosity groups even for the faintest stars. The diagram of a star field, drawn up for the stars of a given interval of apparent magnitude, can be used to derive the density function and the luminosity function and, in favorable circumstances, to clarify the conditions of absorption. A complicated distribution

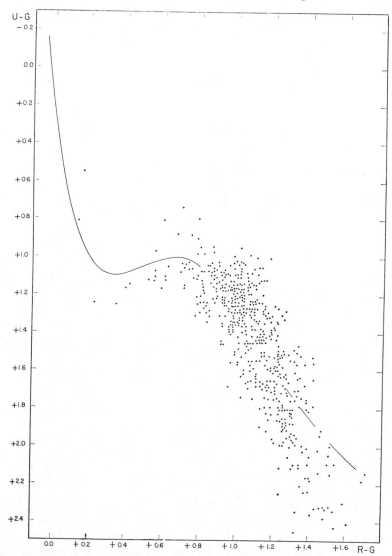

FIG. 14.—$U - G$, $R - G$ diagram of main-sequence stars between 11 and 17 mag. in a star field at galactic latitude $+78°$ (Helm 1958).

of the absorbing material may, on the other hand, make it impossible to apply the method.

In Figures 13 and 14 two diagrams are shown. Both are made up from main-sequence stars between 11 and 17 mag. The first diagram was obtained from a field in the Milky Way (Becker and Steinlin 1956), the second from a field near the galactic pole (Helm 1958). Both diagrams show clearly that the three-color photometry indicates differences in the numbers of stars of different types without actually using spectral types.

There are two points of interest in connection with the application of the two-color diagram or the color difference–color index diagram in stellar statistics. Do the stars of different luminosity classes differ in their positions in the diagram, and, if so, is it possible to identify them according to their classes by photometric means alone, even in the case of interstellar absorption? A final answer cannot as yet be given because there have not been enough tests made so far of the different photometric systems. It seems that supergiants (luminosity class I) with spectral classes from about B3 to A5 can be recognized in the diagram if there is no absorption but cannot be separated from reddened class V stars or from white dwarfs. Stars of early spectral types (luminosity classes II, III, and IV) hardly differ in their position from stars of class V, but, since the giants and supergiants are very rare, this lack of differentiation has little effect on the results obtained by using the diagram in stellar statistics. The situation is different for medium- and late-type giants and supergiants. Main-sequence stars, even with very low apparent magnitudes, are not very distant in contrast to the giants and supergiants. It would therefore be rather interesting to separate the stars of class V from the other luminosity classes in the diagram. At the present time, it is not possible to say whether this can be done. It appears that giants and supergiants can hardly be reliably separated from each other by photometry, and as for the separation of giant and class V stars, the results seem to contradict each other. According to Johnson and Morgan (1953), giants and main-sequence stars can be separated only if they are medium- or late-type K because the $U - B$ color index is appreciably larger for these stars than for the reddest main-sequence stars. According to Becker (1952b), the G and K giants lie on a separate branch below the curve of the main-sequence stars in the two-color diagram of the R, G, U system. The separation between these branches is large enough that it should be possible to separate the two types with reasonable accuracy. The application of the method on some star fields points in the same direction (Becker, Müller, and Steinlin 1955; Becker and Steinlin 1956).

It has been shown that the separation of giants and main-sequence stars in the two-color diagram depends on selecting the best position not only for the U band but for the other two spectral bands as well. In this respect the R, G, U system appears to be superior to the U, B, V system. However, it should be noted that the possibility of identifying the yellow and red giants does not depend solely on the position in the two-color diagram but also on the statistical data concerning the space distribution and the relative frequency of giants and dwarf stars.

REFERENCES

ARP, H. C.   1957   *A.J.*, **62**, 129.
                                    1958a *Ap. J.*, **128**, 166.
                                    1958b *A.J.*, **63**, 118.
ARP, H. C., and
  JOHNSON, H. L.   1955   *Ap. J.*, **122**, 171.
BARBIER, D.   1952   *Ann d'ap.*, **15**, 113.
BECKER, W.   1938   *Zs. f. Ap.*, **15**, 225.
                                    1942   *A.N.*, **272**, 179.
                                    1946   *Veröff. Obs. Göttingen*, No. 79.
                                    1948   *Ap. J.*, **107**, 278.
                                    1951a *Zs. f. Ap.*, **29**, 66.
                                    1951b *Ibid.*, p. 177.
                                    1952a *Ibid.*, **30**, 164.
                                    1952b *Ibid.*, **31**, 249.
BECKER, W., and
  HARTWIG, G.   1937   *Zs. f. Ap.*, **14**, 259.
BECKER, W., MÜLLER,
  E. A., and STEINLIN, U.   1955   *Zs. f. Ap.*, **38**, 81.
BECKER, W., and
  STEINLIN, U.   1956   *Zs. f. Ap.*, **39**, 188.
BECKER, W., and
  STOCK, J.   1954   *Zs. f. Ap.*, **34**, 1.
BONSACK, W. K., GREEN-
  STEIN, J. L., MATHIS,
  J. S., MELBOURNE,
  W. G., NEUGEBAUER,
  G., NEWBURN, R. L.,
  OLSEN, K. H., TIFFT,
  W. G., WAHLQUIST,
  H. D., and WALLER-
  STEIN, G.   1957   *Ap. J.*, **125**, 139.
BRILL, A.   1923   *A.N.*, **219**, 353.
CHALONGE, D., and
  DIVAN, L.   1952   *Ann. d'ap.*, **15**, 201.
FITCH, W. S.   1957   *A.J.*, **62**, 108.
GOLAY, M.   1955   *Pub. Obs. Genève*, Nos. 51 and 53.
                                    1960   *Ibid.*, No. 60.
GREENSTEIN, J. L.   1946   *Ap. J.*, **104**, 403.
HALL, J. S.   1934   *Ap. J.*, **79**, 145.
HARDIE, R. H.   1955   *Ap. J.*, **122**, 256.
HARRIS, D. L.   1956   *Ap. J.*, **124**, 665.
HELM, W.   1958   Thesis, University of Basel.
HILTNER, W. A., and
  IRIARTE, B.   1958   *Ap. J.*, **128**, 443.
HILTNER, W. A., and
  JOHNSON, H. L.   1956   *Ap. J.*, **124**, 367.

Johnson, H. L.	1955	*Ann. d'ap.*, **18**, 292.
	1958	*Lowell Obs. Bull.*, No. 90.
	1959	*Ibid.*, No. 99.
Johnson, H. L., and Iriarte, B.	1958	*Lowell Obs. Bull.*, No. 91.
Johnson, H. L., and Morgan, W. W.	1953	*Ap. J.*, **117**, 313.
Johnson, H. L., and Sandage, A.	1956	*Ap. J.*, **124**, 379.
King, E. S., and Ingalls, R. L.	1930	*Harvard Ann.*, Vol. **85**, No. 11.
Kraspan, E.	1957	Thesis, University of Basel.
Lindholm, E. H.	1957	*Ap. J.*, **126**, 588.
Mawridis, L.	1958	*Zs. f. Ap.*, **45**, 98.
Morgan, W. W., and Mayall, N. U.	1957	*Pub. A.S.P.*, **69**, 291.
Öpik, E., and Livländer, R.	1925	*Pub. Obs. Tartu*, Vol. **26**, No. 3.
Öpik, E., Livländer, R., and Silde, O.	1935	*Pub. Obs. Tartu*, Vol. **28**, No. 2.
Roman, N. G.	1956	*Ap. J.*, **123**, 184.
Sandage, A.	1958	*Ap. J.*, **128**, 150.
Schmidt, H.	1958	*Zs. f. Ap.*, **44**, 129.
Schmidt, K. H.	1956	*Mitt. Obs. Jena*, No. 21.
Schmidt, Th.	1958	*Zs. f. Ap.*, **46**, 145.
Stebbins, J., and Whitford, A. E.	1943	*Ap. J.*, **98**, 20.
Steinlin, U.	1956	*Zs. f. Ap.*, **39**, 210.
Stoy, R. H.	1959	Private communication.
Strömgren, B.	1950	*Trans. I.A.U.*, **7**, 404.
	1951	*A.J.*, **56**, 142.
Vaucouleurs, G. de	1959	*Lowell Obs. Bull.*, No. 97.
Woolley, R. v. d. R.	1956	*Vistas in Astronomy*, ed. A. Beer (London: Pergamon Press), **2**, 1095.

CHAPTER 14

The Stellar Temperature Scale and Bolometric Corrections

D. L. HARRIS III*

T.E.N.S. Corporation, Bethesda, Maryland

§ 1. INTRODUCTION

IN ASTROPHYSICAL investigations the concept of temperature enters in many different forms; for example, there is excitation temperature appearing in Boltzmann's equation, ionization temperature appearing in Saha's equation, and color temperature appearing in Planck's law. However, it seems that the *effective temperature*, T_e, in the relation between the stellar luminosity, L, and the stellar radius, R,

$$L = 4\pi R^2 \sigma T_e^4 \,, \tag{1}$$

defines a more fundamental temperature scale and will be adopted here. The radiation constant, σ, in equation (1) is equal to 5.67×10^{-5} c.g.s. units.

Unfortunately, there are only a few stars for which the luminosity and radius are known with sufficient accuracy to give a direct determination of effective temperature. Therefore, we shall utilize information derived from theoretical model atmospheres and from color temperatures (or colors themselves) to interpolate between the direct determinations of the effective temperature. A brief discussion of color temperatures will be found at the end of the chapter.

Equation (1) can be expressed in terms of bolometric absolute magnitudes, or

$$M_b = M_b \text{ (sun)} - 5 \log R + 5 \log R \text{ (sun)} - 10 \log T_e$$
$$+ 10 \log T_e \text{ (sun)} \,, \tag{2}$$

* The editor records with deep regret the premature decease of Dr. Daniel L. Harris III, on April 29, 1962. He will long be remembered by his friends and associates who experienced his kindness and generous co-operation. His scientific work was noted for its precision and imagination.

which reduces to

$$M_b = 42.31 - 5 \log R - 10 \log T_e , \qquad (3)$$

if we put T_e (sun) $= 5784°$ (Allen 1950); M_b (sun) $= +4.69$ mag., corresponding to our adopted visual magnitude of the sun of -26.81 mag. (Harris 1961);
and express the radii of stars in terms of the solar radius.

As bolometric magnitudes are not normally measured, it is necessary to introduce the concept of a bolometric correction, BC, which is defined by

$$M_b - M_v = BC , \qquad \text{or} \qquad m_b - m_v = BC , \qquad (4)$$

where M_v is the visual absolute magnitude corresponding to the visual magnitude, m_v, and m_b is an observed bolometric magnitude.

Besides the introduction of bolometric corrections in connection with the
stellar temperature scale, relation (4) is important in the comparison of observations with astrophysical theory; the absolute bolometric magnitude is a much
more fundamental quantity than the conventional visual absolute magnitude
employed in studies of galactic structure.

In this chapter we shall base our discussion on Kuiper's (1938) classic investigation of bolometric corrections and the stellar temperature scale. In particular,
we shall use the MK classification of stellar spectra and the modern photoelectric magnitude and color scale (Stebbins and Whitford 1945; Johnson and
Morgan 1953) in preference to those used by Kuiper, but the main modifications
arise from considerations based on theoretical stellar atmospheres which have
been developed in the last twenty years.

§ 2. EMPIRICAL BOLOMETRIC CORRECTIONS
FOR LATE-TYPE STARS

Because of the absorption by the earth's atmosphere, especially in the ultraviolet portion of the spectrum, it is not possible to observe the bolometric magnitude of a star directly; eventually, rocket and/or satellite observations may
provide direct information in this regard. However, for stars of spectral type F5
and later the radiometric magnitudes, m_r, observed by Pettit and Nicholson
(1928) are reasonably good approximations after the correction, $-\Delta m_r$, is applied to reduce the observed value to "no atmosphere." The correction (Kuiper
1938) varies only between -0.4 and -0.6 mag. for spectral types F5–M6, so
that small errors in the assumed stellar temperature scale (required in the evaluation of the correction) will hardly affect the derived bolometric magnitude.

We assume that

$$m_b = m_r - \Delta m_r + 0.60 , \qquad (5)$$

so that the bolometric corrections given by dwarf stars of type G will agree, on
the average, with Kuiper's results. The bolometric magnitudes for individual
stars computed in this manner differ only slightly from those given by Kuiper
(1938, Table 7).

Table 1 gives the bolometric corrections for various spectral types and luminosity classes. The values for the supergiants are uncertain, as they are based on a very limited number of stars. Table 2 gives the bolometric corrections for various values of the color index, $B - V$, for stars of luminosity class V and III and for the color index, $R - I$, for the late-type giants. Table 3 gives the bolometric corrections for main-sequence stars as a function of visual absolute magnitude.

The bolometric corrections for the late-type stars are in good agreement with those published by Eggen (1956) and by Popper (1959), both investigations utilizing Pettit and Nicholson's observed radiometric magnitudes. No significant

TABLE 1
BOLOMETRIC CORRECTIONS—SPECTRAL TYPES

MK Type	V	III	Ib	MK Type	V	III	Ib
F5......	−0.04	....	−0.04	K0.....	−0.19	−0.37	....
F8......	− .05	....	− .06	K1.....	−0.22	−0.44	−0.95
G0......	− .06	....	....	K2.....	−0.25	−0.54	....
G2......	− .07	....	....	K3.....	−0.35	−0.76	....
G5......	− .10	....	....	K4.....	....	−1.00	....
G8......	−0.15	−0.27	−0.7:	K5.....	−0.71	−1.18	−1.15:
G9......	....	−0.32	....	K7.....	−1.02	....	....

TABLE 2
BOLOMETRIC CORRECTIONS—COLOR INDICES

$B - V$	V	III	$R - I$	III
0.4......	−0.04	....	0.3.....	−0.47
0.5......	−0.05	....	0.4.....	−0.65
0.6......	−0.07	....	0.5.....	−1.02
0.7......	−0.11	....	0.6.....	−1.24
0.8......	−0.17	....	0.7.....	−1.46
0.9......	−0.25	−0.25	0.8.....	−1.67
1.0......	−0.41	−0.33	0.9.....	−1.88
1.1......	−0.58	−0.47	1.0.....	−2.09
1.2......	−0.74	−0.62	1.1.....	−2.30
1.3......	−0.90	−0.78	....	....
1.4......	−1.07	−0.94	....	....
1.5......	....	−1.10	....	....

TABLE 3
BOLOMETRIC CORRECTIONS—ABSOLUTE MAGNITUDE (MAIN SEQUENCE)

M_v	BC	M_v	BC	M_v	BC	M_v	BC
5.0......	−0.10	6.5.....	−0.30	8.0.....	−0.90	9.5....	−1.52
5.5......	− .14	7.0.....	− .48	8.5.....	−1.11	10.0....	−1.72
6.0......	−0.20	7.5.....	−0.70	9.0.....	−1.31	10.5....	−1.93

improvement can be made until more observed radiometric magnitudes become available.

For dwarf M-type stars the bolometric corrections are large and very uncertain. The values for YY Gem, M0.5 V, that have been published are as follows: -1^m32 (Kuiper 1938), -1^m4 (Kopal 1955), and -1^m30 (Limber 1958). For later types, Limber (1958) obtains -2.24 mag. for M4 V; -2.81 mag. for M6 V; and -3.8 mag. for M8 V based on extrapolations using infrared colors. Kuiper's remark that a radiometric magnitude of Barnard's star at M5 V is needed to settle the question of the bolometric corrections for the late-type M dwarfs still applies.

§ 3. THEORETICAL BOLOMETRIC CORRECTIONS

For stars of early spectral type it is possible to compute the bolometric corrections as a function of effective temperature, utilizing models of stellar atmospheres. For the earliest-type stars, we have used the bolometric corrections tabulated by Underhill (1957) based on models computed by McDonald and

TABLE 4

THEORETICAL BOLOMETRIC CORRECTIONS—
EFFECTIVE TEMPERATURE

$T_e \times 10^{-3}$	$\log T_e$	BC	$T_e \times 10^{-3}$	$\log T_e$	BC
50°	4.70	-4^m70	12°	4.08	-0^m60
40	4.60	-4.03	10	4.00	$-.30$
30	4.48	-3.16	9	3.95	$-.18$
25	4.40	-2.62	8	3.90	$-.12$
20	4.30	-1.94	7	3.85	$-.07$
15	4.18	-1.16	6	3.78	-0.04

Underhill (1952) and Pecker (1950). For later-type stars, we have used the values compiled by Popper (1959) based on models computed by Hunger (1954), Osawa (1956), and Saito (1956). The relationship between these theoretical bolometric corrections and the effective temperature are tabulated in Table 4.[1]

It should be noted that the values based on Popper's compilation differ by nearly 0.2 mag. from those given by Kuiper (1938, Table 6). However, the earlier results were also based on theoretical model atmospheres, and the modern results are considered to be more reliable.

§ 4. FUNDAMENTAL EFFECTIVE TEMPERATURES

In addition to the sun, there is a small number of stars whose effective temperatures can be determined; these are stars with measured angular diameters or double-line eclipsing binaries that have measurable parallaxes. The angular diameter of Sirius has been measured by Brown and Twiss (1956) and an effective temperature of 9350° calculated by Popper (1959). The angular di-

[1] [Cf. Table 7 for the relation between spectral type and effective temperature.—EDITOR.]

ameters of late-type giant stars observed by Pease (1931) lead to the effective temperatures listed in Table 5 (Kuiper 1938, Table 11). Popper suggests that the limb darkening of these stars may be much more extreme than that adopted by Kuiper, which would make the tabulated effective temperatures systematically too high. This aspect merits further investigation.

TABLE 5

FUNDAMENTAL EFFECTIVE TEMPERATURES

Star	Spectral Type	T_e	log T_e	Source
μ_1 Sco.......	B1.5 V	27,500°	4.44	Harris (text)
α CMa......	A0 V	9,350	3.97	Popper (1959)
β Aur.......	A2 V	10,500	4.02	Popper (1959)
Sun.........	G2 V	5,784	3.76	Allen (1950)
YY Gem....	M1 V	3,650	3.57	Popper (1959)
α Boo......	K2 IIIp	4,090	3.61	Kuiper (1938)
α Tau.......	K5 III	3,780	3.58	Kuiper (1938)
α Sco........	M1 Ib	3,230	3.51	Kuiper (1938)
α Ori........	M2 Iab	3,460	3.54	Kuiper (1938)
β Peg........	M2 II–III	3,080	3.49	Kuiper (1938)
o Cet........	M6±*	2,360±	3.37±	Kuiper (1938)

* Long-period variable.

TABLE 6

EFFECTIVE TEMPERATURES FROM MODEL ATMOSPHERES

Star	Spectral Type	T_e	log T_e	Source
	O5	44,600°	4.65	Underhill (1957)
	O9	36,800	4.57	Underhill (1957)
	B2 V	27,800	4.44	Underhill (1957)*
α Lyr..........	A0 V	9,500	3.98	Hunger (1954)
	A3 V	8,900	3.95	Osawa (1956)
	A9 V	7,560	3.88	Osawa (1956)
σ Boo.........	F2 V	6,800	3.83	Code (1954)

* The average of six.

The results listed for the spectroscopic binaries differ only slightly from the earlier values computed by Kuiper, with the exception of the value for μ_1 Scorpii. The increase of over 10,000° arises from the use of a significantly smaller parallax (Bertiau 1958), so that both the absolute magnitude and the bolometric correction are larger.

The higher temperature determined for μ_1 Scorpii is in good agreement with the results obtained from the theoretical model atmospheres and is in agreement with the results obtained by Hoyle (1960) from the theory of stellar evolution. However, the temperature derived from observations must be considered as very uncertain because of the critical dependence of the calculated value on the parallax used in the reduction.

Effective temperatures determined from theoretical model atmospheres fall into two classes: those based on complete model atmospheres (Osawa 1956; Underhill 1957) and those based on features of the stellar spectrum of an individual star (Code 1954; Hunger 1954). These values of effective temperatures based on model stellar atmospheres are listed in Table 6.

§ 5. THE EFFECTIVE-TEMPERATURE–SPECTRAL-TYPE RELATIONSHIP

The effective-temperature–spectral-type relationship was first derived for the MK system of Keenan and Morgan (1951), using the temperature scales of

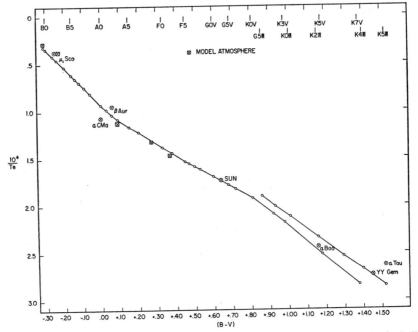

Fig. 1.—A comparison of the effective-temperature–spectral-type relation, with the individual points representing the values of fundamental temperatures, ⊗, and those derived from model atmospheres, ☒.

Kuiper (1938) and of Stebbins and Whitford (1945), the latter being based on their six-color photometry. Our tabulated relation differs from that of Keenan and Morgan in the following respects: (a) we have taken the effective temperature of a B0 V star to be equal to 30,000° instead of 25,000°; (b) the effective temperatures of stars earlier than G2 V have been adjusted so that the reciprocal effective temperature varies smoothly with the $B - V$ color index; (c) the reciprocal effective temperatures of stars later than G2 V are adjusted to vary smoothly with the $B - R$ six-color index, the same relationship being assumed to obtain for stars of luminosity classes V and III (Fig. 1).

TABLE 7

RELATION BETWEEN SPECTRAL TYPE, BOLOMETRIC CORRECTIONS, AND EFFECTIVE TEMPERATURE

SPECTRAL TYPE		COLOR B − V	EFFECTIVE TEMPERATURE			
MK	BC		Revised	Keenan, Morgan	Kuiper	Underhill, Popper
O9	−3.34	−0.31	31,900°	....	31,600°	36,800°
B0	−3.17	−0.30	30,000	25,000	25,100	....
B1	−2.50	−0.26	24,200	22,500	22,900	27,900
B2	−2.23	−0.24	22,100	20,300	20,400	22,700
B3	−1.77	−0.20	18,800	18,000	18,600	27,400
B5	−1.39	−0.16	16,400	15,600	15,500	....
B6	−1.21	−0.14	15,400	....	14,500	....
B7	−1.04	−0.12	14,500	....		
B8	−0.85	−0.09	13,400	12,800	12,300	....
B9	−0.66	−0.06	12,400	11,800	....	
A0	−0.40	0.00	10,800	11,000	10,700	9400
A1	−0.32	0.03	10,200	10,300	....	9220
A2	−0.25	0.06	9730	9700	9680	9030
A3	−0.20	0.09	9260	9100	....	8860
A5	−0.15	0.15	8620	8700	8530	8440
A7	−0.12	0.20	8190	8100	....	8100
F0	−0.08	0.33	7240	7600	7500	7140
F2	−0.06	0.38	6930	7000	....	6820
F5	−0.04	0.45	6540	6600	6470	6490
F6	−0.04	0.47	6450	6390	....	6420
F7	−0.04	0.50	6320	....	....	6300
F8	−0.05	0.53	6200	6150	....	....
G0	−0.06	0.60	5920	6000	6000	....
G2	−0.07	0.64	5780	5730	5710	
G5	−0.10	0.68	5610	5520	5360	
G8	−0.15	0.72	6490	5320	....	
K0	−0.19	0.81	5240	5120	4910	
K2	−0.25	0.92	4780	4760	4650	
K3	−0.35	0.98	4590	4610	....	
K5	−0.71	1.18	3970	4400	3900	
K7	−0.02	1.38	3520	4000	....	
G5 III	−0.22	0.86	5260	4650	4620	....
G8 III	−0.27	0.93	4980	4440	....	4800
K0 III	−0.37	1.01	4720	4200	4230	4650
K2 III	−0.54	1.16	4280	3810	....	4400
K3 III	−0.76	1.29	3950	3660	....	4050
K4 III	−1.00	1.40	3730	....	....	....
K5 III	−1.18	1.52	3500	3550	3580	....

The use of colors (or color temperatures) to smooth and interpolate effective temperatures for earlier-type stars does not appear to offer any particular difficulty, if the effects of the ultraviolet absorptions are not present to any great extent in the short-wavelength filter bands. However, for later-type stars, Bahng (1958) suggested that long-wavelength colors were preferable for temperature classification and demonstrated that a K2 III star which nearly matched in color a K4 V star in the red regions of the spectrum showed large differences in the blue and ultraviolet regions. Popper (1959) has published a revision of Keenan and Morgan's temperatures of giants that is in satisfactory agreement with our revision.

Table 7 gives the effective-temperature–spectral-type relationship obtained from our compilation, as well as the temperatures found by Keenan and Morgan, by Kuiper, and by Underhill and Popper. The bolometric corrections in the second column correspond to the effective temperature scale in the fourth column and to those in Tables 1 and 4.

§ 6. COLOR TEMPERATURES

The *color temperature* is the temperature of a black body having the same relative intensity distribution, or color, as that of the source under observation.

TABLE 8

COMPARISON OF EFFECTIVE TEMPERATURE
WITH COLOR TEMPERATURES

Spectral Type	T_e	T_{5000}	T_{4250}	T_{3500}
B0 V.........	30,000°	33,000°	39,800°	23,000°
B5 V.........	16,400	22,500	23,400	14,200
A0 V.........	10,800	15,300	16,700	10,000
A5 V.........	8620	11,000	13,000	8900
F0 V.........	7240	8950	9900	7600
F5 V.........	6540	7700	7600	7300
F8 V.........	6200	6900	6500	7000

As stellar sources do not radiate as black bodies, the color temperature will vary with frequency. However, as we have seen, the amount of information concerning the effective temperatures of stars is so limited that it is necessary to utilize other observations to effect an interpolation between the directly determined values.

Code has given a comprehensive discussion of stellar energy distribution in Volume 6, chapter 2, of this series, to which the reader is referred for details. The comparison of the color temperatures and our effective temperatures is given in Table 8, based on Code's compilation for stars with spectral types earlier than the sun. The three color temperatures correspond to regions at $\lambda\lambda$ 5000, 4250, and 3500.

For later-type stars the crowding of absorption lines makes measurements of gradients very difficult. However, long-wavelength photoelectric colors are available for discussion. Following Bahng (1958), we have illustrated the variations in temperatures derived from colors in different portions of the spectrum by comparing the mean of two K7 V stars with the mean of two K5 III stars given in the six-color photometry lists. Using different color combinations, we have computed the corresponding T_1 temperatures (Stebbins and Whitford 1945) and give the differences in Table 9. The large difference obtained for the short-base-line color, $V - B$, is similar in magnitude to that found by Kuiper from Becker's (1935) short-base-line colors.

TABLE 9

DIFFERENCES IN COLOR TEMPERATURES FOR K7 V AND K5 III STARS

SPECTRAL TYPE	T_e	T_1 TEMPERATURES			
		$V-B$	$V-G$	$B-R$	$V-I$
K7 V............	3520°	3690°	3620°	3520°	3640°
K5 III..........	3500	3140	3270	3490	3420
Difference....	20°	550°	350°	30°	220°

§ 7. SUMMARY AND CONCLUSIONS

The revised tables of bolometric corrections and effective temperatures given in this chapter differ in many instances only slightly from those given in earlier compilations. It is hoped that the incorporation of the results from model stellar atmospheres and the utilization of more accurate spectral classification and photoelectric colors has resulted in a set of tables that are consistent with the best information now available.

The bolometric corrections for early-type stars are based on model stellar atmospheres, which have progressed a great deal during the last decade. However, for late-type stars we are still using the results obtained by Pettit and Nicholson (1928) made over thirty years ago—a modern comprehensive series of radiometric observations extending to fainter main-sequence stars would be very valuable.

It would be of interest to extend the list of stars with known angular diameters to obtain more directly determined effective temperatures. The data on the known eclipsing binaries might well be extended to include other stars, as well as to improve the information on the stars listed in Table 5.

It is anticipated that considerable progress will be made in the comparison of theory and observation of stellar spectra that will improve the relationship between spectral type and effective temperature. This knowledge will then improve the relationship between computed bolometric corrections and spectral type, or color, which at present is rather uncertain. The comparison of our effective-temperature–spectral-type relation shown in Figure 1, with the individual points representing the values of fundamental temperatures and those derived from model atmospheres, indicates that there is still much to be done to improve the relationship.

REFERENCES

ALLEN, C. W.	1950	*Observatory*, **70**, 154.
BAHNG, J. D. R.	1958	*Ap. J.*, **128**, 572.
BECKER, W.	1935	*Veröff. Berlin-Babelsberg*, Vol. **10**, Heft 6, p. 8.
BERTIAU, F. C.	1958	*Ap. J.*, **128**, 533.
BROWN, R. H., and		
TWISS, R. Q.	1956	*Nature*, **178**, 1046.
CODE, A. D.	1954	*Proceedings of the N.S.F. Conference on Stellar Atmospheres*, ed. M. H. WRUBEL (Bloomington: University of Indiana Press), p. 14.
EGGEN, O. J.	1956	*A.J.*, **61**, 361.
HARRIS, D. L., III	1961	*Planets and Satellites*, ed. G. P. KUIPER and B. M. MIDDLEHURST (Chicago: University of Chicago Press), chap. 8.
HOYLE, F.	1960	*M.N.*, **120**, 22.
HUNGER, K.	1955	*Zs. f. Ap.*, **36**, 42.
JOHNSON, H. L., and		
MORGAN, W. W.	1953	*Ap. J.*, **117**, 313.
KEENAN, P. C., and		
MORGAN, W. W.	1951	*Astrophysics*, ed. J. A. HYNEK (New York: McGraw-Hill Book Co., Inc.), p. 20.
KOPAL, Z.	1955	*Ann. d'ap.*, **18**, 379.
KUIPER, G. P.	1938	*Ap. J.*, **88**, 429.
LIMBER, D. N.	1958	*Ap. J.*, **127**, 363.
McDONALD, J. K., and		
UNDERHILL, A. B.	1952	*Ap. J.*, **115**, 577.
OSAWA, K.	1956	*Ap. J.*, **123**, 517.
PEASE, F. G.	1931	*Ergebn. d. exakt. Naturwiss.*, **10**, 84.
PECKER, J. C.	1950	*Ann. d'ap.*, **13**, 433.
PETTIT, E., and		
NICHOLSON, S. B.	1928	*Ap. J.*, **68**, 279.
POPPER, D. M.	1959	*Ap. J.*, **129**, 647.
SAITO, S.	1956	*Kyoto Contr.*, No. 69.
STEBBINS, J., and		
WHITFORD, A. E.	1945	*Ap. J.*, **102**, 318.
UNDERHILL, A. B.	1957	*Pub. Dom. Ap. Obs. Victoria*, **10**, 357.

CHAPTER 15

Empirical Data on Stellar Masses, Luminosities, and Radii

D. L. HARRIS III

T.E.N.S. Corporation, Bethesda, Maryland

AND

K. Aa. STRAND AND C. E. WORLEY

U.S. Naval Observatory, Washington, D.C.

§ 1. INTRODUCTION

DIRECT information concerning the masses of individual stars is obtained from the study of the orbital motions of the components of visual double-star systems which have measurable trigonometric parallaxes. Another source is the double-line spectroscopic binaries, which are also eclipsing variables.

In the present chapter are compiled the empirical data that are the best available at the present time for evaluating stellar masses, the mass-luminosity relation, and stellar radii. Compared with the data available some 40 years ago (Hertzsprung 1919), it will be noted that some progress has been made, but there is still much to be done in regard to improving present data by obtaining new observations.

§ 2. ORBITS OF VISUAL BINARIES

At the present time, orbits have been determined for approximately 500 double stars. The most recent catalogue was published by Baize (1950) and contains orbits for 252 binary systems. New or revised orbits are currently being published in *Circulaires d'Information de la Commission des Étoiles Doubles de l'Union Astronomique Internationale.*

A considerable number of the published orbits are not sufficiently well determined to allow the use of the orbital elements—i.e., the period, P, and the semimajor axis, a—in a mass determination. As a rule, orbits with periods exceeding 200 years belong in this category. Only a small fraction of the well-determined orbits can be used in investigations requiring stellar masses determined with fairly high accuracy because in the majority of the cases the systems have too small parallaxes.

It will be recalled that the total mass of a binary system, $\Sigma\mathfrak{M}$, is determined from Kepler's third law, which can be expressed by the formula

$$\log \Sigma\mathfrak{M} = 3 \log a - 2 \log P - 3 \log \pi ,$$

where π is the parallax of the system.

In cases where the orbit is well determined, the error in $3 \log a - 2 \log P$ is small, with the result that the error in $\Sigma\mathfrak{M}$ will depend primarily on the error of the parallax. In these cases we have

$$\Delta (\log \Sigma\mathfrak{M}) = -3\Delta (\log \pi) .$$

Since, in general, a trigonometric parallax cannot be determined with a prob_able error less than $\pm 0\overset{''}{.}005$, it is seen that, for binary systems with parallaxes less than $0\overset{''}{.}050$, the masses have probable errors in excess of 30 per cent.

The limiting distance at which accurate masses can be obtained for systems with well-determined orbital elements severely limits the number of well-deter-mined stellar masses. Approximately 20 systems have well-determined orbital elements, and parallaxes in excess of $0\overset{''}{.}1$, while a similar number have parallaxes between $0\overset{''}{.}05$ and $0\overset{''}{.}1$. Another 25 systems with well-determined orbital ele-ments could give valuable data on stellar masses if lacking parallax and mass-ratio data were obtained.

In Table 1 are listed 64 visual binary systems within 25 parsecs of the sun for which orbital elements have been determined. The first column identifies the star by its number in the Aitken double-star catalogue. If the star is not in this catalogue, its Bonner or Cordoba *Durchmusterung* number is given. The star is further identified by its name. The second column lists the right ascension and declination for the epoch 1900. In the third column are given the magnitudes of the two components, which were derived from the known total magnitude of the system and the magnitude difference between the components. The combined magnitudes were selected in order of preference from (*a*) photoelectric visual (*V*) magnitudes, (*b*) photometric visual magnitudes in the *Henry Draper Catalogue*, and (*c*) *Durchmusterung* magnitudes.

For approximately half the stars, photometric (including photovisual) deter-minations of the magnitude differences are available, and, for these pairs, two decimal magnitudes are given if the combined magnitudes were available from the first two sources mentioned in the previous paragraphs.

The fourth column lists the spectral types, which were selected in order of preference from (*a*) MK (Yerkes) system, (*b*) Mount Wilson system, and (*c*) Henry Draper system. The MK spectra are identified by their luminosity classes. The following two columns need no explanations, while the final column lists pertinent information in regard to the data in the previous columns.

TABLE 1

Orbits of Visual Binaries within 25 Parsecs of the Sun

ADS/BD Name	Pos. 1900 R.A. Dec.	Mag {A B}	Sp. {A B}	a P (Years)	π Abs.	Source of Orbit	Notes
61 Σ 3062	00^h01^m0 +57°53'	6.53 7.31	dG4 dG8	1".43 106.8	+0".043	Baize, *J. d. Obs.*, **40**, 197, 1957	1, 3
490 13 Cet	00 30.1 −04 09	5.6 6.3	F8 V	0.244 6.91	+ .064	Luyten, *Ap. J.*, **78**, 225, 1933	1, 3, 4, 5
520 β 395	00 32.2 −25 19	6.3 6.4	G5 V	0.67 25.0	+ .074	Van den Bos, *Union Obs. Circ.*, No. 98, p. 342, 1937	
671 η Cas	00 43.0 +57 17	3.47 7.22	G0 V dM0	11.99 480	+ .174	Strand, unpublished	
L 726–8	01 34.0 −18 28	12.5 12.9	dM5.5e dM5.5e	5.57 200	+ .370	Van de Kamp, *A.J.*, **64**, 236, 1959	2, 3, 4, 7
1733 Hastings 1	02 11.0 −18 41.0	8.1 9.9	dK4	1.70 169	....	Horeschi, *A.N.*, **284**, 57, 1958	1, 2, 3, 4
1865 A 2329	02 22.5 +03 59	9.4 9.6	dM1.5	0.55 25.2	+ .071	Finsen, *Union Obs. Circ.*, No. 98, p. 344, 1937	1, 3, 4
ε Ceti −12°501 φ 312	02 34.7 −12 18	5.49 5.49	F5 IV–V	0.11 2.62	+ .066	Finsen, *M.N. Astr. Soc. South Africa*, **14**, 84, 1955	1
3093 o² Eri BC	04 10.8 −07 49	9.6 11.1	DA dM4e	6.89 248	+ .204	Van den Bos, *B.A.N.*, **3**, 128, 1926	4
3841 α Aur	05 09.3 +45 54	0.9 0.9:	G5 III G0 III	0.054 0.28	+ .075	Merrill, *Ap. J.*, **56**, 44, 1922	2, 3, 4
−31°2902 Hu 1339	05 56.6 −31 02	8.4 8.9	K5	0.94 72.0	+0.051	Baize, *J. d. Obs.*, **35**, 68, 1952	1, 3, 4

TABLE 1—Continued

ADS/BD Name	Pos. 1900 R.A. Dec.	Mag. {A B}	Sp. {A B}	a / P (Years)	π Abs.	Source of Orbit	Notes
Ross 614	$06^h24^m.3$ $-02°44'$	11.3 14.8	M4	$0".98$ 16.5	$+0".252$	Lippincott, A.J., 55, 236, 1951; 60, 379, 1955	4
5423 Sirius	06 40.8 −16 35	− 1.43 8.52	A1 V DA	7.50 50.09	+ .376	Van den Bos, J. d. Obs., 43, 145, 1960	2, 3, 5
6175 Castor	07 28.2 +32 06	1.99 2.85	A1 V A5m	6.30 420	+ .074	Rabe, A.N., 284, 97, 1958	
6251 Procyon	07 34.1 +05 29	0.38 10.7:	F5 IV-V	4.55 40.65	+ .287	Strand, Ap. J., 113, 1, 1951	4
6420 9 Pup	07 47.1 −13 38	5.6 6.2	G0 V	0.58 23.2	+ .068	Woolley and Symms, M.N., 97, 445, 1937	4
6650 ζ Cnc AB	08 06.5 +17 57	6.15 6.50	F8 V	0.88 59.7	+ .047	Gasteyer, A.J., 59, 243, 1954	4
6664 Hu 115	08 08.4 −13 36	9.6 10.0	dM0	0.69 58.5	+ .056	Baize, J. d. Obs., 44, 22, 1961	1, 2, 3, 4
6914 β 208	08 34.8 −22 19	5.3 6.7	dG6	1.9 214	+ .061	Hirst, M.N. Astr. Soc. South Africa, 2, 100, 1942	1, 2, 3, 4
7114 ι UMa BC	08 52.4 +48 26	10.8 11.0	M1	0.70 40	+ .068	Worley, unpublished	3, 4
+42°1956 Kuiper	08 54.2 +42 11	4.13 6.20	F5 V	0.61 22.2	+ .075	Baize, J. d. Obs., 38, 40, 1955	2
+77°361 Kuiper	09 06.3 +77 40	10.7 11.0	K5	0.57 16.0	+ .047	Baize, J. d. Obs., 40, 172, 1957	1, 2, 3, 4
7284 Σ 3121	09 12.0 +29 00	7.9 8.0	dK4	0.66 34.2	+0.058	Van den Bos, Union Obs. Circ., No. 99, p. 448, 1938	4

TABLE 1—Continued

ADS/BD Name	Pos. 1900 R.A. Dec.	Mag { A / B	Sp. { A / B	a / P (Years)	π Abs.	Source of Orbit	Notes
ψ Vel −39°3651	09h26m8 −40°02′	4.1 / 4.6	F2 IV	0″.92 / 34.1	+0″.064	Van den Bos, *A.J.*, **51**, 198, 1945	4
8119 ξ UMa	11 12.9 +32 06	4.28 / 4.75	G0 V	2.56 / 59.7	+ .128	Rakowiecki, *Wiadom Matematika*, **46**, 125, 1938	1, 3, 5
8148 ι Leo	11 18.7 +11 05	4.03 / 6.70	F2 IV	1.96 / 204.5	+ .048	Rabe, *A.N.*, **184**, 97, 1958	1, 2, 3
8197 OΣ 235	11 26.7 +61 38	5.76 / 7.08	F6 V	0.78 / 71.9	+ .052	Aitken, *Pub. Lick Obs.*, **12**, 72, 1914	1, 3
8573 β 28	12 24.9 −12 50	6.6 / 8.7	dF8	1.51 / 180	+ .049	Muller, *J. d. Obs.*, **38**, 19, 1955	1, 3, 4
8630 γ Vir	12 36.6 −00 54	3.48 / 3.50	F0 V / F0 V	3.75 / 171.4	+ .092	Strand, *Ann. Leiden Obs.*, **18**, 77, 1937	
8804 α Com	13 05.1 +18 03	5.04 / 5.07	F5 V	0.67 / 25.8	+ .054	Pavel, *A.N.*, **277**, 156, 1949	
8862 Hu 644	13 15.4 +48 19	9.2 / 10.1	dM2	1.40 / 49.0	+ .085	Baize, *J. d. Obs.*, **32**, 50, 1949	1, 3, 4
8891 ζ UMa Aa	13 19.9 +55 27	2.25	A2 V	0.011 / 0.056	+ .040	Russell, *Pub. A.S.P.*, **39**, 313, 1927	1, 2, 3, 4
9031 Σ 1785	13 44.5 +27 29	7.59 / 8.03	dK6 / dK6	2.42 / 155.0	+ .075	Strand, *A.J.*, **60**, 42, 1955	
−60°5483 α Cen	14 32.8 −60 25	− 0.04 / 1.17	G2 V / dK5	17.58 / 79.92	+ .761	Heintz, *Circ. d'Information*, No. 19, 1959	1, 3, 4
9352 Hu 575	14 38.0 +19 55	9.7 / 10.0	dM0	0.63 / 52	+0.044	Muller, *Bull. Astr.*, **16**, 208, 1951	1, 4

277

TABLE 1—Continued

ADS/BD Name	Pos. 1900 R.A. Dec.	Mag. {A, B}	Sp. {A, B}	a / P (Years)	π Abs.	Source of Orbit	Notes
9413, ξ Boo.	14h46m.8 +19°31'	4.67 / 6.83	G8 V / K4 V	4".88 / 150	+0".149	Strand, *Ann. Leiden Obs*, **18**, 90, 1937	2, 5
9494, 44 Boo.	15 00.5 +48 03	5.28 / Var	dG1 / G2+G2	4.01 / 254	+.080	Gennaro III, *Atti R. Obs. Padova*, No. 66, 1940	
9617, η CrB.	15 19.1 +30 39	5.64 / 5.91	G2 V	0.84 / 41.6	+.065	Danjon, *Bull. Astr.*, **1**, 11, 191, 1938	1, 3
9716, OΣ 298.	15 32.5 +40 08	7.46 / 7.62	dK4 / dK5	0.88 / 56	+.052	Stephens, *Pub. A.A.S.*, **9**, 170, 1939	1, 3
9909, ξ Sco AB.	15 58.9 -11 06	4.90 / 4.92	F5 IV	0.72 / 45.7	+.039	Baize, *Astronomie*, **56**, 157, 1942	1, 3
10075, Σ 2052.	16 24.5 +18 38	7.7 / 7.8	dK2	2.23 / 236	+.058	Siegrist, *Pub. Madrid Obs.*, Vol. 1, No. 11, 1952	1, 2, 3, 4
10157, ζ Her.	16 37.5 +31 47	2.89 / 5.55	G0 IV / dK0	1.37 / 34.4	+.105	Baize, *J. d. Obs.*, **32**, 53, 1949	
−8°4352, Kuiper.	16 50.1 -08 09	9.7 / 9.8	dM3e	0.218 / 1.715	+.157	Voute, *Pub. Riverview Obs.*, **2**, 43, 1946	3, 4, 6
+45°2505, Kuiper.	17 10.6 +45 47	10.0 / 10.4	dM4	0.71 / 13.02	+.157	Baize, *Astronomie*, **66**, 76, 1952	4
−34°11626, Melb 4.	17 12.1 -34 53	6.3 / 7.2	dK5	1.84 / 42.1	+.139	Baize, *J. d. Obs.*, **29**, 17, 1946	3, 4
10585, A 351.	17 27.4 +29 26	9.6 / 10.0	K4	0.60 / 60.0	+.055	Baize, *J. d. Obs.*, **38**, 42, 1955	1, 2, 3, 4
10598, Σ 2173.	17 25.2 -00 59	5.97 / 6.08	G8 IV-V	1.02 / 46.1	+0.052	Duncombe and Ashbrook, *A.J.*, **57**, 92, 1952	3

TABLE 1—*Continued*

ADS/BD Name	Pos. 1900 R.A. Dec.	Mag. {A B}	Sp. {A B}	a / P (Years)	π Abs.	Source of Orbit	Notes
10660 26 Dra	17^h34^m0 +61°57'	5.33 8.04	G1 V	1".50 74.2	+0".065	Hall, *A.J.*, **54**, 106, 1949	
10786 μ Her BC	17 42.5 +27 47	10.3 10.8	dM4	1.36 43.2	+ .119	Couteau, *Bull. Astr.*, **23**, 127, 1960	1, 3, 4
11046 70 Oph	18 00.4 +02 32	4.20 5.98	K0 V dK6	4.56 87.85	+ .199	Strand, *Ann. Leiden Obs.*, **18**, 136, 1937	
11077 99 Her	18 03.2 +30 33	5.12 8.42	F7 V	1.07 53.7	+ .061	Ames and Pratt, *A.J.*, **63**, 41, 1958	
11871 β 648	18 53.3 +32 47	5.36 7.46	G0 V	1.24 61.2	+ .053	Schrutka-Rechtenstamm, *A.N.*, **268**, 229, 1940	1
−37°13048 γ CrA	18 59.7 −37 12	4.84 5.08	F8 V	2.07 119.3	+ .053	Dawson, *SDS*, notes for 18ʰ	1, 2, 3
12096 B 427	19 03.9 −19 58	7.0 7.2	K0	0.13 2.68	. . . .	Voronov, *Tashkent Obs.*, *Circ.*, No. 27, 1934	1, 2, 3, 4
12889 Σ 2576	19 41.8 +33 22	8.30 8.38	dK5	2.15 243	+ .047	Baize, *J. d. Obs.*, **38**, 44, 1955	2, 3
13461 OΣ 400	20 06.9 +43 39	7.7 8.2	dG4	0.48 84.4	+ .045	Wierzbinski, *J. d. Obs.*, **40**, 29, 1957	1, 2, 3, 4
−37°13741 Rus 321	20 20.4 −37 43	6.5 7.7	K2 IV–V	0.79 135	+0.050	Jones (Eggen, *M.N.*, **120**, 445, 1960)	1, 2, 3, 4

TABLE 1—*Continued*

ADS/BD Name	Pos. 1900 R.A. Dec.	Mag. {A B}	Sp. {A B}	a / P (Years)	π Abs.	Source of Orbit	Notes
14773...... δ Equ.	21h09m.6 +09°36'	5.2 5.3	F7 V	0".26 5.70	+0".056	Luyten and Ebbighausen, *Pub. Obs. U. Minnesota*, **2**, 25, 1934	4
14787...... τ Cyg.	21 10.8 +37 37	3.84 6.39	F0 IV	0.85 49.8	+ .049	Van Biesbroeck, *A.J.*, **48**, 169, 1940	
−58°7893...... φ 283.	21 39.4 −58 08	9.6 9.7	M	0.234 6.32	+ .054	Van den Bos, *Union Obs. Circ.*, No. 109, p. 370, 1950	1, 3, 4
15971...... ζ Aqr AB.	22 23.7 −00 32	4.31 4.51	F2 IV	4.01 600	+ .043	Franz, *A.J.*, **63**, 329, 1958	1, 2, 3
15972...... Kru 60.	22 24.4 +57 12	9.77 11.43	dM3 dM4e	2.39 44.46	+ .254	Hall, *A.J.*, **57**, 47, 1952	
16326...... A 632.	22 47.9 +57 11	8.3 8.8	K5	1.07 90.0	....	Dommanget, *Ann. R. Obs. Belgique*, **6**, 45, 1953	1, 3, 4
17175...... 85 Peg.	23 56.9 +26 33	5.82 8.86	G3 V	0.83 26.27	+0.081	Hall, *A.J.*, **54**, 102, 1949	1, 3

NOTES TO TABLE 1

1. Parallax or improved parallax needed.
2. Poor orbit.
3. Mass ratio needed.
4. Improved magnitudes or Δm needed.
5. At least one component is a spectroscopic binary.

6. The parallax is a weighted mean for both Wolf 629 and Wolf 630.
7. There is a new orbit by Luyten (*Pub. Obs. U. Minnesota*, Vol. **2**, No. 16, 1961) which gives $a = 2".38$, $P = 54^y.5$. The value of a^3/P^2 changes little, however.

It should be noted that, for nearly half the systems, parallaxes or improved parallaxes are needed, as well as mass ratios and improved magnitudes or magnitude differences between the components. Eighteen orbits have been designated poor, although five of these have short enough periods to allow a better orbit determination if they are observed sufficiently over the next decade.

§ 3. MASS RATIOS OF VISUAL BINARIES

The determination of the individual masses in a binary system requires the knowledge of the orbit of at least one of the components referred to the center of gravity of the system. If the masses of the individual components are $\mathfrak{M}_A$ and $\mathfrak{M}_B$, a, the semimajor axis of the relative orbit and a_A the semimajor axis of the "absolute" orbit of component A, then we have

$$\frac{\mathfrak{M}_B}{\mathfrak{M}_A + \mathfrak{M}_B} = \frac{a_A}{a}.$$

The fractional mass of the fainter component in terms of the combined mass of both components is usually defined as the mass ratio, B.

The determination of the "absolute" orbit of either component requires the study of the motions in an "absolute" reference frame. At present this is done almost exclusively by photography with long-focus refractors, using as a reference frame a system of "background" stars. In the past, micrometer measurements were used in the same manner, but the majority of the mass ratios were obtained from meridian-circle positions (Boss 1937).

While, theoretically, a short arc with a measurable curvature should be sufficient to establish the ratio between the dimensions of the relative and absolute orbits for a given system, observations over a long time interval are generally required to attain the necessary precision.

In the case of close binaries which are not resolved on the photographic plate, the resulting finite image will be the center of light of the two components. If we assume that the measured position of the blended image is the weighted center of light-intensity, and β the fractional distance of the primary to the photocenter in terms of the distance between the two components, then we have

$$\beta = \frac{l_B}{l_A + l_B},$$

where l_A and l_B are the luminosities of the components. If the difference of magnitude between the components, Δm, is introduced, we have $\beta = 1/(1 + 10^{0.4\Delta m})$.

Experiments with artificial binaries (Hall 1951) show minor systematic deviations from the theoretical relation for values of Δm larger than 2. Since the value of B is small in these cases, the choice between the theoretical and the experimental value has little effect on the resulting mass ratio.

With the fractional difference of photocenter to barycenter being $B - \beta$, the

TABLE 2

MASSES AND LUMINOSITIES OF VISUAL BINARIES

ADS/BD Name	Sp. $\begin{cases} A \\ B \end{cases}$	Σ Mass Mass Ratio	$\log \begin{cases} \mathfrak{M}_A \\ \mathfrak{M}_B \end{cases}$	$m_v \begin{cases} A \\ B \end{cases}$	$M_v \begin{cases} A \\ B \end{cases}$	$M_b \begin{cases} A \\ B \end{cases}$
61..... Σ 3062.....	dG4 dG8	3.22 0.59	+0.12 +0.28	+ 6.53 + 7.31	4.69 5.47	4.60 5.33
520..... β 395.....	G5 V	1.19 0.5	−0.22 −0.22	+ 6.3 + 6.4	5.6 5.7	5.5 5.6
671..... η Cas.....	G0 V dM0	1.42 0.38	−0.06 −0.27	+ 3.47 + 7.22	4.67 8.42	4.61 7.35
1865..... A 2329.....	dM1.5	0.73 0.5	−0.44 −0.44	+ 9.4 + 9.6	8.7 8.9	7.5 7.6
−12°501..... ε Cet.....	F5 IV–V	0.67 0.5	−0.47 −0.47	+ 5.49 + 5.49	4.59 4.59	4.6 4.6
3093..... o² Eri BC.....	DA dM4e	0.63 0.31	−0.36 −0.71	+ 9.6 +11.1	11.2 12.6	10.8 10.4
3841..... α Aur.....	G5 III G0 III	4.50 0.53	+0.33 +0.38	+ 0.9 + 1.0:	0.28 0.4:	0.1 0.2:
Ross 614.....	M4	0.22 0.35	−0.85 −1.10	+11.3 +14.8	13.3 16.8	11.1 13.0
5423..... Sirius.....	A1 V DA	3.16 0.33	+0.33 +0.02	− 1.43 + 8.52	1.45 11.4	1.22 11.1
6251..... Procyon.....	F5 IV–V	2.41 0.27	+0.25 −0.19	+ 0.38 +10.7:	2.67 13.0	2.63 12.4–12.9
6420..... 9 Pup.....	G0 V	1.15 0.51	−0.25 −0.23	+ 5.6 + 6.2	4.8 5.4	4.7 5.2
6650..... ς Cnc AB.....	F8 V	1.84 0.46	0.00 −0.07	+ 6.15 + 6.50	4.51 4.86	4.46 4.80
7114..... ι UMa BC.....	M1	0.68 0.5	−0.47 −0.47	+10.8 +11.0	10.0 10.2	8.3 8.4
+42°1956..... Kuiper.....	F5 V	1.09 0.41	−0.19 −0.35	+ 4.13 + 6.20	3.51 5.58	3.47 5.43
7284..... Σ 3121.....	dK4	1.26 0.51	−0.21 −0.19	+ 7.9 + 8.0	6.7 6.8	6.3 6.4
−39°3651..... ψ Vel.....	F2 IV	2.55 0.49	+0.11 +0.10	+ 4.1 + 4.6	3.1 3.6	3.1 3.6
8630..... γ Vir.....	F0 V F0 V	2.31 0.49	+0.07 +0.05	+ 3.48 + 3.50	3.50 3.52	3.46 3.48
8804..... α Com.....	F5 V	2.86 0.51	+0.15 +0.16	+ 5.04 + 5.07	3.70 3.73	3.66 3.69
9031..... Σ 1785.....	dK6 dK6	1.40 0.49	−0.15 −0.16	+ 7.59 + 8.03	6.97 7.41	6.51 6.76
−60°5483..... α Cen.....	G2 V dK5	1.94 0.46	+0.02 −0.05	− 0.04 + 1.17	4.36 5.57	4.29 5.42

TABLE 2—*Continued*

ADS/BD Name	Sp. {A B}	Σ Mass Mass Ratio	log {$\mathfrak{M}_A$ $\mathfrak{M}_B$}	m_v {A B}	M_v {A B}	M_b {A B}
9352..... Hu 575.....	dM0	1.09 0.43	−0.21 − .33	+ 9.7 +10.0	7.9 8.2	7.1 7.2
9413..... ξ Boo.....	G8 V K4 V	1.56 0.46	− .08 − .14	+ 4.68 + 6.78	5.54 7.64	5.39 6.89
9617..... η CrB.....	G2 V	1.25 0.47	− .18 − .23	+ 5.63 + 5.92	4.69 4.98	4.62 4.88
9716..... OΣ 298.....	dK4 dK5	1.54 0.5	− .11 − .11	+ 7.46 + 7.62	6.04 6.20	5.83 5.96
9909..... ξ Sco AB.....	F5 IV	3.01 0.5	+ .18 + .18	+ 4.90 + 4.92	2.86 2.88	2.82 2.84
10075..... Σ 2052.....	dK2	1.02 0.5	− .29 − .29	+ 7.65 + 7.83	6.47 6.65	6.18 6.30
10157..... ζ Her.....	G0 IV dK0	1.88 0.41	+ .05 − .11	+ 2.89 + 5.55	2.99 5.65	2.93 5.49
−8°4352..... Kuiper.....	dM3e	0.91 0.5	− .34 − .34	+ 9.7 + 9.8	10.7 10.8	8.7 8.7
+45°2505..... Kuiper.....	dM4	0.55 0.50	− .56 − .56	+10.0 +10.4	11.0 11.4	8.8 9.1
−34°11626..... Melb 4.....	dK5	1.31 0.41	− .11 − .27	+ 6.3 + 7.2	7.0 7.9	6.5 7.1
10598..... Σ 2173.....	G8 IV–V	3.55 0.5	+ .25 + .25	+ 5.97 + 6.08	4.55 4.66	4.48 4.58
10660..... 26 Dra.....	G1 V	1.95 0.45	+ .03 − .06	+ 5.33 + 8.04	4.49 7.20	4.43 6.65
11046..... 70 Oph.....	K0 V dK6	1.56 0.42	− .05 − .18	+ 4.20 + 5.98	5.70 7.48	5.54 6.80
11077..... 99 Her.....	F7 V	1.87 0.37	+ .07 − .16	+ 5.12 + 8.48	4.04 7.40	3.99 6.76
11871..... β 648.....	G0 V	3.42 0.43	+ .29 + .17	+ 5.35 + 7.47	3.97 6.09	3.91 5.87
12889..... Σ 2576.....	dK5	1.62 0.5	− .09 − .09	+ 8.30 + 8.38	6.66 6.74	6.31 6.37
14773..... δ Equ.....	F7 V	3.08 0.49	+ .20 + .18	+ 5.2 + 5.3	3.9 4.0	3.9 4.0
14787..... τ Cyg.....	F0 IV	2.10 0.42	+ .09 − .06	+ 3.84 + 6.39	2.29 4.84	2.25 4.75
−58°7893..... φ 283.....	M	2.04 0.5	+ .01 + .01	+ 9.6 + 9.7	8.3 8.4	7.3 7.3
15972..... Kru 60.....	dM3 dM4e	0.42 0.38	− .59 − .80	+ 9.77 +11.43	11.79 13.45	9.55 10.64
17175..... 85 Peg.....	G3 V	1.56 0.48	− .09 −0.12	+ 5.82 + 8.86	5.36 8.40	5.23 7.34

semimajor axis of the photocentric orbit, a, is related to the semimajor axis of the relative orbit, a, by the equation

$$a = (B - \beta)a \, ,$$

from which B can be determined if a, a, and β (Δm) are known.

The majority of the mass ratios given in Table 2 were obtained from the compilations by Strand and Hall (1954) and van de Kamp (1954), who also listed the sources from which they were derived. Equal masses, $B = 0.5$, were assumed for systems where Δm was 0.2 or less, and no mass ratio had been determined.

§ 4. THE EMPIRICAL MASS-LUMINOSITY RELATION

The existence of a statistical relation between the intrinsic luminosity and the mass of a star was first stated by Halm (1911). This conclusion was based on the correlation of mass with spectral type and spectral type with luminosity. Hertzsprung (1919) stated the relation explicitly by the formula

$$\log \mathfrak{M} = -0.06 \, (M_v - 5) \, ,$$

where $\mathfrak{M}$ is the mass and M_v is the absolute visual magnitude of the star. The formula agrees fairly well with recent data. Among the many investigations published on the mass-luminosity relation can be mentioned those by Eddington (1926), Parenago (1937), and Kuiper (1938). More recent discussions based on improved observational data are those by Strand and Hall (1954) and van de Kamp (1954).

From the compilation of binary systems in Table 1, forty-one systems were selected for a discussion of the mass-luminosity relation and are listed in Table 2. These are the systems which, in the opinion of the authors, have sufficient observational data for such a discussion. Systems from Table 1, for which one or both components are known to be composite stars, such as 13 Cet (ADS 490), a Gem (ADS 6175), ξ UMa (ADS 8119), and 44 Boo (ADS 9494), were excluded.

The first column of Table 2 identifies the systems, using the same designations as in Table 1. The second column lists the spectra of the two components. The masses in the third column were computed from the orbital elements (a, P) and parallaxes listed in Table 1. On the basis of the known mass ratios, the logarithms of the masses of the individual components are given in the fourth column. The fifth column contains the data on visual magnitudes given in Table 1, while the sixth column lists the absolute magnitudes as computed from the known trigonometric parallaxes and the visual magnitudes. The last column contains the bolometric absolute magnitudes, using the bolometric corrections from chapter 14.

Figure 1 represents the empirical mass-luminosity relation, with the logarithms of the individual masses plotted against their absolute bolometric magnitudes. If the values of high weights are considered, it is noted that they form, with a few exceptions, a rather narrow sequence from $M_b = 0$ to $M_b = +11$, with a slight change of slope at $M_b = +7.5$. For the stars brighter than 7.5 bolometric magnitude, we find the approximate relation

$$M_b = 4.6 - 10.0 \log \mathfrak{M} ,$$

while, for the stars fainter than $M_b = +7.5$, we have

$$M_b = 5.2 - 6.9 \log \mathfrak{M} .$$

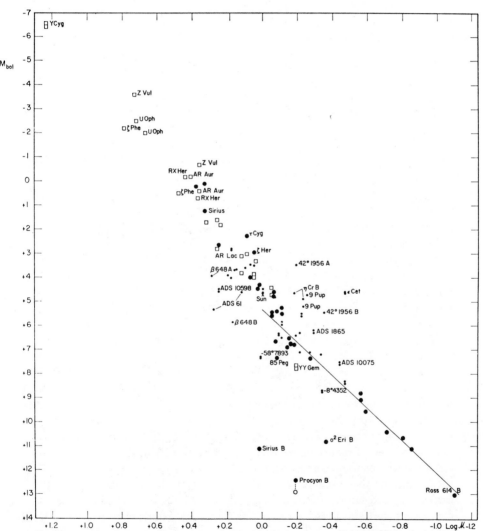

FIG. 1.—The empirical mass-luminosity relation. Visual binaries of high weight are indicated by large filled circles; those of low weight by small filled circles. Eclipsing binaries are indicated by unfilled squares. The solid line represents the adopted mass-luminosity relation for the late-type dwarf stars.

Whether the change in slope is real or caused by the bolometric corrections used for the faint dwarfs cannot be decided at this time.

Three white dwarfs, the companions to Sirius, Procyon, and o^2 Eri, lie below the mass-luminosity relation by some magnitudes. The companion to 85 Peg is underluminous for its mass by approximately 1 mag., and this deviation is larger than can be ascribed to errors in the available data.

Note that both τ Cyg A and ζ Her A, which have mass determinations of high weight, lie approximately 1 mag. above the general mass-luminosity relation. According to present theories of stellar evolution, both these subgiants should be brighter than main-sequence stars of similar masses, and this is just what we find.

In the distribution of the values of lower weight, there are a considerable number of large deviations from the general relation. In all cases, as shown in Figure 1, both components of a particular double star show the same large deviations, which nearly always can be ascribed to a poorly determined trigonometric parallax.

An extension of the mass-luminosity relation to the stars more luminous than $M_b = 0$, for which no data are available from visual binaries, can be based on the data obtained from those double-lined spectroscopic binaries that are also eclipsing binaries. As in the case of the visual binaries, it is also desirable to limit the eclipsing binaries to be included in the discussion to those systems classified as "reliable" in the sense of providing reliable values of masses, radii, and colors of the two components.

A tentative list of "reliable" systems was assembled from compilations by Kopal (1955) and Popper (1957). The list was critically reviewed by D. M. Popper and resulted in the 13 systems listed in Table 3. Ten of the systems have main-sequence components, while two systems are composed of subgiants (Z Her and AR Lac). One system consists of a main-sequence star and a giant (Z Vul). The data for the sun are given for a comparison.

The table will be discussed further in the next section, and we shall here concern ourselves only with the data pertaining to the mass-luminosity relation. It will be noted from Figure 1 that the data for the visual and the spectroscopic binaries agree in the region where they overlap.

There appears to be no change in the relation for M_b brighter than 0 except for a slight change of slope, which is not too well established in view of the limited material. From the observational data available at the present time, it can be concluded that there exists a well-defined relation between the mass and the bolometric magnitude of a main-sequence star. It also appears that the earlier-type subgiants, such as Sirius A and Procyon A, and giants like the two components of Capella (α Aur) satisfy the same mass-luminosity relation as do the main-sequence stars. The subgiants τ Cyg and ζ Her and the subdwarf companion to 85 Peg, all of which have reliable mass determinations, show marked deviations from the mass-luminosity relation.

TABLE 3

DATA ON "RELIABLE" SPECTROSCOPIC BINARIES

STAR	POSITION 1900 R.A.	POSITION 1900 Dec.	SPECTRUM A	SPECTRUM B	MASS A	MASS B	RADIUS A	RADIUS B	ABS. BOL. MAG. A	ABS. BOL. MAG. B	LOG MASS A	LOG MASS B
WW Aur....	06^{h}25^{m}9	+32°32'	A5–7	A7	1.81	1.75	1.9	1.9	+1.6	+1.8	+0.26	+0.24
AR Aur....	05 11.7	+33 40	B8	B9.5	2.55	2.30	1.8	1.8	−0.2	+0.4	+0.41	+0.36
Y Cyg....	20 48.1	+34 17	O9.5	O9.5	17.4	17.2	5.9	5.9	−6.5	−6.5	+1.24	+1.24
YY Gem..	07 28.4	+32 05	M1e	M1e	0.64	0.64	0.62	0.62	+7.7	+7.7	−0.19	−0.19
Z Her....	17 53.6	+15 09	F4 IV–V	K0 IV	1.22	1.10	1.6	2.6	+3.0	+3.3	+0.09	+0.04
RX Her....	18 26.0	+12 33	B9.5	A1	2.75	2.33	2.4	2.0	−0.2	+0.7	+0.44	+0.37
TX Her....	17 15.5	+42 00	A5	F0	2.1	1.8	1.8	1.5	+1.7	+2.8	+0.32	+0.26
AR Lac....	22 04.6	+45 15	G2	K0	1.32	1.31	1.54	2.86	+3.8	+3.1	+0.12	+0.12
UV Leo...	10 33.0	+14 47	G0	G2	0.9	0.9	1.10	0.99	+4.4	+4.7	−0.05	−0.05
U Oph....	17 11.5	+01 19	B5	B6	5.30	4.65	3.4	3.1	−2.5	−2.0	+0.72	+0.67
WZ Oph...	17 01.8	+07 55	G0	G0	1.11	1.11	1.37	1.35	+3.9	+3.9	+0.05	+0.05
ζ Phe....	01 04.2	−55 47	B6 V	A0 V	6.1	3.0	3.4	2.0	−2.2	+0.5	+0.79	+0.48
Z Vul....	19 17.5	+25 23	B3–4 V	A2–3 III	5.4	2.3	4.7	4.7	−3.6	−0.7	+0.73	+0.36
(Sun)...			G2 V		1.0		1.0		+4.7			

§ 5. THE RADII OF THE STARS

The largest source of information regarding the radii of stars is derived from eclipsing binaries which are also double-lined spectroscopic binary systems. From the photometric solution, one obtains the relative radii of the two components in terms of their orbital separation, along with the inclination of the orbit, while the spectroscopic solution gives the quantities $\mathfrak{M}_1 \sin^3 i$, $\mathfrak{M}_2 \sin^3 i$, and $a \sin i$. Here $\mathfrak{M}_1$ and $\mathfrak{M}_2$ refer to the masses of the two components, and a is the semimajor axis of the orbit in absolute units (kilometers). By combining the results of the two solutions, one obtains the individual masses and radii.

TABLE 4

DATA ON ECLIPSING BINARIES OF LOWER WEIGHTS

Star	Spectral Type	log Mass	log Radius	M_b
μ^1 Sco............	B1.5 V (B3)	1.15 0.97	0.72 0.76	−4.9 −4.2
β Aur...........	A2 V	0.37 0.35	0.40 0.36	+0.4 +0.6
V 356 Sgr........	B3 A2 II	1.08 0.67	0.69 1.04	−3.9 −2.8
ζ Aur............	K4 Ib B7 V	0.92 0.75	2.20	−4.4 ....
31 Cyg..........	K3 Ib B3 V	1.26 0.95	2.24 0.67	−4.9 −3.8
32 Cyg..........	K6 I B3 V	1.36 0.91	2.55 0.59	−5.6 −3.4

Unfortunately, as Struve (1957) has emphasized, "there are many 'abnormal' double stars, and few, if any, that can be described as entirely 'normal.'" If, in addition, one restricts the discussion to "reliable" systems (Popper 1957), it is found that only a small number of systems is available. It is to be noted that improvements in observational techniques are gradually extending this list of reliable systems.

The spectral types, masses, and radii of the thirteen selected eclipsing binary systems are listed in Table 3. The absolute bolometric magnitudes given in the last two columns have been computed by using the effective temperature scale derived earlier and the relation

$$M_b = 42.31 - 10 \log T_e - 5 \log R,$$

in order that these stars may be plotted on a mass-luminosity diagram.

Table 4 gives six more eclipsing binary systems of lower weight which are of interest. μ^1 Sco and β Aur were used earlier in connection with the derivation of the effective temperature scale, while the remaining four systems consist of a B-type star and a larger, cooler companion. Wilson (1960) and Popper (1961) have discussed the difficulties involved in the analysis of these latter systems, but they are included here because they provide the only determinations, unreliable as they may be, of the radii of supergiants.

Table 5 gives the mass, radii, and bolometric magnitudes of seven eclipsing systems of the W UMa type based on Kopal's (1955) compilation. These "contact" binary systems appear to deviate from the mass-luminosity relation for "normal" main-sequence stars. In addition to the results obtained from eclipsing

TABLE 5

DATA ON W UMA SYSTEMS

Star	Spectral Type	log Mass	log Radius	M_b
44 Boo.........	G2 G2	0.00 − .30	−0.05 − .22	+4.9 +5.8
VW Cep........	G5 K1	+ .04 − .52	+ .04 − .15	+4.5 +6.1
YY Eri.........	G5 G5	.00 − .22	.00 − .05	+4.7 +4.9
SW Lac.........	G3 G3	.00 + .08	.00 − .10	+4.7 +5.0
ER Ori.........	G2 G2	− .40 − .52	− .05 − .05	+4.9 +4.9
W UMa........	G0 G0	+ .04 − .30	− .05 − .15	+4.7 +5.2
AH Vir.........	K0 K0	+ .15 −0.22	+ .11 −0.15	+4.6 +5.9

binaries, there are a few other stars for which the radii may be determined. As observational techniques and theoretical studies progress, this small list may also expand in length.

Direct determinations made by Pease (1931) of the apparent diameters of stars by means of an interferometer have been used in the discussion of the effective temperatures of late-type giants. In the case of Aldebaran, K5 III, the angular diameter of 0".020 may be combined with the trigonometric parallax of 0".048 to give $R = 48 R_{(sun)}$. The parallaxes of the other stars observed by Pease are too small to be used in this manner to determine the absolute radii. More recently the angular diameter of Sirius has been measured by Brown and Twiss (1956), who found $d = 0".0068 \pm 0".0005$. With the large trigonometric parallax of 0".377 of Sirius we find $R = 2.05 R_{(sun)}$, assuming Popper's (1959) correction for limb darkening.

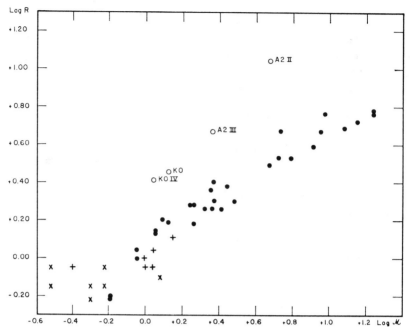

Fig. 2.—The empirical mass-radius relation. Eclipsing binaries from Tables 3 and 4 are indicated by filled circles. Four stars lying above the general relation are indicated by open circles. Crosses indicate the brighter components of the W UMa systems listed in Table 5, while ×'s indicate the fainter components.

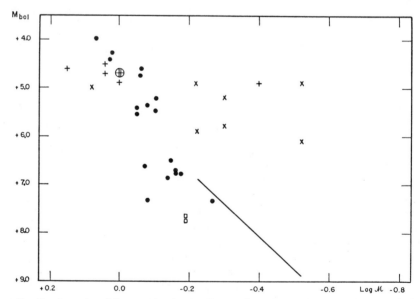

Fig. 3.—A portion of the mass-luminosity diagram from Fig. 1 is here reproduced, with the addition of the W UMa systems from Table 5. Crosses indicate the brighter components, ×'s the fainter components and ⊕ the sun.

The apparent diameter of the supergiant M-type star, Antares, has been determined to be 0".041 (uncorrected for limb darkening) from the photoelectric light-curves of its occultation by the moon (Cousins and Guelke 1953; Evans, Heydenrych, and van Wyk 1953). This may be compared with Pease's value of 0".040 determined interferometrically. Unfortunately, the parallax is too small to be reliable. Earlier observations of β Cap and ν Aqr by Whitford (1939) failed to show measurable diameters.

The mass-radius relation for stars in the vicinity of the main sequence is given in Figure 2, in which all the systems listed in Tables 3, 4, and 5 are plotted. The four stars, shown as open circles, lie above the main sequence according to their luminosities; the obvious separation between them and the main-sequence stars is undoubtedly due to selection effects.

The "contact" binaries evidently deviate from "normal" main-sequence stars in the mass-radius, as well as in the mass-luminosity, plot. A portion of the mass-luminosity diagram is shown in Figure 3, where the individual stars refer to entries in Table 5 and the lines represent the mean relations derived from visual binary systems. It appears that the deviations of the "contact" binaries from the relations for "normal" stars are much more pronounced for the less massive components of the systems. It is quite difficult to obtain "reliable" photometric and spectroscopic solutions for these systems, which may account for a good part of the scatter in the diagrams.

REFERENCES

BAIZE, P.	1950	*J. d. Obs.*, **33**, 1.
BOSS, B.	1937	*General Catalogue of 33342 Stars for the Epoch 1950* (Washington D.C.: Carnegie Institution of Washington), Appendix II.
BROWN, R. H., and TWISS, R. Q.	1956	*Nature*, **178**, 1046.
COUSINS, A. W. J., and GUELKE, R.	1953	*M.N.*, **113**, 776.
EDDINGTON, A. S.	1926	*The Internal Constitution of the Stars* (Cambridge, England: Cambridge University Press); new edition (New York: Dover Publications, Inc., 1959).
EVANS, D. S., HEYDENRYCH, J. C. R., and VAN WYK, J. D. N.	1953	*M.N.*, **113**, 781.
HALL, R. G., JR.	1951	*A.J.*, **55**, 215.
HALM, J.	1911	*M.N.*, **71**, 610.
HERTZSPRUNG, E.	1919	*A.N.*, **208**, 89.
KAMP, P. VAN DE	1954	*A.J.*, **59**, 447.
KOPAL, Z.	1955	*Ann. d'ap.*, **18**, 379.
KUIPER, G. P.	1938	*Ap. J.*, **88**, 472.
PARENAGO, P. P.	1937	*A.J., U.S.S.R.*, **14**, 33.

PEASE, F. G. 1931 *Ergebn. d. exakt. Naturwiss. Berlin,* **10,** 84.
POPPER, D. M. 1957 *J.R.A.S. Canada,* **51,** 51.
1959 *Ap. J.,* **129,** 647.
1961 *Ibid.,* **134,** 828.
STRAND, K. AA., and
HALL, R. G., JR. 1954 *Ap. J.,* **120,** 322.
STRUVE, O. 1957 *J.R.A.S. Canada,* **51,** 106.
WHITFORD, A. E. 1939 *Ap. J.,* **89,** 472.
WILSON, O. C. 1960 *Stellar Atmospheres,* ed. J. L. GREENSTEIN ("Stars and Stellar Systems," Vol. **6** [Chicago: University of Chicago Press]), p. 436.

CHAPTER 16

Polarization of Starlight

JOHN S. HALL

Lowell Observatory

AND

K. SERKOWSKI

Warsaw University Observatory and Lowell Observatory (1959–1961)

§ 1. INTRODUCTION

Polarization is one of the observed properties of stellar light. Nevertheless, until 1946, astronomers generally believed that starlight was not polarized —there were no indications of anisotropy which could produce polarization. In this year Babcock (1947) discovered the circularly polarized Zeeman components of the absorption lines in spectra of peculiar A-type stars. In the same year Chandrasekhar (1946) and Chandrasekhar and Breen (1947) were investigating theoretically the atmospheres of early-type stars in which the scattering of light by free electrons played a predominant role. They found that 11.7 per cent of light emanating from a given point at the stellar limb might be plane-polarized, with the electric vector parallel to the limb. They predicted that this polarization might be detected when the early-type component of an eclipsing binary was being occulted by its late-type companion. Investigations carried out in an effort to observe this effect led to the discovery of interstellar polarization by Hall (1949) and Hiltner (1949a). This serendipital discovery is another of the many which seem so prevalent in the field of astronomy.

§ 2. METHODS OF MEASURING POLARIZATION

2.1. PARAMETERS DESCRIBING POLARIZATION

Let us consider the partially plane-polarized light, having a total intensity I, for which the position angle of the plane of vibration of the electric vector, in the equatorial co-ordinate system, is θ. We may represent this light as the sum of two plane-polarized components. We shall denote by I_{max} the intensity of the plane-polarized component for which the position angle of the plane of vibration is θ, and by I_{min} that for which the position angle is $\theta + 90°$; the amount of polarization, p, expressed in stellar magnitudes is

$$p = 2.5 \log \frac{I_{max}}{I_{min}}. \tag{1}$$

The partially plane-polarized light may also be represented as a sum of the plane-polarized light of intensity PI and natural light of intensity $(1 - P)I$. The degree of polarization, P, satisfies the equation

$$P = \frac{I_{max} - I_{min}}{I_{max} + I_{min}} = \frac{\ln 10}{5} p = 0.4605p. \tag{2}$$

In order to make a statistical analysis of polarization data or to eliminate systematic errors in observations, it is often necessary or desirable to add or subtract double sine waves having different phases and amplitudes. This can be done most readily by describing polarization by means of the parameters I, Q, U, and V, introduced by Stokes (1852). Their properties were discussed by Chandrasekhar (1946, 1950), van de Hulst (1957), and McMaster (1961). The Stokes parameters for the partially plane-polarized light considered by us are (cf. Behr 1959b)

$$I = I_{max} + I_{min}, \tag{3}$$

$$Q = (I_{max} - I_{min}) \cos 2\theta = PI \cos 2\theta, \tag{4}$$

$$U = (I_{max} - I_{min}) \sin 2\theta = PI \sin 2\theta, \tag{5}$$

$$V = 0. \tag{6}$$

The parameter V describes the degree of ellipticity; for circularly polarized light, $V = \pm I$, where the plus sign should be taken for right-handed, and the minus sign for left-handed, polarization. The natural light is equivalent to a mixture of any two independent (without phase relationships) streams having equal intensity and the parameters Q, U, V, differing only by sign.

In astronomical applications it is convenient to introduce the Stokes parameters expressed in magnitudes, which are defined by

$$p_x = \frac{Q}{0.4605I} = p \cos 2\theta, \tag{7}$$

$$p_y = \frac{U}{0.4605I} = p \sin 2\theta, \tag{8}$$

$$p_v = \frac{V}{0.4605I}. \tag{9}$$

The first two of the parameters were introduced by Behr (1956) and Davis (1955). Denoting by θ_G the position angle of the plane of vibration in the galactic co-ordinate system and replacing θ in equations (7) and (8) by the angle $(\theta_G - 90°)$ in order to relate them conveniently to the galactic co-ordinate system, we obtain the Stokes parameters, expressed in magnitudes and galactic co-ordinates,

$$Q_G = p \cos 2 \, (\theta_G - 90°) , \tag{10}$$

$$U_G = p \sin 2 \, (\theta_G - 90°) . \tag{11}$$

If the amount of polarization is so small that p^2 may be neglected (this condition is fulfilled in most astronomical applications), the increments of the parameters p_x and p_y, resulting from instrumental polarization, are independent of the values of the parameters themselves. For this reason, as was pointed out by Wesselink (1958) and Behr (1959b), the instrumental polarization is most conveniently described in terms of the parameters p_x and p_y.

The Stokes parameters can be expressed by the differences between the magnitudes of a star observed through an analyzer oriented in different position angles:

$$p_x = m(90°) - m \, (0°) , \tag{12}$$

$$p_y = m(135°) - m(45°) . \tag{13}$$

Here $m(\phi)$ is the magnitude of a star observed through an analyzer (e.g., a Polaroid sheet) transmitting only the plane-polarized light for which the position angle of the plane of vibration is ϕ. To obtain p_v, let us insert a quarter-wave plate in front of the analyzer. This quarter-wave plate should be oriented so as to introduce a phase difference of 90° between the components of the electric vector, for which the position angles of the plane of vibration are 0° and 90°, respectively. Denoting by $m^*(\phi)$ the magnitude of a star observed by a quarter-wave plate so oriented and the analyzer, we have

$$p_v = m^*(45°) - m^*(135°) . \tag{14}$$

Since in most cases the errors of magnitude measurements obey the Gaussian law of errors, the same law is obeyed by the errors of the Stokes parameters expressed in magnitudes. The mean errors of these parameters are independent of their true values. This cannot be said about the parameters p and θ. Also the observed value, p, of the amount of polarization is systematically greater than the true value, p_0. As shown by Serkowski (1958b), the most probable observed value, p, is connected with the true value, p_0, by the relation

$$p = \begin{cases} (p_0^2 + \tfrac{1}{2}\pi\epsilon^2)^{1/2} & \text{for } p_0 \approx 0 \\ (p_0^2 + \epsilon^2)^{1/2} & \text{for } p_0 \gg \epsilon , \end{cases} \tag{15}$$

where ϵ is the mean error of each of the parameters p_x and p_y. The mean error, ϵ_p, of the amount of polarization, understood as the r.m.s. deviation of the observed value of p from the most probable value given by equations (15), is

$$\epsilon_p = \begin{cases} \epsilon(2 - \tfrac{1}{2}\pi)^{1/2} & \text{for } p_0 \approx 0 \\ \epsilon & \text{for } p_0 \gg \epsilon . \end{cases} \tag{16}$$

The r.m.s. deviation, δ_p, of the observed amount of polarization from the true value, p_0, is, of course, larger and equals

$$\delta_p = \begin{cases} \epsilon \sqrt{2} & \text{for } p_0 \approx 0 \\ \epsilon & \text{for } p_0 \gg \epsilon . \end{cases} \tag{17}$$

The mean error, ϵ_θ, of the position angle, θ, is

$$\epsilon_\theta = \begin{cases} \dfrac{\pi}{\sqrt{12}} \text{ radians} = 51°96 & \text{for } p_0 \approx 0 \\[2ex] \dfrac{1}{2} \dfrac{\epsilon}{p} \text{ radians} = 28°65\dfrac{\epsilon}{p} & \text{for } p_0 \gg \epsilon. \end{cases} \tag{18}$$

Although the use of the Stokes parameters greatly facilitates corrections and the statistical analysis of results, we believe that polarization data should continue to be published as magnitude differences and position angles (in equatorial and galactic co-ordinates) of the electric vector maximum.

2.2. Photographic Measurements of Polarization

As may be seen from equations (12) and (13), for determining each of the Stokes parameters, p_x and p_y, the magnitude difference should be measured between the two images of a star on a photographic plate obtained at position angles of an analyzer differing by 90°. To eliminate the influence of changing atmospheric extinction, these two images should be exposed simultaneously, and, to lessen the influence of non-uniformity of the photographic emulsion and the development process, they should be as near each other as practicable.

The above conditions are fulfilled if, in front of the photographic plate, we place a plane-parallel calcite plate cut parallel to its natural cleavage planes. Because of the birefringence of calcite, two images of each star will be formed on the photographic plate—the ordinary and extraordinary one—polarized in perpendicular planes. The magnitude difference between these two images formed by a properly oriented calcite plate gives the corresponding Stokes parameter expressed in magnitudes. The mean error of determining the Stokes parameter from one exposure is about the same as the error of determining the magnitude difference between two neighboring stars on a photographic plate, i.e., of the order of ± 0.04 mag. The mean error of the Stokes parameter determined from 16 plates is therefore ± 0.01 mag. High-quality calcite plates, as large as 8 cm. in diameter, may be obtained, and almost all of this large field on the photographic plate can be utilized for polarization measurements. This method of measuring polarization was used successfully by Markowitz and Hall (1950), Markowitz (1951), Gossner (1952), Behr (1955), and van den Bergh (1956).

In these investigations the shapes of the ordinary and extraordinary images are not identical. The ordinary image has a regular, circular shape, but the extraordinary image is distorted by astigmatism resulting from the oblique direction of rays which traverse the calcite plate. As pointed out by Lodén (1958), a small change in the focus of the telescope causes large changes in the shape of the extraordinary image. To avoid these errors, Serkowski (1958c, 1960b) and, independently, Bartl (1959) proposed to use two identical plane-parallel calcite plates oriented so that their principal sections were perpendicular to one another. The light which is ordinary in the first crystal is extraordinary in the second and vice versa. Hence both images of a star given by crossed calcite plates have the same shape and are formed in the same plane perpendicular to the direction of the initial light-rays.

For each region investigated, at least eight exposures should be made, each on a separate plate, the calcite crystals being rotated after each exposure by 45°. In this way, possible small systematic differences between the two images, as well as the influence of the neighboring stars on a star being measured, can, to a first approximation, be eliminated. Reliable results, however, can be obtained only if stellar images are far from being crowded.

According to Lodén (1958), accurate photographic measurements of polarization may be obtained with the self-standardizing quadruple-image polarigraph constructed by Öhman (1956). It consists of two Wollaston prisms and a plane-parallel quartz plate mounted in a collimated beam. Although the method has the advantage of providing photometric calibration, it has the disadvantage of introducing systematic errors for off-axis stars. This objection against the self-standardizing polarigraph applies also to a single Wollaston prism used for photographic measurements of polarization by Dombrovskii (1949, 1952, 1957), Janssen (1946), and Hiltner (1947).

The photographic method of measuring polarization is important as an efficient means of measuring polarization of faint stars because the polarization of stars fainter than the fifteenth magnitude is difficult to measure accurately by the photoelectric method, even with large telescopes.

2.3. Photoelectric Measurements of Polarization

The present photomultiplier tubes have two disadvantages which must be taken into consideration when measuring polarization. First, their sensitivity is different for light polarized in different planes. This effect is very conspicuous in the RCA 1P21 photomultipliers for which the cathode is usually not normal to the direction of incident light. It is also true for E.M.I. photomultipliers with their "end-on" cathode; the difference in sensitivity may be as large as 3 per cent. In this latter case the effect may be caused by the inclination of the first dynode of the "venetian-blind" type. Some of the light passes through the semi-transparent cathode and produces photoelectrons from the first dynode.

To avoid this effect, the photomultiplier tube was rotated together with an analyzer in the polarimeter constructed by Hiltner (1951a). A simpler way of avoiding this effect is to place a Lyot (1929) quartz depolarizer immediately in front of the photomultiplier; this method was first used in the polarimeter constructed by Hall (1948).

Another bad feature of photomultiplier tubes results from large changes in sensitivity over the area of the cathode. To minimize systematic errors due to the influence of this effect, the image of the telescope objective should be formed on the cathode so that it does not move as the analyzer is rotated. This condition is fulfilled if the analyzer is exactly plane-parallel and its surfaces are perpendicular to the axis of rotation. In the case of photomultiplier tubes rotating together with an analyzer, the axis of rotation should always point toward the center of the telescope objective. This last condition is sometimes difficult to accomplish because of flexure in the telescope.

As shown by Behr (1956, 1960), the inhomogeneous sensitivity of photocathodes causes a single sine wave to be superimposed on the double sine wave, representing the changes of the photocurrent due to stellar polarization alone, as the analyzer is rotated through 360°.

Three types of photoelectric polarimeters have been used—the d.c. polarimeter, the a.c. polarimeter, and the differential polarimeter. In the d.c. polarimeter, the analyzer placed before the photomultiplier tube can be set in several position angles. In each position angle of the analyzer, the magnitude of a star is measured. It is most convenient when the analyzer can be set in eight position angles, at 45° intervals. Then the magnitude differences between the position angles differing by 90° give directly the Stokes parameters expressed in magnitudes, according to equations (12) and (13). The first d.c. polarimeter for measuring stellar polarization was built by Hiltner (1949b, 1951a). Polarimeters of this type were constructed later by Dombrovskii (1953, 1957), van P. Smith (1956), Grigoryan (1957a), Hoag and Smith (1959), and Krzeminski (1959).

A polarimeter of the a.c. type was constructed by Hall (1948, 1952, 1953) and Hall and Mikesell (1950). The analyzer (plane-parallel calcite plate) is made to rotate about the optical axis of the telescope with a frequency of 15 c.p.s. Hence the polarized component of the illumination which strikes the photocathode changes sinusoidally with a frequency of 30 c.p.s. This alternating photocurrent is amplified and transformed electronically, so that the parameters describing polarization can be registered by a recorder or punched on cards (Hall and Hoag 1958). The calibration of measurements is obtained by means of an inclined plane-parallel glass plate introducing constant polarization. Systematic errors are eliminated by observations with and without a Lyot depolarizer.

The a.c. polarimeter with an analyzer rotating with sufficiently high frequency should eliminate the influence of atmospheric scintillation on the measurements. As shown by Mikesell, Hoag, and Hall (1951), the scintillation of two perpendicularly polarized components is almost exactly the same, and the ratio of the simultaneous intensities of these components is not affected by the scintillation.

Instead of using a rapidly rotating analyzer, the ill effects of scintillation may also be eliminated if two photomultiplier tubes are illuminated by perpendicularly polarized components of stellar light. Such differential polarimeters were constructed by Hiltner (1951*b*, 1952, 1959), Behr (1956), Thiessen (1958), Fessenkov (1959), Gehrels and Teska (1960), and Serkowski (unpublished). The Wollaston prism or plane-parallel calcite plate is used for splitting the lightbeam. Since the ratio of two photocurrents is, in most cases, near unity, it is more convenient to measure the difference between currents instead of the ratio. The accuracy so far obtained with differential polarimeters for bright stars is much higher than that obtained with d.c. or a.c. polarimeters. According to Behr (1959*b*), an observation lasting 12 minutes gives a mean error of each of the Stokes parameters of ± 0.0007 mag., while the corresponding value obtained with d.c. or a.c. polarimeters is about ± 0.003 mag. Such gain in accuracy takes place only for bright stars, for which atmospheric scintillation is the main factor limiting the accuracy of the measurements.

In the differential polarimeter the influence of scintillation is reduced to a large extent but is not completely eliminated. The residual influence of scintillation is still the main source of errors when observing bright stars. Because of atmospheric scintillation, the illumination of the telescope's objective (or mirror) is inhomogeneous and rapidly changing. This, as pointed out by Behr (1956, 1960), has the following consequences:

1. In every point of the image of the objective formed on the photocathode the illumination changes rapidly. Because of the lack of homogeneity in the sensitivity of the photocathode, this causes fluctuations in the photocurrent.

2. In refractors, the objective introduces polarization if its illumination is not symmetrical with respect to its center. This polarization may be as large as a few hundredths of a magnitude and can be computed from Fresnel's formulae. Similar effects are observed in the case of mirrors, which in most cases polarize incident light differently in different portions of their surface, as pointed out by Reimer (1957), Dollfus (1957), Thiessen and Broglia (1959), and Behr (1960).

The objectives of telescopes are also likely to introduce circular polarization (Serkowski 1960*a*). This affects both the amount of polarization and the position angle of the plane of vibration. This circular polarization can be easily measured directly and taken into account in the reductions.

§ 3. BASIC OBSERVATIONAL RESULTS

3.1. POLARIZATION AND THE MILKY WAY

More than 4000 stars have been investigated photoelectrically for polarization. Most of them are O- and B-type stars, for which polarization measurements were made by Hall (1958) and Hiltner (1951*a*, 1954*a*, *d*, 1956) and for southern stars by van P. Smith (1956). The measurements contained in the catalogues of the last two authors are included in Hall's (1958) catalogue of 2592 stars, together with his own observations. Polarization data for about 500 nearby stars have been published by Behr (1959*b*) and for 31 cepheids by Schmidt

(1958*a*). For nearly 400 stars of different types, polarization was also measured photoelectrically by Dombrovskii (1958), with somewhat less accuracy than that obtained by the others. The surveys of polarization in Kapteyn Selected Areas were made by Bartl (1959), Lodén (1960, 1961*a*, *b*), and Tripp (1956). Polarization of globular clusters was measured by Blamont and Courtès (1954). All these data show that the amount of polarization decreases rapidly with increasing galactic latitude. The largest amounts of polarization are observed in the Milky Way belt. Nevertheless, polarization as large as 0.002 mag. was detected by Behr (1959*b*) near the northern and southern galactic poles.

The longitude dependence of the amount of polarization for stars farther than several hundred parsecs may be represented by a double sine wave, with minima at galactic longitudes, $l^{\mathrm{II}} = 50°$ and $230°$ (Fig. 1). These are approximately

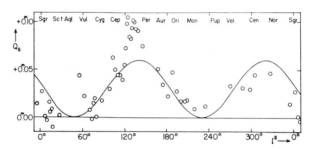

FIG. 1.—The mean values of the Stokes parameter Q_G (the component of the polarization parallel to the galactic plane), in intervals of galactic longitude, l^{II}, chosen so that the average number of stars in the interval is 25. No one point is based on less than 20 stars. Only stars with $|b^{\mathrm{II}}| < 3°0$ and more than 600 pc distant were used. The double sine wave is arbitrarily drawn with minima at $l^{\mathrm{II}} = 50°$ and $230°$.

the directions of galactic spiral arms as determined by Morgan, Whitford, and Code (1953) from the distribution of the O-type associations. The corresponding galactic longitudes obtained by Behr (1959*b*) from polarization of stars nearer than 250 pc in both low and high galactic latitudes are $l^{\mathrm{II}} = 62°$ and $242°$, with mean errors of $\pm 5°$.

The longitude dependence is still more evident if, instead of the amounts of polarization, we use the Stokes parameter Q_G (defined by eq. [10]). In Figure 1 the mean values of Q_G computed by Serkowski (1962) are shown as a function of galactic longitude; all the stars measured photoelectrically have been taken into account, for which $|b^{\mathrm{II}}| < 3°0$ and the distance is larger than 600 pc. It is apparent that the minimum values of Q_G are equal to zero within the limits of error.

The fact that the planes of vibrations are, on the average, parallel to the galactic equator means that the mean values of θ_G and U_G are 90° and 0°, respectively. It is quite obvious that θ_G assumes completely random values in those galactic longitudes for which the mean values of Q_G and U_G vanish. Also, the mean deviation of θ_G from the average value of 90° is smallest in those galactic longitudes in which mean Q_G assumes the maximum value. It was pointed out by Shain (1957) and Schmidt (1958b) that the mean values of θ_G are not exactly equal to 90° for all galactic longitudes but show a systematic trend. Explanations of this longitude dependence were proposed by Shain (1957), Behr (1959b), and Serkowski (1960a, 1962), but the problem is still unsolved. Instead of considering the longitude dependence of θ_G, it is more convenient to consider such dependence for U_G (Fig. 2), the mean values of which, in contrast to those of θ_G, are equally well defined for all galactic longitudes.

The interstellar origin of polarization was recently questioned by Thiessen (1961, 1962), who explains the polarization of starlight by synchrotron radiation in stellar atmospheres. This hypothesis does not seem to fit the observations satisfactorily. Detailed criticism of Thiessen's arguments is given by Behr (1961) and by Warwick (1961).

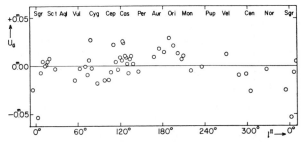

Fig. 2.—The mean values of the Stokes parameter U_G for the same stars as those used in Fig. 1.

3.2. Wavelength Dependence of Polarization and Extinction

The amount of polarization for a given longitude is positively correlated both with the distance of a star and with its interstellar reddening. Hiltner (1956) and Schmidt (1958b) showed that the ratio of the amount of polarization, p, to visual extinction, A_v, both expressed in magnitudes, does not exceed the value

$$\left(\frac{p}{A_v}\right)_{max} = 0.065 \pm 0.005 \,(\text{m.e.}) \,. \tag{19}$$

The existence of this maximum value suggests that both polarization and extinction are produced by the same kind of interstellar particles.

The wavelength dependence of polarization has quite a different character from that of interstellar extinction. The extinction in the visual region is approximately proportional to λ^{-1}, while the polarization is more nearly independent of λ. The wavelength dependence of interstellar polarization was investigated for several stars by Hiltner (1950; his recent results were summarized by van de Hulst, 1957) and by Gehrels (1960a). Their results are shown in Figure 3. Polarization is given in this figure on an arbitrary scale as a function of λ^{-1}.

Polarization of seven stars was also measured in wavelengths λλ 3710, 4300, and 5160 by Behr (1959a). For all these stars, except α Cygni, the polarization in the ultraviolet is slightly smaller than in the blue. The polarization in yellow for some stars is smaller than in the blue; for others, larger. Recently Kruszewski (1962) found a positive correlation between the ratio of amounts of polarization in blue and yellow colors and the ratio of polarization to interstellar extinction. A plausible explanation of these effects will be discussed in the next section.

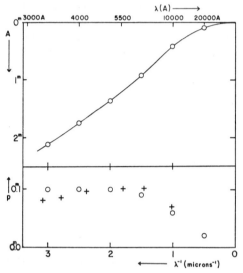

Fig. 3.—The observed color dependence of extinction (*upper diagram*) and polarization (*lower diagram*), expressed in arbitrary magnitude scales. The open circles are values compiled by van de Hulst (1957) from extinction measured by Whitford (1948) and corrected in the ultraviolet by Miss Divan (1954) and from unpublished polarization measurements by Hiltner. The crosses are Gehrels (1960a) values.

§ 4. OPTICAL PROPERTIES OF INTERSTELLAR DUST

4.1. Distribution Parameter

The interstellar polarization may be explained by absorption and scattering of stellar light by interstellar dust, provided that this dust shows some kind of anisotropy. Two conditions are necessary for producing the anisotropy in the orientation of dust grains. First, the grains must be either birefringent or aspherical; we shall assume that an axis of symmetry can be distinguished in each grain. Second, there must exist some mechanism for orienting the grains; this mechanism will also have an axis of symmetry. It seems most probable that the dust grains are oriented by galactic magnetic fields.

Davis and Greenstein (1951) and Davis (1955) describe the degree of alignment of the dust grains by the distribution parameter, F, defined by

$$F = \tfrac{1}{3} - \langle \cos^2 a_z \rangle , \tag{20}$$

where a_z, according to the notation of these authors, is the angle between the axis of symmetry of a grain and the axis of symmetry of the orientation mechanism and $\langle \cos^2 a_z \rangle$ is an average value for all grains. If the dust grains are oriented completely at random, we have $F = 0$. If the axes of all the grains are parallel to the axis of symmetry of the orienting mechanism, we have $F = -\frac{2}{3}$ and if all are perpendicular, $F = \frac{1}{3}$.

The extinction produced by a single dust grain (extinction = absorption + scattering) is described by three extinction cross-sections, σ_E, σ_H, and σ_S. Each of these cross-sections is an area of an opaque non-scattering screen perpendicular to the direction of the incident light which would cause the same extinction as that of the dust grain under consideration. The cross-sections σ_E, σ_H, and σ_S correspond to the axis of symmetry of a grain parallel to the electric vector, the magnetic vector, and the direction of propagation of the incident light, respectively.

Let us average the extinction cross-sections for all the grains, the orientation of which is described by the distribution parameter F. We shall denote by S_r and S_l the mean extinction cross-sections for the plane-polarized light with $\theta_G = 0°$ and $90°$, respectively. As shown by Serkowski (1962), the increments of the Stokes parameters, Q_G and U_G, and interstellar absorption, A (in magnitudes), over the path ds are

$$dQ_G = \frac{5}{2 \ln 10} (S_r - S_l) n_g \cos 2 (\theta_G - 90°) ds, \qquad (21)$$

$$dU_G = \frac{5}{2 \ln 10} (S_r - S_l) n_g \sin 2 (\theta_G - 90°) ds, \qquad (22)$$

$$dA = \frac{5}{4 \ln 10} (S_r + S_l) n_g ds. \qquad (23)$$

In these equations, n_g is the number of grains per unit volume. The equations are valid if p^2 is negligible compared with unity and if θ_G is the position angle of the axis of symmetry of the orienting mechanism in the path interval ds.

Davis (1959) expresses S_r and S_l as functions of extinction cross-sections of individual grains, the distribution parameter, and the angle ν' between the direction of the magnetic field and the direction of the incident light. When the dust grains are the same size and when the magnetic field is parallel to the galactic plane, we find the approximate relations

$$S_r - S_l = \frac{3}{2} (\sigma_E - \sigma_H) F \sin^2 \nu', \qquad (24)$$

$$S_r + S_l = \frac{2}{3}(\sigma_E + \sigma_H + \sigma_S) + (\sigma_E + \sigma_H - 2\sigma_S)(1 - \frac{3}{2} \sin^2 \nu') F. \qquad (25)$$

The ratio of polarization to extinction can now be expressed by means of the extinction cross-sections. Let us consider only the regions of the sky where the polarization is large. In these regions we have $\theta_G \approx 90°$, and hence, by equations

(10) and (11), $Q_G \approx p$, $U_G \approx 0$. Substituting equations (24), (25), and $\theta_G = 90°$ in equations (21) and (23), averaging, and integrating them along the path from the star, we obtain

$$p = \frac{5}{2 \ln 10} \frac{3}{2} (\sigma_E - \sigma_H) n_v S F \sin^2 v', \tag{26}$$

$$A = \frac{5}{2 \ln 10} \frac{1}{3} (\sigma_E + \sigma_H + \sigma_S) n_v S + A_1 (F, v'), \tag{27}$$

where S is the distance to a star and A_1 (F, v') is a small term depending on the orientation of the dust grains. This last term may cause the color dependence of interstellar extinction to depend on the direction in which we are looking, in accordance with results of Hiltner and Johnson (1956), Greenberg (1960b), Greenberg and Meltzer (1960), and Wilson (1960). Neglecting this term we finally obtain

$$\frac{p}{A} = \frac{9}{2} \frac{\sigma_E - \sigma_H}{\sigma_E + \sigma_H + \sigma_S} F \sin^2 v'. \tag{28}$$

Davis (1959) explains the different color dependence of polarization obtained for different stars by Behr (1959a) by differences in the alignment of dust grains. As will be discussed in the next section (eqs. [30] and [31]), Davis and Greenstein (1951) found that the stronger the galactic magnetic field is, the larger are the grains which may be completely aligned by this field. Hence polarization is produced in a strong magnetic field, on the average, by larger dust grains than in a field of lower intensity. The factor $\sigma_E - \sigma_H$ in equation (26) depends on the size of dust grains expressed in terms of wavelength. Let us assume that this factor has a maximum as a function of wavelength. This maximum will be at a longer wavelength in a strong magnetic field where the dust grains producing polarization are, on the average, larger than in the weak field.

4.2. Scattering by Cylindrical and Ellipsoidal Grains

The dust grains producing interstellar polarization may be treated either as needles, which can be approximated by long cylinders, or as ellipsoids. The theory of light-scattering by long cylinders of arbitrary diameter was given by van de Hulst (1950, 1957) and by van P. Smith and van de Hulst (1951). They considered only cylinders with axes perpendicular to the incident light. The results which they obtained for dielectric cylinders with indices of refraction 1.25 and 1.50, for slightly absorbing (i.e., containing an admixture of metals) cylinders with indices of refraction $1.25 - 0.10i$ and $1.50 - 0.10i$, and for iron cylinders with index $1.41 - 1.41i$ are shown in Figure 4. The upper part of this figure shows $(\sigma_E + \sigma_H)/\sigma_{geom}$, which may be assumed to be proportional to the extinction, A; the lower part gives $(\sigma_E - \sigma_H)/\sigma_{geom}$, which is proportional to polarization. Here σ_{geom} is the geometrical cross-section equal to $2ab$, where a and b are the radius and length of the cylinder, respectively. Since the ratio $2a/\lambda$ is the abscissa, Figure 4 gives the theoretical dependence of extinction and polarization on λ^{-1} for cylindrical grains of diameter $2a$. Each of the curves in Figure 4 fits approximately the observed color dependences shown in Figure 3 if a suitable size, a, of dust grains is assumed for a given value of refractive index (cf. Gehrels 1960*b*).

The cross-sections for arbitrarily oriented cylinders with index of refraction $m \to 1$ were computed by Wilson (1960). In this limiting case no polarization results.

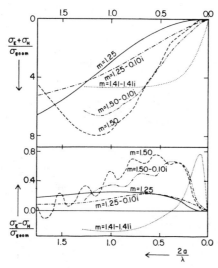

Fig. 4.—Theoretical dependence of extinction and polarization on λ^{-1} for cylindrical grains of diameter $2a$.

There is no exact theory of light-scattering by ellipsoidal grains of arbitrary size. Van de Hulst (1950) estimated that polarization produced by prolate spheroids with axial ratio $2:1$ is half that of infinite cylinders of the same equatorial diameter. The approximate calculations have also been made by Stevenson (1953), Greenberg (1960*a*), and Shatilov (1960). Cross-sections for ellipsoids have been obtained experimentally by Greenberg (1960*b*), who observed the scattering of 3-cm microwaves on ellipsoidal models of comparable dimensions. The results are shown in Figure 5. The upper part of this figure shows the values

$$2\,\frac{\bar\sigma}{\sigma_{\text{geom}}} = \begin{cases} \dfrac{\sigma_E + \sigma_H + 4\sigma_S}{3\,\sigma_{\text{geom}}} & \text{for } \nu' = 0°, \\[2ex] \dfrac{\sigma_E + \sigma_H + 2\sigma_S}{2\,\sigma_{\text{geom}}} & \text{for } \nu' = 90°, \end{cases} \tag{29}$$

which are proportional to extinction if $F = \tfrac{1}{3}$ and $\nu' = 0°$ (direction parallel to orienting force) or $\nu' = 90°$ (direction perpendicular to orienting force), respectively (cf. eqs. [27] and [25]). The lower part gives $(\sigma_E - \sigma_H)/\sigma_{geom}$ that is proportional to polarization, p [Greenberg (1960b) denotes σ_E, σ_H, σ_S, by $\sigma_{E||}$, $\sigma_{E\perp}$, and $\sigma_{K||}$, respectively]. The curves for prolate spheroids with the ratio of their semiaxes $b/a = 2$ and short cylinders of length twice the diameter are shown. The values $2\pi a^2$ and $8a^2$, respectively, are assumed for σ_{geom}. Greenberg's models were made of lucite having a refractive index of 1.61. It may be seen from Figure 5 that only the lucite grains for which $2a/\lambda$ is between 0.25 and 0.55 show a

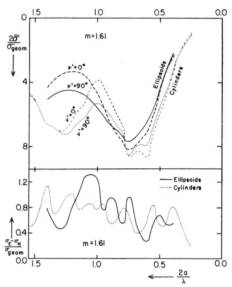

Fig. 5.—The experimental values of $2\,\bar\sigma/\sigma_{geom}$ (proportional to extinction) and $(\sigma_E - \sigma_H)/\sigma_{geom}$ (proportional to polarization) for prolate spheroids of axial ratio 2:1 and for short cylinders. The extinction-curves are given for direction parallel ($\nu' = 0°$) and perpendicular ($\nu' = 90°$) to the force orienting the dust grains. The curves are computed from data obtained by Greenberg (1960b) from microwave experiments. It is evident that the general character of the experimental curves is similar to that of the theoretical curves for $m = 1.50$ presented in Fig. 4.

wavelength dependence of extinction similar to that found for interstellar extinction in the visual region.

From Figures 4 and 5 we may find the maximum values of the ratio of polarization to extinction by means of equation (28). We shall assume $\nu' = 90°$ and $F = \frac{1}{3}$, which means that the axes of all grains are perpendicular to the direction of the orienting force (cf. next section). If we also assume that the middle of the rectilinear portions of the curves in the upper parts of Figures 4 and 5 represent the interstellar extinction around λ 5500, we obtain the values of $(p/A)_{max}$ and the diameters of grains $2a$ given in Table 1 (cf. van de Hulst 1955).

It may be seen from this table that the most effective particles of this group for producing polarization are the iron needles. Another interesting feature of elongated iron grains is that the light-scattering on such grains gives not only linear but also circular polarization (cf. Serkowski 1960a). The properties of iron grains are discussed by Fick (1954, 1955), Güttler (1952), and Zimmermann (1957); their formation is discussed by Spitzer and Schatzman (1949). Schatzman and Bernal (1960) suggest that long iron filaments having very strong polarizing properties are very likely to be present in the interstellar medium.

Cayrel and Schatzman (1954) and more recently Hoyle and Wickramsinghe (1962) suppose that the interstellar polarization is caused by graphite flakes much smaller than visual wavelengths. Because of their molecular structure, such flakes have strange optical properties. The light with the electric vector vibrating in the plane of the flake suffers metallic absorption, while, for the light vibrating in the perpendicular plane, graphite behaves as a dielectric, and

TABLE 1

MAXIMUM VALUES OF p/A FOR DIFFERENT TYPES OF PARTICLES
(Assumed $\lambda = 5500$ A, $F = \frac{1}{3}$, $\nu' = 90°$)

Shape	Index of Refraction	$(p/A)_{max}$	Diameter $(2a)$ of Grains (μ)
Long cylinders (needles)	1.25	0.05	0.7
	1.25−0.10i	.07	.5
	1.50	.15	.3
	1.50−0.10i	.2	.3
	1.41−1.41i	.35	.06
Short cylinders, length/a=4.....	1.61	.15	.25
Prolate spheroids, b/a=2........	1.61	0.2	0.25
Observed.................	....	0.065	....

the extinction cross-section for this component is much smaller. For a given graphite flake or microcrystal, the wavelength dependence of absorption is almost uniform up to a long wavelength cutoff (cf. Platt 1960). One graphite flake per 20 classical dust grains of spherical shape is sufficient to explain the observed polarization of stellar light.

4.3. QUANTUM-MECHANICAL DUST GRAINS

Great difficulty arises in explaining why the dust grains are elongated. The growth of dust grains which are not monocrystals seems to be a symmetrical process, and the grains formed should be nearly spherical. The situation changes if dust grains are much smaller than the sizes given in Table 1. It was pointed out by Platt (1956, 1960) that certain kinds of single molecules or complexes of molecules only about 10 A in diameter may produce appreciable extinction and polarization. Such small particles must have definitely aspherical shapes because of statistical fluctuations in the arrangement of the molecules or atoms.

According to Platt, the highly paramagnetic, unsaturated, large molecules absorb energy at wavelengths about 400 times greater than their diameters. To absorb and re-emit in a given wavelength region, such quantum-mechanical particles are only one two-hundredth the diameter of the classical scattering particles. The total bulk of such particles, sufficient to explain the observed extinction, is therefore much smaller than that of classical particles. If the particles are elongated with length/width $= 1 + \epsilon$, the maximum ratio of polarization to extinction is $(p/A)_{max} = \epsilon/2$. The polarization increases with decreasing size of particles because the shapes of smaller particles are likely to be more aspherical. Since Platt's particles are pure absorbers, the wavelength dependence of extinction for such particles should be almost independent of direction (Greenberg 1960b, c).

Platt (1960) has also suggested that small dust grains are likely to be elongated because of their electric charges. Such rotating grains, with electric charges at the ends, may be aligned by an external magnetic field, with their long axes parallel to the field. The polarization should increase with wavelength for such charged particles, just opposite to that for particles of random asphericity. The direction of the orientation of the "dust strings" which would result from this interesting suggestion does not seem to explain the observed change of polarization with galactic longitude.

§ 5. ALIGNMENT MECHANISMS

Two types of aligning forces have been proposed to explain the alignment of interstellar dust—gas bombardment and magnetic fields. The alignment of dust grains by interaction with gas flowing in a direction perpendicular to the galactic plane was suggested by Gold (1952). According to this author, the long axes of the grains tend to be parallel to the relative velocity. Zirin (1952) suggests that such alignment would be with the long axis normal to the direction of relative motion. Both these arguments were discussed thoroughly by Davis (1955), who showed that the alignment of dust grains by interaction with gas is much too small to explain the observed polarization.

The theory of alignment of dust grains by a weak magnetic field was developed by Davis and Greenstein (1951) and Davis (1958). Because of equipartition of energy between the interstellar dust and gas, the dust grains are spinning with an angular velocity of 10^5–10^6 rad/sec. According to the theory of free rigid bodies, the smallest kinetic energy of rotation for a given angular momentum corresponds to a rotation around the shortest axis of the ellipsoid of inertia. Hence the spinning dust grains tend to rotate around their shortest axis. These axes are aligned parallel to the galactic magnetic field because of the paramagnetic absorption in the granular material. Each volume element inside the dust grain rotating around an axis which is not parallel to the external magnetic field changes its magnetization periodically. The internal damping (so-called paramagnetic absorption) accompanying such changes of magnetization decreases the angle between the axis of rotation and the direction of the magnetic field; therefore, the axis of rotation tends to become parallel to the magnetic field.

The amount of energy lost by the magnetic field due to paramagnetic absorption is proportional to the imaginary part, χ'', of the magnetic susceptibility which characterizes the material in the dust grains; χ'' is proportional to the frequency, ω, with which the magnetic field inside the grain is changing or, in other words, proportional to the angular velocity of the dust grain.

The degree of alignment due to the mechanism considered may be described by means of the distribution parameter, F, defined by equation (20). Since the torques acting on the grain due to paramagnetic absorption are not conservative, the Maxwell-Boltzmann theory does not apply, and only a rather crude estimate of F can be made. Davis and Greenstein (1951) give the following expression for F, valid if the grains are prolate spheroids:

$$F = \begin{cases} F_l & \text{for } |F_l| \ll \frac{1}{3} \\ \frac{1}{3} & \text{for } |F_l| \gg \frac{1}{3} , \end{cases} \tag{30}$$

where

$$F_l = 2.5 \times 10^{18} \frac{B^2}{a\,n_H T^{1/2}} \frac{\chi''}{\omega} . \tag{31}$$

Here B is the magnetic flux density in gauss, a is the average radius of a grain, n_H is the number of gas atoms (or ions) per cm³, and T is the temperature of the interstellar gas. The plane of polarization is the same for both prolate and oblate spheroids. In each case the long dimension of the grains is perpendicular to the magnetic field.

Davis and Greenstein (1951), on the basis of theory and experiments described by Gorter (1947), assume that, for the dust grains whose paramagnetic properties are due to the admixture of iron ions, the ratio $\chi''/2$, encountered in equation (31), equals

$$\frac{\chi''}{\omega} \approx \frac{2.5 \times 10^{-12}}{T_g} , \tag{32}$$

where T_g is the temperature of dust grains. This relation is fulfilled only if the dust grains are not much smaller than 0.01 μ.

Henry (1958) generalized the Davis-Greenstein theory for the case of ferromagnetic dust grains. Equations (30) and (31) remain valid in this case; only the ratio χ''/ω becomes dependent on the ratio of the axes of spheroidal grains. Henry assumes the ratio of axes 2:1 and obtains, for monocrystals of iron or nickel,

$$\frac{\chi''}{\omega} \approx 3 \times 10^{-7}, \tag{33}$$

almost independently of temperature, while for ferrites such as, e.g., Fe_2O_3,

$$\frac{\chi''}{\omega} \approx 2 \times 10^{-10}, \tag{34}$$

for temperatures near to absolute zero. The advantage of the use of ferrite grains in explaining interstellar polarization is their high index of refraction—near to 3 for Fe_2O_3 (cf. Fick 1954, 1955).

The Davis-Greenstein mechanism can also be applied to diamagnetic grains, such as graphite flakes discussed by Cayrel and Schatzman (1954); the planes of the flakes will be aligned perpendicular to the magnetic field. From their data we find that, for graphite,

$$\frac{\chi''}{\omega} \approx \frac{2 \times 10^{-12}}{T_g^2}. \tag{35}$$

If we insert expressions (32)–(35) in equation (31) and assume $n_H T^{1/2} = 100$ (which is approximately valid both for H I regions and for H II regions between the gas clouds), $T_g = 10°$ K, $a = 0.04\ \mu$ for iron grains and graphite flakes, and $a = 0.2\ \mu$ for other materials, we obtain $|F_l| \gg \frac{1}{3}$, and the alignment is practically complete for the following magnetic flux densities:

$$B \gg \begin{cases} 5 \times 10^{-5} \text{ gauss for graphite flakes ,} \\ 3 \times 10^{-5} \text{ gauss for paramagnetic grains ,} \\ 1.2 \times 10^{-6} \text{ gauss for ferrites ,} \\ 1.3 \times 10^{-8} \text{ gauss for iron grains .} \end{cases} \tag{36}$$

Since the estimates of galactic magnetic fields on other grounds show that it is of the order of 10^{-6}–10^{-4} gauss, the alignment of dust grains can be explained satisfactorily by the Davis-Greenstein theory (cf. Burbidge 1953). It may be supposed that the Platt particles are completely aligned even in a very weak field because they are highly paramagnetic and very small.

If the magnetic field is very strong, several orders of magnitude higher than that given by expression (36), the torque on ferromagnetic grains will stop the spinning of the grains. In this case they will be aligned like compass needles, with their long axes parallel to the magnetic field, which was discussed by Spitzer and Tukey (1951). For such grains the magnetic field must be perpendicular to the galactic plane, and the observed longitude dependence of polarization cannot be explained.

§ 6. INTERSTELLAR POLARIZATION AND GALACTIC MAGNETIC FIELDS

6.1. MAGNETIC FIELDS IN SPIRAL ARMS

If the dust grains are aligned by a galactic magnetic field, the longitude dependence of polarization shown in Figure 1 enables one to determine the mean direction of this field. As indicated by equations (21) and (24), the average direction of magnetic lines of force is toward those galactic longitudes in which the mean value of the Stokes parameter Q_G vanishes. The mean direction of the galactic magnetic field derived from polarization data is in good agreement with the directions of the spiral arms outlined by young open clusters and O-type associations but does not agree so well with the spiral arms derived from the distribution of neutral hydrogen as observed in the 21-cm emission line. In fact, the neutral hydrogen appears to be concentrated in a set of rings rather than in spiral arms. The theories of formation of spiral arms (Elvius and Herlofson 1960; Wentzel 1960) explain the differences in distribution of gas and of hot stars but seem to suggest that the magnetic field is directed parallel to the concentrations of gas.

To explain his observations of nearby stars, Behr (1959b) suggests that the magnetic lines of force are helically twisted around the direction of the spiral arm. A similar hypothesis is also discussed by Ireland (1961), who assumes that the magnetic lines of force are wound in tight helices. The turns of the field are ellipses with major axes in the galactic plane and with centers lying on a straight line directed toward galactic longitude $l^{II} = 86°$. The elliptical turns of the field are taken to lie in planes that make an angle of $\sim$40° with the axis of the galactic spiral arm; thus the direction $l^{II} = 46°$ is essentially parallel to the turns. Such distortion can prevent any relative streaming of the gas between the inside and outside of an arm. Ireland's hypothesis seems to explain some previously unexplained features of the observed polarization at the longitudes $l^{II} = 0°$–$90°$. The detailed comparison of this hypothesis with observations was recently done by Stepien (1962).

The polarization measurements of galaxies discussed by Meinel (1953) and de Vaucouleurs (1959) and of globular clusters in M31 (Hiltner 1958) show polarization with the electric vector parallel to the long axis of the galaxy. The photographic polarization measurements of NGC 7331 made by Elvius (1957) show polarization with the electric vector parallel to the long axis of the galaxy but only on the side of the galaxy that has smaller surface brightness and is redder. On the opposite side the electric vectors are perpendicular to the long axis. The amounts of polarization are between 0.04 and 0.09 mag. Elvius suggests that on the bluer side of the galaxy we are observing mainly the scattered light which should be polarized in the plane perpendicular to that of direct starlight.

6.2. STRUCTURE AND DENSITY OF MAGNETIC FIELDS

The polarization of stars behind filamentary nebulae shows very good correlation between the position angles of the filaments and those of the planes of vibration of the transmitted starlight. This was shown in the Pleiades by Hall (1951, 1955, 1958) and van den Bergh (1956) and in other regions by Shain (1955, 1956a, b). From the observed widths of filaments in the Pleiades and their radii of curvature, Parker (1958) estimates that their existence indicates a magnetic field directed along the filaments of not less than 2.5×10^{-6} gauss.

Cowling (1953) has implied that the stretching of the spiral arms will tend to produce an ellipsoidal distribution of magnetic fields, with the major axis of the ellipsoid parallel to the direction of the arms. Takakubo (1955, 1957), in a discussion specifically concerned with the stretching of a spiral arm caused by differential rotation in the galaxy, shows that the time required for aligning the particles is comparable with the lifetime of an element of interstellar turbulence. He finds that magnetic fields caused by the stretching of the spiral arms would have almost enough strength to sustain the polarization mechanism required by the Davis-Greenstein theory.

Variations in the plane of polarization have been used for estimating the magnetic-field strength by Davis (1951) and Chandrasekhar and Fermi (1953). They show that the inertia of interstellar motions of velocity v in a conducting medium of density ρ gives rise to Alfvén waves (cf. van de Hulst 1949) running along the mean direction of the magnetic field B, where

$$B = \left(\frac{4\pi\rho}{3}\right)^{1/2} \frac{v}{a}, \qquad (37)$$

a being the root-mean-square tangent of the angular deviation of the position angle of the magnetic lines of force from its mean value; it is assumed that we are looking perpendicularly to the mean direction of the magnetic field. To estimate a, Davis (1955) assumes that

$$a = a_p n^{1/2}, \qquad (38)$$

where a_p is the root-mean-square deviation of the position angle of the electric vector for the stars considered and n is the number of homogeneous regions along the path to these stars, these regions being separated by distances larger than the wavelength of the variations in B. For stars in the Perseus spiral arm of the galaxy, Davis assumes $a_p = 0.1$ radian and $n = 6$. Taking these values and assuming $\rho = 2 \times 10^{-24}$ gm/cm^3 and $v = 12$ km/sec (Spitzer 1956), the value $B = 1.4 \times 10^{-5}$ gauss is obtained.

To avoid guessing the value of n, Serkowski (1958b) uses the equations relating a with the ratio of variances σ_G^2, σ_U^2 of the Stokes parameters Q_G, U_G for stars at the same distance to the direction perpendicular to the mean direction of the magnetic field. To obtain these equations, he assumed that the Alfvén waves were running along the mean direction of the magnetic field; this means that the fluctuations in the plane perpendicular to this field are superimposed on the uniform field. Since for the association surrounding the double cluster in Perseus the ratio of variances is $\sigma_Q^2/\sigma_U^2 = 0.60 \pm 0.14$(m.e.), this gives

$$a = 0.50 \pm 0.04 \text{(m.e.)} \qquad (39)$$

and hence, by equation (37),

$$B = 7 \times 10^{-6} \text{ gauss .} \qquad (40)$$

From her statistical discussion of 16 O-type associations, Semeniuk (1960) found that the mean value of the mentioned ratio of variances is 0.8 ± 0.1

(m.e.). The fact that this ratio is smaller than unity excludes the possibility that the *isotropic* fluctuations are superimposed on the uniform magnetic field.

H. M. Johnson (1957b) expresses the ratio of polarization to extinction in those galactic longitudes where this ratio is a minimum by means of the mean inclination of the local magnetic field to the mean field. He obtains the mean inclination 0.7 radian, in rather good agreement with the value obtained from the double cluster in Perseus.

All these investigations indicate that the galactic magnetic field is far from being uniform; the fluctuating component perpendicular to the galactic plane is only slightly smaller than the component parallel to the spiral arm.

§ 7. POLARIZATION AND EXTINCTION

7.1. DEPOLARIZATION

The dependence of the ratio of the amount of polarization, p, to the visual interstellar extinction, A_v, on galactic longitude was investigated recently by H. M. Johnson (1957a) and by Th. Schmidt (1958b). This last author found that, for each interval of galactic longitude, this ratio may be described by the equation

$$\frac{p}{A_v} = a - \beta A_v,$$

(41)

where a and β are constants. Comparing the values of coefficients a and β for different galactic longitudes, Schmidt found a strong negative correlation with the dispersion, σ_θ, of the position angles θ_G. Extrapolating this dependence for $\sigma_\theta = 0$, Schmidt finds in this limiting case that

$$\frac{p}{A_v} = 0.^{m}065(\pm 0.005) - 0.^{m}010A_v(\pm 0.001).$$

(42)

The coefficient β, called the "depolarization parameter" by Schmidt, is always positive and proportional to the mean ratio p/A_v for a given longitude. The decrease in the ratio p/A_v with increasing A_v might be explained in two ways. First, the observational errors and intrinsic scatter increase the mean amount of polarization more appreciably for weakly polarized stars than for those which are strongly polarized; second, the decrease in p/A_v with increasing A_v must occur when p and A_v are uncorrelated random quantities.

The ratio p/A_v depends slightly on galactic latitude (Bielicka and Serkowski 1957). As shown by Schmidt (1958b) and Grzedzielski (1959), this dependence is caused by the dependence of p/A_v on A_v, which has already been discussed.

7.2. CORRELATION BETWEEN POLARIZATION AND EXTINCTION

The ratio of polarization to extinction was found by Pacholczyk (1959a) to be larger by 0.004 for the Perseus spiral arm than for the Orion arm. This difference increases slightly if only supergiants are taken into account. Since the selection effects for supergiants are smaller than for other stars, Pacholczyk concludes that the effect is real.

A similar effect is found by Pacholczyk (1959b) for the ratio of polarization to the equivalent width of the interstellar λ 4430 band; this ratio is twice as large for the Perseus arm as for the Orion arm. To explain this effect, theoretical estimates were made by Grzedzielski (1958) showing that the dust grains may be better aligned in the rarefied H II regions between the spiral arms than in the H I regions. However, Hall (1958) did not find any difference between the polarization of stars imbedded in H II regions and that of other stars in the same region of the sky.

The intensities of interstellar absorption bands were suggested to be correlated with polarization by Greenstein and Aller (1950), Hall and Mikesell (1950), Lunel (1954), and other authors. The correlation between polarization and equivalent width of the λ 4430 band was found by Pacholczyk (1959b) and Krzeminski (1959) to be smaller than the correlations between polarization and extinction and between the extinction and the equivalent width of λ 4430 for the same stars. Pacholczyk concludes that the coefficient of partial correlation between the polarization and this equivalent width is negligibly small and that there is no direct connection between polarization and the intensity of interstellar absorption bands, the observed correlation being caused by the fact that both these quantities are correlated with interstellar extinction.

Another feature that seems common to both polarization and extinction is the microscale of fluctuations. The autocorrelation analysis applied by Serkowski (1958b) to the observations of the double cluster in Perseus shows that the microscales of the fluctuations in both the extinction and the polarizing properties of the interstellar medium are equal and smaller than 1.5 parsec. The microscale is a characteristic distance such that the coefficient of correlation between the values in points separated by that distance falls to $1/e$, as compared with unity for zero distance. The fact that both polarization and extinction in the direction of the double cluster in Perseus do not increase with distance for distances larger than 1 kpc was pointed out by Dombrovskii (1959). This is what might be expected because this cluster is 2.3 kpc away and is situated more than 140 pc from the galactic plane, where the density of the interstellar dust is already quite low.

Considering the stars in a given interval of galactic longitude, we observe a strong correlation between polarization and extinction. This is caused by the same dependence of both these factors on distance and on galactic latitude. However, if we consider the group of stars that are all at practically the same distance and the same galactic co-ordinates, the correlation between polarization and extinction in many cases is negligibly small. Some galactic clusters show a correlation between polarization and extinction, while others do not.

Polarization and extinction are well correlated for M29 (Hiltner 1954c), NGC 663 and 1502 (Hoag 1953), NGC 2169 (Krzeminski 1961), and the association VI Cygni (Hiltner 1954b, 1956).

Little or no correlation was found for the open clusters NGC 2244 (Lodén

1956; Hoag and Smith 1959; Grigoryan and Smak 1960), NGC 7243 (Krzeminski 1961), M25 (Serkowski, unpublished), J. Stock's cluster in Perseus (Serkowski 1958b; Larsson-Leander and Serkowski 1959), the double cluster in Perseus (Hiltner 1956; Serkowski 1958a, b), and the associations I Cep and II Per (Grigoryan 1957b), I Lac (Krzeminski and Oskanjan 1961), and III Cep (Serkowski 1960b). For 10 of 16 associations investigated by Semeniuk (1960), the coefficients of correlation between polarization and extinction are less than 0.3.

The lack of correlation between polarization and extinction may be explained if the ratio of dust density, n_g, to the gas density, n_H, is constant in the interstellar medium. If the value of the distribution parameter, F, given for weak magnetic fields by equation (31), is inserted into equation (26), we see that the polarization is proportional to the ratio n_g/n_H. If this ratio is constant, the polarization is independent of the spatial density of dust and hence is not correlated with extinction for stars in open clusters.

The correlation between polarization and reddening, however, is expected if both these effects are produced inside the cluster. In this case the stars imbedded more deeply in the nebula surrounding the cluster will be both more strongly reddened and more strongly polarized. This will be particularly so if the magnetic field is uniform inside the cluster.

REFERENCES

BABCOCK, H. W.	1947	*Ap. J.*, **105**, 105.
BARTL, E.	1959	*Mitt. U.-Sternw. Jena*, No. 39.
BEHR, A.	1955	*Les Particules solides dans les astres* (*Mém. Soc. R. Sci. Liège*, 4th ser., Vol. **15**), p. 547.
	1956	*Nachr. Akad. Wiss. Göttingen, math.-phys. Kl.* 2a, No. 10, p. 205; *Veröff. Göttingen*, No. 114.
	1959a	*Zs. f. Ap.*, **47**, 54; *Veröff. Göttingen*, No. 124.
	1959b	*Nachr. Akad. Wiss. Göttingen, math.-phys. Kl.*, p. 185; *Veröff. Göttingen*, No. 126.
	1960	*Lowell Obs. Bull.*, **4**, 292.
	1961	*Zs. f. Ap.*, **53**, 95; *Veröff. Göttingen*, No. 133.
BERGH, S. VAN DEN,	1956	*Zs. f. Ap.*, **40**, 249; *Veröff. Göttingen*, No. 115.
BIELICKA, K., and SERKOWSKI, K.	1957	*Bull. Acad. Pol.*, **3**, 1113; *Warsaw Repr.*, No. 66.
BLAMONT, J. E., and COURTÈS, G.	1954	*Ann. d'ap.*, **17**, 312.
BURBIDGE, G. R.	1953	*Ap. J.*, **118**, 575.
CAYREL, R., and SCHATZMAN, E.	1954	*Ann. d'ap.*, **17**, 555.
CHANDRASEKHAR, S.	1946	*Ap. J.*, **103**, 351.
	1950	*Radiative Transfer* (Oxford: Clarendon Press), pp. 24 ff. New edition: 1960 (New York: Dover Publications, Inc.).
CHANDRASEKHAR, S., and BREEN, F. H.	1947	*Ap. J.*, **105**, 435.

CHANDRASEKHAR, S., and
  FERMI, E.   1953   *Ap. J.*, **118**, 113.

COWLING, T. G.   1953   *Ciel et Terre*, **69**, 177.

DAVIS, L., JR.   1951   *Phys. Rev.*, **81**, 890.

                     1955   *Vistas in Astronomy*, ed. A. BEER (London and New York: Pergamon Press), **1**, 336.

                     1958   *Ap. J.*, **128**, 508.

                     1959   *Zs. f. Ap.*, **47**, 59.

DAVIS, L., JR., and
  GREENSTEIN, J. L.   1951   *Ap. J.*, **114**, 206; *Mt. W. and Palomar Repr.*, No. 40.

DIVAN, L.   1954   *Ann. d'ap.*, **17**, 456.

DOLLFUS, A.   1957   *Ann. d'ap.*, *Suppl.*, No. 4.

DOMBROVSKII, V. A.   1949   *Doklady Akad. Nauk Armyanskei SSR.*, **10**, 199.

                     1952   *Doklady Akad. Nauk SSSR.*, **82**, 537.

                     1953   *A.J., U.S.S.R.*, **30**, 603.

                     1957   *Vestnik Leningrad. U.*, No. 19.

                     1958   *Ibid.*, No. 1.

                     1959   *Ibid.*, No. 19.

ELVIUS, A.   1957   *Stockholm Obs. Ann.*, Vol. **19**, No. 1.

ELVIUS, A., and
  HERLOFSON, N.   1960   *Ap. J.*, **131**, 304.

FESSENKOV, V. G.   1959   *A.J., U.S.S.R.*, **36**, 1094.

FICK, E.   1954   *Zs. f. Phys.*, **138**, 183.

                     1955   *Ibid.*, **140**, 308.

GEHRELS, TH.   1960*a*   *Lowell Obs. Bull.*, **4**, 300.

                     1960*b*   *A.J.*, **65**, 466 and 470.

GEHRELS, TH., and
  TESKA, TH. M.   1960   *Pub. A.S.P.*, **72**, 115.

GOLD, T.   1952   *M.N.*, **112**, 215.

GORTER, C. J.   1947   *Paramagnetic Relaxation* (New York: Elsevier Publishing Co.).

GOSSNER, J. L.   1952   *A.J.*, **57**, 11.

GREENBERG, J. M.   1960*a*   *J. Appl. Phys.*, **31**, 82.

                     1960*b*   *Lowell Obs. Bull.*, **4**, 281 and 285.

                     1960*c*   *Ap. J.*, **132**, 672.

GREENBERG, J. M., and
  MELTZER, A. S.   1960   *Ap. J.*, **132**, 667.

GREENSTEIN, J. L., and
  ALLER, L. H.   1950   *Ap. J.*, **111**, 328; *Mt. W. and Palomar Repr.*, No. 16.

GRIGORYAN, K. A.   1957*a*   *Soob. Byurakan. Obs.*, **22**, 49.

                     1957*b*   *Izv. Akad. Nauk Armyanskei SSR*, **10**, 57.

GRIGORYAN, K. A., and
  SMAK, J. M.   1960   *Soob. Byurakan. Obs.*, **28**, 3; *Warsaw Repr.*, No. 120.

GRZEDZIELSKI, S.	1958	*C.R.*, **246**, 890; *Contr. Inst. Ap. Paris*, ser. A, No. 235.
	1959	*Acta Astr.*, **9**, 25; *Warsaw Repr.*, No. 82.
GÜTTLER, A.	1952	*Zs. f. Ap.*, **31**, 1.
HALL, J. S.	1948	*A.J.*, **54**, 39.
	1949	*Science*, **109**, 166.
	1951	*A.J.*, **56**, 40.
	1952	*Ibid.*, **57**, 12.
	1953	*Astronomical Photoelectric Photometry*, ed. F. B. WOOD (Washington, D.C.: Am. Assoc. Adv. Sci.), p. 41.
	1955	*Les Particules solides dans les astres* (*Mém. Soc. R. Sci. Li`ge*, 4th ser., Vol. **15**), p. 543.
	1958	*Pub. U.S. Naval Obs.*, Vol. **17**, Part VI.
HALL, J. S., and HOAG, A. A.	1958	*The Present and Future of the Telescope of Moderate Size*, ed. F. B. WOOD (Philadelphia: University of Pennsylvania Press), p. 87.
HALL, J. S., and MIKESELL, A. H.	1950	*Pub. U.S. Naval Obs.*, Vol. **17**, Part I.
HENRY, J.	1958	*Ap. J.*, **128**, 497.
HILTNER, W. A.	1947	*Ap. J.*, **106**, 231.
	1949a	*Science*, **109**, 165.
	1949b	*Ap. J.*, **109**, 471.
	1950	*Phys. Rev.*, **78**, 170.
	1951a	*Ap. J.*, **114**, 241; *Contr. McDonald Obs.*, No. 201.
	1951b	*Observatory*, **71**, 234.
	1952	*A.J.*, **57**, 13.
	1954a	*Ap. J.*, **120**, 41; *Contr. McDonald Obs.*, No. 233.
	1954b	*Ap. J.*, **120**, 178; *Contr. McDonald Obs.*, No. 238.
	1954c	*Ap. J.*, **120**, 367; *Contr. McDonald Obs.*, No. 240.
	1954d	*Ap. J.*, **120**, 454; *Contr. McDonald Obs.*, No. 241.
	1956	*Ap. J. Suppl.*, **2**, 389 (No. 24); *Contr. McDonald Obs.*, No. 269.
	1958	*Ap. J.*, **128**, 9; *Contr. McDonald Obs.*, No. 285.
	1959	*Ap. J.*, **130**, 340; *Contr. McDonald Obs.*, No. 309.
HILTNER, W. A., and JOHNSON, H. L.	1956	*Ap. J.*, **124**, 367; *Contr. McDonald Obs.*, No. 266.
HOAG, A. A.	1953	*A.J.*, **58**, 42, and private communication.
HOYLE, F., and WICKRA-MASINGHE, N. C.	1962	*M.N.*, **124**, 417.
HOAG, A. A., and SMITH, E. VAN P.	1959	*Pub. A.S.P.*, **71**, 32.
HULST, H. C. VAN DE	1949	*Problems of Cosmical Aerodynamics* (Dayton: Central Air Documents Office), p. 45.
	1950	*Ap. J.*, **112**, 1.
	1955	*Les Particules solides dans les astres* (*Mém. Soc. R. Sci. Liège*, 4th ser., Vol. **15**), pp. 393 and 609.

| | 1957 | *Light Scattering by Small Particles* (New York and London: Wiley & Chapman). |

IRELAND, J. G. — 1961 — *M.N.*, **122**, 461.

JANSSEN, E. — 1946 — *Ap. J.*, **103**, 380.

JOHNSON, H. M. — 1957a — *Pub. A.S.P.*, **69**, 130.
1957b — *Ibid.*, p. 256.

KRUSZEWSKI, A. — 1962 — *Pub. A.S.P.*, **74**, 519.

KRZEMINSKI, W. — 1959 — *Acta Astr.*, **9**, 231; *Warsaw Repr.*, No. 93.
1961 — *Acta Astr.*, **11**, 7; *Warsaw Repr.*, No. 108.

KRZEMINSKI, W., and
OSKANJAN, V. — 1961 — *Acta Astr.*, **11**, 1; *Warsaw Repr.*, No. 107.

LARSSON-LEANDER, G.,
and SERKOWSKI, K. — 1959 — *Ark. f. astr.*, **2**, 295; *Stockholm Obs. Medd.*, No. 113.

LODÉN, L. O. — 1956 — *Ark. f. astr.*, **2**, 39; *Stockholm Obs. Medd.*, No. 90.
1957 — *Ark. f. astr.*, **2**, 111; *Stockholm Obs. Medd.*, No. 95.
1960 — *Ark. f. astr.*, **2**, 407; *Stockholm Obs. Medd.*, No. 119.
1961a — *Stockholm Obs. Ann.*, Vol. **21**, No. 7.
1961b — *Ibid.*, Vol. **22**, No. 1.

LUNEL, M. — 1954 — *Ann. d'ap.*, **17**, 234; *Pub. Haute-Provence Obs.*, Vol. **3**, No. 10.

LYOT, B. — 1929 — *Ann. Obs. Paris-Meudon*, **8**, Part 1, 102.

MCMASTER, W. H. — 1961 — *Rev. Mod. Phys.*, **33**, 8.

MARKOWITZ, W. — 1951 — *A.J.*, **56**, 134.

MARKOWITZ, W., and
HALL, J. S. — 1950 — *A.J.*, **55**, 175.

MEINEL, A. B. — 1953 — *Pub. A.S.P.*, **65**, 289.

MIKESELL, A. H., HOAG,
A. A., and HALL, J. S. — 1951 — *J. Opt. Soc. America*, **41**, 689.

MORGAN, W. W.,
WHITFORD, A. E., and
CODE, A. D. — 1953 — *Ap. J.*, **118**, 318.

ÖHMAN, Y. — 1956 — *Stockholm Obs. Ann.*, Vol. **19**, No. 4.

PACHOLCZYK, A. G. — 1959a — *Acta Astr.*, **9**, 17; *Warsaw Repr.*, No. 75.
1959b — *Acta Astr.*, **9**, 90; *Warsaw Repr.*, No. 85.

PARKER, E. N. — 1958 — *Rev. Mod. Phys.*, **30**, 955.

PLATT, J. R. — 1956 — *Ap. J.*, **123**, 486.
1960 — *Lowell Obs. Bull.*, **4**, 268, 278, and 311.

REIMER, L. — 1957 — *Optik*, **14**, 83.

SCHATZMAN, E., and
BERNAL, M. J. M. — 1960 — Private communication.

SCHMIDT, TH. — 1958a — *Zs. f. Ap.*, **45**, 214; *Veröff. Göttingen*, No. 121.
1958b — *Zs. f. Ap.*, **46**, 145; *Veröff. Göttingen*, No. 123.

SEMENIUK, I. — 1960 — Private communication.

SERKOWSKI, K.   1958a   *Rev. Mod. Phys.*, **30**, 952; *Warsaw Repr.*, No. 78.
                         1958b   *Acta Astr.*, **8**, 135; *Warsaw Repr.*, No. 72.
                         1958c   *Postepy astronomii* (Cracow), **6**, 160.
                         1960a   *Lowell Obs. Bull.*, **4**, 296, 301, and 317.
                         1960b   *Acta Astr.*, **10**, 227; *Warsaw Repr.*, No. 105.
                         1962   *Advances in Astronomy and Astrophysics*, ed. Z.
                                 KOPAL (New York and London: Academic
                                 Press), **1**, 289.
SHAIN, G. A.   1955   *A.J. U.S.S.R.*, **32**, 381 and 489.
                         1956a   *Izv. Krim. Obs.*, **16**, 181.
                         1956b   *A.J. U.S.S.R.*, **33**, 469.
                         1957   *Ibid.*, **34**, 3.
SHATILOV, A. V.   1960   *Optika i Spektroskopia*, **9**, 86 and 233.
SMITH, E. VAN P.   1956   *Ap. J.*, **124**, 43.
SMITH, E. VAN P., and
  HULST, H. C. VAN DE   1951   *A.J.*, **56**, 141.
SPITZER, L., JR.   1956   *Ap. J.*, **124**, 20.
SPITZER, L., JR., and
  SCHATZMAN, E.   1949   *A.J.*, **54**, 195.
SPITZER, L., JR., and
  TUKEY, J. W.   1951   *Ap. J.*, **114**, 187.
STEPIEN, K.   1962   *Acta Astr.*, in press.
STEVENSON, A. F.   1953   *J. Appl. Phys.*, **24**, 1134 and 1143.
STOKES, G. G.   1852   *Trans. Cambridge Phil. Soc.*, **9**, 399.
TAKAKUBO, K.   1955   *Sci. Rept. Tohoku U.*, ser. I, **39**, 97; *Sendai Astr.
                                 Rap.*, No. 45.
                         1957   *Sci. Rept. Tohoku U.*, ser. I, **40**, 251; *Sendai Astr.
                                 Rap.*, No. 55.
THIESSEN, G.   1958   *Observatory*, **78**, 256.
                         1961   *Astr. Abh. d. Hamburger Sternw.*, Vol. **5**, No. 9.
                         1962   *Zs. f. Ap.*, **54**, 287.
THIESSEN, G., and
  BROGLIA, P.   1959   *Zs. f. Ap.*, **48**, 81.
TRIPP, W.   1956   *Zs. f. Ap.*, **41**, 84; *Veröff. Göttingen*, No. 116.
VAUCOULEURS, G. DE   1959   *Hdb. d. Phys* (Berlin: Springer), **53**, 336.
WARWICK, J. W.   1961   *Ap. J.*, **134**, 1021.
WENTZEL, D. G.   1960   *Lowell Obs. Bull.*, **4**, 269.
WESSELINK, A. J.   1958   *M.N.*, **118**, 271.
WHITFORD, A. E.   1948   *Ap. J.*, **107**, 102.
WILSON, R.   1960   *M.N.*, **120**, 51.
ZIMMERMANN, O.   1957   *Zs. f. Naturforsch.*, **12a**, 647.
ZIRIN, H.   1952   *Harvard Obs. Bull.*, **921**, 26.

CHAPTER 17

Surveys and Observations of Visual Double Stars

W. H. VAN DEN BOS
Lick Observatory

§ 1. RANDOM SEARCHES

THOUGH a limited number of double stars was found accidentally during the seventeenth and eighteenth centuries, it may be said that double-star astronomy started when Sir William Herschel in 1779 began to search the heavens for optical pairs, hoping to find suitable objects for the determination of stellar parallaxes by differential methods. Double-star astronomy, like Bradley's discovery of aberration and nutation, may therefore be regarded as an unexpected outcome of the search for stellar parallax. In 1803, on the basis of his measures of a number of his discoveries, Herschel was able to demonstrate the existence of orbital motion and hence of true binary systems consisting of pairs of stars revolving round their common center of mass.

On the basis of probability and the distribution of the stars over the sky, it can be shown that the majority of the double stars listed in our catalogues are genuine binary systems. In individual cases, a distinction between binaries and optical pairs can be made only by demonstrating the existence of relative motion of orbital character or of common motion in space. Furthermore, it is not possible to draw a sharp border line between double and multiple stars, on the one hand, and the members of a stellar cluster, on the other hand. All that can be said is that the earlier astronomers were more generous in listing their discoveries than the modern observer, who is content to leave the wider pairs to the proper-motion observer.

The pioneer work of William Herschel was continued by his son John Herschel, J. South, and a few others. The telescopes and micrometers available to these observers did not allow them to make very accurate measurements of the position angles and even less of the angular separations of the double stars. Reliable measurements may be said to have started when Struve obtained the celebrated 9-inch Dorpat refractor in 1824 and used it in his great double-star survey of the sky, from the North Pole to 15° southern declination. He catalogued approximately 3000 pairs (Struve 1837), and the 10,000 measures of their separations and position angles have not been surpassed in accuracy by the best modern micrometric measures. Together with his meridian-circle observations of the positions of these pairs, this work provided a sound foundation for double-star astronomy on which all his successors could build.

W. Struve estimated that he had inspected roughly 120,000 stars down to magnitude 8 or $8\frac{1}{2}$, at an average rate of 400 stars per hour of observing. If allowance is made for the fact that every star had to be picked up in the finder, brought into the field of the main telescope, examined, and, if found double, recorded as such with a rough description and approximate position, it is obvious that only a few seconds could as a rule be devoted to the actual examination. Struve states, in fact, that the first glance sufficed to show whether or not the star was double. While this is true under favorable conditions of seeing, it is hard to believe that Struve enjoyed such conditions on all occasions when he was engaged on the survey; later discoveries prove that a considerable number of double stars that were within the capacity of his telescope escaped detection.

When Struve exchanged Dorpat for Pulkova in 1839, he obtained possession of a 15-inch refractor, and, with this, a resurvey was made of the brighter stars to a limiting magnitude of 7. The survey was carried out mostly by his son Otto Struve and resulted in the discovery of some 500 additional pairs. Many of these, but by no means all, may be considered too difficult to have been detected with the Dorpat refractor.

After the completion of the surveys by the two Struves, no further regular searching was done until the last quarter of the nineteenth century, when Burnham entered the field. Observers concentrated on remeasurement of the double stars found in the surveys, occasionally finding a new pair in the course of their work. While this policy was probably followed under the mistaken impression that the Herschels and Struves had exhausted the supply of double stars, it was all to the good for the normal development of double-star astronomy. The discovery is only the first stage in the history of a double star, and it needs to be followed up by regular measurement, so that the pairs in orbital motion can be found and orbits computed, once the observations warrant this.

Among the outstanding observers of this period, in regard to both quantity and quality, were Dawes, Dembowski, Schiaparelli, and Asaph Hall. Dembowski's contribution of more than 20,000 very accurate measures, in spite of having been made with telescopes with apertures of only 5 and 7 inches, is of fundamental importance in the study of relative motions in the systems discovered up to the last quarter of the nineteenth century.

A new era in double-star discovery started in 1870, when Burnham at Chicago began his search with a 6-inch refractor. He soon proved that a great many double stars remained to be found, especially very close pairs and pairs in which the magnitude difference between the components was large. Working in later years mainly with the Dearborn 18½-, Washburn 15½-, Lick 12- and 36-, and Yerkes 40-inch refractors, he discovered, in all, about 1340 new pairs, many of them of extreme difficulty or having short periods of revolution. He also made thousands of measures of his own discoveries as well as of other pairs. He was the first to show the potentialities of a large refractor, situated in a good climate, when used by a keen-eyed observer. His example was soon followed by Hough, Holden, Stone, Howe, See, and others.

Meanwhile, in the Southern Hemisphere double-star astronomy had developed on much the same lines as in the Northern, though to a far smaller extent. Since the number of observatories in the Southern Hemisphere was (and still is) considerably smaller than in northern latitudes and their telescopic equipment much inferior, a large portion of the discoveries and measures of objects between the equator and about 40° southern declination has been made by observers in the Northern Hemisphere, such as Jacob in India, Scott and Doberck in China, Burnham, and observers at the Cincinnati and Lowell Observatories.

In the Southern Hemisphere itself, the early discoveries were made mainly by John Herschel during his expedition to South Africa in the years 1834–1838. Russell and Hargrave at Sydney added a few hundred pairs, but the most effective observer of the southern skies appeared in the person of Innes. Starting as an amateur astronomer with a small telescope in Australia, Innes soon afterward went to the Cape Observatory, where he discovered about 400 new pairs and made many measures of his own discoveries and other double stars with the 7- and 18-inch refractors. As in the case of Burnham's 6-inch, some of Innes' discoveries with the 7-inch are difficult objects to measure with instruments of much larger aperture.

In 1903 Innes went to Johannesburg as director of a newly established meteorological observatory; by 1906 he had acquired a 9-inch refractor, with which he continued his work of discovery and measurement of double stars, adding about 700 new pairs to his earlier discoveries. In 1925 the 26½-inch refractor came into use, and with this instrument, until his retirement at the end of 1927, he brought the total of his discoveries to about 1600. Other discoveries and measures were contributed by Hussey and Dawson between 1911 and 1936 with the La Plata 17-inch refractor, while many pairs, as in the Northern Hemisphere, were noted by the merdian observers.

§ 2. THE LICK SURVEY

In 1899 Aitken and Hussey at the Lick Observatory started a systematic survey of all the stars contained in the *Bonner Durchmusterung* down to magnitude 9.0 and to declination −14° (later extended to −18°) between right ascensions 1ʰ and 13ʰ and to −22° from 13ʰ to 1ʰ. The greater part of the survey was done with the 36-inch refractor, though the 12-inch was used in many of the earlier searches. The searching was done by means of charts, on which the positions of the BD stars down to magnitude 9.0 (Aitken) or 9.1 (Hussey) were plotted. In this way, many misidentifications made by earlier discoverers could be corrected.

When Hussey left Lick in 1905, Aitken took over his zones and completed the survey in 1915. It resulted in the discovery of about 4300 pairs. Many of these are very close and difficult objects, but many others could have been found in earlier searches, showing how incomplete these were. It must, however, be admitted that a systematic survey can never be exhaustive either. The number of stars to be examined is so large that to restrict the searches to nights of good seeing would mean that the survey could not be completed in a reasonable length of time. Even if this were possible, there would always remain some pairs too close for discovery at the time of inspection, though wide enough to be discovered at other times.

The principal purpose of the survey was to provide reliable material for a statistical study of the distribution of the double stars. The essential difference between random searches and a systematic survey is that the latter gives the ratio between the single stars and the stars found to be double within the limiting separation adopted in the survey (which was 5″ for the fainter stars and progressively wider for stars brighter than magnitude 6). It was found that, on the average, one in every eighteen stars examined was double, which shows that our knowledge of duplicity is still extremely incomplete. Statistical studies of the stellar population within 5 parsecs of the sun, where our knowledge of stellar duplicity approaches completeness, indicate that more than half the stellar population exists in double or multiple systems.

§ 3. SOUTHERN SURVEYS

The general survey made at the Lick Observatory has been supplemented by two surveys made in South Africa. With the 26½-inch refractor of the Union Observatory in Johannesburg, Innes, van den Bos, and Finsen surveyed a large part of the skies between 18° southern declination and the South Pole, examining all the stars down to magnitude 9.0 in the *Cape Photographic Durchmusterung*, while, with the 27-inch refractor of the Lamont-Hussey Observatory in Bloemfontein, Rossiter, Donner, and Jessup examined all the stars down to about 9.5 mag. listed in the various "Durchmusterung" catalogues between the equator and the South Pole. Over 11,000 new pairs were found in these two surveys, with 7500 at Bloemfontein and 3500 at Johannesburg. The surveyors at Bloemfontein used charts, as in the Lick survey, while at Johannesburg the searches were made directly from the *Cape Photographic Durchmusterung*.

§ 4. SPECIAL SURVEYS

In addition to the general surveys already mentioned, surveys have also been carried out for selected groups of stars or as a by-product in other investigations. Kuiper examined all stars north of declination −20° brighter than magnitude 6.5 (Harvard Revised) and all stars of large parallax or with known proper motions larger than 0″.3 per year. A number of interesting binaries were discovered, among them Wolf 630, which has the shortest known period (1.7 years) of any visual binary. A survey of the duplicity of all stars brighter than 6.5 mag. between declination +20° and −75° has been carried out by Finsen with an eyepiece interferometer attached to the $26\frac{1}{2}$-inch refractor at the Republic Observatory.

By June, 1961, 10,579 examinations had been made of 6955 stars, and 64 new binaries were discovered. Many of the new pairs show considerable orbital motion, with one pair, ϵ Ceti, having the second shortest known period (2.6 years) of any visual binary. The survey is now being extended to magnitude 7.5 (Finsen 1961).

A recent survey of known M dwarfs has been carried out by Worley (1962). The initial survey list contained 803 stars, of which 700 were examined. A total of 27 new binaries with separations less than 15″ was detected. Nine pairs were found with separations less than 1″, and two pairs show rapid orbital motion.

A photographic search for companions to stars with large proper motions has been carried out by Van Biesbroeck (1961). A total of 650 stars was observed and 12 companions discovered, including the star with the lowest known luminosity (Van Biesbroeck 1944), the companion to Wolf 1985 = Ross 652.

A considerable number of wide, generally faint, pairs with common proper motions has been discovered by Luyten and Giclas in their proper-motion surveys described in chapter 5. Of particular importance are the pairs consisting of subdwarfs, white dwarfs, and late-type red dwarfs.

Among the searches for visual binaries among the stars fainter than those examined in the general surveys can be mentioned the visual surveys by Jonckheere, Espin, and Milburn, and the faint pairs extracted from the various astrographic catalogues by Barton and others.

A number of interesting binary systems has been found in connection with long-focus photographic astrometry for the purpose of determining trigonometric parallaxes. In several cases the binary nature of a system was found from periodic variations in the proper motions of the brighter component or of the unresolved binary. Similarly, long-focus photography of binary systems has revealed periodic variations in orbital motions of several systems, indicating the presence of invisible companions.

Since the visual surveys for binaries among the faint stars have been carried out with telescopes of moderate sizes compared with the largest ones now available and since the photographic method does not have the resolving power of the visual method, there is no doubt, that many more double stars would be discovered, especially among the faint stars, if telescopes such as the large reflectors were made available for surveys of this kind.

The vast number of stars fainter than the ninth magnitude makes it doubtful whether a general survey would provide the returns that would justify such a large undertaking. Instead, the search for binaries among the fainter stars should be limited to stars with large proper motions, to stars in a limited number of selected areas, or to variables, where the unknown existence of a close companion may falsify the light-curves.

At the present stage of development it appears that the systematic measurement of the multitude of pairs already known is more urgently needed than the addition of a large number of faint pairs discovered indiscriminately. The remeasurement will more than tax the energies of the few astronomers active in this field.

§ 5. GENERAL CATALOGUES

Toward the end of the nineteenth century a large amount of data on double stars had already been accumulated. Since the data were scattered over a large number of publications which were more or less accessible, it required an arduous, rather blind, search through the astronomical literature to find out whether a certain star was known to be double and to collect all available information on it. There was a definite need for a reliable source which could supply the complete information which was wanted. This demand was fulfilled by the publication of general catalogues by Innes (1899) and by Burnham (1906).

The two catalogues and especially Burnham's, generally known by its abbreviation "BDS," have been of inestimable value to astronomers interested in double stars and are still valuable sources of information. In the course of time, however, further accumulation of data, later observations, new discoveries, etc., made their extension and revision desirable. Such a catalogue was published by Jonckheere (1917) and is generally known as the "JDS." It contains new pairs within 105° of the North Pole not yet contained in the BDS and includes the measures of these pairs. Innes (1927) published in mimeographed loose-leaf form a catalogue of binaries between declinations −19° and −90°, known as the "SDS." The most recent general catalogue, listing all known double stars within 120° of the North Pole, generally designated the "ADS," was published by Aitken (1932). After the lapse of more than a quarter of a century since the publications by Innes and Aitken, the number of new pairs which have been discovered has increased to such an extent that there is an urgent need for new catalogues listing all known pairs.

An "Index Catalogue of Double Stars," covering the entire sky, planned by van den Bos and Jeffers (1957) is near completion in the form of a card catalogue. Altogether, the catalogue contains pertinent data on 65,000 binary systems and includes brief summaries of the state of information. Present plans call for a publication of the material in the more compact form of a volume in the "Lick Observatory Publication Series" (Jeffers 1961).

§ 6. CURRENT FILES OF MEASUREMENTS

Card catalogues of all published measures have been kept up to date at two observatories—the Lick Observatory, Mount Hamilton, California, and the Republic Observatory in Johannesburg, South Africa. At Johannesburg the card catalogue covers the same region as the *SDS* (declinations between −19° and − 90°), while at Mount Hamilton the catalogue now covers the entire sky. At the Lick Observatory, all measures made since 1927.0 and some earlier ones omitted from the *ADS* have been recorded on punched IBM cards.

A microfilm copy of the Johannesburg catalogue was transmitted to the Lick Observatory in 1956 and has since been recorded on IBM cards. The combined catalogue contains some 160,000 cards. While it has not been considered expedient to publish the catalogue of observations in book form, the data will be available to those who desire them.

§ 7. CONCLUSION

It is only by continued remeasurement following discovery that double-star astronomy is able to furnish the data which are of the most importance to astronomy in general. The number of reliable orbits and masses is still too small in certain respects for fruitful statistical work and—what is perhaps worse—does not provide a fair sample of the double-star population, as it is subject to severe observational and computational selections, especially where systems with long periods of revolution are concerned.

For the time being, we have to rely on the visual observer, working with some form of micrometer or interferometer, for most of this remeasurement, but for the wider pairs the photographic method has been shown to give results of much greater accuracy. Reliable photographic measurements of the wider pairs have now been made during less than half a century but, if continued over a longer period, will provide the best means of obtaining information on pairs in slow motion.

A great advance in our knowledge could undoubtedly be made if it were found possible to devote some of the observing time of the large reflectors to the observation of double stars. Additional information of great value can also be obtained by well-planned spectroscopic and photometric observations of suitable visual double stars.

REFERENCES

AITKEN, R. G.   1932   *New General Catalogue of Double Stars within 120°
                                          of the North Pole* (Washington, D.C.: Carnegie
                                          Institution of Washington), Vols. 1 and 2.

Bos, W. H. van den, and
    Jeffers, H. M.   1957   *Pub. A.S.P.*, **69**, 322.

Burnham, S. W.   1906   *A General Catalogue of Double Stars within 120° of the North Pole* (Washington, D.C.: Carnegie Institution of Washington), Parts 1 and 2.

Finsen, W. S.   1961   *Pub. A.S.P.*, **73**, 283.

Innes, R. T. A.   1899   *Reference Catalogue of Southern Double Stars* (*Ann. R. Obs. Cape of Good Hope*), Vol. **2**, Part 2.

     1927   "Southern Double Star Catalogue" (loose-leaf mimeograph).

Jeffers, H. M.   1961   Private communication.

Jonckheere, R.   1917   *Catalogue of Measures of Double Stars* (*Mem. R.A.S.*, Vol. **61**).

Struve, W.   1837   *Mensurae micrometricae* (Petropolis).

Van Biesbroeck, G.   1944   *A.J.*, **51**, 61.

     1961   *Ibid.*, **66**, 528.

Worley, C. E.   1962   *A.J.*, **67**, 396.

CHAPTER 18

Surveys and Observations of Physical and Eclipsing Variable Stars

B. V. KUKARKIN AND P. P. PARENAGO*

University of Moscow

§ 1. INTRODUCTION

1.1. DEFINITION

THE term "variable stars" applies in general to all stars of varying brightness. However, in many cases the observed variations are due purely to geometrical causes, and no variability would be detected if the star were oriented differently relative to the sun. These are referred to as "geometrical variables," while "physical variables" are defined as stars having variations in their radiation due to processes taking place in the stars themselves. While this chapter will discuss both types of variable stars, only a very brief account will be given of the eclipsing binaries, which are discussed in more detail in the next chapter.

1.2. THE IMPORTANCE OF VARIABLE STARS

Eclipsing variables furnish the largest amount of data on stellar characteristics, such as size, mass, surface temperature, figure, density distribution in the interior of the star, the composition and extension of the atmosphere, etc. Non-stationary processes taking place in eclipsing variables, such as outflow of matter, etc., also lead to an understanding of stellar evolution in general.

In the case of variable stars with amplitudes larger than half a magnitude, the method of discovery is simple and consists of comparing two photographs taken of one and the same region of the sky, with a sufficiently long time interval between photographs. The comparisons are made with a blink-microscope, a stereocomparator, the superposition of a negative on a positive, or by means of television techniques. Variable stars thus differ significantly from non-vari-

---

* The editor notes with much regret the decease of Professor P. P. Parenago on January 5, 1960.

able stars, in that even an approximate classification of the latter requires investigation with special equipment. This inevitably lowers the limiting magnitude for a given instrument by several magnitudes, while variable stars are easily detected by direct photography almost to the limiting magnitude of the instrument. A telescope with a 12–16-inch aperture is as effective with respect to the discovery and classification of variable stars as the 200-inch telescope is with respect to slit spectrograms. No less essential is the simple detailed classification of the variable stars, which can be obtained from their light-curves almost to the limiting magnitude of a given series of plates. This is often equivalent to the detection of minute physical peculiarities of non-variable stars.

Variable stars of many types, such as supernovae, novae, cepheids, red irregular and semiregular variables, Mira type variables, and others, are stars of very high luminosity. We can detect them with comparative ease not only in distant parts of our Galaxy but also in other galaxies. The analysis of variables of various types in different parts of our Galaxy and other galaxies, as well as a study of their peculiarities, furnishes important data for comparing individual galaxies and various parts within them.

Well-defined relations between luminosity and some other easily determined characteristics, such as the length of the period of variation of cepheids and Mira type variables and the form of the light-curve of novae have been found for many variables. These characteristics have made it possible to use variable stars as special luminosity standards in solving problems of distances, dimensions, and structure of our own and other galaxies.

§ 2. HISTORICAL SUMMARY

The earliest documents on stellar variability were recorded by the Chinese several centuries B.C. and were concerned with the appearances of novae or temporary stars. During a period of almost two thousand years, descriptions of the appearance of novae can be found in chronicles of the people of Europe and the Orient.

An early detailed description of a nova, from its appearance to the naked eye to its disappearance, was given by Tycho Brahe for the famous supernova of 1572. However, the interest created by the appearance of this star and also by the discovery of Mira (o Ceti) in 1596, P Cygni in 1600, the supernova in the constellation of Ophiuchus in 1604, and the rediscovery of Mira in 1609 and 1631 did not lead to a realization of the phenomenon of stellar variability. It was not until 1639 that the Dutch scientists Holwarda and Fullenius showed that Mira is a variable star, which suddenly appears to and disappears from the naked eye. From then on, Mira has been observed systematically, and the year 1639 can be considered the beginning of the study of variable stars.

During the next century and a half, variable stars were detected accidentally, mainly as a result of contradictions between the observed magnitudes and those given in Bayer's *Uranometria* (1603). During the last decades of the eighteenth century, W. Herschel turned his attention to variable stars, and two English astronomers, Goodricke and Pigott, began a systematic search for them. Their work was successful, and toward the end of the eighteenth century twelve variable stars, representing several of the main types, were already known, and it was Goodricke who suggested the correct interpretation of the light-variation of Algol as an eclipsing variable.

The next stage in the studies of variable stars is associated with the German astronomer Argelander. He understood the necessity for a systematic study of known variable stars, which in 1844 had reached almost twenty in number. He developed a simple method for estimating the brightness of variable stars and, with his students, discovered and investigated dozens of new variables. Several variable stars were detected in the search for asteroids started in 1801.

In the middle of the last century, visual observations of variable stars by professional and amateur astronomers became widespread. Toward the end of the nineteenth century and the beginning of the twentieth, observers began to form associations which selected their own observing programs. The most active at the present time are the American Association of Variable Star Observers, the Variable Stars Section of the British Astronomical Association, Astronomisk Selskab (Denmark), Association Française des Observateurs des Étoiles Variables, and the Section of Variable Stars of the New Zealand Royal Astronomical Society. These associations provide visual observations for several hundred variables of large amplitude.

The development of scientific photography during the latter part of the last century led to a revolution in the study of variable stars. The Harvard College Observatory was especially active in this field, and, on the initiative of Pickering, systematic photographic observations of the entire sky were planned, and the search for variable stars was organized. Over a period of several decades, thousands of variable stars were discovered at the Harvard Observatory. In Europe the organization of systematic photographic observations of the sky was especially promoted by Wolf in Heidelberg and Blazhko in Moscow. Hundreds of variables were discovered and studied at these observatories. Studies of variable stars by means of photography became widespread and, during the last 60 years, about 27,000 variables, including those in globular clusters and other galaxies, have been discovered. Approximately 14,000 of these were discovered in the United States, mainly at the Harvard College Observatory; about 8000 in Germany, mainly at the Sonneberg Observatory; about 2000 in the Soviet Union, mainly at the observatories of Moscow and Simeis; and about 2000 in Holland at the Leiden Observatory. At present, systematic photographic observations of the sky are made at the observatories at Sonneberg, Dushanbe (Stalinabad), Odessa, and the Harvard College Observatory. Selected fields in our Galaxy, in globular clusters, and in other galaxies are photographed at many observatories for the purpose of studying the variable stars.

Systematic studies of the spectra of variable stars began simultaneously with the application of photography. Pickering discovered the first spectroscopic binary in 1889 and called attention to the peculiar character of the spectra of some variables. At Pulkova, Belopolsky in 1894 discovered the variation in the radial velocity of cepheids, and it was at about the same time that the first colorimetric observations of variable stars were made. Spectral and colorimetric studies of variables became widely used and led to important discoveries. In particular, some variables showed such spectral characteristics that, from their spectra alone, it was possible to state the presence of light-variations. Progress in theoretical astrophysics led to an understanding of the spectra and of the processes which take place in the atmospheres of variable stars.

The earliest attempts to use photoelectric observations for precise photometry of stars were made in 1913. The pioneers in photoelectric photometry were Stebbins in the United States and Guthnick and Prager in Germany. During the last twenty years, photoelectric observations of magnitudes and colors of variable stars have been further improved and have led to many important discoveries. New detailed features in eclipsing variables and new regularities in the physical variables were discovered. New types of stellar variation were found which would have been impossible to detect by other methods of photometry because of their small amplitude.

At the end of the nineteenth century, systematic investigations of variables in globular clusters were begun with the work of Bailey at Harvard. It was also at Harvard that Miss Leavitt later started the study of variables in the Magellanic Clouds. Variable stars were also studied in other isolated systems, and this played a decisive role in the understanding of their nature and in the recognition of the galaxies as independent systems. Miss Leavitt (1908), while studying the variables in the Magellanic Clouds, discovered the period-luminosity relation for cepheids. Pickering (1912) devoted a special paper to this problem, and a few months later Hertzsprung (1912) called attention to the importance of this relation. The first investigations connected with the determination of the zero point of this relation were made by Shapley (1918). Although special attention has been given to the study of the period-luminosity relation for cepheids, the problem of the zero point and possible multiplicity of this relation cannot yet be considered completely solved (see chap. 21).

Studies dealing with the computation of the orbits of eclipsing variables started during the period 1908–1912. Discounting the first attempts to solve this problem, Blazhko, Russell, and Shapley should be named as the founders of the theory of orbit computations of eclipsing variables. They formulated the main principles involved in the solution of the problem. Further refinements were concerned primarily with the increase in the precision of observations, the detection of numerous additional effects, and the construction of a theory of stellar atmospheres. At the present time the techniques used in computing orbits of eclipsing variables have reached a very high degree of sophistication.

Numerous investigations dealing with the detection and study of the cor-

relations between different characteristics in variables, such as type of variability, length of period, spectrum, peculiarities in the light-curve, etc., began in
the first quarter of this century. These studies have received special attention
during the past decades in connection with the growing amount of observational
data, the increase in the precision of observations, the detailed study of spectra,
and the discovery of variables in distant parts of our Galaxy and in other
galaxies. During the past decades, theories of stellar variability were also developed, and the discovery by Ambartsumian of criteria from which to estimate
the age of some formation of matter in the universe lent importance to the study
of variable stars and their use in solving many problems of stellar cosmogony.

§ 3. THE NOMENCLATURE OF VARIABLE STARS

The great number of variable stars discovered raised the question of a uniform system for their designation, in order to facilitate further identification
and bibliography. The following nomenclature of variables was used during the
second half of the past century and has since been subjected only to minor additions. At present it is adopted as an international system. In each constellation, the stars are named in the order of their discovery by Latin letters beginning with R, S, etc. After Z follow combinations of two letters beginning
with RR, RS to SS to ZZ, etc. If still more designations are needed, they continue with AA, . . . , AZ, BB, . . . , BZ, . . . , QZ. There are 334 such combinations. If the number of variables in a given constellation exceeds 334, the following variables are named by the symbol V and a running number—V 335, V 336,
etc.—with the name of the constellation added. Before World War II the naming of the variable stars was assigned to the Commission on Variable Stars of
the Astronomische Gesellschaft in Germany. After World War II this function
was delegated to a special subcommission of the International Astronomical
Union. Since the Eighth General Assembly of the I.A.U., which was held in
Rome in 1952, this function has been taken over by the compilers of the *General
Catalogue of Variable Stars.*

Besides the variable stars with final designation, there are thousands of stars
with suspected variability for which a system of preliminary designations is
needed. Unfortunately, there are several different systems in existence. For
example, the stars for which data were published in the *Astronomische Nachrichten* were assigned a running number, the year, and the constellation to which
they belong (e.g., 526,1936 Cyg; 122,1937 Cyg; etc.). Sometimes lists of
variables discovered in other places were published in the same journal, and
the stars were given preliminary designations on the same system. However,
this was not done systematically, and after World War II these symbols were
used in only a few cases.

Variable stars discovered at the Harvard College Observatory are given the
designation "HV" and a number in order of discovery. Similarly, variable stars
discovered at the Sonneberg Observatory are given the symbol "S," and those

discovered in the U.S.S.R. the symbol "СПЗ" (Soviet Variable Star) and a number in order of discovery. There are many other systems of preliminary designations, as, for example, the stars detected by Ross carry his name, followed by a number. The symbol "VV" with a current number means that the variable was discovered at the Vatican Observatory, the symbol "OV" that the variable was discovered at the University of Oklahoma, U.S.A., etc. Some investigators do not assign systematic preliminary designations to the variables detected by them. This is the case for numerous variables discovered in Holland. In each list, these variables are designated by either small letters of the Latin alphabet or by a running number.

It should be remembered that preliminary designations of variables are only temporary. After the star has been given a final designation, which is assigned immediately after its first reliable investigation, the preliminary designation is practically never referred to and is needed only as a historical reference. If the star does not deserve a final designation because of incomplete data, it is included in catalogues of suspected variables and is usually later referred to under the number assigned to it in these catalogues.

Variable stars in globular clusters are usually designated by the number of the cluster and a number indicating the order of discovery in the particular cluster. No uniform system of designations has been used for variables in other galaxies. Variable stars in the Magellanic Clouds are usually designated by a preliminary number on the HV system. In other galaxies, they are named after the galaxy in which they are found and given a number for identification.

§ 4. LITERATURE ON VARIABLE STARS

4.1. CATALOGUES AND LISTS OF VARIABLE STARS

During the nineteenth century, catalogues and lists of variable stars were compiled independently, without any uniform plan. At the beginning of this century, the variable stars were named by the Astronomische Gesellschaft, Germany. The catalogues were compiled by Hartwig and published as a supplement to the *Vierteljahrschrift der Astronomischen Gesellschaft*. Lists of newly designated variables were published in *Astronomische Nachrichten*. In 1926 the Babelsberg Observatory began to publish annual catalogues, compiled by Prager until 1937 and subsequently by H. Schneller until 1943. The lists of newly named variables continue to be published in the *Astronomische Nachrichten* and its supplements.

The publication of these catalogues was discontinued during World War II. Catalogues of variable stars can be compiled and edited only in institutions having bibliographical data on all the published investigations of variable stars, which are very numerous and scattered throughout the astronomical literature. Only specialists who devote their time to the study of variable stars are able to follow all these investigations. Prior to World War II a card catalogue of all investigations of variable stars was kept at the Babelsberg Observatory. Its compilation was started by Müller and Hartwig, continued by Prager, and later by Schneller. At present, this catalogue is located at the Postdam Observatory under the responsibility of Schneller.

In 1940 the authors of this chapter began the compilation of a complete card catalogue of all investigations and observations of variable stars at the Sternberg Astronomical Institute in Moscow. Later, Efremov and Kholopov took an active part in this work. The card catalogue was completed in 1947 and is continuously being updated. By 1961 it contained about two hundred thousand summaries of studies of variable stars. The compilation of the card catalogue, which contains all the latest data, has made it possible for the astronomers of the U.S.S.R. to assign designations to new variable stars and to compile catalogues. Between 1946 and 1952, lists of newly discovered variables were compiled in Moscow and printed in a separate publication by the International Astronomical Union (lists Nos. 42–47).

The *General Catalogue of Variable Stars*, containing data on 10,912 objects, was published in 1948. Since new data would be added each year to only 5 per cent of known variables and since, on the average, there would be only 400 new variables, it was decided that an annual supplement to the catalogue would be sufficient. The supplement would contain all the essential changes and the lists of new variables, and it was decided that a new edition of the catalogue should be published only when about one-third of the catalogue needed corrections. Since the supplements include the same data as in the lists of designations, it was decided in 1952 to include these in the supplements. From 1949 to 1958 nine annual supplements have been printed.

In 1958 the second edition of the *General Catalogue of Variable Stars* was published (Kukarkin, Parenago, *et al.* 1958). This catalogue contains data on 14,708 variable stars and had to be published in two volumes. The first volume contains a list and the main data on all the designated variables and the remarks, while the second volume contains various auxiliary tables (a list of variables in the order of right ascensions, a list of stars according to types of variability, a list of identifications, etc.).

Data on numerous stars of suspected variability with no final designations have, from time to time, been compiled into catalogues. In 1929, Zinner published a catalogue which included data on 2191 suspected variable stars. In 1934 and 1937, Prager published two such catalogues, which, together, contain 5829 suspected variable stars.

In 1951 the authors of this chapter, together with Efremov and Kholopov, collected data on all variables discovered after 1937 and added those variables from the catalogues of Zinner and Prager which, up to that time, had not received a final designation; from these data they compiled the *Catalogue of Stars of Suspected Variability* designated the "CSSV." It was divided into two parts; the first part contained data on 5835 stars whose variability seemed to be very probable to the compilers; the second contained data on 2299 stars whose variability seemed doubtful. Many of the stars in these catalogues have been investigated and given a final designation. By 1961, 490 stars of Zinner's catalogue, 2568 stars of both of Prager's catalogues, and 854 stars of the *Catalogue of Stars of Suspected Variability* were given final designation. An additional edition of the *CSSV* is planned and will contain all the variable stars discovered after 1950 which have not yet received a final designation. There are 1000 such stars to date.

Thus data on about 24,000 variable stars in our Galaxy are quite fully represented in various catalogues, which makes it easier to study and use variable stars in various branches of astronomy, including general investigations. A description of the bibliographical references is given in § 4.3.

The catalogues of variable stars in globular clusters are in a convenient form and quite complete. Two catalogues have been published by the David Dunlap

TABLE 1

KNOWN VARIABLES AT DIFFERENT EPOCHS

Year	Variables with Final Designation	Suspected Variables	Total
1929.........	3218	2191	5409
1937.........	6968	8359	15,327
1948.........	10,912	8248	19,160
1961.........	15,504	10,000±	25,500±

Observatory (Sawyer 1939, 1955). The second catalogue contains 1421 objects and includes a complete bibliography and statistical data.

No general catalogue or list has been compiled for variable stars in nearby galaxies. Data are scattered among various articles and publications, and there is not even a bibliographical index to articles on variables in other galaxies, with the exception of the Magellanic Clouds, of which Buscombe, Gascoigne, and de Vaucouleurs (1954) have written a review containing a complete bibliography. It is evident that the rapidly developing study of variable stars in other galaxies emphasizes the need of establishing a similar reference system or index.

4.2. THE NUMBER OF KNOWN VARIABLE STARS

Table 1 illustrates the increase in the number of variable stars discovered in our Galaxy during the last thirty years, excluding variables in globular clusters. The first column gives the year to which the data correspond, the second the number of variables which received a final designation, the third the number of stars of suspected variability, and the fourth the total number of variable stars.

On the average, 400 stars are designated variables each year. This continuous and nearly uniform increase in the number of variable stars shows that only a small percentage of existing variables has been detected. Special photographic studies of variable stars to 16–17 mag. in comparatively large selected fields and to 18–20 mag. in small fields make it possible to estimate their total number to be several million.

Eighty of the 121 globular clusters known at present (1961) have been searched for variable stars, and approximately 1600 were detected. No large increase in this number is expected. Assuming that the total number of globular clusters in our Galaxy is approximately 200, the total number of variables in them can be estimated at 4000. However, only the brightest stars have been studied, and no special search has been made for variables of low luminosity.

In the Magellanic Clouds the number of variables detected so far exceeds 3000, of which about 1000 have been investigated. Again, only stars of high luminosity have been studied, and it is too early to estimate the total number of variables in these galaxies. The same is the case to a higher degree in regard to other nearby galaxies in which several hundred variables have already been detected. It is evident that this is only a very small fraction of the total number of variables in these stellar systems.

4.3. Bibliography of Variable Stars

From time to time, bibliographic references have been published on the basis of the bibliographic cards of variable stars. In 1918–1922 Müller and Hartwig published three volumes of the *Geschichte und Literatur des Lichtwechsels der veränderlichen Sterne*, which contained a complete bibliography of all variable stars designated before 1915. In 1934, Prager published two volumes, containing literature published after 1915 of all variable stars designated before 1913 arranged alphabetically from Andromeda to Ophiuchus. In 1952, Schneller published a third volume, which contained literature on variables designated before 1931 in the constellations from Orion to Vulpecula. In 1941, Prager published a bibliographic reference which contained a list of literature on variable stars designated from 1931 to 1938. In 1957, Schneller published an additional volume of *Geschichte und Literatur*, with a bibliography of new investigations on variables included in the previous volumes and all variables designated before 1938. In 1960 and 1961 he published two additional volumes, with a bibliography of all variables designated between 1938 and 1958. It is his intention to compile additional volumes to be published every few years by the German Academy of Sciences. These will contain new bibliographic data on stars included in the previous volumes, as well as newly designated variables.

Besides the general catalogues, lists and bibliographic indexes which serve the purpose of giving a complete description of the objects and the literature about variable stars, there are specialized references of various types which are compiled and published.

Since 1925, special almanacs for eclipsing variables have been compiled and published at Kraków, at the initiative of Banachiewicz. These give lists and ephemerides useful to observers. The almanac does not include faint stars or southern variables.

Between 1934 and 1938, an almanac was compiled by Okunyev and Tsesevich, first at Leningrad and later at Stalinabad, which contained lists, observational results, and ephemerides of short-period cepheids. Since 1960 the ephemerides of some RR Lyrae stars were computed by Tsesevich at Odessa and published by Kordylewski in the *Ephemerides of Eclipsing Binaries* at Kraków.

Special lists of eclipsing variables, including critical reviews of data on these stars and recommendations to observers, were also published. The first were compiled independently by Dugan (1934) and Martynov (1934). The last revised list was compiled by Wood (1953). It gives data on 918 eclipsing variables and recommendations in regard to their study.

Tables to facilitate the computation of orbits of eclipsing variables have also been published. The most useful were compiled by Tsesevich (1947) and Merrill (1950).

It is often difficult to find and identify a variable star, especially if it is faint. The best means of identification is a chart of the surrounding stars. Toward the end of the last century, Hagen (1889–1927) began the preparation of an atlas of charts of variable stars. Over a period of 30 years, charts of about 400 variables, predominantly Mira type variables, were published. Charts of about 500 variables of Mira, U Gem, and some other types are compiled and distributed by the American Association of Variable Star Observers.

During the last 20 years, identification charts have often been published, together with the information on discovered variables. Such charts have been compiled for all faint variables discovered in the Netherlands and in the U.S.S.R. Some lists of new variables discovered in Germany were also accompanied by charts. Unfortunately, there are still several thousand faint variables which lack identification charts.

Over the years, variable stars have attracted the attention of many astronomers, which explains the large number of monographs devoted to variable stars. A selection of such monographs is listed at the end of the chapter.

§ 5. CLASSIFICATION OF VARIABLE STARS

5.1. HISTORICAL

The great variety in the light-changes of variable stars led long ago to attempts to classify these stars according to their most characteristic features. For many decades the features of the light-variations, such as the amplitude, the period, and the form of the light-curve, were the main criteria used for classification. Later on, following the development of stellar spectroscopy, the physical peculiarities of the atmospheres of the objects were added as a means of classification. It was also found that certain types of variable stars occupied specific regions of the spectrum-luminosity or color-luminosity diagrams. In recent years, studies of the space distribution of variables and investigations of the kinematic properties of variables of similar type have been made. These showed that the distribution of variables in our Galaxy, whether in the disk, the intermediate, or the spherical components, or in isolated stellar systems such as globular clusters, the Magellanic Clouds, or other galaxies, is closely connected with the place they occupy in the color-luminosity diagram and with their morphologic features (e.g., period and light-curve). Lately it has become possible to estimate the upper limit of the age of some variables according to the ideas of Ambartsumian. This adds a new criterion for classifying variable stars.

The success of theoretical astrophysics and the understanding of the processes taking place in stellar atmospheres, together with hypotheses concerning the internal structure of stars and stellar energy sources, provide one more essential criterion for the classification of the variable stars—namely, their common origin. It is certain that this criterion will become more important as the numerous observed peculiarities of variable stars receive a firm theoretical basis. At present, observations of brightness and spectra of variables, in combination with their space distribution and velocities, are far from having been fully explained by theory and for a long time will determine the principles of a detailed classification of variable stars.

It is evident that no classification can describe the whole variety of processes and phenomena characteristic of nature. However, a well-founded classification, which selects and distributes the objects according to the most essential multi-dimensional features, will without doubt be able to reveal the most significant features determining the nature of a given aggregation of objects.

It is unfortunate that in the classification of variable stars the strict use of such terms as "class," "type," and "subtype" is absent. Such terms are already applied to objects of many different categories. For this reason, an attempt is made here to use a stricter application of these terms. The term "class" will be used only for the main aggregations of variable stars, which, according to our present knowledge, have the same cause for their variability. In each class the most characteristic groups of variables with similar peculiarities of light-variation and spectrum will be defined as "types." Finally, separate groups of variable stars of a given type which differ in some fine morphologic feature or are members of various components of our Galaxy or other stellar system will be defined as "subtypes."

5.2. General Classification

On the basis of the peculiarities in the light-variations of variable stars, the processes in their atmospheres, or their origin, the variable stars can be divided into three classes: (1) eruptive variable stars, (2) pulsating variables, and (3) eclipsing variables. In naming these three classes, an attempt has been made to express the most essential characteristics of each class. A more detailed classification according to type, with examples, is given in the following three sections.

5.3. ERUPTIVE VARIABLE STARS

The light-variations of eruptive variable stars result from deep internal causes, which point to a non-stable condition of these stars. A thorough study of these interesting objects started fairly recently, and, except for the novae, the data are still very limited. In the past few years many investigators have paid special attention to these objects, and some types of variable stars in this class were discovered only recently.

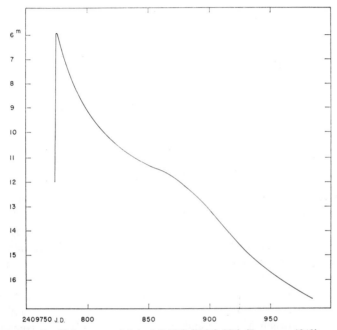

FIG. 1.—Light-curve of S And (1885) (NGC 224) (Parenago 1949)

The following more detailed classification of eruptive variable stars is proposed: (1.1) supernovae, (1.2) novae, (1.3) nova-like variables, (1.4) U Geminorum and Z Camelopardalis type variables, (1.5) RW Aurigae type variables, (1.6) UV Ceti type variables.

Supernovae (type 1.1) are characterized by a sudden increase in brightness, with the result that the brightness increases by more than 20 mag. for several days. During the next several hundred days the brightness decreases to its pre-eruptive values. The brightness of a supernova at maximum is comparable with that of a whole galaxy, and its absolute magnitude amounts, on the average, to -15.5. A typical light-curve of a supernova is shown in Figure 1. According to Kopylov (1955a), supernovae in our Galaxy form a flat subsystem.

Novae (type 1.2) are also characterized by sudden flares. Their brightness increases by 10–12 mag. over a period of several days, followed by a return to the former brightness over a period which varies from several hundred days to several decades. Novae show a large variation in amplitude, in duration of flares, and in the forms of their light-curves. According to Vorontsov-Velyaminov (1940), the decrease in brightness after the outburst is at first approximately inversely proportional to the length of time after the outburst. Then it changes until it is approximately inversely proportional to the cube of the time. These idealized light-curves are smoothed, and the small secondary variations often observed on the descending branch are neglected. About fifty novae flare up annually in the Galaxy; on the average, we observe only one or two.

Some novae have sharp maxima followed by a rapid decrease in brightness, while others show a more gradual decline. The first type is characterized by higher luminosity at maximum than the second type. According to McLaughlin (1945), the absolute magnitude at maximum is determined by the length of time, t_3, in days after maximum during which the nova decreases by 3 mag. According to the latest determination by Kopylov (1955b), we have,

$$M_{max} = -13.7 + 3.6 \log t_3 ,$$

while for the supernovae, according to the same source, we have

$$M_{max} = -31.9 + 9.5 \log t_3 .$$

Kopylov came to the conclusion that the novae in the Galaxy belong to the intermediate component.

The spectra of novae shortly before and during maximum are always absorption spectra and are similar to those of A- and F-type supergiants. Immediately after maximum, bright bands appear in the spectrum, but the absorption lines of the same elements continue to be present on their violet sides. Gradually the spectrum becomes more complex, and absorption and emission lines, corresponding to high excitation and ionization in the expanding envelope, appear. The velocities of expansion increase, and the emission band widths correspond to velocities of expansion of hundreds and thousands of km/sec. Then forbidden lines appear, and the absorption lines and the continuous spectrum become weaker and completely disappear.

DQ Herculis 1934 requires special mention because it was discovered to be a close binary. Both the increase and the decrease in brightness of this nova were slow, with the exception of the rapid decrease in brightness from sixth to twelfth magnitude, which took place half a year after the principal maximum at first magnitude, following which it rapidly again became of the sixth magnitude, as shown in Figure 2. The photoelectric observations by Walker (1954, 1956, 1958) showed the star to be an Algol-type variable with an unusually short period of 0.19362 day and an amplitude of about 1.5 mag. Unfortunately, the eclipse is not total, there is no noticeable secondary minimum, and the light-curve varies in shape, which, together with other circumstances outlined below, greatly hinder the reliable determination of its physical characteristics. According to

Walker, it can be assumed that the radii of the components are of the order of 0.1 solar radius, the masses from 0.5 to 1.5 solar masses, and densities from 10^3 to 10^4 the solar density. A unique feature of the light-curve of the star is the occurrence between phases $0.110P$ and $0.325P$ of rapid variations in light having a period of 1.180 minutes and a range of 0.07 mag. in the ultraviolet. From scanty observations made before the 1934 outburst, it appears possible that DQ Herculis was then an eclipsing variable, but with a period of 0.19321 day

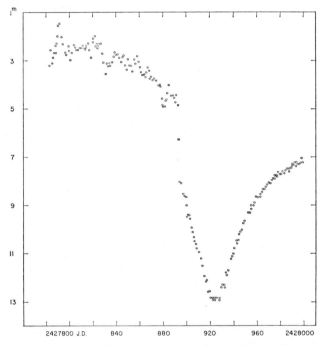

Fig. 2.—Light-curve of DQ Her (1934) (Campbell 1942b)

(Ahnert 1958). The increase in the period after the outburst would indicate a loss of 0.43 per cent of the mass of the system.

If the early period is correct, then it is necessary to accept the idea that outbursts with an amplitude of 14 mag. are not capable of essentially changing the characteristics of such a close pair. It is extremely interesting that the eclipsing variable of the Algol type—UX Ursa Majoris—which has practically the same period as DQ Herculis (0.19667 day), is in many respects similar to this nova. It is not improbable that UX Ursa Majoris was once a nova which flared up in the past or will flare up sometime in the future.[1]

The fact that after an outburst the brightness of a nova becomes the same

[1] Walker (1962) has discovered that Nova T Aurigae 1891 with light-outbursts very similar to those of DQ Herculis is also a close binary with a period of 0.2043635 day, and Kraft (1963) has observed that Nova V 603 Aquilae and Nova GK Persei 1901 are also close binaries.

as before the outburst shows that there are no substantial changes in the physical nature of a nova during an outburst, and it may be assumed that if a nova was a variable before the outburst, it remains one after the outburst, and if before the outburst there were no variations in brightness, there will be none after.

Nova-like variables (type 1.3) vary greatly. They are similar to the novae in the peculiarities of their spectra, and some also have sudden flare-ups, but usually with smaller amplitudes than the regular novae. Included among the novalike variables are the recurrent novae which differ little from ordinary novae except for the smaller amplitude of the outburst. The data on recurrent novae are summarized in Table 2. It is not reliably established that UW Persei belongs to the recurrent novae. The time interval between the flares (mean cycle) is of a stationary character but may vary by as much as one-fifth from its mean

TABLE 2

DATA ON RECURRENT NOVAE

Nova	Max.–Min.	Year of Outburst	Mean Cycle (Days)	log P
T CrB.......	2.0–10.8	1866, 1946	29,000	4.46
RS Oph.....	5.3–12.3 pg	1898, 1933, 1958	11,000	4.04
UW Per.....	13.5–17 pg	1901, 1913	4000	3.60
T Pyx.......	7.0–14.0 pg	1890, 1902, 1920, 1944	6650	3.82
WZ Sge......	7.0–15.5 pg	1913, 1946	11,900	4.08
V 1017 Sgr...	7.2–14.3 pg	1901, 1919	6400 (?)	3.81
U Sco........	8.8–17.6 pg	1863, 1906, 1936	13,400	4.13
VY Aqr.....	8.0–<16	1907, 1962	20,000	4.30

value. WZ Sagittae is a spectroscopic binary with the shortest known period of 0.05666884 day (Krzeminski 1962).

If it is assumed that all ordinary novae are recurrent novae, with a time interval between outbursts of several thousand years, then it is estimated that the total number of stars in the Galaxy which will flare as novae should be of the order of 10^5–10^6. Among stars of this type, R Coronae Borealis and variables similar to it occupy a special place. Stars of this type usually have G–K spectra, which show a relatively high carbon abundance. In contrast to recurrent novae, they remain at maximum brightness most of the time. Their minima are of different durations, varying from several months to several years, and with depths of from 1 to 9 mag. For a given star there are times when the minima follow one another rapidly, and there have been cases when there was no minimum during 10 or more years.

In contrast to these stars, others, such as Z Andromedae, very often have a rather stable cycle and vary more or less continuously. The period of Z Andromedae remains at 700 days over a long period of time (Fig. 3), while the amplitude varies considerably. Such stars could be considered as belonging to the ordinary semiregular variables if it were not for their characteristic nova-like spectra, which show comparatively rapid variations. Z Andromedae type stars are usually called "symbiotic stars" because they display a "combination spectrum" of a low-temperature absorption spectrum (commonly of type M) and high-excitation emission lines.

U Geminorum type variables (type 1.4) are characterized by a rapid rise in brightness, with an amplitude of from 2 to 6 mag. which lasts for several days.

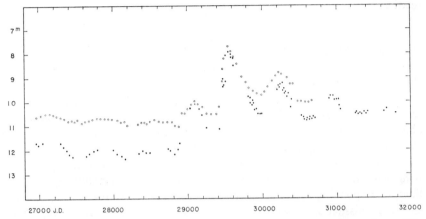

Fig. 3.—Photographic (*dots*) and visual (*circles*) light-curves of Z And (Payne-Gaposchkin 1946).

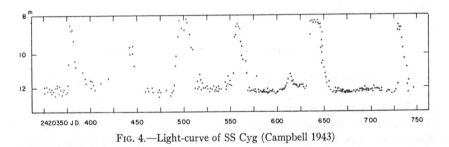

Fig. 4.—Light-curve of SS Cyg (Campbell 1943)

The duration of the increase in brightness varies from several hours to several days, and the decrease usually takes longer, the flare lasting about 20 per cent of the time. The intervals (cycles) between flares are subject to accidental fluctuations, but each star follows a definite cycle. Individual stars of this type have cycles of between 10 and several hundred days. For some stars, like Z Camelopardalis, changes in behavior are observed. Sometimes the outbursts stop, and the variable remains constant in brightness at a magnitude intermediate between maximum and minimum. The light-curve of SS Cygni in Figure 4 is typical of the U Geminorum type variables.

The mean amplitude of a flare A of the U Geminorum type stars is rather closely related to the mean cycle P (Kukarkin and Parenago 1934). Vorobyeva (1960) gives, with a rather large dispersion, the relation

$$A = 0.84 + 1.64 \log P,$$

where A is expressed in magnitudes and P in days. Kopylov (1954) finds that recurrent novae do not fully satisfy this relation. For the stars in Table 2 the relation is

$$A = -7.0 + 3.7 \log P.$$

On account of the small dispersion in the values of $\log P$, the few stars in the group, and the small number of outbursts observed, it is necessary to consider this still an open question.

At maximum brightness, the U Geminorum type stars have continuous spectra with weak absorption lines of hydrogen, Ca II, and He I, with widths of about 20 A. The continuous spectrum corresponds approximately to spectral class A0. At minimum, the spectrum has bright bands of hydrogen, He I, and Ca II, with the same width as above. No noticeable displacement of the bands is detected in either case. The absorption spectrum at minimum has narrow lines, corresponding to the spectrum of a dwarf G5 star. Joy (1956) observed that the emission and absorption lines of SS Cygni show periodic variations, with a period of 0.276244 day, one of the components having only absorption lines, the other only emission lines. From the computed elements he derived the following values for the masses and semimajor axes of the two components ($i = 90°$):

$$\mathfrak{M}_{abs} = 0.20 \odot, \qquad \mathfrak{M}_{em} = 0.18 \odot,$$
$$a_{abs} = 437,000 \text{ km}, \qquad a_{em} = 463,000 \text{ km}.$$

Joy estimated the absolute magnitudes of the components to be approximately equal, $+5.5$. Adopting $T_e = 5500°$, he derived the radius of the absorption component equal to $0.90\odot = 625,000$ km. Adopting $T_e = 20,000°$, the radius of the emission component was found to be $0.15\odot = 105,000$ km. Thus the distance between the surfaces of the components is 170,000 km (for $i = 90°$) or more. Since Grant (1955) did not detect a noticeable eclipse, i must be less than 60°. Adopting, with Joy, $i = 50°$, we find

$$\mathfrak{M}_{abs} = 0.42 \odot, \qquad \mathfrak{M}_{em} = 0.40 \odot.$$
$$a_{abs} = 560,000 \text{ km}, \qquad a_{em} = 600,000 \text{ km},$$

and a distance between the surfaces of 427,000 km. The close proximity of the components is possibly characteristic of U Geminorum type stars and has no apparent connection with the flares of these stars. Since the mean cycle of SS Cygni is 50 days, it is about 180 times longer than the orbital period, but it brings the U Geminorum type stars to a closer relationship with Nova DQ Herculis. According to Kraft (1962), at least four stars of U Geminorum type are very close binaries with periods of from 0.17 to 0.39 day. U Geminorum type stars are very similar to recurrent novae and in many respects can be considered novae in miniature. No distinguishing criteria for separating the Z Camelopardalis variables from the U Geminorum type have as yet been established.

RW Aurigae type variables (type 1.5) are characterized by irregular light-variations, which range in amplitude from a fraction of a magnitude to 3 or 4 mag. Sometimes these stars undergo large variations during intervals of 1–2 days and even over as short a period as several hours, and sometimes the brightness does not essentially change over several weeks. Their color index is smaller at maximum and larger at minimum brightness. Most of the stars belong to spectral classes from F to M and are named T Tauri stars by Joy (1945) and Herbig (1952), but they are found among all spectral classes from B to M.

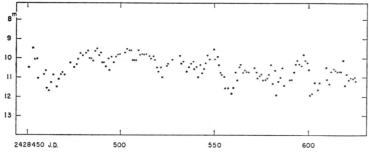

FIG. 5.—Light-curve of T Ori (Parenago 1954*b*)

Hydrogen emission lines, at least Hα, of varying intensity and often Ca II are observed in their spectra. The absolute magnitudes are mostly within the limits of +2 to +6; more often they are subgiants. On the H-R diagram they form a cloud or T-band (Parenago 1950, 1954*a*; Kholopov 1958; Strand 1958). Recently it was found that the spectra of some stars of this type—such as NX Monocerotis and VY Orionis—show strong continuous emission, large polarization in the ultraviolet, reaching 30–50 per cent, and fluctuations in the ultraviolet with a time scale of about 1 minute and a range of 1 mag., with excesses reaching 1.5 mag. (Hunger and Kron 1957). All these phenomena indicate the presence of relativistic electrons.

Many of the stars of this type are connected with diffuse nebulae and associations. The cause of light-variations can in no case be the obscuration of these stars by dust, as was once supposed for variable stars in the Orion Nebula Cluster, where there are several hundreds of such stars. The light-variation for T Orionis is shown in Figure 5.

UV Ceti type variables (type 1.6) are characterized by sudden flares of very short duration, as shown in Figure 6. Usually in the course of several minutes the brightness increases by several times, sometimes by several orders of magnitude, and then returns to its previous value over a period of several hours. At maximum, a strong continuous emission is observed. As a rule, these stars are dwarfs of spectral class M.

5.4. PULSATING VARIABLE STARS

The variations in brightness of pulsating variable stars can be explained by pulsation processes taking place in their atmospheres and upper layers. The pulsation periods of some variables in this class remain practically constant during many decades, undergoing only slight variations of a secular, as well as of an accidental, nature. Other variables of this class have a less well-defined

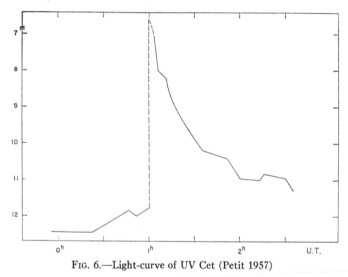

FIG. 6.—Light-curve of UV Cet (Petit 1957)

periodicity, and the length of the cycle varies by several per cent from one pulsation to the next. Finally, a fraction of the pulsating variables do not have an established periodicity, and large irregularities are observed in the variations in the brightness and in the spectrum. As a class, pulsating variables are found in all components of our Galaxy, in globular clusters, and in other galaxies.

Pulsating variables show a close correlation between the length of the period and the spectrum and, for some types, also between the length of the period and the luminosity, which makes them very convenient objects for solving problems of determining distances to galaxies and other stellar systems.

The total radiation of most of the known pulsating variables changes from minimum to maximum by a factor of 1.5–2, although for some stars the change is only a few per cent. On account of peculiarities in the radiation and the presence of strongly varying molecular absorption bands in the visible region of the spectrum of some pulsating variables, the light-variations seem to be large, in certain cases up to a factor of 10^3–10^4.

The following more detailed classification of pulsating variables according to type is proposed: (2.1) irregular variables, (2.2) semiregular variables, (2.3) Mira type stars, (2.4) long-period cepheids, (2.5) short-period cepheids, (2.6) β Canis Majoris type variables, and (2.7) other pulsating variables.

Irregular variables (type 2.1) are characterized by slow, wavelike light-variations without well-pronounced periodicity. As a rule, variables of this type are low-temperature stars, mostly of class M. They are either giants or subgiants and are found in all parts of our Galaxy.

Semiregular variables (type 2.2) are characterized by rather well-defined periodicities, which, however, are subject to considerable variations. The light-curves undergo changes from period to period, and the presence of two or more oscillations of different periods and amplitudes is characteristic of many of these stars. As a rule, variables of this type are of spectral class M, but some belong to spectral classes G–K, in particular, the RV Tauri subtype stars.

Among the semiregular variables several groups can be distinguished. RV Tauri subtype stars are characterized by light-curves with primary and second-ary minima. In many cases these minima interchange after several years, but the periods, usually between 20 and 140 days, remain rather constant, with varia-tions not exceeding one-sixth of the mean value of the period. For some stars of this type, periodic variations in the mean magnitude exceeding the principal period by fifteen to twenty times are observed. The absolute visual magni-tudes of these stars are about −2.5. The spectra usually belong to classes G Ib and are very similar to the spectra of long-period cepheids. At the principal minimum, absorption bands of TiO appear in the spectra, which are classified as K5–M. Near the principal minimum, hydrogen emission often appears in the form of red and violet components of the absorption lines. The radial velocities show curves similar to the light-curves, with a minimum preceding in time the principal light-minimum by 0.4 of the period. If these curves are integrated, they show that the radius of the atmosphere reaches its maximum near the principal light-minimum and its minimum soon after the secondary minimum of the light-curve.

The AF Cygni subtype stars of spectral classes M II–III form the most nu-merous group of semiregular variables, with periods of from 50 to 300 days and with an absolute visual magnitude about −1. Their periods undergo variations up to ± one-third of the mean value, which is usually well defined for long inter-vals of time. The spectral classes do not show noticeable variations with the phase of the light-curve, and the radial velocities vary within narrow limits, but their relation to the light-curves has not as yet been investigated.

μ Cephei or α Orionis subtype stars belong to supergiants M of luminosity classes Ia–Ib and seldom to luminosity class II. The periods vary from 80 to 200 days. Periodic variations of the mean magnitude exceeding the principal period by about ten times are often observed. The radial velocities vary little and have amplitudes of from 5 to 15 km/sec. In the case of α Orionis, the radius is largest near minimum brightness and smallest near maximum.

The comparatively rare cyclic variables show light-variations with first one period, then a second period, and sometimes even a third. These periods conform approximately to the relation

$$P_1:P_2:P_3 = 1:1.5:2.$$

The spectra are usually type M, but some have spectral classes K and G.

There are other special semiregular variables which differ from those described above. For example, the light-variations of SV Ursa Majoris and WY Andromedae are similar to those of AF Cygni subtype stars, but their spectra are of type G–K I*b* as well as M, and the stars belong to the spherical component

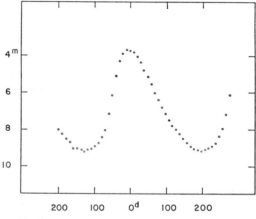

FIG. 7.—Light-curve of Mira (Campbell 1942*a*)

of the Galaxy. It is very likely that a fraction of the RV Tauri type stars also belong to the spherical component of the Galaxy, while other semiregular variables belong to the flat and intermediate components.

Mira type stars (type 2.3) have periods ranging from 70 to between 700 and 800 days. The individual periods of a given star show irregular variations up to 15 per cent of the mean value of the period, and only in a few cases, like R Hydrae and R Aquilae, can the variations in the period be considered regular. The form of the light-curves of a certain star is usually the same from one period to the next, and the ascending branch is usually somewhat shorter than the descending branch, as shown in the light-curve of Mira in Figure 7. For periods shorter than 300 days, the light-curves are smooth, while for periods exceeding 300 days they have a halt or a wave in the ascending branch. For a small number of stars, this wave is so large that the maximum appears to be double. The visual or photographic amplitudes for the individual stars range from 3 to 10 mag., with an average range of 5 mag. According to Pettit and Nicholson (1933), the radiometric amplitudes are small and average 1 mag. According to calculations by Merrill, who adopted a mean amplitude of 5 mag., the temperature range from 2350° K at maximum brightness to 1800° K at minimum brightness accounts for 3 mag. of the variation, while the other 2 mag. are explained by the obscuring effect of the molecular bands, which become stronger at the lower temperatures at minimum light.

The spectra of Mira type stars are usually of type M, but some are of type N or S. They have hydrogen emission lines, which give the spectra such a characteristic appearance that several such stars were discovered from the appearance of the spectra on objective-prism plates rather than from the light-variation. The hydrogen emission lines first appear near the middle of the ascending branch of the light-curve and disappear shortly before minimum brightness, when bright iron and magnesium lines appear. The absorption spectrum shows practically no change with the phase of the light-variations.

TABLE 3

THE PERIOD-LUMINOSITY RELATION FOR MIRA TYPE VARIABLES

	P (DAYS)						
	100	175	200	300	400	500	600
M_{pg}.....	-2.1	-2.5	-2.2	-0.9	0.0	$+0.4$	$+0.6$

The diameters, computed from radiometric observations, reach a minimum near maximum brightness and a maximum near the middle of the descending branch of the light-curve. Relative to the mean value of the diameter, the variations are about one-sixth. However, radial velocities determined from absorption lines show the largest velocity of recession at maximum brightness and the largest velocity of approach at minimum brightness, which is the reverse of what is observed for the cepheids. The observations indicate that the photosphere and the atmosphere apparently do not pulsate with the same phase. The velocities determined from emission lines are smaller than those found from absorption lines by an amount depending on the phase of the light-variations. Soon after maximum brightness the difference ranges from $+10$ to $+30$ km/sec but decreases to near zero at minimum, when the emission lines disappear. The total amplitude of the radial velocity-curve from the emission lines is therefore smaller than the amplitude derived from the absorption lines.

The period-luminosity relation for Mira type stars is the reverse of that for the cepheids because the visual or photographic magnitude decreases with increasing period. According to Kukarkin (1949), the absolute photographic magnitude at maximum is related to the period, as shown in Table 3.

Since the spectral types change from approximately M2.5 for a period of 150 days to M6 for a period of 500 days, the absolute bolometric magnitudes depend very slightly on the length of the period. The exact relation depends on the accuracy of the bolometric corrections and on the effects of the absorption bands and cannot as yet be considered as definitive.

The motions of the Mira type stars show that they do not form a homogeneous system and that they belong to all three components of the Galaxy. Stars with periods exceeding 400 days show a small velocity dispersion and therefore belong to the disk component. For periods of from 90 to 150 days and from 200 to 400 days, the dispersion is larger, and such stars probably belong to the intermediate galactic component. Surprisingly, stars with periods of from 150 to 200 days but seldom those from 200 to 250 days show a very large dispersion, characteristic of the galactic halo. This was discovered by Merrill (1923). Merrill, Deutsch, and Keenan (1962) have shown that the relative abundance of metals varies with the different groups of Mira variables.

Long-period cepheids (type 2.4) have periods that are subject to only very slight variations. The periods of the individual stars range from 1.5 to 80 days. All variables of this type are supergiants of spectral type from F to K, and their spectra and temperatures vary approximately in phase with their brightness. A well-defined correlation between the length of period and the luminosity is characteristic of long-period cepheids. The light-curves of δ Cephei and W Virginis are shown in Figures 8 and 9. The photographic amplitudes of long-period cepheids are approximately 1.5 times larger than the visual amplitudes. The bolometric amplitudes of δ Cephei and η Aquilae were determined by Pettit and Nicholson (1933) from radiometric observations and were found to be equal to 0^m56, which is exactly half the photographic amplitudes (1^m12) as determined from photoelectric observations. The radial velocity-curve of a long-period cepheid is almost a mirror reflection of the light-curve, with the largest velocity of approach at maximum brightness and the largest velocity of recession at minimum brightness. The variation in the radius of the atmosphere found by integrating the radial velocity-curve leads to the conclusion that the radius is largest at the middle of the descending branch of the light-curve and smallest at the middle of the ascending branch. The variations in the radius of the photosphere can easily be found from the light-curve (i.e., luminosity) and the temperature, which varies in phase with the light-variations, with the maximum temperature usually preceding maximum brightness by a few hundredths of a period. It was found that the radius of the photosphere is smallest during maximum brightness and temperature and vice versa. This shows that the photosphere and the atmosphere pulsate with different phases.

Many characteristics of long-period cepheids are related to the length of the period. While the spectral class at maximum brightness is not dependent on the length of the period and averages F6 Ib, the spectral class at minimum is correlated with the length of the period and changes from F8 for periods of 1 or 2 days to K0 for periods of several weeks. The amplitudes of the light-curves, A

(in magnitudes), and the radial velocities, $2K$ (in km/sec), increase statistically with increasing period and can be expressed approximately by the formula

$$2K = 35A_{pg} = 70A_{bol}.$$

Hertzsprung (1926) first detected that the form of the light-curve shows a close dependence on the length of the period. This is shown in Figure 10.

The best-known relation for the long-period cepheids is the period-luminosity relation, which is discussed in detail in chapter 21 by Kraft. According to Kraft, the latest detailed revision gives the following relation between the absolute blue magnitude, M_B, and the period, P:

$$M_B = -1.33 - 2.25 \log P.$$

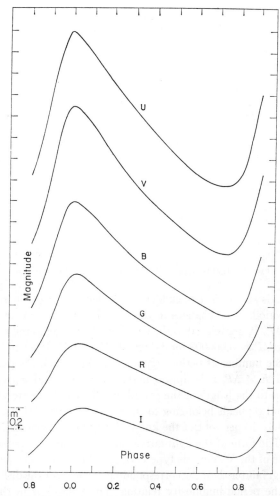

FIG. 8.—Light-curves of δ Cep in six colors (Stebbins 1945)

The zero point in this equation has been derived from the cepheids in the vicinity of the sun and is not the same for the different subsystems (Kukarkin 1954; Sandage 1958).

The period–mean-density relation for the cepheids can be expressed by the formula

$$P\rho^{1/2} = Q.$$

Kraft (1961) finds that Q equals 0.048, if P is expressed in days and ρ in units of the solar density. He also finds that the observations do not exclude the possibility that Q, instead of being constant, has a tendency to increase with increasing period according to the formula $Q = 0.0389 + 0.00146P$. The periods

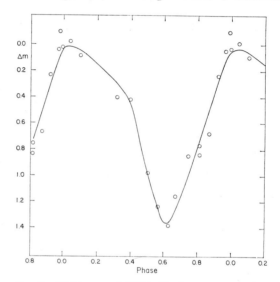

Fig. 9.—Light-curve of W Vir (Gordon and Kron 1949)

of many cepheids are subject to sudden small changes, either increasing or decreasing the periods. The changes in the period, expressed in fractions of the mean period, $\Delta P/P$, are related to the length of the period as follows (Parenago 1956, 1958): $\Delta P/P = 0.000003$ for 3 days; 0.0001 for 10 days; and 0.001 for 50 days. If E is the number of periods (epochs) during which the period remains constant, then $E \times \Delta P/P$ is approximately constant and equals 0.10. The features related to the length of the period mentioned above are valid for ordinary long-period cepheids belonging to the disk component of our Galaxy.

Approximately 10 per cent of the known long-period cepheids belong to the galactic halo. The form of the light-curves for these stars corresponds approximately to those of the W Virginis type variables, but they have shorter periods and are 1.5 mag. fainter than the corresponding cepheids of the disk component, according to the period-luminosity relation. The variations in the periods of

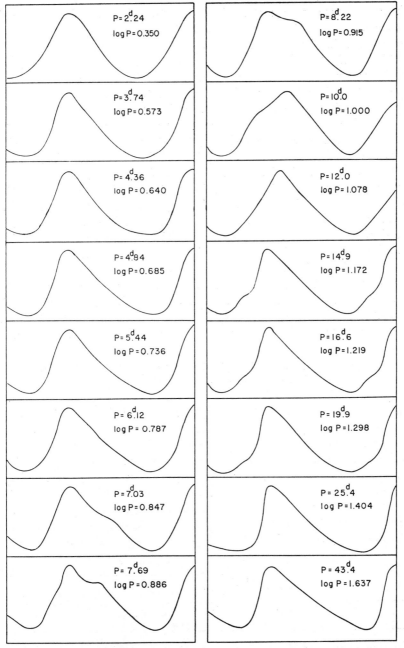

Fig. 10.—Light-curves of long-period cepheids showing the dependence of the form of the light-curve on the length of the period (Parenago and Kukarkin 1947).

these stars are more frequent and larger than those for the cepheids of the disk component, but $E \times \Delta P/P$ is nearly constant and averages 0.54 for the stars which have been investigated so far.

Short-period cepheids (type 2.5), also known as RR Lyrae type or cluster-type variables, have periods between 1.5 hours and 1.5 days. These variables have spectral types between A and F, and their spectra and temperatures vary approximately in phase with the brightness, similar to the long-period cepheids. The absolute magnitudes within each stellar system are surprisingly constant but are not the same in the various systems (Kukarkin 1954; Sandage 1958). The mean absolute photographic magnitude of short-period cepheids, according to the latest determinations, is $+0^m.5$ (Pavlovskaya 1953, and others). The majority of the short-period cepheids in our Galaxy belong to the galactic halo with a nearly spherical symmetry with respect to the center of the Galaxy (Kukarkin 1947), and their motions have an exceedingly large velocity dispersion. Many of these variables are found in globular clusters, occupying a definite place in the color-magnitude diagram. Apparently, there are also some short-period cepheids which belong to the disk component of our Galaxy. The light-curve of RR Lyrae is shown in Figures 11a and 11b. It is very likely that the RR Lyrae type variables with the very short periods (<0.2 day) have low luminosities ($M \sim +3^m$) and belong to the disk population, and Preston (1959) noted that the metal abundances were different in the different groups of these variables.

β Canis Majoris (or β Cephei) type variables (type 2.6) are pulsating stars of spectral types B1–B3 and luminosity classes III–IV. They have periods between 0.15 and 0.25 day and amplitudes of about a tenth of a magnitude. Only 16 stars of this type are known at present. Characteristic of β Canis Majoris type stars is the existence of two very close periods, which differ by only several minutes, leading to a beat frequency. For example, ν Eridani has periods of 4^h10^m and 4^h16^m, with the corresponding amplitudes in the radial-velocity variations of 49 and 22 km/sec, respectively, and with the amplitudes of light-variation $0^m.114$ and $0^m.067$. This leads to a beat with a 7-day period. β Canis Majoris stars have the period-spectrum relation shown in the accompanying table. This relation may be called a period-luminosity relation, but it is the

	SPECTRUM				
	B2 IV	B2 II	B1 IV	B1 III	B1 II–III
Period (day)........	0.165	0.190	0.210	0.247	0.251

change in luminosity class and not the spectral type that should be emphasized. The light-curves and radial-velocity variations show that the pulsations of these stars correspond almost exactly to the theoretical pulsation, if a minimum radius corresponds to maximum brightness. Probably all variables of this type among the bright B stars of the northern sky are known. The light-curves of β Cephei in six colors are shown in Figure 12.

During recent years, variables with small amplitudes in their light-variations of spectral class A with an anomalous metallic-line intensity and periodic variations in light and spectrum have been discovered. They have periods of several days and were named $α^2$ Canis Venaticorum type variables. Besides these, some

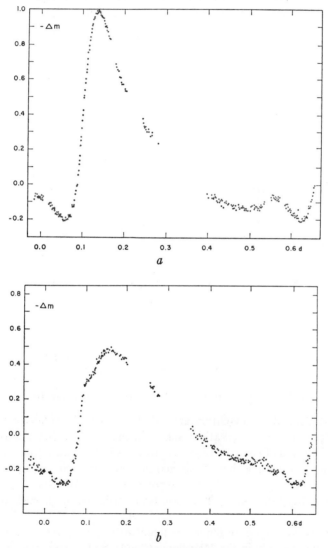

FIG. 11.—Light-curves of RR Lyr at different phases of the secondary period. Each dot represents a single photoelectric observation (Walraven 1949).

stars of spectral type F also have small periodic light and spectrum variations with periods of several hours. These are called δ Scuti type stars and have absolute magnitudes close to +3. It is very likely that we have here also processes of atmospheric pulsations. At present we know very little about these stars and temporarily classify them as "other pulsating stars" (type 2.7).

5.5. Eclipsing Variable Stars

The light-variations of eclipsing variables, as can be inferred from their name, are due to the eclipse of one component of a close double star by the other com-

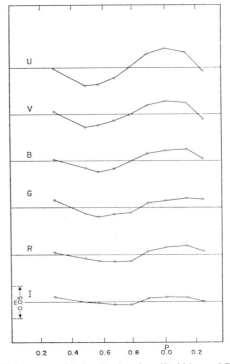

Fig. 12.—Light-curves of β Cep in six colors (Stebbins and Kron 1954)

ponent during their revolution around the center of gravity of the system. Precise photometric observations and detailed studies of their spectra have led to the detection of complex physical processes in their atmospheres and in the envelopes surrounding them. This makes it necessary to consider some of the eclipsing binaries as stars which have not as yet attained a stable configuration. The instability causes small, but observable, variations in the radiation of these stars.

Eclipsing variables are found predominantly in the disk component of our Galaxy and possibly in the Magellanic Clouds. So far, they have not been detected in globular clusters, although there is evidence that some of the eclipsing binaries of our Galaxy belong to the galactic halo. The determination of eclipsing binary orbits is described elsewhere (cf. Vol. **2**, chap. 24).

The following formal classification of eclipsing variables is generally used: (3.1) Algol-type variables, (3.2) β Lyrae type variables, (3.3) W Ursa Majoris type variables.

Algol-type variables (type 3.1) have nearly constant brightness between eclipses, the components having the form of slightly flattened spheroids. The lack of constant brightness between minima may also be caused by physical effects in their atmospheres. The periods of stars of this type range from $4\frac{1}{2}$ hours

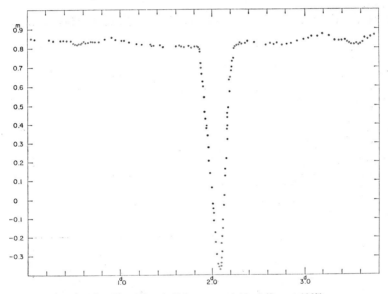

FIG. 13.—Photoelectric light-curve of Algol (Smart 1937)

to many years, depending on the components, which may range from subdwarfs to supergiants. The light-curve of Algol (β Persei) is shown in Figure 13.

β Lyrae type variables (type 3.2) are characterized by continuous light-variations between minima. This is caused by the components having the form of triaxial ellipsoids or more complicated figures, with the result that the area of the projected surfaces on the plane of the sky changes continuously during the process of revolution. The periods are between $\frac{1}{2}$ day and 200 days. The light-curve of DO Cassiopeiae is shown in Figure 14.

W Ursa Majoris type variables (type 3.3) also have continuous light-variations, the secondary minimum hardly differing from the principal minimum. This is due to the fact that the components which are almost contacting triaxial ellipsoids are very closely similar to each other. The periods of stars of this type are between 0.06 and 1 day. The light-curve of VW Cephei is shown in Figure 15.

It should be pointed out that the classification presented here is based on the character of the light-curves and does not account for the physical peculiarities of the components of these close double-star systems.

A classification based on the physical nature of the components seems preferable, like the one proposed by Krat (1937), which is given below:

a) Both components belong to spectral types O–B9. The ellipticity effect of the components is usually large, since dimensions of the components are large relative to the size of the orbit. The orbital periods are several days.

b) The faint component belongs to spectral types A0–F5. The periods are between a fraction of a day and several days. The ellipticity effect is nearly always present.

c) One of the components is a subgiant. The ellipticity effect is small and the

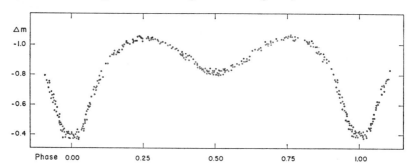

FIG. 14.—Photoelectric light-curve of DO Cas (Schneller and Daene 1952)

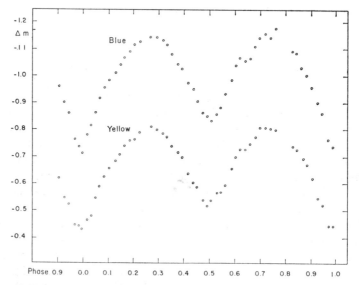

FIG. 15.—Photoelectric light-curves of VW Cep in blue and yellow light (McNamara and Stern 1950).

reflection effect large. The periods are usually longer than 1 day. This is the most numerous group among the stars that have been investigated.

d) Both the components are main-sequence stars, the companion being of spectral types later than F5. The periods range from a fraction of a day to 4 days. The ellipticity and reflection effects are very small.

e) These are W Ursa Majoris type stars. The periods are less than 1 day. Both components are of spectral types between F5 and M.

f) Both components, or at least one of them, are giants. The periods equal several hundred days and more.

Krat's classification can be further detailed as follows: in group *e* some of the stars can be subdwarfs, and in group *f* supergiants are more frequent than giants. In addition, cases of outflow of matter from one or both components should be noted. These cases appear with increasing frequency in the course of a detailed study of eclipsing variables.

§ 6. STATISTICS ON VARIABLE STARS

6.1. THE PROBABILITY OF DISCOVERY

With the exception of a small number of variable stars of special types, which are detected as a result of special measurements with photoelectric photometers, variable stars, as a rule, are discovered by comparing two photographs of the same area of the sky, separated by a certain interval of time, as described at the beginning of this chapter.

In order to determine the completeness of our knowledge of the number of variable stars in a given region of the sky, we must consider the probability of discovering variable stars. Assume that, in the region of the sky being searched for variables by means of comparing two photographs, there are N variable stars and that P is the mean value of the probability of discovering one of the variables by comparing two plates. The expected number of discovered variables after an nth comparison is

$$A_n = N P (1 - P)^{n-1} .$$

The total expected number of variable stars which should be discovered during n comparisons is found as a result of the summation of n terms of the above equation:

$$\sum_1^n A_n = NP \frac{1 - (1 - P)^n}{1 - (1 - P)} = N [1 - (1 - P)^n] .$$

The values of N and P can be determined if the numbers A are known from successive comparisons of independent pairs of plates. In this way Hoffmeister (1933) found that, on the average, the probability of discovery is 0.1 if one pair of plates is compared. By a somewhat different method, van Gent (1933) arrived at a probability of 0.33.

Experience has shown that it can be assumed that a comparison of about fifteen pairs of plates is necessary in order to discover half the variables in a given field and that, for the discovery of 90 per cent, no less than fifty pairs are needed. However, it should be remembered that this is true only for the average types of variable stars and that the discovery of some variables is excluded, such as eclipsing binaries with very long periods and no minima during the interval the photographs were taken or novae if they had no flares. The probability of discovery depends on many factors. For a given length of exposure, each instrument has an optimum range of magnitudes within which variable stars are usually discovered. The probability of discovery depends on the optical qualities of the instruments, the uniformity of the photographs, and the interval of time between the plates. If the interval between the plates is sufficiently large, the probability of discovering Mira type variables is about 0.7, that of discovering cepheids with large amplitudes is 0.2, while the probability of discovering eclipsing and semiregular variables is considerably smaller and in some cases nearly zero.

The usual practice at astronomical observatories dealing with the discovery of variable stars is to compare no less than ten pairs of plates taken over a large interval of time. In this way, sufficiently homogeneous data are derived that can be used for statistical purposes. At any rate, the uniformity with which variables are discovered in areas for which a dozen or more pairs of photographs have been compared makes it possible to make preliminary conclusions in regard to the abundance of different types of variables in relation to galactic co-ordinates, position in space, etc.

6.2. Observed Distribution According to Type

The list on page 361 illustrates the frequency distribution according to type of variable stars which had received final designations prior to 1961. While this distribution does not represent the actual number of variable stars in the Galaxy (see § 6.4), the numbers do indicate the chance of studying variable stars of different types. The larger the number of known variables of a given type, the greater is the chance of finding their space distribution and their kinematic and physical peculiarities.

6.3. Special Surveys of Variable Stars

For some decades after the general application of photography to astronomy, variable stars were usually discovered by comparing only one or two pairs of plates. Although hundreds of variables were discovered in this manner, the data were not statistically uniform. Since the 1920's, special searches for variable stars in selected areas of the sky have been made at various places by means of photography, using instruments of medium size with limiting magnitudes between 15.5 and 17.5. The purpose of these searches was to discover all variable stars within the limiting magnitudes. Such studies received wide application at the Harvard College Observatory and also at the observatories in Leiden, Sonneberg, and Moscow. A search for variables in a small number of areas was made at the observatories of Bergedorf, Hamburg, and Berlin-Babelsberg, at the Simeis and Engelhardt observatories, at the Edinburgh Observatory, at Castel Gandolfo, and at several other places.

1.1. Supernovae	7
1.2. Novae	156
1.3. Nova-like variables	79
1.4. U Geminorum type variables	137
1.5. RW Aurigae type variables	797
1.6. UV Ceti type variables	16
Total number of eruptive variables	1192
2.1. Irregular variables	1427
2.2. Semiregular variables	1848
2.3. Mira type variables	3795
2.4. Long-period cepheids	624
2.5. Short-period cepheids	2561
2.6. β Canis Majoris type variables	16
2.7. Other pulsating variables	15
Total number of pulsating variable stars	10,286
3.1. Algol-type variables	1870
3.2. β Lyrae type variables	312
3.3. W Ursa Majoris type variables	258
3.0. Unclassified eclipsing binaries	448
Total number of eclipsing binaries	2888
0.0. Known variables which have not been studied as yet	1141
Total number of variable stars	15,507

An extensive program on the study of variables in a wide belt of the Milky Way and in selected areas of high galactic latitudes was initiated by Shapley at the Harvard College Observatory and at its station at Bloemfontein in South Africa. Two hundred and six principal fields of variable stars and more than 300 additional fields were selected. These fields, each covering about 80 square degrees, provide valuable data for stars brighter than 16.5 mag. and in some cases as faint as 17.5 mag. By 1957, all or part of the results of 58 fields had been published. At the Harvard Observatory not only newly discovered variables but also those detected previously were investigated. In each field the variables were discovered by comparing more then a dozen pairs of plates, and the data can be considered sufficiently homogeneous for statistical studies.

At the Sonneberg Observatory many areas of the sky, each with an area of about 100 square degrees, have been photographed systematically. These areas are mainly in the plane of the Milky Way or at low galactic latitudes. At present, 53 selected areas have been investigated. The variables were discovered by comparing several dozen pairs of plates, and in each area the new variables, as well as those discovered previously, were studied. In this respect the investigations made by the Sonneberg Observatory were similar to those of the variable-star fields at Harvard, and the data can be considered homogeneous and suitable for statistical studies.

At the Sternberg Astronomical Institute in Moscow and at its station in Crimea, about 100 square degrees surrounding a number of Kapteyn selected areas are photographed systematically. At present, five areas have been investigated. Newly discovered variables, as well as those known previously, are studied in each field, and these results are also suitable for statistical investigations.

At the Leiden Observatory and at its southern station in Johannesburg, South Africa, several hundred photographs of many selected fields of the Milky Way were taken at the initiative of Hertzsprung. Most of the fields were investigated at Leiden, but some fields were studied at Groningen, Louvain, Lwow, and Wroclaw. Usually a comparison was made of photographs taken with intervals of several hours to several days and, only in rare cases, intervals of several weeks or months. Hence mainly short-period cepheids and eclipsing variables were detected. The Leiden material is very complete with respect to variables with rapid light-variations, but it is far from complete for variables with long periods. In addition, studies were made almost exclusively of variables discovered as a result of plate comparisons, and numerous variables already known but not detected during the comparisons were not investigated. For these reasons, the Leiden material can be used only to a limited extent for statistical investigations.

With the exception of the Leiden fields, the material described above can be used to study the distribution of different types of variable stars as related to their position in our Galaxy. Several similarities were found in the distribution of different types of variables in reference to galactic latitude and longitude, and, for the most frequent types, surfaces of equal density in our Galaxy were drawn. As in the case of the long-period cepheids, a considerable inhomogeneity was found for other types. Most long-period cepheids belong to the disk component of our Galaxy, but a considerable fraction forms a well-defined spherical subsystem, similar to the subsystem of globular clusters.

The first studies of very faint variables in small areas were made during the 1940's and 1950's. From photographs taken with the 100-inch reflector covering an area of 0.34 square degree at low galactic latitude, Baade discovered 285 variable stars to a limiting magnitude of 20, which have been studied by Gaposchkin (1955). Oosterhoff (1960) investigated two areas of 0.63 square degree each, also in low galactic co-ordinates, which had been photographed with the 60-inch reflector at the Mount Wilson Observatory. In these areas he discovered 19 and 18 variables, respectively. These data are comparable with the investigations of variables in selected fields described above.

At the present time the study of selected fields of variable stars is being continued with instruments of medium size and with the 48-inch Schmidt telescope at Mount Palomar, and various areas of the sky are being studied at many different observatories. All these investigations will considerably broaden our knowledge concerning the space distribution of variable stars, which is of great importance in connection with the solution of problems on the structure of our Galaxy. They also lead to the possibility of estimating the total number of variable stars of various types.

There are, at the present time, 121 known globular clusters, of which 80 have been searched for variable stars. From these it has been found that the relative abundances of bright variables differ considerably from cluster to cluster. So far, mainly short-period cepheids have been discovered, but it should be noted that a systematic search for variables among the main-sequence stars has not been made and would require plates taken with large telescopes.

A comprehensive study of variables in other galaxies is just at its beginning, but comprehensive data have been obtained on the Large and Small Magellanic Clouds, mainly due to the work of Shapley and his collaborators and by Arp (1960) in recent years. In these galaxies, more than 3000 variables were discovered, and, of these, 1000 have already been investigated. Most of the variables were found to be long-period cepheids. Recently Thackeray (1958) discovered short-period cepheids in the globular clusters in the Magellanic Clouds. A number of Mira type, irregular, and semiregular variables were also found, and about ten novae have been noted. As in the case of globular clusters, only the intrinsically bright stars have been studied, and it is necessary to begin a systematic search for variables among the numerous fainter stars which can be observed only with large telescopes in the Southern Hemisphere.

In more distant galaxies, only the brightest stars can be studied. Predominantly novae, supernovae, long-period cepheids, and some other irregular variables are known in galaxies that have been searched for variable stars, but no exhaustive studies can be made. However, Baade (1956), using photographs of the Andromeda Nebula taken with the 200-inch reflector, was able to reach some interesting conclusions on the variations in the characteristics of cepheids as a function of their distance from the nucleus.

The purpose of the above-mentioned investigations was to study all the variables that could be reached in the selected fields or in isolated stellar systems. On the basis of these investigations, important conclusions can be drawn in regard to distances and structural features of the metagalaxy and the structure and the dynamics of our Galaxy.

Besides the faint variable stars, there are numerous bright variable stars distributed over the whole celestial sphere. Several attempts have been made to study all variables to a certain limiting magnitude. In 1936 the Commission on Variable Stars of the Academy of Sciences of the U.S.S.R. proposed a program to observe all variables brighter than the twelfth photographic magnitude at their maximum brightness. The celestial sphere was divided into 176 regions of equal area, and these were assigned to different investigators. World War II interrupted the completion of this plan, but many regions were studied and hundreds of variables investigated.

After World War II, it became evident that it was better to concentrate this work at a small number of observatories which had large collections of photographs. It would then be possible not only to study all variables brighter than the twelfth magnitude but also to make a systematic search for new bright variable stars. At the present time, bright variable stars are being studied at observatories in Sonneberg, Dushanbe (Stalinabad), Odessa, Bamberg, and Moscow and at the private observatories of R. Weber in Paris and L. Romano in Treviso. The Harvard College Observatory is also participating in this work, and it is expected that these studies will be completed in the near future.

Toward the end of the 1930's, investigations of variable stars brighter than the tenth magnitude at maximum brightness were started at the Harvard College Observatory by S. Gaposchkin and C. Payne-Gaposchkin (1946——). The results of this valuable contribution contain data on 1504 variable stars. However, it is unfortunate that most of the variables investigated already had final designations and that hundreds of suspected variables were left unstudied. This shortcoming will be corrected when the work mentioned in the previous paragraphs is completed.

The attempts which have been made to carry out complete surveys of variables can be summarized as follows:

1. A sufficiently complete survey of variables to a limiting magnitude between 16 and 17 has been attained in about 60 widely distributed selected fields. These investigations have already furnished very valuable data in the study of the structure of our Galaxy, and the work is being continued.

2. A similar survey of variables to a limiting magnitude between 18 and 20 has also been made in a limited number of small fields, and these investigations will be expanded considerably in the near future.

3. Many globular clusters and the nearby galaxies have been searched for variable stars and have contributed valuable information. This work will be continued on an expanded scale.

4. Homogeneous data on variables brighter than 12 mag. over the whole sky will soon be available.

6.4. ESTIMATE OF THE TOTAL NUMBER OF VARIABLES IN THE GALACTIC SYSTEM

For some types of variable stars it has been possible to study the variations in the space density over a large region of the solar neighborhood in a direction perpendicular to the galactic plane and along the radius vector from the galactic center. As a rule, the space density is well represented by functions of the form

$$D(z) = D_0 e^{-z} \quad \text{or} \quad D(R) = D_0 e^{-R},$$

where D_0 is the density in the solar neighborhood, z the distance from the galactic plane, and R the distance in this plane from the galactic center. Thus each galactic subsystem of variable stars of a given type can be characterized by two gradients:

$$\frac{\partial \log D}{\partial R} = -m, \quad \frac{\partial \log D}{\partial z} = -l.$$

Parenago (1948) showed that these gradients can be used to estimate the total number of objects of a given type in our Galaxy. He deduced the following expression for the total number of objects:

$$N = \frac{1.3 D_0}{m^2 l} 10^{R_0 m},$$

where D_0 is the density in the solar neighborhood and R_0 the distance of the sun from the galactic center.

The computed number of variable stars of the types for which determination of the gradient was possible, is as follows: novae, 1.0×10^6; semiregular and irregular variables, 7.0×10^4; Mira type, 1.4×10^6; long-period cepheids, 0.5×10^5; short-period cepheids, 1.7×10^5. It should be emphasized that these are only rough estimates, since the variation in the gradients with the galactic co-ordinates has been accounted for only approximately.

MONOGRAPHS ON VARIABLE STARS*

HAGEN, J. G.	1913–	
	1921	*Die veränderlichen Sterne* (Freiburg: Herder), Part I.
FURNESS, C. E.	1915	*An Introduction to the Study of Variable Stars* (Boston and New York: Houghton Mifflin Co.).
SCHILLER, K.	1923	*Die Einführung in das Studium der veränderlichen Sterne* (Leipzig: J. A. Barth).
STEIN, J.	1923	*Die veränderlichen Sterne* (Freiburg: Herder), Vol. **2**, Part II.
LUDENDORFF, H.	1928	"Die veränderlichen Sterne," *Hdb. d. Ap.*, (Berlin: Springer), Vol. **6**.
	1936	Appendix, *Hdb. d. Ap.*, (Berlin: Springer), Vol. **7**.
STRATTON, F. J. M.	1928	"Novae," *Hdb. d. Ap.* (Berlin: Springer), Vol. **6**.
	1936	Appendix, *Hdb. d. Ap.* (Berlin: Springer), Vol. **7**.
BRUGGENCATE, P. TEN	1931	"Die veränderlichen Sterne," *Ergebn. d. exakt. Naturwiss.* (Berlin: Springer), Vol. **10**.
	1933	Russian translation, Moscow and Leningrad.

* Arranged chronologically.

SIEDENTOPF, H. 1932 "Untersuchungen zur Theorie der periodischen Veränderlichen," *A.N.*, **245**, 85–118.

JACCHIA, L. 1933 "Le Stelle variabili," *Pub. Bologna Obs.*, **2**, 173 (No. 14).

VORONTSOV-VELYAMINOV, B. 1935 *New Stars and Galactic Nebulae* (in Russian) (Moscow and Leningrad: United Scientific and Technical Press).

KUKARKIN, B. V., and PARENAGO, P. P. 1937 *Physical Variable Stars* (in Russian) (Moscow and Leningrad: United Scientific and Technical Press).

MERRILL, P. W. 1938 *The Nature of Variable Stars* (New York: Macmillan Co.).

PAYNE-GAPOSCHKIN, C., and GAPOSCHKIN, S. 1938 *Variable Stars* ("Harvard Observatory Monographs" [Cambridge: Harvard Observatory]).

PARENAGO, P. P., and KUKARKIN, B. V. 1938 *Variable Stars and Their Method of Observation* (in Russian) (Moscow and Leningrad).

1947 Second edition (in Russian) (Moscow and Leningrad: State Press for Technical and Theoretical Literature).

1953 Czech translation (Prague: Nakladetelstoi Ceskolovenske Akademie Ved.).

MARTYNOV, D. YA. 1939 *Stellar Variability*, Vol. **2**: *Eclipsing Variables* (in Russian) (Moscow and Leningrad).

MERRILL, P. W. 1940 *Spectra of Long-Period Variable Stars* (Chicago: University of Chicago Press).

CAMPBELL, L., and JACCHIA, L. 1941 *The Story of Variable Stars* (Philadelphia: Blakiston Co.).

CECCHINI, G., and GRATTON, L. 1942 *Le Stelle nuove* (Milan: Pub. Roy. Astr. Obs.).

KOPAL, Z. 1946 *An Introduction to the Study of Eclipsing Variables* ("Harvard Observatory Monographs" [Cambridge: Harvard Observatory]).

FLORJA, N. F., KUKARKIN, B. V., MARTINOFF, D. J., PARENAGO, P. P., TSESEVICH, V. P., and ZVEREV, M. S. 1947 *Methods of Observing and Investigating Variable Stars* (in Russian) (Moscow and Leningrad: State Press for Scientific and Theoretical Literature).

KUKARKIN, B. V. 1948 *Variable Stars* (in Russian) ("Progress of Astronomy," Vol. **4** [Moscow and Leningrad]).

VORONTSOV-VELYAMINOV, B.	1948	*Gaseous Nebulae and the Novae* (in Russian) (Moscow and Leningrad: Publishing House of the Academy of Sciences of the U.S.S.R.).
	1953	German translation (Berlin).
KUKARKIN, B. V.	1949	*Investigations of the Structure and Evolution of the Stellar Systems on the Basis of Variable Stars* (Moscow: State Press for Technical and Theoretical Literature).
	1953	Czech translation (Prague: Nakladatelstoi Ceskolovenske Akademie Ved.).
	1954	German translation (Berlin: Akademie Verlag).
PAYNE-GAPOSCHKIN, C.	1954	*Variable Stars and Galactic Structure* (London: University of London, Athlone Press).
AMBARTSUMIAN, V. A. (ed.)	1955	*Non-stable Stars: Fourth Cosmogonical Conference 26–29 Oct. 1954 at Moscow* (Moscow: Publishing House of the Academy of Sciences of the U.S.S.R.).
HERBIG, G. H. (ed.)	1957	*Non-stable Stars: Symposium No. 3 of the International Astronomical Union at Dublin* (London: Cambridge University Press).
PAYNE-GAPOSCHKIN, C.	1957	*The Galactic Novae* (Amsterdam: North Holland Publishing Co.; New York: Interscience Publishers).
ARAKELIAN, M. (ed.)	1957	*The Non-stable Stars: Symposium of 20–22 Sept. 1956 at Byurakan* (Erevan: Publishing House of the Academy of Sciences of the Armenian S.S.R.).
PAYNE-GAPOSCHKIN, C.	1958	"The Novae," *Hdb. d. Phys.* (Berlin, Göttingen, and Heidelberg: Springer), Vol. **51**.
LEDOUX, P., and WALRAVEN, TH.	1958	"Variable Stars," *Hdb. d. Phys.* (Berlin, Göttingen, and Heidelberg: Springer), Vol. **51**.
ZWICKY, F.	1958	"Supernovae," *Hdb. d. Phys.* (Berlin, Göttingen, and Heidelberg: Springer), Vol. **51**.
WENZEL, W.	1961	*Einige Eigenschaften der unregelmässiger veränderlichen Sterne geringer Leuchtkraft* (Pub. Sonneberg Obs., Vol. **5**, No. 1).

REFERENCES

AHNERT, P.	1958	*Mitt. veränderliche Sterne* (Sonneberg), No. 373.
ARP, H. C.	1960	*A.J.*, **65**, 404.
BAADE, W.	1956	*Mitt. Astr. Gesellsch.*, 1955, p. 51.
BAYER, J.	1603	*Uranometria*
BUSCOMBE, W., GASCOIGNE, S. C. B., and VAUCOULEURS, G. DE	1954	*Suppl. Australian J. Sci.*, **17**, 3 (No. 3).
CAMPBELL, L.	1942a	*Harvard Repr.*, No. 250, p. 12.

	1942*b*	*Ibid.*, p. 35.
	1943	*Ibid.*, No. 259, p. 20.
DUGAN, R. S.	1934	*Princeton Contr.*, No. 15.
GAPOSCHKIN, S. I.	1955	*Peremennye Zvezdy*, **10**, 337.
GENT, H. VAN	1933	*B.A.N.*, **7**, 21.
GORDON, K. C., and		
KRON, G. E.	1949	*Ap. J.*, **109**, 178.
GRANT, G.	1955	*Ap. J.*, **122**, 566.
HAGEN, J. G.	1889–	
	1927	*Atlas Stellarum Variabilium*, Ser. I–VII.
HERBIG, G. H.	1952	*J.R.A.S. Canada*, **46**, 222.
HERTZSPRUNG, E.	1912	*A.N.*, **192**, 261.
	1926	*B.A.N.*, **3**, 115.
HOFFMEISTER, C.	1933	*A.N.*, **250**, 401.
HUNGER, K., and		
KRON, G. E.	1957	*Pub. A.S.P.*, **69**, 347.
JOY, A. H.	1945	*Ap. J.*, **102**, 169.
	1956	*Ibid.*, **124**, 317.
KHOLOPOV, P. N.	1958	*A.J.*, *U.S.S.R.*, **35**, 434.
KOPYLOV, I. M.	1954	*Doklady Acad. Nauk U.S.S.R.*, **99**, 515.
	1955*a*	*Izv. Crimean Ap. Obs.*, **13**, 76.
	1955*b*	*A.J.*, *U.S.S.R.*, **32**, 48.
KRAFT, R. P.	1961	*Ap. J.*, **133**, 39.
	1962	*Ap. J.*, **135**, 408.
	1963	Private communication.
KRAT, V. A.	1937	*Pub. Astr. Obs. Engelhardt*, No. 19, p. 3.
KRZEMINSKY, W.	1962	*Pub. A.S.P.*, **74**, 66.
KUKARKIN, B. V.	1947	*A.J.*, *U.S.S.R.*, **24**, 269.
	1949	*Peremennye Zvezdy*, **7**, 57.
	1954	*Astr. Circ. Acad. Sci.*, *U.S.S.R.*, No. 155, p. 12.
KUKARKIN, B. V., and		
PARENAGO, P. P.	1934	*Veränderliche Sterne* (Gorki), **4**, 249.
KUKARKIN, B. V.,		
PARENAGO, P. P.,		
EFREMOV, YU. I., and		
KHOLOPOV, P. N.	1958	*General Catalog of Variable Stars* (2d ed.; Moscow: Publishing House of the Academy of Sciences of the U.S.S.R.).
LEAVITT, H. S.	1908	*Harvard Ann.*, **60**, 87 (No. 4).
McLAUGHLIN, D. B.	1945	*Pub. A.S.P.*, **57**, 69.
McNAMARA, H., and		
STERN, H. V.	1950	*Pub. A.S.P.*, **62**, 114.
MARTYNOV, D. YA.	1934	*Bull. Engelhardt Obs.*, No. 2, p. 3.
MERRILL, J. E.	1950	*Princeton Contr.*, No. 23.
MERRILL, P. W.	1923	*Ap. J.*, **78**, 320.
MERRILL, P. W.,		
DEUTSCH, A. J., and		
KEENAN, P. C.	1962	*Ap. J.*, **136**, 21.

OOSTERHOFF, P. TH.	1960	Private communication.
PARENAGO, P. P.	1948	*A.J., U.S.S.R.*, **25**, 123.
	1949	*Peremennye Zvezdy*, **7**, 122.
	1950	*Ibid.*, p. 169.
	1954*a*	*Trudy Astr. Inst. Sternberg*, **25**, 1.
	1954*b*	*Ibid.*, p. 214.
	1956	*Astr. Circ. Acad. Sci., U.S.S.R.*, No. 173, p. 11.
	1958	*Peremennye Zvezdy*, **11**, 236.
PARENAGO, P. P., and KUKARKIN, B. V.	1947	Monograph: *The Variable Stars and Their Method of Observation* (in Russian) (Moscow: State Press for Technical and Theoretical Literature), p. 53.
PAVLOVSKAYA, E. D.	1953	*Peremennye Zvezdy*, **9**, 349.
PAYNE-GAPOSCHKIN, C.	1946	*Ap. J.*, **104**, 362.
PAYNE-GAPOSCHKIN, C., and GAPOSCHKIN, S. I.	1946	*Harvard Ann.*, Vol. **115** and **118**.
PETIT, M.	1957	*Peremennye Zvezdy*, **12**, 13.
PETTIT, E., and NICHOLSON, S. B.	1933	*Ap. J.*, **78**, 320.
PICKERING, E. C.	1912	*Harvard Circ.*, No. 173.
PRESTON, J. W.	1959	*Ap. J.*, **130**, 507.
SANDAGE, A.	1958	*Ap. J.*, **127**, 513.
SAWYER, H. B.	1939	*Pub. David Dunlap Obs.* (Toronto), Vol. **1**, No. 4.
	1955	*Ibid.*, **2**, 33.
SCHNELLER, H., and DAENE, H.	1952	*A.N.*, **281**, 25.
SEVERNY, A. B.	1948	*Izv. Crimean Ap. Obs.*, Vol. **1**, Part 2, p. 3.
SHAPLEY, H.	1918	*Ap. J.*, **48**, 154.
	1930	*Harvard Mono.*, No. 2.
SMART, W. M.	1937	*M.N.*, **97**, 404.
STEBBINS, J.	1945	*Ap. J.*, **101**, 49.
STEBBINS, J., and KRON, G. E.	1954	*Ap. J.*, **120**, 192.
STRAND, K. AA.	1958	*Ap. J.*, **128**, 14.
THACKERAY, A. D.	1955	*M.N.*, **118**, 117.
TSESEVICH, V. P.	1947	Compendium: *Variable Stars* (in Russian), **3**, 494.
VOROBYEVA, V. A.	1960	*Peremennye Zvezdy*, **13**, 72.
VORONTSOV-VELYAMINOV, B. A.	1940	*Ap. J.*, **92**, 283.
WALKER, M. F.	1954	*Pub. A.S.P.*, **66**, 230.
	1956	*Ap. J.*, **123**, 68.
	1958	*Ibid.*, **127**, 319.
	1962	*Information Bulletin on Variable Stars* (Commission 27 of the I.A.U.), No. 2.
WALRAVEN, TH.	1949	*B.A.N.*, **11**, 19.
WOOD, F. B.	1953	*Pub. U. Pennsylvania, Astr. Ser.*, Vol. **8**.

CHAPTER 19

Empirical Data on Eclipsing Binaries

FRANK BRADSHAW WOOD

Flower and Cook Observatory, University of Pennsylvania, Philadelphia, Pennsylvania

§ 1. HISTORY

THE systematic study of eclipsing variables begins with the discovery by Goodricke (1783) of the nature and period of light-variations of Algol and his suggestion that the observed changes could "hardly be accounted for otherwise than either by the interposition of a large body revolving round Algol, or some kind of motion of its own, whereby part of its body, covered with spots or such like matter, is periodically turned towards the earth." An earlier discovery of the light-variation by Montanari and Maraldi was known to Goodricke only after he had made an independent discovery and found the general nature of the variation and the period.

Until nearly the end of the nineteenth century, discovery of new systems proceeded slowly. The development of photography gave tremendous impetus to the discovery and classification of variables and to the derivation of light-elements. The few theoretical studies of this time were hampered by the complexity of the relations between the light-changes and the elements of the system and by lack of adequate observational material. The development of more precise observing techniques and the practice of observing the entire light-curve were complemented by the theoretical work of Russell (1912*a*, *b*). This presented a general theory which permits the calculation of the eclipse and orbital elements from the light-curve in any given case. It is essentially on this theoretical treatment that all later work has been based.

Beginning about 1941, spectrographic and photometric observations began to show effects not explicable in terms of the older theory and indicated that, in some of the earlier cases, the complications in the light- and velocity-curves were really caused by the stars and were not a result of observational errors. It is clear now that many of these complications are associated with circumstellar streams of gas, complex in character and unstable or metastable in nature. Much stimulating work leading to better understanding of these systems has already been done (e.g., Sahade *et al.* 1959).

It is well known that from studies of light- and velocity-curves of eclipsing systems it is possible to derive such fundamental properties as radii, masses, and densities. An excellent summary of how these are obtained has been given by Pierce (1951) and a much more detailed description by Russell and Merrill (1952). Merrill (1950, 1953) has published tables and nomographs for use with various coefficients of limb darkening. These permit rapid computation of the initial elements and demonstrate graphically the geometry of the eclipse in any given case. Plaut (1950, 1953) has published solutions for all known systems brighter than magnitude 8.5. Mergentaler (1950) and O'Connell (1951) have discussed systems with asymmetric light-curves.

Other properties connected with the study of stellar atmospheres which can be derived from the light-curve include coefficients of limb darkening, "reflection" or reradiation effects, and in a few cases stellar atmospheric extinction effects found when a relatively small star passes behind the tenuous outer atmosphere of a late-type supergiant. In rare cases, when the period of rotation of the line of apsides of an elliptical orbit can be measured, it is even possible to determine the degree of central condensation of at least one of the components. One of the most active fields of study at present is the evolution of close double-star systems.

§ 2. CATALOGUES AND PUBLICATIONS

The *Second General Catalogue of Variable Stars* (Kukarkin *et al.* 1958) lists 14,708 variable stars which have been named. Many known variables have not yet been named, and discovery of new variables is continuing. This indicates clearly that the problem of assembling and disseminating variable-star data is a major one. For many purposes, eclipsing variables are included with other types of variables; the pertinent catalogues and other publications are described in chapter 18. In addition, however, there exist catalogues and publications dealing solely with eclipsing variables. Historically, three centers have been active in this type of work. One of these is at the Kraków Observatory. Another was at the Princeton University Observatory until 1950, when it was transferred to the Flower and Cook Observatory of the University of Pennsylvania. A third is at the Engelhardt Observatory, near Kazan. More recently, Commission 42 of the International Astronomical Union has taken an active part in the distribution of information and co-ordination of work in the field.

The work at Kraków was started by Banachiewicz in 1925. The publication, *Rocznik Astronomiczny Obserwatorium, International Supplement*, appears annually. Edited now by Kordylewski, this presents ephemerides for a large number of eclipsing variables. Currently observed times of minima also appeared in the editions from 1949 to 1959. From 1960 on, these will be published in separate *Eclipsing Variables Circulars*, issued a few times each year. The

1960 edition of the *Rocznik* gives a detailed list of almost 4000 known or suspected eclipsing binaries. In addition to the catalogues of the literature and observed minima, the archives of the Kraków Observatory contain about 150,000 estimates of brightness from 1920 to the present; these are being continued with the application of photoelectric methods in some cases. Szafraniec (1959, 1961) has published most of the observations for the years 1920–1950. Finally, a catalogue is being prepared at Kraków which will give the residuals between observed minima and those computed from linear elements. About 100 stars are thus being studied for variation of period.

At Princeton University Observatory, under the supervision of Dugan, a catalogue was prepared in 1922 listing all the published material concerning eclipsing systems, together with abstracts of this material. Dugan kept the catalogue abreast of published (and much unpublished) material until his death in 1940. He used the material in it to compile the first edition of *A Finding List for Observers of Eclipsing Variables* (Dugan 1934). From 1940 to 1950 the catalogue was maintained by Pierce, who published the second *Finding List* (Pierce 1947). At the untimely death of Pierce in 1950, the catalogue and associated material were transferred to the Flower and Cook Observatory of the University of Pennsylvania. In 1953, the third edition of the *Finding List* was published (Wood 1953). The purpose of these publications is not that of a general catalogue or a bibliographical collection but rather, as Dugan first stated, "as an aid to observers of eclipsing variables in selecting a program rapidly, easily, and without exasperation." The finding lists contain the basic observational data for each system—position, brightness, ranges, spectra, light-elements, etc.—together with references to charts, comparison stars, and the more important earlier light- and velocity-curves, solutions, and period studies. It is limited to stars brighter than the thirteenth magnitude. The next edition was published in 1963 (Koch *et al.* 1963). The card catalogue contains a much more extensive collection of material on all eclipsing stars; information from it is supplied on request.

The Engelhardt Observatory also continues a bibliographical card catalogue of eclipsing stars. As of January 1, 1959, this contained 3225 stars, including suspected variables, with a total of 38,374 brief abstracts. For the same date, the catalogue of spectroscopic binaries contained 2235 systems, with 17,042 references. From this the Engelhardt astronomers have published a bibliographical catalogue of spectroscopic binaries from 0 to 6 hours of right ascension, (Martynov 1961).

At the 1958 meetings of the International Astronomical Union, steps were taken to make Commission 42 (Étoiles Doubles Photométriques) active in the collection and dissemination of information concerning the increasing amount of work being done in the field. Active work of the commission had started in a smaller way in 1955, when, under the leadership of O'Connell and Merrill, a co-operative arrangement was established among the various photometric and spectrographic observers of the eclipses of VV Cephei and ε Aurigae. The Flower and Cook Observatory served as co-ordinating center for this experiment. The arrangement resulted in a great deal of informal exchange of data; more formally, nine information bulletins were issued and distributed to all participants and to all others who expressed interest. The intercommunication between spectrographic and photometric observers was especially fortunate and eliminated the earlier practice by which each observer usually either discussed his own observations without knowledge of other data or else waited for years for this finally to appear in published form.

In 1958, four systems were selected for similar co-operative programs. In each case, the principal criterion was that the advantages of continued observation over a specified interval outweighed the difficulties inherent in trying to combine different sets of photometric observations. The systems selected are ζ Aurigae, VW Cephei, β Lyrae, and AR Cassiopeiae, with co-ordinating centers at Tølløse, Leiden, Stockholm, for the first three, respectively, and with that of the last currently uncertain. Preliminary results for β Lyrae and VW Cephei indicate success for these programs. In addition to these specific programs, an astronomer completing a light- or velocity-curve of any eclipsing system is requested to send the results in advance of publication directly to the president of Commission 42.

§ 3. PERIOD AND PERIOD CHANGES

It is now thoroughly established that in many eclipsing systems the periods are subject to change. In rare cases the plot against epoch of the differences between observed and computed minima is sinusoidal, with the residuals from primary and secondary changing in phase and by the same amount. These cases can be explained by changing light-time as the system moves around the center of mass of a triple or multiple system of which it is a part. In other cases, a sinusoidal variation of residuals is found, but the secondary displacement is in the direction opposite to that of the primary. These can be explained by the rotation of the lines of apsides of elliptical orbits. The details of the theory, worked out by Cowling (1938) and Sterne (1939) have been applied by Russell (1939) and others to individual systems. The basic relation is

$$\frac{P}{P'} = C_1 \left(\frac{R_1}{a}\right)^5 \left(1 + \frac{16\,\mathfrak{M}_2}{\mathfrak{M}_1}\right) + C_2 \left(\frac{R_2}{a}\right)^5 \left(1 + \frac{16\,\mathfrak{M}_1}{\mathfrak{M}_2}\right).$$

Here P is the orbital period and P' the period of rotation of the line of apsides; R_1 and R_2 are the radii of the stars and a the distance between their centers; $\mathfrak{M}_1$ and $\mathfrak{M}_2$ are the masses. The constants, C_1 and C_2, depend on the distribution of density in the stars. The relation does not hold for large orbital eccentricities or for stars nearly in contact. De Kort (1956) has suggested a method of determining the apsidal period when observations have continued over only a fraction of it.

Many eclipsing systems show period changes which do not follow any regular pattern. The first general study of such changes was made by Dugan and Wright (1939). Their general conclusion that in many systems sudden lengthening or shortening of the periods can occur in an unpredictable and apparently erratic manner has been confirmed by all later investigations. In some cases the period varies almost continuously; in others a long interval of constant period (as closely as can be observed) is followed by one or more relatively sudden changes. Figure 1 shows a plot against epoch of the residuals between observed and computed times of minimum for R CMa, from recent work by Koch. Examples for W UMa type systems have been summarized by Binnendijk (1957).

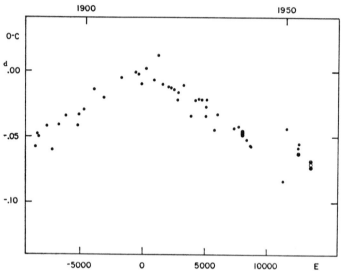

Fig. 1.—Residuals from linear elements of R CMa, as given by Koch. Ordinates are differences between observed and computed times of minimum in fractions of a day; abscissae are epochs. The six large points toward the right represent photoelectric determinations of primary; the large open circle is a photoelectric determination of secondary. Information concerning the other points is summarized in *Princeton Contr.*, No. 21, p. 23.

These sudden changes are of the general order of 10^{-6} of the period but in rare cases may be appreciably greater. They offer some difficulties in interpretation. Early attempts by Markowitz (1933) and Kuiper (1941) provide mechanisms for changes in one direction only, but it is soundly established by observation that changes can occur in either direction. On the basis of the data available in 1950, Wood (1950) noted that, in systems showing such changes, one component was near the surface of dynamical instability and showed that a possible cause could be the violent ejection of matter from localized regions of the stellar surface. Svechnikov (1955) has applied these ideas in a more detailed study of four systems and has estimated the luminosity of the gaseous envelopes formed. He has shown that the calculated variations of light and the intensity of the emission lines are not in conflict with the observational data. Huang (1956) has presented a more elaborate treatment, and Kwee (1958) has investigated the effect of mass transfer between the components; to date, no mechanism other than mass ejection has promised solution. However, much more work is required before we can understand the details of such variation.

§ 4. TABLES OF ECLIPSING BINARIES

The following tables have been compiled from the Card Catalogue of Eclipsing Variables maintained at the University of Pennsylvania. The headings are

TABLE 1

SYSTEMS WITH LIMB DARKENING COMPUTED FROM
RELIABLE PHOTOMETRIC OBSERVATIONS

System	Spectral Type	Computed Limb Darkening	λ	References
β Aur........	A2 IV	0.57 ± 0.17	4500	H. N. Russell, $Ap.\ J.$, 102, 1, 1945
AR Aur......	B9 V	$.49 \pm 0.08$	4500	C. M. Huffer and O. J. Eggen, $Ap.$
	B9 V	$.52 \pm 0.09$		$J.$, 106, 1947
YZ Cas.......	A3	$.49 \pm 0.04$	4500	G. E. Kron, $Lick\ Obs.\ Bull.$, 19, 59,
	[F5]	$.45 \pm 0.11$		1939
		$.33 \pm 0.03$	6700	$Ap.\ J.$, 96, 173, 1942
		$.48 \pm 0.11$		
α CrB........	A0 V	$.20 \pm 0.06$	7230	G. E. Kron and K. C. Gordon, $Ap.$
				$J.$, 118, 55, 1953
TW Dra......	A5	$.11 \pm 0.12$	4370	R. L. Baglow, $David\ Dunlap\ Pub.$,
		(alt. sol. 0.25)		2, 1, 1952
		$.27 \pm 0.11$	5100	
		(alt. sol. 0.37)		
RR Lyn......	A6s	$.64$	4500	S. Nekrasova and K. Irshenko, $Peremennye\ Zvezdy$ ("Variable Stars"), 5, 323, 1940, from Huffer's p.e. observations
β Per........	B7 V	$.76$	4340	D. Chalonge, L. Divan, and G. Cayrel de Strobel, $Contr.\ Inst.\ Ap.$, Ser. A, No. 167, 1954
		$.76$	4500	G. Cayrel de Strobel, D. Chalonge, and L. Divan, $Mem.\ Soc.\ Astr.\ Ital.$, 26, 257, 1955 ($Assiago\ Contr.$, No. 61)
AG Per......	B4	$.58$	4500	S. Nekrasova and K. Irshenko, $Peremennye\ Zvezdy$ ("Variable Stars"), 5, 323, 1940
X Tri........	A3	$.52 \pm 0.10$	4250	W. Krat, $Engelhardt\ Bull.$ (Kazan),
	[G5]	$.62 \pm 0.20$		No. 3, p. 3, 1934
		$.33$	5500	From Jordan's pg* and Dugan's v*
		$.21$		observations
AH Vir......	K0	$.73 – 0.80$	3950	M. Kitamura, H. Tanabe, and T.
		$.64 – 0.73$	4750	Nakamura, $Pub.\ Astr.\ Soc.\ Ja$-
		$.57 – 0\ 66$	5600	pan, 9, 119, 1957
RS Vul.......	B5 V	Between 0.18 and 0.27	5100	R. L. Baglow, $David\ Dunlap\ Pub.$, 2, 1, 1952
		$.44*$	5500	W. Krat and S. Nekrasova, $Pere$-
		$0.47*$	4250	$mennye\ Zvezdy$ ("Variable Stars"), 4, 409, 1935, from Baker's pg* and Dugan's v* observations

* Computed from the light-curve between eclipses.

TABLE 2

Systems Showing Apsidal Motion

System	P' (Years)	$(P'/P) \times 10^{-3}$	e	Source
GL Car.......	25	3.8	0.157	U. van Wijk, J. B. Rogerson, and A. Skumanich, *A.J.*, **60**, 95, 1955
AR Cas.......	413	24.9	.247	R. M. Petrie, *A.J.*, **51**, 22, 1944
V346 Cen.....	160	9.2	.15	R. S. Dugan and F. W. Wright, *Princeton Contr.*, No. 19, p. 10, 1939; H. N. Russell, *Ap. J.*, **90**, 648, 1939
Y Cyg........	47	5.7	.144	R. S. Dugan, *Princeton Contr.*, No. 12, 1931
V477 Cyg.....	436	67.8	.235	J. A. Pearce, *Pub. Dom. Ap. Obs., Victoria*, **10**, 447, 1958
CO Lac.......	35	8.4	.028	W. Zonn, *Torun Bull.*, **9**, 18, 1950
GN Nor......	400	25.6	.18	J. de Kort, *Ric. Astr.*, **3**, 119, 1954
δ Ori A.......	113	7.2	.085	P. Pismis, G. Haro, and O. Struve, *Ap. J.*, **111**, 509, 1950
AG Per.......	72	13.0	.067	J. Ashbrook, *A.J.*, **55**, 2, 1949
YY Sgr.......	312–360	46.7	.163	G. Keller and D. N. Limber, *Ap. J.*, **113**, 637, 1951
V523 Sgr.....	≥214	≥33.6	≥ .17	J. de Kort, *B.A.N.*, **9**, 273, 1942
V526 Sgr.....	184	35.0	.256	D. J. K. O'Connell, *M.N.*, **108**, 334, 1948
TX UMa.....	32	3.8	.024	F. B. Wood, *Princeton Contr.*, No. 21, p. 18, 1946
AO Vel.......	50	11.5	.12	P. Th. Oosterhoff and C. J. van Houten, *B.A.N.*, **11**, 63, 1949
α Vir........	133	12.1	.154	O. Struve, J. Sahade, S. S. Huang, and V. Zebergs, *Ap. J.*, **128**, 310, 1958
HD 321230...	566	59.6	0.506	T. E. Sterne, *M.N.*, **99**, 666, 1939

TABLE 3

Systems Showing Variable Period, Other Than That Caused by Apsidal Motion

RT	And	DO	Cas	V548	Cyg	UW	Lac	RT	Per
TT	And	EN	Cas	W	Del	VX	Lac	RW	Per
UU	And	GT	Cas	TT	Del	AR	Lac	ST	Per
WZ	And	GU	Cas	Z	Dra	Y	Leo	WY	Per
XZ	And	RR	Cen	RR	Dra	RW	Leo	XZ	Per
AB	And	SV	Cen	SX	Dra	T	LMi	Y	Psc
BX	And	LT	Cen	TW	Dra	RV	Lyr	RT	Scl
XZ	Aql	U	Cep	S	Eql	BV	Lyr	V467	Sco
V342	Aql	VW	Cep	UX	Eri	β	Lyr	μ¹	Sco
ST	Aqr	XX	Cep	YY	Eri	UX	Mon	RS	Sct
RW	Ara	CQ	Cep	RX	Gem	GM	Nor	U	Sge
RS	Ari	SS	Cet	AL	Gem	U	Oph	RS	Sgr
RZ	Aur	R	CMa	AY	Gem	SW	Oph	BN	Sgr
AM	Aur	RY	Cnc	BO	Gem	V502	Oph	BQ	Sgr
β	Aur	TU	Cnc	Z	Her	BM	Ori	RW	Tau
TY	Boo	TY	Cnc	SZ	Her	EQ	Ori	λ	Tau
UW	Boo	U	CrB	TU	Her	ER	Ori	X	Tri
44i	Boo	RS	CVn	TX	Her	FH	Ori	UX	UMa
Y	Cam	SW	Cyg	UX	Her	FL	Ori	W	UMa
SV	Cam	SY	Cyg	AK	Her	U	Peg	S	Vel
RW	Cap	UW	Cyg	BO	Her	TY	Peg	UY	Vir
FV	Car	WW	Cyg	CC	Her	UX	Peg	AG	Vir
RX	Cas	ZZ	Cyg	CT	Her	AT	Peg	AH	Vir
RZ	Cas	BR	Cyg	SY	Hya	AQ	Peg	RR	Vul
TV	Cas	CV	Cyg	FG	Hya	BB	Peg	RS	Vul
ZZ	Cas	GM	Cyg	RS	Ind	DI	Peg	AT	Vul
AO	Cas	MR	Cyg	RT	Lac	β	Per	BU	Vul
BM	Cas	V346	Cyg	SW	Lac	Z	Per		
CW	Cas	V382	Cyg	TW	Lac				

TABLE 4

SYSTEMS WITH WELL-DETERMINED ABSOLUTE DIMENSIONS

Name	R_1 (☉)	R_2 (☉)	$\mathfrak{M}_1$ (☉)	$\mathfrak{M}_2$ (☉)	Sp.₁	Sp.₂	Reference
σ Aql........	4.3	3.4	6.9	5.5	B3 V	B3 V	From ptm. data in *Groningen Pub.*, No. 54, 1950, and spec. data in *Yerkes Pub.*, **7**, 275, 1939
β Aur........	2.5	2.3	2.3	2.2	A2 IV	A2 IV	*Ap. J.*, **129**, 659, 1959
ζ Aur........	190.	7.0	14.	8.0	K4 Ib	B8	*Pub. Dom. Ap. Obs., Victoria*, **11**, 33, 1958
SX Aur.......	5.2	4.3	10.8	5.7	B3.5	B6	*Ap. J.*, **97**, 394, 1943
TT Aur.......	4.5	4.0	6.7	5.3	B3	B3	*Ap. J.*, **73**, 77, 1931
WW Aur.......	1.9	1.9	1.8	1.8	A7 V	A7 V	*Ap. J.*, **129**, 659, 1959
AR Aur.......	1.8	1.8	2.5	2.3	B9 V	B9 V	*Ap. J.*, **129**, 659, 1959
44i Boo......	0.9	0.6	1.0	0.5	G2	G2	*A.J.*, **60**, 355, 1955
UW CMa.......	18.6	14.8	19.	23.	O7f	O7f	*Pub. A.S.P.*, **71**, 151, 1959
AO Cas.......	13.9	8.9	19.	23.	O9 III	O9 III	From ptm. data in *Ap. J.*, **108**, 28, 1948, and spec. data in *Ap. J. Suppl.*, **4**, 157, 1959
U Cep........	2.9	4.7	4.7	1.9	B8	G8 III	*Ap. J.*, **112**, 542, 1950
VW Cep.......	1.1	0.7	1.1	0.3	dG5	dK1	From ptm. data in *Groningen Pub.*, No. 54, 1950, and spec. data in *Ap. J.*, **108**, 490, 1948
AH Cep.......	6.1	6.1	16.5	14.2	B0 Vn	B0 Vn	*Ap. J.*, **106**, 313, 1947
U CrB........	5.2	3.7	6.7	2.5	B5	B9	From ptm. data in *Ap. J.*, **128**, 595, 1958; and spec. data in *Pub. A.A.S.*, **8**, 219, 1935
RS CVn.......	1.8	4.8	1.8	1.7	F4n	dG8	*Ap. J.*, **113**, 637, 1951
32 Cyg.......	353.	3.9	22.7	8.1	K5 I	B3 V	*Ap. J.*, **126**, 30, 1957
Y Cyg........	5.9	5.9	17.1	17.3	B0 IV	B0 IV	*Princeton Contr.*, No. 12, 1931
V444 Cyg.....	2.2	9.8	14.4	29.6	WN6	O6	*Ap. J.*, **111**, 454, 1950
V477 Cyg.....	1.5	1.2	2.4	1.6	A3	F5	*Pub. Dom. Ap. Obs., Victoria*, **10**, 447, 1958
V695 Cyg (31 Cyg)...	17.4	4.7	18.	9.	K3 Ib	B3 V	*Pub. Dom. Ap. Obs., Victoria*, **11**, 1, 1958
WW Dra.......	2.7	4.9	4.0	2.3	G2	K0	*Ap. J.*, **94**, 407, 1941

TABLE 4—Continued

Name	R_1 (☉)	R_2 (☉)	$\mathfrak{M}_1$ (☉)	$\mathfrak{M}_2$ (☉)	Sp.₁	Sp.₂	Reference
YY Eri	1.0	0.9	1.0	0.6	G5	G5	Tokyo Ann., 2d Ser., 3, 227, 1953
YY Gem	0.6	0.6	0.6	0.6	dM1e	dM1e	Ap. J., 115, 301, 1952
Z Her	2.4	2.6	1.2	1.1	F4 V	K0 V	Ap. J., 124, 196, 1956
RX Her	2.4	2.0	2.7	2.3	A0	A0	Ap. J., 129, 659, 1959
TX Her	1.6	1.6	2.0	1.8	A5	F0	From ptm. data, Peremennye Zvezdy ("Variable Stars"), 11, 26, 1956, and spec. data in Pub. Dom. Ap. Obs., Victoria, 1, 207, 1920
VZ Hya	1.2	1.0	1.2	1.1	F5	F5	Princeton Contr., No. 21, 1946
SW Lac	1.0	0.8	1.0	1.2	G3 p	G3 p	Ap. J., 125, 372, 1957
AR Lac	1.8	2.9	1.3	1.3	F8	K2 III	From ptm. data in Princeton Contr., No. 21, p. 10, 1946, and spec. data in Ap. J., 113, 299, 1951
CM Lac	1.1	0.9	2.0	1.5	A2	A7	A.J., 63, 106, 1958
UV Leo	1.2	1.2	1.4	1.3	G0	G2	Zs. f., Ap., 34, 99, 1954
UX Mon	4.4	8.4	1.5	3.4	A5	dG1p	Ap. J., 126, 69, 1957
U Oph	3.1	2.9	4.0	3.9	B5 V	B5 V	Mem. Soc. Astr. Ital., nuova ser., 29, 381, 1958
ER Ori	0.9	0.9	0.4	0.3	G2	G2	Tokyo Ann., 5, 3, 1957
AG Per	3.7	2.6	5.2	4.6	B4	B5	Washburn Pub., 15, 192, 1931
ζ Phe	3.4	2.0	6.1	3.0	B6 V	A0 V	M.N., 119, 143, 1959
μ¹ Sco	5.6	6.2	14.0	9.2	B3 V	B6	M.N., 108, 398, 1948
V356 Sgr	4.9	12.7	12.1	4.7	B3 V	A2 II	Ap. J., 121, 56, 1955
W UMa	0.9	0.7	1.1	0.5	dG0	dG0	From ptm. data in Ap. J., 79, 369, 1934, and spec. data in Pub. A.S.P., 62, 115, 1950
TX UMa	2.4	4.0	3.1	0.9	B9	gF2	Princeton Contr., No. 21, p. 18, 1946
AH Vir	1.3	0.7	1.4	0.6	K0	K0	From ptm. data in Pub. Astr. Soc. Japan, 9, 119, 1956, and spec. data in Ap. J., 107, 96, 1948
Z Vul	4.7	4.7	5.4	2.3	B4 V	A3 III	Ap. J., 126, 53, 1957

self-explanatory. Descriptions of criteria used in selecting material in each of the tables follow.

Table 1 lists the systems whose limb-darkening coefficients have been computed from reliable photometric observations. This makes no attempt to include all systems for which a darkening coefficient has been reported on unreliable evidence. Systems which have not been observed sufficiently between minima to produce strong rectifications have been omitted, since coefficients thus computed are certain to be illusory. For the same reason, systems have been omitted when observations at different epochs have led to strikingly different darkening

TABLE 5

SYSTEMS WITH ECCENTRIC ORBITS OR DISPLACED SECONDARY
MINIMA, BUT NO CONFIRMED APSIDAL MOTION

TW	And	DI	Cen	32	Cyg	SS	Lac	ζ	Phe
WZ	And	KT	Cen	SW	Cyg	AU	Lac	Y	Psc
XZ	And	LZ	Cen	MR	Cyg	UV	Leo	UU	Psc
QS	Aql	V350	Cen	V380	Cyg	RR	Lyn	TY	Pup
QY	Aql	V380	Cen	V382	Cyg	RU	Mon	ZZ	Pup
V805	Aql	V383	Cen	V448	Cyg	TU	Mon	DD	Pup
V889	Aql	V384	Cen	V453	Cyg	AR	Mon	DM	Pup
RR	Ari	V495	Cen	V456	Cyg	AU	Mon	μ^1	Sco
ϵ	Aur	RS	Cep	V470	Cyg	FW	Mon	FU	Sco
ζ	Aur	XX	Cep	V541	Cyg	HI	Mon	V453	Sco
TT	Aur	AH	Cep	V695	Cyg	IM	Mon	RY	Sct
EO	Aur	CO	Cep	W	Del	AY	Mus	μ	Sgr
SS	Cam	CW	Cep	TW	Dra	U	Oph	RS	Sgr
GR	Car	SW	CMa	RZ	Eri	V451	Oph	XZ	Sgr
GW	Car	CE	CMa	SV	Gem	BM	Ori	V1647	Sgr
RX	Cas	α	CrB	μ	Her	EY	Ori	BU	Vel
YZ	Cas	U	CrB	RX	Her	GG	Ori	UY	Vir
ZZ	Cas	RW	CrB	UX	Her	AQ	Peg	BD	Vir
CC	Cas	W	Cru	DI	Her	AT	Peg	RS	Vul
EP	Cas	UW	Cru	SX	Hya	EE	Peg		
IT	Cas	UX	Cru	AI	Hya	RT	Per		
SV	Cen	RS	CVn	RV	Hyi	AB	Per		

coefficients. Systems such as AR Lac, which is itself an intrinsic variable, have not been included, since computed coefficients in such cases have no meaning. No system has been included for which the elements have been published only in abstract, without discussion or observational data.

Table 2 lists systems in which rotation of the line of the apsides has been determined either from variation of period or variation of the longitude of periastron determined from radial-velocity observations. Doubtful or suspected cases have been omitted.

Table 3 lists systems for which variation of period, other than that caused by apsidal motion, has been reported to date.

Table 4 lists systems with well-determined absolute dimensions. Because of the many departures from the usual mass-luminosity relation shown by eclipsing variables, only systems for which spectrographic values of the mass ratios are

TABLE 6

SELECTED SYSTEMS OF SPECIAL INTEREST

V694 Aql	Algol-type light-curve; period = 0^d45
ε Aur	Infrared component; many puzzles
ζ Aur	Atmospheric eclipse; many puzzles
44i Boo	Variable light-curve; member visual binary
δ Cap	Metallic-line star
RX Cas	Giants; intrinsic variable; shell
SX Cas	Shell; intrinsic variable cA6 + G6
ZZ Cas	B3; period 1^d24, $e = 0.2$
AO Cas	O stars; variable in period, spectra, and light-curve
BM Cas	Intrinsic variable, A5 I, period = 197^d
CC Cas	O9 IV + O9 IV; member of aggregate?
GG Cas	B6 + K0 III; discrepancy between light- and velocity-curves
V644 Cen	Period greater than 200 years
U Cep	Shell or stream; asymmetric light-curve
VV Cep	B3 + gM2; shell; period = 7430^d
VW Cep	Variable light-curve; period = 0^d28
CQ Cep	O7 + WN6; variation in spectrum
CX Cep	Asymmetric light-curve; spectrum WN5
R CMa	Small mass faint component; other puzzles
UW CMa	High-luminosity O stars; remarkable changes in emission lines; gas stream
RZ Cnc	K1 III + K4 III; Ca II emission
32 Cyg	B3 V + K5 I; period = 1141^d
KU Cyg	F4 Ia + M0 III; period = 38^d
MY Cyg	Metallic-line star
PV Cyg	Spectrum N; red color index + 2^m95
V444 Cyg	Wolf-Rayet component; intrinsic variation
V695 Cyg(31)	B5 V + K3 Ib; period = 3800^d
RZ Eri	Emission in spec.; one component metallic-line star
DQ Her	Old nova; peculiar light-curve and spectrum; period = 4^h39^m
AR Lac	Intrinsic variation; peculiar spectrum
RR Lyn	Brighter component metallic-line star
β Lyr	Shell; many peculiarities
UX Mon	Large fluctuations in spectrum and light
RZ Oph	F3e Ib + cK5; period = 262^d
FO Ori	Duration of eclipse = 1/46 period
AR Pav	Symbiotic spectrum; period 605^d
β Per	First known eclipsing variable, but still many puzzles
RY Per	Low ρ; different rv-curves in H and He
UU Psc	Peculiar light-curve
V383 Sco	Spectrum F0 Ia; period = 4900^d
W Ser	Peculiar and variable light-curve; peculiar spectrum
CV Ser	Wolf-Rayet component (WC7 + B)
υ Sgr	Peculiar spectra; B8p + F2p; period = 139^d
μ Sgr	Spectrum B8 Iap; period = 180^d
V777 Sgr	Spectrum A + K5 Ib; period = 936^d
RW Tau	Shell or stream; peculiar spectrum; B8 Ve + K0 IV
BL Tel	cF8 + M(?); intrinsic variation; period = 777^d
UX UMa	Variable light-curve; large variations in spectrum; period less than 0^d2

available have been included. Even a few of these have been excluded when the authors indicated lack of confidence in the reliability of the results. Densities and absolute magnitudes are not given, since these can easily be computed from radii, masses, and spectra. For any detailed consideration of an individual case, reference should, of course, be made to the original studies cited in the eighth column.

Table 5 lists systems for which the radial velocity-curves have shown eccentric orbits or in whose light-curves the secondary minima have been displaced from the position midway between primaries but for which apsidal motion has not yet been established with certainty. Future studies of apsidal motion might well consider these systems. Systems for which the spectrographic studies have shown only small eccentricities have generally been omitted, since it is known that gas streams can cause spurious eccentricities.

Finally, Table 6 lists selected systems of special interest. No effort has been made to be comprehensive, since this would involve a prohibitively long publication. The effort has rather been to illustrate various cases of particular interest found among eclipsing systems.

REFERENCES

BINNENDIJK, L.	1957	*J.R.A.S. Canada*, **51**, 83.
COWLING, T. G.	1938	*M.N.*, **98**, 734.
DUGAN, R. S.	1934	*Princeton Contr.*, No. 15.
DUGAN, R. S., and		
WRIGHT, F. W.	1939	*Princeton Contr.*, No. 19.
GOODRICKE, J.	1783	*Phil. Trans.*, **73**, 474.
HUANG, S. S.	1956	*A.J.*, **61**, 49.
KOCH, R. H.,		
SOBIESKI, S., and		
WOOD, F. B.	1963	*Pub. U. Pennsylvania*, Astronomical Serv., Vol. **9**.
KORT, J. DE	1956	*Vistas in Astronomy*, ed. A. BEER (London: Pergamon Press), **2**, 1187.
KUIPER, G. P.	1941	*Ap. J.*, **93**, 133.
KUKARKIN, B. V.,		
PARENAGO, P. P.,		
EFREMOV, YU. I., and		
KHOLOPOV, P. N.	1958	*General Catalogue of Variable Stars* (2d ed.; Moscow: Publishing House of the Academy of Sciences of the U.S.S.R.).
KWEE, K. K.	1958	*B.A.N.*, **14**, 131.
MARKOWITZ, W.	1933	*Ap. J.*, **77**, 337.
MARTYNOV, D. YA.	1961	*Bibliography of Spectroscopic Binary Stars* (Moscow: Academy of Science, U.S.S.R.).
MERGENTALER, J.	1950	*Wrocław Contr.*, No. 4.
MERRILL, J. E.	1950	*Princeton Contr.*, No. 23.
	1953	*Ibid.*, No. 24.

O'CONNELL, D. J. K.   1951   *Riverview College Pub.*, No. 10 (Vol. **2**, No. 6).
PIERCE, N. L.   1947   *Princeton Contr.*, No. 22.
                           1951   *Astrophysics*, ed. J. A. HYNEK (New York, To-
                                   ronto, and London: McGraw-Hill Book Co.,
                                   Inc.), chap. 11.
PLAUT, L.   1950   *Groningen Pub.*, No. 54.
                           1953   *Ibid.*, No. 55.
RUSSELL, H. N.   1912a   *Ap. J.*, **35**, 315.
                           1912b   *Ibid.*, **36**, 54.
                           1939   *Ibid.*, **90**, 641.
RUSSELL, H. N., and
   MERRILL, J. E.   1952   *Princeton Contr.*, No. 26.
SAHADE, J., HUANG, S. S.,
   STRUVE, O., and
   ZEBERGS, V.   1959   *Trans. Amer. Phil. Soc.*, N.S., Vol. **49**, Part 1.
STERNE, T. E.   1939   *M.N.*, **99**, 451.
SVECHNIKOV, M. A.   1955   *Peremennye Zvezdy*, **10**, 262.
SZAFRANIEC, R.   1959   *Acta Astr.*, Suppl. No. 3.
                           1961   *Ibid.*, Suppl. No. 4.
WOOD, F. B.   1950   *Ap. J.*, **112**, 196.
                           1953   *Pub. U. Pennsylvania*, Astronomical Ser., Vol. **8**.

CHAPTER 20

The Calibration of Luminosity Criteria

A. BLAAUW

Kapteyn Laboratory, Groningen

§ 1. INTRODUCTION

THE determination of spectroscopic absolute magnitudes involves two steps: (a) the choice of the luminosity-sensitive quantity—for instance, a line-intensity ratio I—and its measurement in the spectra of the observed stars, and (b) the calibration of I versus the absolute magnitude. The choice of the quantity I is usually based on empirical evidence with regard to its variation with absolute magnitude, combined with an understanding of the observed behavior on the basis of the theory of stellar atmospheres. This choice will not be discussed in the present chapter. We shall deal only with step b, the calibration.

The modern systems of luminosity classification and the observational work invested in them reflect the kind of problems for which these systems were developed. The most extensive efforts have been made for the early-type stars, because of the imminence of the problems of spiral structure, galactic rotation, and properties of the interstellar matter, although these spectral types themselves represent only a tiny fraction of the galactic stellar population. For the same reasons supergiants of somewhat later types may be expected to be given much attention in the near future. Local problems connected with interstellar matter have stimulated the development of spectroscopic luminosity criteria for A and F stars. Relatively little has been done lately on the stars of later types. Here the problem is complicated by the fact that we deal with a mixture of stars of different stellar populations. Yet it is this very aspect that is likely to make these stars the object of intensive investigation in the future, particularly in connection with the problem of separating the kinematic and distributional properties of the various population components.

In view of this, the present treatment of the calibrations will deal with two main categories: (a) the early-type stars, i.e., mainly the spectral types O and B, and (b) the stars of later types. Galactic clusters will be dealt with briefly in connection with the early types.

383

We shall first discuss the stars of late spectral types because, prior to the present stage of research, these were observed in large numbers by the Mount Wilson observers (Adams, Joy, Humason, and Brayton 1935) and their results remain of interest in modern research. The Mount Wilson results are affected by certain systematic errors which were investigated at length by Strömberg, Russell and Moore, van Rhijn, and others. The rather complicated analysis of some of these authors may have created the impression that the systematic errors are of an intricate nature and the Mount Wilson results therefore less useful. We shall present a more concise description of the nature of the system- atic errors and show that the Mount Wilson data remain valuable in some re- spects. This fact has been somewhat overlooked in recent years. It is important to realize that the Mount Wilson material comprises more than 4000 stars of types later than A5, a number far exceeding that available at present in any other system of classification. Current work on the later spectral types will sub- sequently be described.

Among the modern programs of photometric or spectrophotometric lumi- nosity determination the calibration of which will *not* be discussed in this chap- ter are the following:

a) The photographic spectrophotometry of Chalonge and collaborators. An extensive account of this program has been given by Chalonge (1958). The luminosity calibration of the three measured quantities: D (the Balmer dis- continuity), λ_1 (a wavelength defined by the slope of the Balmer decrement), and ϕ_0 (the absolute gradient of the continuum in the interval from λ 3800 to λ 4800), has been undertaken by Berger. It makes use of the difference between the absolute magnitudes of components of double stars, for which the lumi- nosity of the fainter component is known from other sources—for instance, the MK classification. Preliminary accounts were given by Berger (1957, 1958) and a more complete one in his thesis (Berger 1962).

b) The narrow-band photoelectric photometry of Strömgren and his collab- orators. For accounts of this program we refer to chapter 9 by Strömgren. The H β photometry for early-type stars is referred to in § 3.32, below.

c) The low-dispersion objective-prism photographic spectrophotometry of the Stockholm and Uppsala schools. For recent accounts of the problems con- nected with the luminosity calibration in these programs we refer to Sinnerstad (1961*a, b*) and to Ljunggren and Oja (1961).

§ 2. THE SPECTRAL TYPES A TO M

2.1. THE EARLY MOUNT WILSON WORK

Adams, Joy, Humason, and Brayton (1935) published spectroscopic absolute magnitudes of 4179 stars, mostly later than A5 and north of declination $-26°$. We shall refer to this program as the "early Mount Wilson work" to avoid con- fusion with the modern work at the same observatory discussed later in this chapter. The list of Adams and collaborators was the result of many years of research since the work of Adams and Kohlschütter in 1916. References to these earlier investigations are given in the paper by Adams *et al.* Their absolute magnitudes are based on visual estimates of relative line intensities, calibrated empirically against the absolute magnitude. In this calibration the stars within each spectral subdivision were grouped according to the estimated line-intensity ratios, and for these groups mean absolute magnitudes were derived from the trigonometric parallaxes (for the main-sequence stars) and from the proper motions (for the giants). It is important to notice that separate reduction-curves were constructed for the domains of the giants, the subgiants, and the main-sequence stars. The transition regions in between these became the weakest part of the calibration. The existence of a "subgiant" region in between the main sequence and the "normal" giants had been suggested by earlier work of Strömberg (1933, 1936).

The derived absolute magnitudes were used by Adams *et al.* in the construction of an HR diagram. This is reproduced in Figure 1; it represents stars selected according to apparent brightness (those brighter than the sixth visual magnitude) and therefore includes the giants in a much larger volume of space than the dwarfs; had the stars been selected per volume of space, then the high luminosities would have been represented in much smaller relative numbers. This diagram exhibits a feature which later gave rise to considerable discussion (and some confusion): the main-sequence and the giant branches are characterized by very small dispersions around the mean absolute magnitude for a given spectral type; even the subgiants appear as a distinct, narrow, intermediate branch. It appears that, in each of these branches, for a given spectral type the observed dispersion around the mean absolute magnitude is less than would be expected from the observational errors in the line-intensity ratios. This is contradictory in itself and, moreover, leaves no room for the not negligible cosmic dispersion of the absolute magnitudes.

Subsequent analyses have shown that this feature is a consequence of the interplay of two circumstances: (*a*) the main-sequence and the giant branches in the HR diagram represent areas of maximum density with respect to their surroundings, and (*b*) the calibration-curves, used for these separate areas, were constructed after the stars were grouped according to the observed line-intensity ratios. These circumstances allowed the observational and cosmic errors in the intensity ratios to affect the calibration in a systematic way.

Since the understanding of this effect is of importance, not only for the use of the early work, but also for modern work on the calibration of luminosity criteria, we shall discuss it at some length in the following paragraphs. In modern work the accidental and cosmic errors affecting the measures of luminosity criteria are smaller than those affecting the early Mount Wilson work. However, the systematic trend to be feared in the results remains the same as long as the calibration procedure remains basically unchanged, i.e., if it groups the stars according to the measured values of the luminosity-sensitive quantity.

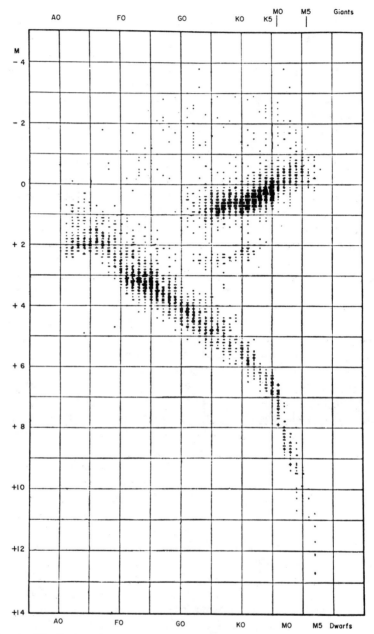

Fig. 1.—Distribution of the spectroscopic visual absolute magnitudes of Adams, Joy, Humason, and Brayton in the HR diagram, as it was given by these authors. Their calibration procedure, with separate reduction-curves for the main-sequence, subgiant, and giant branches, has led to the spuriously small dispersion of absolute magnitudes within each of these branches (see the text).

2.11. *The nature of the systematic errors in the early Mount Wilson spectro-scopic absolute magnitudes.*—Let $F(M)$ be the frequency distribution of the (true) absolute magnitudes for the spectral type considered. For the actual cases considered, $F(M)$ always applies to the stars selected according to apparent magnitude. For most types, the function $F(M)$ may be assumed to have a peak around the main sequence. In some cases, secondary maxima will occur corresponding to the giant branch and, perhaps, in the supergiant and the subgiant regions. We consider the regions around these maxima separately, in accordance with the fact that separate reduction-curves were used for them by Adams *et al.*

For the sake of the argument, we shall assume that we are dealing with a Gaussian-shaped $F(M)$ for such a region:

$$F(M)\,dM = \frac{1}{\sigma\sqrt{(2\pi)}}\, e^{-(M-M_0)^2/2\sigma^2}\,dM\,. \qquad (1)$$

Once the cause of the systematic errors in the spectroscopic parallaxes has been recognized for this case, the reasoning can be easily extended to differently shaped $F(M)$.

We shall further assume that (a) a unique relation exists between the observed luminosity parameter I (for instance, an equivalent width or a line-intensity ratio) and the true absolute magnitude M; and (b) this relation is linear:

$$M = aI + \beta\,. \qquad (2)$$

Again the reasoning can easily be extended to the more realistic, but somewhat more complicated, cases of non-linear relations.

It is clear that in the present case the frequency distribution of the values of I is also Gaussian:

$$D(I)\,dI = \frac{1}{\sigma_i\sqrt{(2\pi)}}\, e^{-(I-I_0)^2/2\sigma_i^2}\,dI\,, \qquad (3)$$

with

$$\sigma = a\sigma_i \quad \text{and} \quad M_0 = aI_0 + \beta\,. \qquad (4)$$

The reasoning is illustrated by means of Figure 2, in which division a represents $F(M)$, division c represents relation (2), and $D(I)$ is shown in division b.

Let us now assume that the following conventional procedure is used in the calibration: a group of stars is chosen within narrow limits of a value of the measured parameter, i.e., within $I_1 \pm \Delta I/2$. For these, the mean true absolute magnitude is determined by means of a geometric procedure—for instance, the trigonometric parallaxes or the secular parallax based on the reflex of the solar motion. In both these cases a mean parallax may be determined: $\bar{p}(I_1)$. We next derive the absolute magnitude of the stars concerned from the relation $\bar{M} = \bar{m} + 5 + 5\,\langle \log p\rangle$. Before this can be done, we shall have to take into account the difference between $\langle \log p\rangle$ and $\log \bar{p}$; we assume this to be taken care of.

If the afore-mentioned assumption of a unique relation between I and the absolute magnitude holds true, then $\bar{M}$ will be approximately equal to $M(I_1)$. The difference may be due to accidental errors in the trigonometric parallaxes or to errors in the proper motions and to peculiar motions of the stars in case the secular parallax method is used; this difference is, actually, of a random nature. Thus, if we imagine $\bar{M}$ to be plotted against I_1 for different values of I_1,

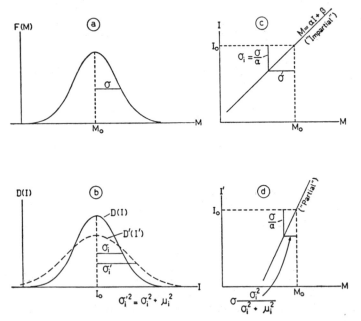

Fig. 2.—Illustration of the influence of accidental errors in the measured quantity, I, on the determination of the spectroscopic absolute magnitudes. *a:* The (Gaussian) distribution of true absolute magnitudes, $F(M)$. *b:* The (also Gaussian) distribution $D(I)$ of the quantity I on the assumption of the strict linear relation between M and I represented by *c*. The dashed line in *b* represents the (Gaussian) distribution $D'(I')$ of the quantity I', which includes accidental observational and cosmic errors of I. *d:* The reduction-curve obtained if, for stars grouped according to I', I is plotted against the mean absolute magnitude derived from trigonometric or secular parallaxes. Full drawn line represents M–M'_s; dashed line gives best fit.

the corresponding points will be scattered randomly with respect to a mean relation, and this latter is the relation $M = aI + \beta$ sought for. If this relation is used in combination with accurately measured values of I for the individual stars, then absolute magnitudes are derived free of systematic errors.

The actual state of affairs is different, in that the available measured values of I are *not* uniquely related to the true absolute magnitudes, because (*a*) the measures of I contain observational errors and (*b*), even if exactly measured, the values of I may not be uniquely related to M because of cosmic "errors." We shall assume that these cosmic errors are of a random nature and may be combined with the observational errors in forming combined random "errors" in I. These errors will further be assumed to have a Gaussian distribution, with mean error μ_i. We shall show that these *random* errors in I lead to *systematic* errors in the resulting absolute magnitudes if a conventional procedure like the one just described is followed.

Instead of the error-free distribution (3) of I, we now have the frequency distribution of measured values I':

$$D'(I') \, dI' = \frac{1}{\sigma_i' \sqrt{(2\pi)}} \, e^{-(I'-I_0)^2/2\sigma_i'^2} \, dI' . \qquad (5)$$

This is also shown in Figure 2, *b*. Obviously, the mean value, I_0, is not affected; hence $I_0' = I_0$, but

$$\sigma_i'^2 = \sigma_i^2 + \mu_i^2 . \qquad (6)$$

We choose stars within narrow limits around the *observed* value I_1', i.e., within $I_1' \pm \Delta I'/2$. The *true* values I for these stars scatter around I_1' in an asymmetric way, such that the mean true value $\bar{I}$ for these stars is given by

$$\bar{I} = I_1' + \frac{\mu_i^2}{D'(I_1')} \left(\frac{d D'}{d I'} \right)_{I'=I_1'} + \text{terms of higher order in } \mu_i^2, \text{ which we shall neglect.}$$

For a derivation of this relation see, for instance, Trumpler and Weaver (1953, par. 1.51). Hence we obtain, with formulae (5) and (6),

$$\bar{I} = I_2' - (I_1' - I_0) \frac{\mu_i^2}{\sigma_i'^2}$$

and

$$\frac{\sigma_i^2 + \mu_i^2}{\sigma_i^2} (\bar{I} - I_0) = (I_1' - I_0) . \qquad (7)$$

Thus the ratio $(I_1' - I_0)/(\bar{I} - I_0)$ is independent of I' and is a function of the ratio of the mean error μ_i and the dispersion σ_i. It is always larger than 1.

We determine the mean parallax for the stars in the interval $I_1' \pm \frac{1}{2}\Delta I'$ and, from it and the apparent magnitudes, the mean absolute magnitude, $\bar{M}$. The individual values of the true absolute magnitudes, M, for the stars concerned will scatter over a certain range; but, in view of relation (2), we have $\bar{M} = a\bar{I} + \beta$, i.e., $\bar{M} = M(\bar{I})$. In drawing the calibration-curve, one plots this $\bar{M}$ against the measured value I_1', not against $\bar{I}$. Hence, instead of obtaining the correct relation $M = aI + \beta$, one now obtains a relation (M, I'), which again is linear but in which all intervals $I' - I_0$ are larger by a factor $(\sigma_i^2 + \mu_i^2)/\sigma_i^2$ as compared with the original intervals $I - I_0$. This is illustrated in Figure 2, *d*. It shows the calibration-curve that is obtained by plotting the selected values of I' against the mean absolute magnitudes found from the trigonometric or secular parallaxes. The curves of Figure 2, *c* and *d*, coincide for the point $M(I_0)$

but have different slopes in the sense that, for the same range in M, the empirically obtained relation of Figure 2, d, corresponds to a larger range of the measured quantity (I') than does the curve of Figure 2, c, which relates true values of I with M. Stated otherwise: for equal intervals in I and I', the interval in M in Figure 2, d, is reduced in the ratio $\sigma_i^2/(\sigma_i^2 + \mu_i^2)$ with respect to the corresponding interval in Figure 2, c.

Now if, in the determination of spectroscopic parallaxes, we start from the observed quantities I' and read corresponding values of M from Figure 2, d, these values will again have a Gaussian distribution, but its dispersion will be different from that of the original distribution $F(M)$ for two reasons: (a) by using the relation of Figure 2, d, the resulting distribution of M will be compressed in the ratio $\sigma_i^2/(\sigma_i^2 + \mu_i^2)$, and (b) we start from the distribution $D'(I')$ for which the dispersion σ_i' is larger than that of $D(I)$ in the ratio σ_i'/σ_i.

Accordingly, we end up with a dispersion of derived values of M which differs from the dispersion σ of the true values by a factor

$$\frac{\sigma_i'}{\sigma_i} \frac{\sigma_i^2}{\sigma_i^2 + \mu_i^2} = \frac{1}{\sqrt{(1 + \mu_i^2/\sigma_i^2)}}. \tag{8}$$

Hence the finally obtained distribution of spectroscopic absolute magnitudes has a *smaller* dispersion than that of the true absolute magnitudes.

We shall denote the spectroscopic absolute magnitudes thus obtained by M_s and their distribution by $F_s(M_s)$. We then have

$$F_s(M_s)\, dM_s = \frac{1}{\sigma_s \sqrt{(2\pi)}} e^{-(M_s - M_0)^2/2\sigma_s^2}\, dM_s, \tag{9}$$

with

$$\sigma_s = \frac{\sigma}{\sqrt{(1 + \mu_i^2/\sigma_i^2)}}. \tag{10}$$

If we further define μ by $\mu = a\mu_i$, so that μ is the mean error of the absolute magnitude corresponding to the mean error μ_i of the line-intensity ratio when converted by means of relation (2) (shown in Fig. 2, c), then $\mu_i/\sigma_i = \mu/\sigma$, and hence

$$\sigma_s = \frac{\sigma}{\sqrt{(1 + \mu^2/\sigma^2)}}. \tag{11}$$

The foregoing explains in a qualitative way the curiously small dispersion in the distribution of the spectroscopic absolute magnitudes which was noted in the Mount Wilson material (Fig. 1); it is always smaller than the dispersion of the true absolute magnitudes. Discussions of this systematic effect have been published by Russell and Moore (1938, 1940), Strömberg (1939, 1940, 1941), and van Rhijn (1939). In these investigations, the adjective "impartial" was assigned to the reduction line of Figure 2, c, and to the absolute magnitudes derived with it, and the adjective "partial" to the line of Figure 2, d, and the corresponding absolute magnitudes.

When spectroscopic absolute magnitudes are used in current problems, the question arises which one of these two kinds of absolute magnitudes, partial or impartial, to select. If the stars in the sample have not been selected according to the measured value of I, the observational and cosmic errors in I may be assumed to have a random character and to cancel for large numbers in the sample. In that case, the "impartially" derived absolute magnitudes, i.e., those obtained with the reduction-curve of Figure 2, c, are the ones to be used.

The absolute magnitudes given in the Mount Wilson catalogue of Adams *et al.* and, in fact, those in most lists of spectroscopic luminosities are given in the "partial" system derived by means of the relation of Figure 2, d. Part of the investigations by Russell and Moore, van Rhijn, and Strömberg have dealt with the problem of reducing the published "partial" values to "impartial" ones. We shall not discuss here in detail the methods applied in these investigations and only refer to the main points, insofar as they are useful to know for work with the Mount Wilson data.

2.12. *The analyses of Russell and Moore.*—Russell and Moore base their treatment on an analysis of the correlation between the spectroscopic *parallaxes*, derived from the "partially" determined Mount Wilson spectroscopic *absolute magnitudes*, and the trigonometric and secular parallaxes. However, in the final paragraphs of their concluding article (Russell and Moore 1940) the authors return to the absolute magnitudes. Linear relations between the "partial" and the "impartial" absolute magnitudes are derived from linear relations between the "partial" and the "impartial" spectroscopic parallaxes. The authors state that these linear approximations are valid in the range of values concerned.

The treatment distinguishes between the main-sequence stars of the various spectral types between A1 and M5 and the giant branch from G0 to M6. First of all, the mean absolute magnitude per spectral subgroup is established by means of trigonometric and secular parallaxes. It is given in Table 12 of Russell and Moore's final paper and denoted S_1 by them. These means differ by a few tenths of a magnitude at most from the mean values, S_0, of Adams *et al.*; the latter are tabulated by Russell and Moore in Table 2 of *Ap. J.*, **87**, 407; the differences are given in the line $S_1 - S_0$ of the tables on page 418 of *Ap. J.*, Vol. **87**. For practical purposes, we may first adjust the spectroscopic absolute magnitudes of Adams *et al.* by this amount and then assume S_1 to represent the absolute magnitude of maximum frequency, i.e., the value M_0 in our considerations in the preceding section.

It follows from the considerations in the preceding section that, for a given star, the difference between the impartially derived absolute magnitude M and the mean value for the spectral subgroup, $M - M_0$, can be obtained from the difference between the partially derived value M_s and M_0, by means of the relation

$$M - M_0 = (M_s - M_0) \frac{\sigma^2 + \mu^2}{\sigma^2}. \tag{12}$$

Using Russell and Moore's symbol S_1 for M_0, this may be written in the form

$$M = M_s + \frac{\mu^2}{\sigma^2}(M_s - S_1).\qquad(13)$$

This is equivalent to the expression

$$M'_s = M_s + A\,(M_s - S_1),\qquad(14)$$

given at the end of Russell and Moore's $Ap.\ J.$, Vol. **92**, paper, where M'_s stands for the impartially derived absolute magnitude (our M), M_s is always the partially derived one, and A is equivalent to μ^2/σ^2.

Russell and Moore gave $A = 1.22$ for the main-sequence stars and $A = 0.33$ for the giants. These values are means from various spectral subclasses and were derived by means of analyses of the correlations between the spectroscopic parallaxes and trigonometric parallaxes, the regression lines being defined by grouping the stars on the basis of (a) the spectroscopic parallax and (b) a quantity $H = m + 5\log\nu$, ν being the proper motion. This latter quantity is correlated to the absolute magnitude, but its accidental errors may be assumed to be independent of those in the trigonometric parallaxes, as well as of those in the spectroscopic luminosity criteria. The cited values of A are taken from the third column of Table 10 of Russell and Moore's paper in $Ap.\ J.$, Vol. **92**, using the relation $A = 1/l - 1$.

The dispersion of the true absolute magnitudes, σ, is called W by Russell and Moore, and the mean error of an impartially derived absolute magnitude, μ, is denoted θ'' by them. The values of these quantities are also given in the above-mentioned Table 10 of their paper and were slightly revised in the subsequent discussion. For the main-sequence stars, $\sigma = \pm0.69$ mag. and $\mu = \pm0.64$ mag., whereas, for the giants, $\sigma = \pm1.04$ mag. and $\mu = \pm0.53$ mag. (see Sec. 27 of Russell and Moore's paper).

These values do not strictly reproduce the above value of A according to the relation $A = \mu^2/\sigma^2$, as they would give $A = 0.86$ for the main sequence and $A = 0.26$ for the giants. The reason for the difference is due mainly to the fact that the system of partially reduced values of the spectroscopic absolute magnitudes as given by Adams $et\ al.$ first required to be improved (because the material of trigonometric parallaxes had been increased) before they could be submitted to a discussion of the impartial versus the partial system. This involved a factor of about 1.2 to be included in the value of A for the main sequence. Moreover, it must be kept in mind that Russell and Moore probably have strongly underestimated μ for the giants (see § 2.14).

2.13. *The analyses of van Rhijn and Strömberg.*—Almost simultaneously with Russell and Moore's final investigation, van Rhijn (1939) analyzed the spectroscopic absolute magnitudes of Adams $et\ al.$ He first computed corrections to these (partially derived) absolute magnitudes, using improved trigonometric and statistical parallaxes. The resulting corrections are given in van Rhijn's

Table 4 and reproduced in Table 1 of this chapter. Van Rhijn used the spectral classes A, F, G, K, and M without finer subdivision. For the absolute magnitudes around M_0, his corrections agree well with those found by Russell and Moore. Van Rhijn next discussed the partial and impartial procedures already referred to. We shall restrict ourselves to the results pertaining to the impartially derived quantities. The mean error μ of an impartially derived absolute magnitude is found to be ± 0.54 mag. ± 0.04 (p.e.) for the main sequence and ± 1.00 mag. ± 0.15 (p.e.) for the giants (van Rhijn's Table 9). Good agreement exists with Russell and Moore's mean error for the main sequence; the mean errors for the giants according to the two investigations are discordant, but their probable errors are also rather large.

TABLE 1

Van Rhijn's (1939) Systematic Corrections, ΔM_s, To Be Applied to
Spectroscopic Absolute Magnitudes, M_s, of Adams,
Joy, Humason, and Brayton (1935)

Spectral Type	M_s	ΔM_s	Spectral Type	M_s	ΔM_s
A......	≤ 0.0	-0.7	K......	≤ -0.5	-1.3
	$+1.0$	-0.5		0.0	-0.8
	$+2.0$	$+0.1$		$+0.4$	0.0
	$+3.0$	$+0.2$		$+0.7$	$+0.5$
				$\geq +2.0$	0.0
F......	≤ 0.0	-1.2			
	$+2.0$	-1.0	M......	≤ -2.0	-0.9
	$+3.0$	-0.2		-1.0	-0.4
				0.0	0.0
G......	≤ -2.0	-1.0		$\geq +1.0$	0.0
	-1.0	-0.7			
	0.0	-0.1			
	$+1.0$	$+0.3$			
	$\geq +2.0$	0.0			

The investigations by Strömberg were carried out at about the same time as those of Russell and Moore and of van Rhijn. Strömberg also discussed the correlations between the spectroscopic absolute magnitudes, and absolute magnitudes obtained from trigonometric parallaxes, distinguishing between (a) grouping of the stars according to the spectroscopic absolute magnitudes, producing the partial calibrations, and (b) grouping according to the independent quantity $H = m + 5 \log \nu$ referred to before. Strömberg's first investigation (1940) dealt with the G0–K2 dwarfs, and his second one (1941) with the F, late K, and M dwarfs. Strömberg's papers clearly demonstrated the different regression lines corresponding to the partial and the impartial calibration as illustrated in our Figure 2. He determined the mean error of an impartially determined spectroscopic absolute magnitude (denoted θ'' by him) for the main-sequence spectral classes F–M. The mean of these, ± 0.54 mag., agrees well with van Rhijn's result and fairly well with Russell and Moore's.

2.14. *Modern use of the early Mount Wilson catalogue.*—We shall now illustrate the effects described in the preceding sections and consider to what extent
the early Mount Wilson material may be adapted to modern use.

Consider, first, the F-type stars. For these, we now have at our disposal a
number of fairly accurately determined individual parallaxes, either trigonometric or from modern spectroscopic work. Thus Oke (1957, 1959) lists accurate
visual absolute magnitudes determined at the David Dunlap Observatory for
62 stars classified between F2 and F9 by Adams *et al.* Oke's work will be referred
to in more detail in § 2.31. The probable errors of the absolute magnitudes given
by Oke are about ±0.2, and his absolute magnitudes are practically free of
systematic errors.

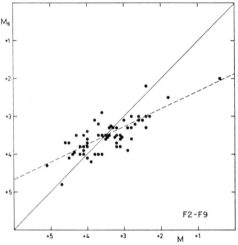

Fɪɢ. 3.—Spectroscopic visual absolute magnitudes, M_s, for F2–F9 stars given by Adams,
Joy, Humason, and Brayton, plotted against modern values, M, mostly taken from Oke
(1957, 1959). The plot illustrates the contracted scale of M_s due to the calibration procedure.

In Figure 3 these absolute magnitudes, denoted by M, are plotted against
the values given by Adams, which are denoted by M_s. We notice that they are
not scattered around the 45° line but that the scale of the Mount Wilson values
is considerably reduced—approximately in the ratio $f = 0.45$, which is the
effect explained in § 2.11. The calibration of the Mount Wilson luminosity criteria was done by means of the partial line of Figure 2, *d*, and consequently the
scale of the derived absolute magnitudes was compressed in the ratio $f = \sigma^2/$
$(\sigma^2 + \mu^2)$. Substituting Russell and Moore's values $\sigma = \pm 0.69$ mag. and $\mu =$
± 0.64 mag. for the main sequence in general, we find $f = 0.54$, which, within
the possible errors of σ and μ, accounts for the observed value of f.

According to § 2.12, impartial absolute magnitudes M_s' may be derived from
the Adams values by means of formula (14). Using $A = 1.22$, given by Russell
and Moore, correcting the Adams values by $S_1 - S_0 = 0.1$ mag., and using the

values of S_1 of Table 12 of Russell and Moore's $Ap. J.$, Vol. **92**, paper, we obtain the corrected values M'_s, which have been plotted against Oke's values in Figure 4. We notice that the points now scatter roughly parallel to the 45° line, indicating that the true scale has been recovered for the values M'_s. The vertical scatter with respect to the 45° line should be due mainly to the observational errors in the Mount Wilson estimates. We find from the vertical residuals a mean error of ±0.65 mag., in agreement with the value ±0.64 mag. quoted by Russell and Moore.

It thus appears that the spectroscopic absolute magnitudes of F2–F9 stars of Adams *et al.*, if corrected in the way indicated above, are approximately on the

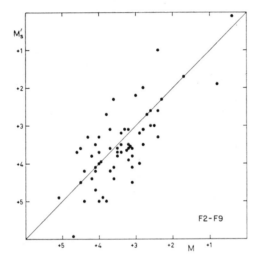

Fig. 4.—Visual absolute magnitudes M'_s for the stars of Fig. 3, obtained by correcting the values of M_s of Adams *et al.* by means of formula (14), are plotted against the same values of M as in Fig. 3. Full drawn line represents $M = M'_s$.

system of modern luminosity determinations, although of lower accuracy. Their probable errors are ±0.43 mag., as compared with about ±0.2 for those of Oke. The significance of this result lies in the fact that the Mount Wilson classifications are available for 782 main-sequence F2–F9 stars.

For the main-sequence G stars a similar situation is encountered. If the correction to M_s (the value of Adams *et al.*) is applied in the manner described, we obtain corrected values M'_s which show a good correlation with the modern values and no scale difference.

For the K stars the situation is different. It is illustrated in Figure 5 for types K0–K5. Adams' values M_s are plotted against modern ones, for which we took, for the subgiants and giants, those given by Wilson and Bappu (1957), whose work will be discussed in more detail in § 2.33, and, for the main sequence, the absolute magnitudes given by Oke (1957, 1959) derived either from trigono-

metric parallaxes or from Oke's spectroscopic criteria or from both. To these latter were added a few values given for main-sequence stars by Wilson and Bappu.

We notice that the dwarfs scatter approximately along the 45° line. Hence
the values of Adams *et al.* appear to be a close approximation to the modern
ones. Application of the corrections by using Russell and Moore's σ and μ would
lead to an expanded vertical scale for these stars. The residuals with respect to
the 45° line in Figure 5 allow an estimate of the errors in the Adams values;
we find the probable error to be only about ± 0.20 mag. It is clear that the early
Mount Wilson absolute magnitudes for the K dwarfs may still form valuable

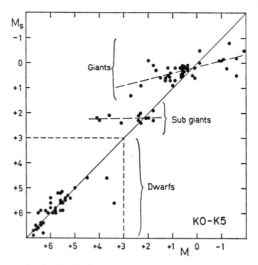

FIG. 5.—Spectroscopic visual absolute magnitudes M_s for K0–K5 stars given by Adams,
Joy, Humason, and Brayton, plotted against modern trigonometric and spectroscopic values.
In the domain of the dwarfs, the scale of the two systems appears to be about equal, whereas
for the giants and subgiants the scale of M_s is strongly compressed. Full line represents $M = M_s$;
dashed lines give best fits to dots in giant and subgiant regions.

material as they stand. The question why application of formula (14) in this
case leads to an overcorrection would require special investigation which is
beyond the scope of this chapter and probably not justified, in view of the relatively small number of stars of these types in the Mount Wilson list.

The entirely different situation with regard to the subgiants and giants is
shown in the upper part of Figure 5. The giants scatter around the dashed line
with a slope which indicates that, for these uncorrected Adams values, the scale
has been compressed by a factor of about 0.24. Instead of the corresponding
correction factor of about 4, the factor predicted by means of formula (12) is
only 1.33, using Russell and Moore's value of $A = \mu^2/\sigma^2$. We suspect that
Russell and Moore have considerably underestimated the mean error μ of the
spectroscopic absolute magnitudes; they found $\mu = \pm 0.53$ mag., whereas van

Rhijn found $\mu = \pm 1.00$ mag. (see § 2.13). The correction factor 4 would require $\mu = 1.7\ \sigma$. With the accidental errors so strongly dominating the cosmic dispersion, it is obviously meaningless to try to introduce corrections to the Adams values for the giants. For the subgiants the situation is similar, as will be seen from Figure 5. Here, too, the whole range of luminosities has been compressed within about half a magnitude in the early Mount Wilson calibration procedure.

2.2. THE YERKES MK SYSTEM

The Yerkes MK system, developed by Morgan and Keenan, is based on low-dispersion Yerkes spectra (125 A/mm at Hγ) and aims at setting up a visual classification system ". . . as precise as possible which can be extended to stars of the eighth to twelfth magnitude with good systematic accuracy." The system is "to be taken as a sort of adaptation of work published at many observatories over the last fifty years" (Morgan, Keenan, and Kellman 1943). In order to achieve this purpose, the system is closely correlated with color temperature, and it classifies luminosities into five main luminosity classes—I, II, III, IV, V, in order of decreasing luminosity. The system is defined by the standard stars in the original *Atlas of Stellar Spectra* of Morgan, Keenan, and Kellman (1943) and somewhat revised by the new list of standards published by Johnson and Morgan (1953). It has become of great value for modern galactic research. We shall discuss the calibration of these luminosity classifications.

The question of the calibration is dealt with only briefly in the Introduction to the original *Atlas*. Reference is made to the use of trigonometric parallaxes, dynamical parallaxes, cluster parallaxes, and distances derived from interstellar line intensities and from the effects of galactic rotation. No numerical values are given for the absolute magnitudes, the preliminary ones are only represented in a diagram (Fig. 2 of the Introduction) as more or less continuous functions of spectral type for each luminosity class. As more stars were classified in the system, more accurate values of the mean luminosities per subclass became available. A brief summary of these was given by Keenan and Morgan (1951), but they did not give details as to the computations.

We shall describe here subsequent investigations insofar as they refer to spectral types A and later on the main-sequence and the giant branches. Earlier types and supergiant calibrations in the MK system are treated in § 3.

2.21. *Miss Roman's work on the F5–K5 stars of luminosity classes II–V.*—Roman (1952) has observed and classified 641 non-variable stars in this spectral range, brighter than 5.5 visual magnitude and north of declination $-20°$. The calibration is performed by means of trigonometric parallaxes and proper motions (i.e., secular parallaxes). The proper motions were used only for the intrinsically brighter groups, in order to strengthen the results from the trigonometric parallaxes. In general, only the proper motions yielded significant results for luminosity classes II and II–III.

The results and the adopted mean visual absolute magnitudes are given by

Roman in her Table 1. These cover the range of spectral and luminosity classes mentioned before, with the exception of the class II for types F5–G5 and class V for types G5 and later. For these, Roman copies the values suggested by Keenan and Morgan (1951).

For some of Roman's subgroups of spectral and luminosity class, the calibration is based on small numbers of stars. Thus, for classes IV and V, the numbers used according to her Table 1 are only between 10 and 20 per spectral subclass. (These probably include some stars not in Roman's list, for it contains only 2 F5 IV, 1 F6 IV, 0 F8 IV, 5 F5 V, 6 F6 V, 7 F8 V, and 5 G0–G2 V stars.) In such cases the statistical errors in the treatment by means of proper motions and trigonometric parallaxes tend to become large. It is therefore of some importance that it can be shown, largely independent of Miss Roman's treatment, that her calibrations are essentially correct.

This procedure makes use of the early Mount Wilson work, discussed in the preceding sections. We may assume that the MK luminosity classes III and V, which contain the majority of the stars, correspond to the ridge lines in the HR diagram as it has been given by Adams *et al.* (see Fig. 1 and § 2.1). The calibration of these Mount Wilson luminosities has been carefully discussed by van Rhijn (1939) in the paper already referred to in § 2.32. We accordingly proceed as follows:

For the stars of MK luminosity class III or V in Roman's list (all of which occur in the early Mount Wilson catalogue) we take the absolute magnitudes from the catalogue of Adams *et al.*, apply the corrections given by van Rhijn, and then compute the mean absolute magnitude for the subgroup. In this case it is of little consequence whether the "partially" reduced spectroscopic absolute magnitudes are used or whether they are reduced to the "impartial" system, since the mean values to be obtained are always close to the average for the spectral subclass; this is the value called M_0 in § 2.11, which is not affected by a difference in slope of the calibration-curve. The essential point in using the Mount Wilson data is that we implicitly make use of the fact that the calibration of these was based on a much larger number of proper motions and parallaxes than were available to Roman.

The results are shown in Table 2. The upper division refers to luminosity class III. Its third column gives the mean spectroscopic absolute magnitude of the stars concerned according to Adams *et al.*; the next column gives van Rhijn's corrections read from Table 4 of *Groningen Publications*, No. 49, and reproduced in our Table 1; and the column "$M_{s,\,corr}$" gives the sum of these. Roman's values are in the sixth column. We find that, except for class G8 III, the values of Roman are almost exactly reproduced. The discrepancy for class G8 III suggests that Roman's result deserves further checking. It is somewhat surprising that it deviates from the general trend in the luminosities from K0 III to K5 III.

In the next division the few class V stars in Roman's list are treated in the same way. Notwithstanding the small numbers of stars, the procedure via the

Mount Wilson luminosities leads again to mean values "$M_{s, corr}$" in the next to last column which confirm in a most satisfactory way the values of Roman.

In view of the small numbers of stars for these main-sequence classes, we have added a second check in the third division of Table 2, making use of the MK classifications given for a number of bright stars by Mustel, Galkin, Kumaigorodskaya, and Boyarchuk (1958) and based on spectrophotometry at the Crimean Astrophysical Observatory. There is only little overlap between this list

TABLE 2

COMPARISON OF ROMAN'S CALIBRATIONS FOR LATE-TYPE MK LUMINOSITY CLASSES III, IV, AND V, WITH VALUES DERIVED VIA THE EARLY MOUNT WILSON SPECTROSCOPIC ABSOLUTE MAGNITUDES, M_s, AND VAN RHIJN'S SYSTEMATIC CORRECTIONS, ΔM_s

MK Type	n	$\langle M_s \rangle$	$\langle \Delta M_s \rangle$	$M_{s, corr}$	M_{Roman}	From Trig. Parallaxes
G8 III.	63	+0.65	+0.17	+0.8	0.0	. . . .
K0 III.	88	+0.63	+0.38	+1.0	+0.7	. . . .
K1 III.	33	+0.60	+0.33	+0.9	+0.8	. . . .
K2 III.	53	+0.46	+0.10	+0.6	+0.9	. . . .
K3 III.	61	+0.27	−0.27	0.0	+0.1	. . . .
K4 III.	31	+0.22	−0.37	−0.2	−0.1	. . . .
K5 III.	31	+0.13	−0.54	−0.4	−0.2	. . . .
F5 V.	5	+3.0	−0.2	+2.8	+3.3	. . . .
F6 V.	6	+3.5	0.0	+3.5	+3.6	. . . .
F8 V.	7	+3.7	+0.1	+3.8	+3.9	. . . .
G0–G2 V.	5	+4.4	0.0	+4.4	+4.4	. . . .
F0 V.	3	+2.6	−0.5	+2.1	. . . .	+2.9
F5 V.	4	+3.5	0.0	+3.5	+3.3	+3.2
F6 V.	6	+3.4	0.0	+3.4	+3.6	+3.5
F7 V.	7	+3.7	+0.1	+3.8	. . . .	+3.4
F8 V.	5	+3.8	+0.1	+3.9	+3.9	+3.8
G0 V.	13	+4.3	0.0	+4.3	} +4.4	+4.3
G2 V.	3	+4.3	0.0	+4.3		+4.8
G8 V.	3	+5.4	0.0	+5.4	. . . .	+5.5
K0 V.	4	+5.6	0.0	+5.6	. . . .	+5.6
G5–K1 IV. . . .	11	+2.8	0.0	+2.8	+3.2	. . . .

and Miss Roman's. Mean absolute magnitudes are computed via the old Mount Wilson values in the same way as described before with the results in the column "$M_{s, corr}$." The spectral classes F0 V, G8 V, and K0 V have been included. Again we find excellent agreement with Roman's values. In the last column of this division of the table we list mean visual absolute magnitudes derived directly from the trigonometric parallaxes; the individual values were also taken from Mustel et al., who borrowed them from a compilation by Nikonov, Nekrasova, Polosukhina, Rachkovsky, and Chuvayev (1957). The agreement with the preceding columns is entirely satisfactory.

Finally, we have also applied the above procedure of using the Mount Wilson data to check the absolute magnitudes of the eleven stars in Roman's list of luminosity Class IV between G5 and K1. This check is justified because we are dealing with the subgiant region which forms a separate "ridge" in the HR diagram of Adams *et al.* for which the authors used separate reduction curves. For this reason, the question of the "partial" versus "impartial" procedure is not important. The rather uncertain results are given in the last division in Table 2 and show a fair agreement with the Roman results.

2.22. *Other data for late-type main-sequence stars.*—The calibration of the late main-sequence MK types can be supplemented by means of data for the nearest stars. These have been given by Gliese (1956) and by Evans, Menzies, and Stoy (1957, 1959). Table IV of the 1957 paper can be somewhat improved by adding the information contained in Table III of the 1959 paper. The data of Gliese and those of Evans, Menzies, and Stoy show good agreement and form the basis for the adopted calibrations as described in §2.24.

2.23. *Osawa's work on the main-sequence A-type stars.*—Osawa (1959) has observed and classified 533 B8–A2 stars brighter than 6.5 visual magnitude and between $+10°$ and $+40°$ declination. Of these, those stars of luminosity class V were selected which, according to a preliminary estimate, are located within about 150 pc from the sun. From mean parallaxes, based on separate analyses of the upsilon and of the tau components, the mean absolute magnitude was derived for type A0 V. Stars of classes B8–A3 were included, but assumed differences in luminosity with respect to A0 were used to obtain the final value for A0 V. The resulting mean absolute magnitude for this subgroup is $+0.5$, and the corresponding values for the neighboring spectral classes are B8 V, -0.5; B9 V, 0.0; B9.5 V, $+0.3$; A0 V, $+0.5$; A1 V, $+0.8$; A2 V, $+1.2$; A3 V, $+1.8$.

2.24. *Summary of calibrations for classes A–M, II–V.*—Table 3 assembles, below the dashed line, the adopted calibrations for the MK types B8–M, luminosity classes II–V. The figures printed in normal size represent the calibrations accounted for in §§ 2.22 and 2.23. These include (*a*) for luminosity classes II to IV–V the results of Roman, slightly revised on the basis of the upper and lowest divisions of Table 2; (*b*) for luminosity class V, types B8–A3 the results of Osawa; (*c*) for F5–G2, luminosity class V, the results of Roman, slightly revised on the basis of both Table 2 and the results of Gliese and of Evans, Menzies, and Stoy referred to before; (*d*) for G5–K5, luminosity class V, the results of Gliese, of Evans, Menzies, and Stoy, and of Mustel and collaborators (see Table 2); (*e*) for K7–M4, luminosity class V, the results of Gliese. The remaining figures, printed in small size, have been taken from Keenan and Morgan (1951) except for types A5–F2, luminosity class V, which were estimated by the author of this chapter from a variety of sources. The values taken from Keenan and Morgan represent the most scarcely populated parts of the HR diagram. For the description of the early-type and supergiant calibrations, see § 3.2.

2.3. CALIBRATION PROCEDURES IN SOME OTHER MODERN SYSTEMS

Since the introduction of the MK system, several programs of spectroscopic luminosity determinations based on quantitative measurements have been

TABLE 3*

MEAN VISUAL ABSOLUTE MAGNITUDES FOR MK LUMINOSITY CLASSES

TYPE	V	IV–V	IV	III–IV	III	II–III	II	Ib	Iab	Ia	Ia–0
O6	−5.5										
8	−5.2										
9	−4.8		−5.3		−5.7		−6.0	−6.1	−6.2	−6.2	
B0	−4.4		−4.8		−5.0		−5.4	−5.8	−6.2	−6.2	−8.1
1	−3.6		−4.1		−4.4		−5.0	−5.7	−6.2	−6.6	−8.2
2	−2.5		−3.3		−3.6		−4.8	−5.7	−6.3	−6.8	−8.2
3	−1.7		−2.5		−2.9		−4.6	−5.7	−6.3	−6.8	−8.3
5	−1.0		−1.8		−2.2		−4.4	−5.7	−6.3	−7.0	−8.3
7	−0.4		−1.2		−1.6		−4.0	−5.6	−6.4	−7.1	−8.3
8	−0.5 +0.1		−0.7		−1.0			−5.6	−6.5	−7.1	−8.3
9	0.0 +0.6		−0.2		−0.4		−3.8	−5.5	−6.5	−7.1	−8.4
A0	+0.5 +1.0		+0.3					−5.2	−6.6	−7.1	−8.4
1	+0.8 +1.5		+0.7		−0.9		−3.0	−5.1	−6.6	−7.3	−8.4
2	+1.2						−2.9	−5.0	−6.7	−7.5	−8.5
3	+1.5		+1.0:		−0.3		−2.8	−4.8	−6.8	−7.6	−8.5
5	+1.8						−2.7	−4.8	−6.9	−7.7	−8.5
7	+2.0		+1.7:		+0.3		−2.6	−4.8		−8.0	
F0	+2.4						−2.5	−4.7	−6.6	−8.5	−8.7
2	+2.8						−2.5	−4.6	−6.6	−8.4	−8.8
5	+3.2	+2.8	+1.9		+1.0		−2.3	−4.6	−6.4	−8.2	
6	+3.5	+2.8	+1.9				−2.2	−4.6	−6.4	−8.1	
8	+4.0	+2.9	+1.9		+1.0		−2.2	−4.6	−6.3	−8.0	
G0	+4.4		+2.6				−2.1	−4.5	−6.3	−8.0	−9.0
2	+4.7		+2.9		+0.4		−2.0	−4.5	−6.2	−8.0	
5	+5.1		+3.0				−2.6 −2.0	−4.5	−6.2	−8.0	
8	+5.5		+3.0	+1.3	+0.4	−1.0	−2.6 −2.0	−4.5	−6.1	−8.0	
K0	+5.9		+3.0	+1.3	+0.8	−0.8	−2.6 −2.0	−4.4	−6.1	−8.0	
1	+6.1		+3.0	+1.3	+0.8	−0.8	−2.6 −2.0	−4.4	−6.1	−8.0	
2	+6.3				+0.8	−0.8	−2.6 −2.0	−4.4	−6.0	−8.0	
3	+6.5				+0.1	−1.0	−2.6 −2.0	−4.4	−6.0	−8.0	
4	+6.8				−0.1	−1.0	−2.6 −2.0	−4.4	−5.9	−8.0	
5	+7.2				−0.3	−1.0	−2.6 −2.0	−4.4	−5.9	−8.0	
7	+8.1										
M0	+8.7				−0.4		−2.4				
1	+9.4										
2	+10.1				−0.4		−2.4	−4.8	−5.6	−7.0	
3	+10.7										
4	+11.2				−0.5						

* Values below the dashed line are discussed in § 2.2 and generally refer to stars selected according to apparent magnitude. The other values are discussed in § 3.2. They generally refer to stars selected per volume of space rather than per apparent magnitude. For the difference between these two kinds of absolute magnitudes, see § 3.24. Among the early types, different evolutionary stages of the clusters or associations containing the stars considered may cause considerable systematic deviations from the tabular absolute magnitudes. Figures printed in normal type represent calibrations discussed in this chapter; those in small type are mostly taken from Keenan and Morgan (1951).

carried out. None of these has produced data as numerous as the list of Adams *et al.* Some of them will be briefly dealt with in this section, with special reference to the question of the calibration of the measured criteria. Only trigonometric and cluster parallaxes were used in these programs—no statistical parallaxes.

In all these cases, the calibrations suffer from the scarcity of stars with reliable parallaxes in the giant region. The situation may be illustrated by means of the color-magnitude plot for 245 stars with trigonometric parallaxes larger than 0".049 in Figure 6, which has been reproduced from Eggen (1955). This selection contains most of the stars for which the individual absolute magnitudes are determined geometrically with sufficient accuracy for calibration purposes. Below 0".050 the relative accuracy of the trigonometric parallaxes and, hence,

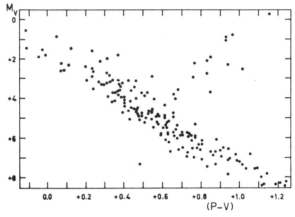

Fɪɢ. 6.—The color-luminosity array for 245 stars with trigonometric parallaxes in excess of 0".049 according to Eggen (1955), excluding white dwarfs and types later than K5.

of the absolute magnitudes diminishes rapidly (compare, for instance, the data for stars with trigonometric parallaxes larger than 0".02 plotted by Eggen [1957]). The calibration of the giants therefore remains rather weak. Of the clusters, only the Hyades provide accurate data, unless additional clusters whose distances are indirectly determined are included.

2.31. *Oke's work on F5–K2 stars.*—Oke (1957, 1959) used line strengths, measured on microphotometer tracings of David Dunlap Observatory spectrograms with a dispersion of 33 A/mm at Hγ. The luminosity parameter used is $R = \log d_i/\log d_j$, where d_i is the depth of the luminosity-sensitive line and d_j that of the luminosity-non-sensitive line. The spectral groups G5–K1 and F5–G2 were treated separately.

The material for groups G5–K1 covers the MK luminosity classes III–V. The luminosity calibration is essentially based on 24 stars, whose trigonometric parallaxes give M_v with probable errors below 0.2 mag., plus three Hyades giants. The absolute magnitudes range from +7 to +0.6. This range of luminosities is, at least for $B - V$ around 0.76, covered by one continuous curve, and in this respect the procedure differs from that adopted by Adams. This curve is shown in Figure 7, which is a reproduction of Figure 1 of Oke's first article. Separate (R, M) relations are obtained by subdividing the low-luminosity part of the material into groups according to $B - V$. Taking into account the errors of the trigonometric parallaxes, Oke concludes, from the scatter of the points with respect to this curve, that the true mean error of an absolute magnitude read from it with R does not exceed ± 0.3 mag.

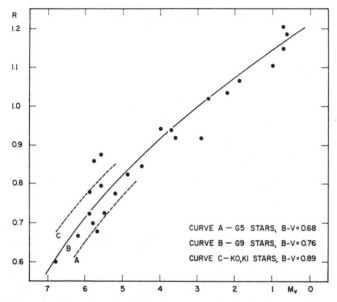

CURVE A — G5 STARS, B-V = 0.68
CURVE B — G9 STARS, B-V = 0.76
CURVE C — K0,K1 STARS, B-V = 0.89

Fig. 7.—Line strengths, $R = \log d_i / \log d_j$, versus visual absolute magnitude as used by Oke (1957) for G5–K1 stars, for different intervals of $B - V$.

Group F5–G2 covers the MK luminosity classes IV and V only. Separate calibration-curves are obtained for the stars with $0.53 \leq B - V \leq 0.67$ (F8–G2) and $B - V \leq 0.53$ (F5). The former, covering the absolute magnitudes $M_v = +5$ to $+2.3$, is based on 20 stars and the sun; the latter, covering $M_v = +6$ to $+3$, on only 10 stars. The mean error in M_v as found from these curves and the measured spectral criterion is estimated to be ± 0.3 mag.

Using these calibration-curves, Oke, in his second article, gives spectroscopic absolute magnitudes for 22 stars with $B - V < 0.53$, for 36 stars with $0.53 \leq B - V \leq 0.67$, and for 34 stars with $B - V > 0.67$; most of these stars also have trigonometric parallaxes of fair accuracy. From these stars, together with 91 stars with good trigonometric or cluster parallaxes, Oke constructs a $B - V$, M_v diagram, for the study of the stars in the region below the M67 sequence. The material of spectroscopic parallaxes appears to serve the particular purpose of this diagram satisfactorily. However, for M_v brighter than $+1$, only very few stars can be incorporated in the study.

2.32. *The work by Hossack and Halliday on G8–K1 stars.*—Hossack (1954) has measured relative line strengths mostly of early K-type stars with an oscilloscope microphotometer on David Dunlap Observatory spectrograms which have a dispersion of 33 A/mm at $H\gamma$ and were used earlier in the radial-velocity programs. For the calibration, the observed line-intensity ratios are plotted against the MK luminosity classes, and for the luminosity classification a continuous scale is introduced, essentially identical with the MK luminosity scale but using Arabic decimal numbers instead of the Roman ones. This allows a finer luminosity classification than the MK system. The internal probable error for a single plate is found to be about ±0.15 luminosity class (based on three line ratios). For K0 and K1 stars, this corresponds to about ±0.4 mag.

Halliday (1955) has used this method for the luminosity classification of 227 G8–K1 stars, for the purpose of finding their luminosity function and space motions. The luminosity classifications were transformed into visual absolute magnitudes by adopting the calibration for the MK classes by Roman (1952) and by Keenan and Morgan (1951) and interpolating linearly for the decimal values. The system of luminosities is therefore essentially that of the MK system discussed in § 2.2 and is affected by the same systematic errors. A summary of recent work along these lines has been given by Heard (1956).

2.33. *The method of Wilson and Bappu for types G, K, and M.*—Wilson and Bappu (1957) have found that the logarithms of the widths of the bright reversals in the H and K absorption lines of G, K, and M stars are a linear function of the visual absolute magnitude over a range of 15 mag. They gave measures of this quantity and the derived absolute magnitudes for 185 stars of types G0 and later, chosen from the Johnson and Morgan (1953) list of MK standard stars and some additional objects. The measures were made on 10 A/mm Mount Wilson and Palomar spectrograms. The method is of great interest because of the wide range of spectral type and luminosity to which it is applicable, but it is limited by the circumstances that high-dispersion spectrograms are required and that the reversal, being situated at the bottom of the absorption lines, can be observed only for relatively bright stars. The essentially linear relation between M_v and the logarithm of the width of the reversal over the range of absolute magnitudes fainter than $M_v = -1$ is shown by Wilson and Bappu's (1957) Figure 3, where the measured quantity, $\log W$, is plotted against the M_v derived from stars with large trigonometric parallaxes—i.e., those for which (p.e. of par.)/par. <0.25). Application of this method to the stars with accurate photoelectric colors, for the purpose of studying in particular the distribution in the color-magnitude diagram below the M67 giant branch, has been published by Wilson (1959a, 1961).

The calibration adopted in the latter papers is based on the assumption of a

strictly linear relation between M_v and log W and the following few, but accurately observed, stars: the sun ($M_v = +4.84$) and the four giants in the
Hyades ($M_v = +0.68, +0.66, +0.54, +0.80$),

$$M_v = -14.94 \log W + 27.59 .$$

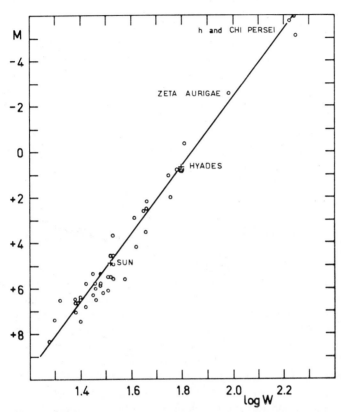

FIG. 8.—Relation between the logarithm of the width of the H and K emission reversals,
log W, and visual absolute magnitude as given by Wilson (1959a, 1961). A linear relation is
adopted, defined by the measures of the sun and of the giants of the Hyades, which are indicated by plus signs.

Tests of this relation by means of the Hyades, 24 giant stars with accurate parallaxes, 29 main-sequence stars with accurate parallaxes, Praesepe, and h and χ
Persei show no significant deviations from this relation. The cosmic scatter is
found to correspond to a probable error of ±0.20 mag. for the giants and a somewhat larger value, ±0.34, for the main-sequence stars, possibly due to rotational
broadening. The linear relation and the way it satisfies the observations, including the individual stars with accurate parallaxes, is shown in Figure 8
(Wilson 1959b, 1961).

§ 3. TYPES O AND B AND SUPERGIANTS

3.1. The Fundamental Data on Absolute Magnitudes

The interest in accurate knowledge of the space distribution of the early-type stars, particularly of the supergiants, has led to the observation of large numbers of stars of these types. Most numerous are the classifications in the MK system, mostly made by Morgan himself, the majority of which have been published in papers by Morgan, Code, and Whitford (1955), Hiltner (1956), and in other, smaller lists. In the following the emphasis will be on the problem of the calibration of this system. Other systems of luminosity measurements include the photographically determined equivalent widths of Hγ published by Petrie (1953, 1956), Petrie and Moyls (1956), and Beer (1961) for O–B5 stars and by Petrie and Maunsell (1950) for B8–A3 stars; photographically determined equivalent widths of Hγ, Hδ, H8, and other lines published by Hack (1953); photoelectrically observed strengths of Hβ and of the Balmer discontinuity by Strömgren (1958) and Crawford (1958, 1960, 1961); photoelectric measures in five wavelength regions by Walraven and Walraven (1960); and photoelectric measures in seven wavelength regions by Borgman (1960). This modern work was preceded by various programs of historical interest, of which we mention especially that of Williams (1936). For a more complete historical review we refer to Petrie (1956).

The problem of the accurate calibration of these estimates or measurements has for many years been a rather difficult one, particularly for the supergiants, because of the lack of nearby stars. No trigonometric parallaxes can be used, and mean secular parallaxes are small and hence uncertain. Yet it seems that a satisfactory solution has lately been reached. It is based on (a) the determination of the distances of clusters or associations containing early-type stars and supergiants by the main-sequence fitting procedure which starts from the well-known distance of the Hyades; and (b) a check on these distances, particularly that of the Perseus double cluster, by means of a direct tie-in with the Scorpio-Centaurus association and making use of the multicolor photoelectric measurements. These two procedures will be described first and, next, the calibrations resulting from the absolute magnitudes thus obtained.

3.11. *The main-sequence fitting procedure, starting from the Hyades.*—The procedure is illustrated in Figure 9, in which the absolute visual magnitude, M_v, is plotted against $B - V$, freed from interstellar absorption. The drawn line, running from $(B - V)_0 = +1.2$, $M_v = +7.7$, to $(B - V)_0 = -0.35$, $M_v = -5.5$, represents the zero-age main sequence (denoted in the following by "ZAMS"). It is also represented in Table 4. This is the main sequence for stars which have completed the Kelvin contraction but have not evolved further as a consequence of hydrogen-burning in the interior. The curve-fitting procedure is based on the assumption that, for star clusters of the age of the Hyades (10^9 years) and younger, the ZAMS is identical, i.e., unaffected by differences in initial chemical composition. Once the $(B - V)_0$, V_0 diagram has been obtained for a given cluster or association, the distance modulus is derived from the vertical fit with the ZAMS for the unevolved part of the observed sequence. For the development of the method, we refer to papers by Johnson and Hiltner (1956), Sandage (1957), Johnson (1957), Johnson and Iriarte (1958), and Johnson (1960).

The accuracy with which the position of the ZAMS has been defined is of basic importance for the distances obtained by means of the curve-fitting procedure and hence for the calibration of the luminosity criteria. We shall therefore describe this definition in some detail.

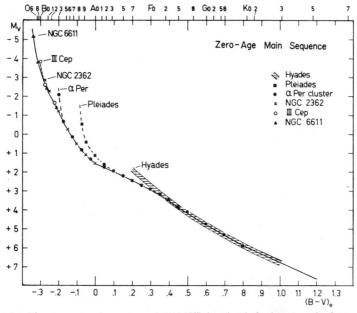

Fig. 9.—The zero-age main sequence ("ZAMS") for visual absolute magnitudes, as defined by the non-evolved parts of the main sequences of the clusters indicated in the diagram.

TABLE 4

THE ZERO-AGE MAIN SEQUENCE

$B - V$	M_v	$B - V$	M_v	$B - V$	M_v
−0.35........	−5.50:	+0.05.......	+1.80	+0.50.......	+4.20
− .30........	−3.30	+ .10.......	+2.00	+0.60.......	+4.80
− .25........	−2.10	+ .15.......	+2.25	+0.70.......	+5.40
− .20........	−1.10	+ .20.......	+2.50	+0.80.......	+5.90
− .15........	−0.20	+ .25.......	+2.70	+0.90.......	+6.30
− .10........	+0.60	+ .30.......	+2.95	+1.00.......	+6.80
− .05........	+1.15	+ .35.......	+3.20	+1.10.......	+7.20
0.00........	+1.55	+0.40.......	+3.55	+1.20.......	+7.65

The geometric distance on which the whole scheme is based is that of the *Hyades*. Since the elements of the motion of the Hyades cluster with respect to the sun are accurately known and the proper motions are large and well determined (Heckmann and Lübeck 1956), individual distances can be derived for the Hyades members. These individual distances, together with the U, B, V photometry of Johnson and Knuckles (1955), have been used by Heckmann and Johnson (1956) for the construction of an accurate $B - V, M_v$ diagram. The main sequence is well defined in this diagram and reproduced in our Figure 9 by the hatched band ranging from $(B - V)_0 = +0.2$ to $+1.0$; this has been drawn symmetrically with respect to the ridge line of Heckmann and Johnson's plot. The correction for interstellar absorption is negligible for our present purpose. (There is some evidence for reddening based on the presence of some polarization of the light of the Hyades stars.)

Evolutionary effects are present in the upper part of the Hyades main sequence (and, naturally, in the red giants, which are not reproduced in Fig. 9) but not in the lower part. This lower part therefore represents the first step in constructing the ZAMS. The next step consists of fitting to this the main sequence of the *Pleiades*. This is reproduced in Figure 9 by the series of squares; we only use the part at $(B - V)_0 < +0.8$ (below this value the main sequence is not well defined). Data have been taken from Johnson and Mitchell (1958); the small corrections for reddening and absorption (0.035 and 0.11 mag., respectively, according to Johnson and Morgan 1953) were not applied because they hardly affect the position of the part of the main sequence that we use. The Pleiades main sequence coincides exactly with the lower part of the Hyades main sequence for an adopted distance modulus of 5.55. The coincidence covers the region $B - V = +0.4$ to $+0.8$ ($M_v = +3.5$ to $+6.0$).

The next extension of the ZAMS is obtained by means of the α *Persei moving cluster*, for which U, B, V photometry has been published by Mitchell (1960). Mitchell measured a large number of stars for which proper motions by Heckmann, Dieckvoss, and Kox (1956) indicated possible membership. The $V, B - V$ plot by Mitchell shows clearly the main-sequence ridge line extending from $B - V = +0.6$ up to about -0.1. It is represented in Figure 9 by filled circles, after corrections for reddening (0.08 mag.) and visual absorption (0.24 mag.) had been applied. Perfect fit with the Pleiades main sequence occurs between $B - V = +0.1$ and $+0.45$ if the distance modulus 6.15 is adopted for the α Per cluster. The figure reveals the evolution away from the main sequence for the Pleiades brighter than $M_v = +2$, $B - V < +0.1$; the deviations are in good agreement with the values estimated by Johnson (1960) by means of theoretical data.

A further extension is obtained by means of the cluster *NGC 2362*. Photometry was published by Johnson and Morgan (1953) and a color-magnitude diagram, corrected for reddening and absorption (0.11 and 0.33, respectively), by Johnson and Hiltner (1956). The main-sequence ridge line is fairly well defined between $B - V = -0.25$ and about -0.05. It has been plotted in Figure 9 by crosses for the interval $B - V = -0.275$ to 0.0. Good coincidence with the sequence for the α Per cluster occurs between $B - V = -0.175$ and 0.0. Evolutionary effects in the upper part of the α Per cluster sequence are clearly present. The distance modulus for NGC 2362, adopted to obtain the fit with the α Per cluster, is 10.8.

In order to extend the ZAMS still farther toward the blue, we have added data for the *III Cep association* and for *NGC 6611*. Photometry of III Cep (Blaauw, Hiltner, and Johnson 1959) gives some information on its main sequence for $B - V = -0.25$ to -0.30; the corresponding points are marked by open circles in Figure 9. More important for the uppermost extension of the ZAMS are the data for NGC 6611 published by Walker (1961). This is one of the very young clusters studied by this author and the one extending farthest into the blue. From Walker's data we derive the position of the—presumably unevolved— main sequence up to $(B - V)_0 = -0.35$. It coincides well with the lower part of the III Cep sequence. The two have only little overlap with the main sequence of NGC 2362; the tie-in is based mainly on the interval $B - V$ between -0.20 and -0.25. The adopted distance moduli are 9.3 for III Cep and 12.6 for NGC 6611. The ZAMS thus obtained reaches up to about $M_0 = -5.5$ for $B - V = -0.35$.

3.12. *Application to h and χ Persei.*—An important example of the application of the curve-fitting method is the distance determination of the association around h and χ Persei, because this provides a large number of the supergiants on which the calibrations are based. Photometry of stars in the inner part of the association, belonging to the two clusters, has been published by Johnson and Morgan (1955). The $M, B-V$ diagram based on it, corrected for interstellar reddening and absorption, was published by Johnson and Hiltner (1956). The ridge line of the unevolved main sequence is fairly well defined for the interval $B - V = -0.17$ to -0.05. Fitting this to the ZAMS of Figure 9 at $B - V = -0.05, -0.10,$ and -0.15 gives for the distance modulus the values 11.7, 11.7, and 11.9, respectively. The mean value, 11.8, is the same as that adopted by Johnson, Hoag, Iriarte, Mitchell, and Hallam (1961) in their list of cluster distances based on the main-sequence fitting procedure. We shall show in § 3.13 that this value is confirmed by an independent method.

3.13. *Direct connection of h and χ Persei with the Scorpio-Centaurus association.*—The curve-fitting procedure described in the preceding section starts from a basic geometric distance of high accuracy (the Hyades), but the various steps leading to the distance modulus of the early-type clusters and hence to the luminosities of the supergiants introduce considerable accumulating errors.

Another procedure for deriving these distance moduli with a comparable degree of precision starts from the Scorpio-Centaurus association, which also has a geometrically determined distance. The distance is less well determined than that of the Hyades, but the Sco-Cen association contains early-type stars, and hence the intermediate steps of the curve-fitting procedure are avoided. The early-type stars cover a fairly wide band in the HR diagram above the zero-age main sequence, which is probably due to the fact that these stars represent different evolutionary stages (Blaauw 1959). In the case of the h and χ Persei clusters and association, which we shall discuss as an example of the application of the alternate procedure, we also have a number of stars in the region of the HR diagram above the main sequence. The procedure utilizes the fact that this array for h and χ Per partly overlaps with that of the Sco-Cen association. For the exact establishment of this overlap, we make use of the multicolor narrow-band photometry by Walraven and Walraven (1960) and by Borgman (1960). The method has been described in detail by Borgman, and its principle was illustrated in the Walravens' paper. The following outlines its application to h and χ Per, which produces strong evidence in support of the distance scale established by the procedure of the previous section.

The multicolor photometry allows the definition of certain photometric quantities, denoted here by p and r, which have the following properties: (a) they are free from interstellar reddening; (b) they are a function of spectral type and luminosity and hence permit the absolute magnitude to be written as a function of p and r, $M_v = f(p, r)$.

We assume, as in the curve-fitting procedure, that no differences occur in the chemical composition of the Scorpio-Centaurus stars and those of h and χ Per. The absence of such differences seems to be even more plausible than for the clusters involved in the curve-fitting procedure, which cover a wider range in age.

The relation $M_v = f(p, r)$ for the Scorpio-Centaurus association can be empirically established for a limited range of spectral type and luminosity. Within this, the cosmic errors of the absolute magnitudes predicted by means of p and r are of the order of ± 0.30 (p.e.).

We now assume that, for h and χ Per stars falling within this range of p and r, the relation $M_v = f(p, r)$ also holds and accordingly compute values of M_v for a number of them. This yields individual distance moduli and hence an average distance modulus for h and χ Per.

In an exploratory investigation by the author of this chapter, the quantities p and r were defined by

$$p = (P - N) - 0.417 (M - L); \quad r = (R - Q) - 0.519 (M - L),$$

where L, M, N, P, Q, and R represent the intensities measured by Borgman (1960) in narrow-wavelength regions. Their effective wavelengths range from λ 3295 for R to λ 5240 for L. The coefficients 0.417 and 0.519 were chosen in such a way as to make p and r independent of interstellar reddening (assuming the reddening law to be uniform). Since Borgman's list contained only the stars in the northern part of the Scorpio-Centaurus association and since those in the more southern part represent a different evolutionary stage, the material was extended by using the photometry of Walraven and Walraven (1960) for these latter stars. The reddening-free quantities $[B - U]$ and $[U - W]$ obtained by these authors could be converted with sufficient approximation into the quantities p and r by means of the stars in common.

The visual absolute magnitudes of the Scorpio-Centaurus stars were taken from Hardie and Crawford (1961), who used new U, B, V photometry and Bertiau's (1958) distances; for stars not in the first authors' list, we used Bertiau's values. As in the case of the curve-fitting method, the absolute magnitudes of the reference stars are used without corrections for duplicity because the apparent magnitudes of the h and χ Per stars are not corrected in this respect.

It then turns out that, for the area $0.12 < p < 0.35$, $0.00 < r < 0.20$ of the p, r array, the absolute magnitudes can be satisfactorily represented by the linear relation

$$M_v = -4.55 + 14.4\,p - 5.1\,r. \tag{15}$$

This range for p and r roughly corresponds to the range in spectral types B2–B7 and in absolute magnitudes, -2.8 to -0.7. Borgman's (1960) list contains six stars in h and χ Per for which p and r lie within the range for which relation (15) has been established, although some of them lie in the border area near the higher luminosities. From the absolute magnitudes computed with equation (15) and the apparent magnitudes corrected for interstellar absorption, we find for the individual distance moduli the values 10.9, 11.0, 11.9, 12.0, 12.2, and 12.3, and the average value, 11.7 ± 0.2 (p.e.). This probable error is an internal one. For a more complete discussion of the possible errors see § 3.14. Current work by Borgman, which includes still fainter stars in the double cluster, leads to a provisional mean distance modulus of h and χ Per of 11.8 (private communication).

The alternate method based on the Scorpio-Centaurus association thus fully confirms the result of the curve-fitting method for h and χ Per. Provisional analyses of the Orion association stars measured by Borgman (1960) lead to a distance modulus of 7.9 ± 0.2, as compared with 8.1 by the curve-fitting method (Johnson *et al.* 1961). It should be borne in mind that there is a basic uncertainty of about ± 0.12 (p.e.) mag. in the distance moduli of the Scorpio-Centaurus stars due to possible errors in the elements of the stream motion (Bertiau 1958, Table 6) and the possibility of an additional error due to an erroneous interpretation of the proper motions (Bertiau 1958), which in our opinion seems unlikely. The good agreement of the two procedures inspires confidence in the correctness of the distance scale now available by these two procedures.

3.14. *Evaluation of systematic errors.*—The absolute magnitudes of the early-type stars obtained by the procedures described in the preceding sections are affected by the systematic errors which entered with the various steps taken. As an example, we consider again these errors in the case of the Perseus double cluster. They are summarized in Table 5 for the two procedures.

In the curve-fitting procedure, we distinguish (*a*) the error in the adopted distance of the Hyades; (*b*) the errors in the adopted reddening and total visual interstellar absorption for each cluster, including the error due to an incorrect ratio between total absorption and color excess; (*c*) the errors involved in the curve-fitting itself for the construction of the zero-age main sequence up to $M_v = -1$; (*d*) the errors in the reddening and absorption of the h and χ Per stars; and (*e*) the error in fitting the main sequence of h and χ Per to the zero-age main sequence.

TABLE 5

BREAKDOWN OF ERROR IN DISTANCE MODULUS OF h AND
χ PERSEI OBTAINED BY TWO PROCEDURES

Source of Error	Probable Error (Mag.)
Main-sequence fitting procedure:	
a) Distance modulus of Hyades..............................	±0.05
b) Reddening and visual absorption of Hyades...................	≤ ± .05
Same for Pleiades.......................................	≤ ± .05
Same for α Persei cluster.................................	≤ ± .05
Same for NGC 2362......................................	≤ ± .05
c) Curve-fitting of	
Pleiades–Hyades.......................................	≤ ± .05
α Persei cluster–Pleiades...............................	≤ ± .05
NGC 2362–α Persei cluster..............................	± .10
d) Reddening and visual absorption of h and χ Persei.............	± .15
e) Zero-age main-sequence fit of h and χ Persei..................	±0.10
Total probable error in distance modulus......................	±0.23
Connection with Scorpio-Centaurus association:	
a) Distance modulus Scorpio-Centaurus........................	±0.15
β) Reddening and visual absorption of Scorpio-Centaurus..........	≤ ± .05
γ) Definition of relation $M(p,r)$...............................	± .05
δ) Application of relation $M(p,r)$ to h and χ Persei stars..........	± .18
ε) Reddening and visual absorption of h and χ Persei stars........	±0.15
Total probable error in distance modulus......................	±0.29

The accuracy of the adopted distance of the Hyades may be judged from the work by van Bueren (1952), Pearce (1955), Heckmann and Lübeck (1956), and others. The main uncertainty arises from the error in the stream velocity, as was pointed out by Pearce, but it is insignificant compared with the other causes of error listed above. The other errors have been estimated from the published observational data.

In the direct connection between h and χ Persei and Scorpio-Centaurus we distinguish (*a*) the error in the adopted distances of the Scorpio-Centaurus stars; (*β*) the errors in the reddening and absorption of these stars; (*γ*) the error introduced by the definition of the relation $M_v(p, r)$; (δ) the error introduced by the application of this relation to h and χ Per stars; and (ϵ) the errors in the reddening and absorption of the h and χ Per stars. Errors δ and ϵ are common to the two procedures.

In Table 5, the error a has been estimated from data given by Bertiau (1958, Table 6), and we have included a contribution due to a possible systematic error in the proper-motion system. The second error has been estimated from the photometry of Hardie and Crawford (1961) and the data given by Bertiau. The total estimated systematic error in the distance modulus of the h and χ Per stars appears to be about ± 0.23 and ± 0.29 mag. for the two procedures. This corresponds to an error of ± 13 per cent in the distance.

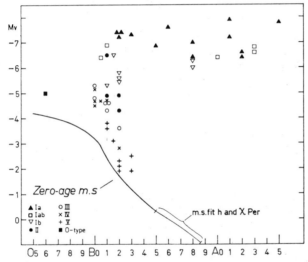

Fig. 10.—The HR diagram of the stars in h and χ Per with MK spectral classifications, as an example of the contribution of a cluster or association to the calibration of the MK luminosity classes for high-luminosity stars.

3.2. The MK System for the Early Types and Supergiants

The most reliable calibration of the MK luminosity classifications for the high-luminosity classes is now obtained by means of the main-sequence fitting procedure described in § 3.11. Members of clusters and associations which have been classified in the MK system can be used if the distance of the cluster or association and hence the individual stellar luminosities have been determined by this procedure. Such distances have recently been published for 106 clusters and associations by Johnson, Hoag, Iriarte, Mitchell, and Hallam (1961).

As an example, we show in Figure 10 the data contributed by the h and χ Persei association. They have been taken from Johnson and Morgan (1955) and pertain to the inner parts and a limited part of the outer association. (Data for a larger area are given by Johnson and Hiltner (1956), but it is doubtful whether all these stars belong to the aggregate.) Different symbols mark the various luminosity classes. This association contributes a large fraction of the high-luminosity stars available for calibration. The drawn line represents the zero-age main sequence. Note that its shape in Figure 10 is defined by a different scale of abscissa than in Figure 9. The region of the zero-age main sequence where the fit for h and χ Per was made is indicated. We notice, in passing, the turnoff around B2 or B3 $(B - V = -0.22)$ at about $M_v = -1.5$.

3.21. *Luminosity classes I and II.*—A new, careful compilation of the individual luminosities of stars with these MK classifications has been made by Schmidt-Kaler, who has subsequently used them for a new calibration. First results for the scarce but interesting supergiants of types F0–K7 have been published (Schmidt-Kaler 1961). Those for the earlier types and the resulting calibrations were kindly communicated by the author in advance of publication. Distances of the clusters and associations in which the stars occur were derived from the work of Johnson, Hoag, *et al.*, mentioned in the preceding section, and from unpublished results of W. Becker, who used the M_v, $U - B$ diagram for the curve fitting. Schmidt-Kaler also included some double stars of which one component could be calibrated independently. The calibrations are reproduced in columns II to Ia-0 of Table 3 (see also the summary in Schmidt-Kaler 1962). They must be considered as the most reliable now available. For the types O9–A5, more than 100 stars were used, and for F0–K7 about 60, for one-third of which double-star data, including eclipsing binaries, were incorporated. Column Ia–0 refers to stars with supergiant characteristics; for the introduction of the symbol Ia–0 see *Trans. I.A.U.*, 11A, 346, 1962.

A fair amount of smoothing has been applied in obtaining the tabular values. For the O and early B types, the luminosities of classes I*b*, I*ab*, and I*a* differ little, and it must be borne in mind that the actual luminosities of stars of a particular luminosity class show considerable dispersion with respect to the tabulated values; deviations of one mag. or more are not uncommon. That such large individual differences should occur for the later spectral classes is obvious from the wide range covered by the values in the various columns of Table 3 and the fact that these luminosity classes do not, like luminosity classes III and V, represent ridge lines of higher density in the HR diagram.

3.22. *Luminosity classes III–V.*—The most comprehensive calibration for the early-type classes III–V is the one by Johnson and Iriarte (1958), based both on stars in associations and clusters and on field stars for which Hγ measures were available. The luminosities of these latter were derived from the calibration of the Hγ equivalent widths described in § 3.31. The results are given by the normal-size figures in Table 3 above the dashed line. For O9–B0, III and IV, we use the results by Schmidt-Kaler (cf. § 3.21). For B1 V, B2 V, and B3 V, the tabulated values are in good agreement with the independent determination based on stars in the Scorpio-Centaurus association by Bertiau (1958). They also agree with values given earlier by Blaauw (1956) as a result of an analysis of the proper motions of the nearest B stars. Insofar as these latter were based on the Cassiopeia-Taurus region, it should be borne in mind that the interpretation of the proper motions of these stars has been criticized by Petrie (1958) on the basis of distances independently determined by means of Hγ measurements. Small-size figures in this part of Table 3 represent luminosities according to Keenan and Morgan (1951).

3.23. *Remarks to Table 3.*—The calibrations discussed in the last sections partly overlap with those for the types described in § 2.2. For the stars of spectral types B8–A1, luminosity class V, we have both the values of Osawa and those of Johnson and Iriarte; the former are systematically brighter by about 0.6 mag. This difference is probably due to the way in which the stars were selected, Osawa's choice being based on a selection according to apparent magnitude, whereas the material used by Johnson and Iriarte (containing many stars in the nearer associations) is more nearly applicable to a selection per volume of space. In general, the difference between mean absolute magnitudes per apparent magnitude and per volume of space is given by the expression

$$\Delta M = \frac{\sigma^2}{A(m)} \frac{dA(m)}{dm},$$

the latter being the fainter one. In this formula σ represents the dispersion of the absolute magnitudes around the mean per volume of space, and $A(m)dm$ represents the number of stars between apparent magnitudes m and $m + dm$. The difference observed between the overlapping series of values in Table 3 is of the amount expected.

Some overlap also occurs for the stars of spectral type G5–K2 of luminosity class II, where the difference is also in the expected sense, although here it is less well established.

In view of the different meanings of the calibrations discussed in §2.2 and in the last two sections, we separate them in Table 3 by the dashed line (see also the remarks in the note to the table).

The small-size figures represent the part of the diagram for which no particulars concerning the calibrations have yet been published. The population of these parts of the HR diagram is very sparse; most of these figures have been copied from Keenan and Morgan (1951).

3.3. The Calibration of Hydrogen-Line Intensities for O and B Stars

3.31. *The Hγ intensities.*—Work on the calibration of Hγ intensities has been done by Petrie (1953, 1958), Petrie and Moyls (1956), and Johnson and Iriarte (1958). The extensive investigations by Petrie were reviewed by this author in the 1960 paper. The calibration is based on various sources of data on absolute magnitudes—galactic clusters, visual binaries, and eclipsing binaries. For the O- and early B-type stars, use is made also of a preceding calibration of line intensities for the B8–A3 stars (Petrie and Maunsell 1950). For some of the galactic clusters, mean trigonometric parallaxes were used and, for the Scorpio-Centaurus stars, distances derived from the stream motion with respect to the sun. In the case of visual binaries, the luminosity of the B-type component is derived from the difference between the apparent magnitudes of the two components and the spectroscopic luminosity of the fainter, later-type, component. Eclipsing binaries furnish absolute magnitudes, provided that the stellar temperature scale is known. As a result of these procedures, Petrie adopts the interpolation formula:

$$M_v = -10.96 \times 10^{-0.145W} , \tag{16}$$

where W is the total absorption at Hγ in equivalent angstroms. In addition, small corrections depending on the spectral type, ranging from $+0.3$ for B0 to zero for B7, are to be applied.

Petrie and Moyls (1956) and Beer (1961) have made several tests of this calibration: mean trigonometric parallaxes for the stars not used in the calibration, mean secular parallaxes derived from proper motions and the elements of the solar motion, and mean distances derived from differential galactic rotation and a plausible value of the rotational constant A. The latter two tests would seem to be the strongest. From the proper motions, both Petrie and Moyls and Beer find confirmation of the adopted relation between M_v and W for the lower-luminosity part, say, $M_v > -2$, whereas for the intermediate luminosities $(-2 > M_v > -4)$ relation (16) seems to give somewhat too low luminosities. A similar result is indicated in Beer's differential galactic-rotation test. These corrections are not, however, suggested by the results from double stars.

Johnson and Iriarte (1958) have independently calibrated the Hγ intensities, using the stars in associations and clusters for which both equivalent widths and cluster distances, based on the curve-fitting procedure described in § 3.11, were known. Their calibration is formulated in two different ways: $(a)M_v$ is given as a function of Hγ and spectral type, as in Petrie's case (Tables IVa and IVb of Johnson and Iriarte's paper); (b) as a function of Hγ and $(B - V)_0$ (Table V of Johnson and Iriarte).

The comparison of the absolute magnitudes derived from Petrie's and Johnson and Iriarte's calibrations reveals systematic differences of up to 1 mag. for the stars of intermediate luminosity (around $M_v = -3$), whereas for the fainter $(M_v > -1)$ and brighter $(M_v < -5)$ stars the agreement is fair. The differences are in the sense that Johnson's values are the brighter ones. We are inclined to think that these latter are more nearly correct because they were based on the cluster distances from the main-sequence fitting procedure, which are probably more reliable than the data available at the time of Petrie's calibration. At least part of the systematic difference must be due to this cause: the distance moduli used by Petrie (1952) for the three clusters providing the majority of the standard stars are 5.0 for the Pleiades, 5.8 for the α Per cluster, and 7.8 for the Orion association, whereas the values in Johnson's system (for instance, Johnson et al. 1961) are 5.5, 6.1, and 8.1, respectively. Part of the difference may also be due to the fact that the effect of duplicity has nowhere been eliminated from Johnson and Iriarte's work, whereas it is eliminated to some extent in Petrie's procedure insofar as known double stars were used.

3.32. *Other hydrogen lines.*—These will be dealt with only briefly, because they have not yet been measured as extensively as $H\gamma$, although there may be more emphasis on other lines than $H\gamma$ in the future. If both $H\gamma$, or $H\beta$, and other lines have been measured, as in the work of Mrs. Hack (1953), these latter may be calibrated via the $H\gamma$ or $H\beta$ values.

The calibration of the $H\beta$ intensities measured in the programs of Strömgren and Crawford has been discussed by Crawford (1958, 1961) and by Hardie and Crawford (1961), with emphasis on the data provided by the II Scorpio association (i.e., the northern part of the Scorpio-Centaurus group) and the I Ori and the I Lac associations. The groups provide stars in restricted areas of the color-magnitude diagram and hence the relations between $H\beta$ and M_v for groups of different ages. An example is the relation $(M_v, H\beta)$ found by Hardie and Crawford for II Sco, which, in the case of single stars, gives a cosmic dispersion of about 0.3 mag. and, for all stars combined, a cosmic dispersion of about 0.5 mag. Extension of this work to more groups may be expected to produce accurate luminosities as a function of $H\beta$ and either spectral type, $(B - V)_0$ or $(U - B)_0$, and to show the variations of these relations as a function of the age of the group.

The author wishes to mention that parts of this chapter were prepared during a stay in 1961 at the Dyer Observatory of Vanderbilt University, Nashville, Tennessee, arranged by the Foreign Visiting Professors Program of the National Science Foundation and the American Astronomical Society.

REFERENCES

ADAMS, W. S., JOY, A. H., HUMASON, M. L., and BRAYTON, A. M.	1935	*Ap. J.*, **81**, 187; *Contr. Mt. W. Obs.*, No. 511.
BEER, A.	1961	*M.N.*, **123**, 191.
BERGER, J.	1957	*Problèmes de populations stellaires et de structure de la galaxie* (Paris: Centre National de la Recherche Scientifique), p. 57.
	1958	*J. d. Obs.*, **41**, 105.
	1962	*Ann. d'ap.*, **25**, 1,77.
BERTIAU, F. C.	1958	*Ap. J.*, **128**, 533; *Contr. McDonald Obs.*, No. 291.
BLAAUW, A.	1956	*Ap. J.* **123**, 408.
	1959	*I.A.U. Symposium*, No. 10, p. 105; *Ann. d'ap. Suppl.*, No. 8.
BLAAUW, A., HILTNER, W. A., and JOHNSON, H. L.	1959	*Ap. J.*, **130**, 69; *Contr. McDonald Obs.*, No. 304.
BORGMAN, J.	1960	*B.A.N.*, **15**, 255.

BUEREN, H. G. VAN   1952   *B.A.N.*, **11**, 385.

CHALONGE, D.   1958   *Ric. Astr. Spec. Astr. Vaticana*, **5**, 345; *Stellar Populations*, ed. D. J. K. O'CONNELL, S.J. (Amsterdam: North-Holland Publishing Co.).

CRAWFORD, D.   1958   *Ap. J.*, **128**, 185; *Contr. McDonald Obs.*, No. 287.

   1960   *Ap. J.*, **132**, 66; *Contr. McDonald Obs.*, No. 325.

   1961   *Ap. J.*, **133**, 860; *Contr. Kitt Peak National Obs.*, No. 9; *Dyer Obs. Repr.*, No. 16.

EGGEN, O.   1955   *A.J.*, **60**, 401; *Lick Obs. Bull.*, No. 538.

   1957   *A.J.*, **62**, 45; *Lick Obs. Bull.*, No. 549.

EVANS, D. S., MENZIES, A., and STOY, R. H.   1957   *M.N.*, **117**, 534.

   1959   *Ibid.*, **119**, 638.

GLIESE, W.   1956   *Zs. f. Ap.*, **39**, 1.

HACK, M.   1953   *Ann. d'ap.*, **16**, 417.

HALLIDAY, I.   1955   *Ap. J.*, **122**, 222; *Comm. David Dunlap Obs.*, No. 37.

HARDIE, R. H., and CRAWFORD, D. L.   1961   *Ap. J.*, **133**, 843.

HEARD, J. F.   1956   *Vistas in Astronomy*, ed. A. BEER (London: Pergamon Press), **2**, 1357.

HECKMANN, O., DIECK-VOSS, W., and KOX, H.   1956   *A.N.*, **283**, 109.

HECKMANN, O., and JOHNSON, H. L.   1956   *Ap. J.*, **124**, 477.

HECKMANN, O., and LÜBECK, K.   1956   *Zs. f. Ap.*, **40**, 1.

HILTNER, W. A.   1956   *Ap. J. Suppl.*, **2**, 389; *Contr. McDonald Obs.*, No. 269.

HOSSACK, W. R.   1954   *Ap. J.*, **119**, 613; *Comm. David Dunlap Obs.*, No. 35.

JOHNSON, H. L.   1957   *Ap. J.*, **126**, 121.

   1960   *Lowell Obs. Bull.*, **5**, 17.

JOHNSON, H. L., and HILTNER, W. A.   1956   *Ap. J.*, **123**, 267; *Contr. McDonald Obs.*, No. 263.

JOHNSON, H. L., HOAG, A. A., IRIARTE, B., MITCHELL, R. I., and HALLAM, K. L.   1961   *Lowell Obs. Bull.*, **5**, 133.

JOHNSON, H. L., and IRIARTE, B.   1958   *Lowell Obs. Bull.*, **4**, 47.

JOHNSON, H. L., and KNUCKLES, C. F.   1955   *Ap. J.*, **122**, 209.

JOHNSON, H. L., and MITCHELL, R. I.   1958   *Ap. J.*, **128**, 31.

JOHNSON, H. L., and MORGAN, W. W.   1953   *Ap. J.*, **117**, 313; *Contr. McDonald Obs.*, No. 216.

   1955   *Ap. J.*, **122**, 429; *Contr. McDonald Obs.*, No. 261.

KEENAN, P. C., and
  MORGAN, W. W.   1951   *Astrophysics*, ed. J. A. HYNEK (New York: Mc-Graw-Hill Book Co., Inc.), p. 12.

LJUNGGREN, B., and
  OJA, T.   1961   *Ann. Uppsala Obs.*, Vol. **4**, No. 10.

MITCHELL, R. I.   1960   *Ap. J.*, **132**, 68.

MORGAN, W. W., CODE,
  A. D., and WHITFORD,
  A. E.   1955   *Ap. J. Suppl.*, **2**, 41.

MORGAN, W. W.,
  KEENAN, P. C.,
  and KELLMAN, E.   1943   *An Atlas of Stellar Spectra* (Chicago: University of Chicago Press).

MUSTEL, E. R., GALKIN,
  L. S., KUMAIGOROD-
  SKAYA, R. N., and
  BOYARCHUK, M. E.   1958   *Pub. Crimean Ap. Obs.*, **18**, 3.

NIKONOV, V. B.,
  NEKRASOVA, S. V.,
  POLOSUKHINA, N. S.,
  RACHKOVSKY, D. N.,
  and CHUVAYEV, K. K. 1957   *Pub. Crimean Ap. Obs.*, **17**, 42.

OKE, J. B.   1957   *Ap. J.*, **126**, 509; *Comm. David Dunlap Obs.*, No. 40.
                      1959   *Ap. J.*, **130**, 487; *Comm. David Dunlap Obs.*, No. 44.

OSAWA, K.   1959   *Ap. J.*, **130**, 159; *Contr. McDonald Obs.*, No. 308.

PEARCE, J. A.   1955   *Pub. A.S.P.*, **67**, 23.

PETRIE, R. M.   1953   *Pub. Dom. Ap. Obs.*, **9**, 251.
                      1956   *Vistas in Astronomy*, ed. A. BEER (London: Pergamon Press), **2**, 1346.
                      1958   *M.N.*, **118**, 80; *Contr. Dom. Ap. Obs.*, No. 61.

PETRIE, R. M., and
  MAUNSELL, C. D.   1950   *Pub. Dom. Ap. Obs.*, **8**, 253.

PETRIE, R. M., and
  MOYLS, B. N.   1956   *Pub. Dom. Ap. Obs.*, **10**, 287.

RHIJN, P. J. VAN   1939   *Pub. Kapteyn Astr. Lab.*, No. 49.

ROMAN, N. G.   1952   *Ap. J.*, **116**, 122.

RUSSELL, H. N., and
  MOORE, C. E.   1938   *Ap. J.*, **87**, 389; *Contr. Mt. W. Obs.*, No. 589.
                      1940   *Ap. J.*, **92**, 354; *Contr. Mt. W. Obs.*, No. 636.

SANDAGE, A.   1957   *Ap. J.*, **125**, 435.

SCHMIDT-KALER, TH. 1961   *Zs. f. Ap.*, **53**, 1 and 28.
                      1962   *Die Sterne*, **38**, 220.

SINNERSTAD, U.   1961*a* *Ann. Stockholm Obs.*, Vol. **22**, No. 2.
                      1961*b* *Meddel. Stockholm Obs.*, No. 131.

STRÖMBERG, G.

1933   *Ap. J.*, **78**, 178; *Contr. Mt. W. Obs.*, No. 473.

1936   *Ap. J.*, **84**, 412; *Contr. Mt. W. Obs.*, No. 554.

1939   *Ap. J.*, **89**, 10; *Contr. Mt. W. Obs.*, No. 603.

1940   *Ap. J.*, **92**, 156; *Contr. Mt. W. Obs.*, No. 628.

1941   *Ap. J.*, **93**, 33; *Contr. Mt. W. Obs.*, No. 641.

STRÖMGREN, B.

1958   *Ric. Astr. Spec. Astr. Vaticana*, **5**, 385; *Stellar Populations*, ed. D. J. K. O'CONNELL, S.J. (Amsterdam: North-Holland Publishing Co.).

TRUMPLER, R. J., and
  WEAVER, H. F.

1953   *Statistical Astronomy* (Berkeley and Los Angeles: University of California Press).

WALKER, M. F.

1961   *Ap. J.*, **133**, 438; *Contr. Lick Obs.*, Ser. II, No. 112.

WALRAVEN, T., and
  WALRAVEN, J.

1960   *B.A.N.*, **15**, 67.

WILLIAMS, E. G.

1936   *Ap. J.*, **83**, 305; *Contr. Mt. W. Obs.*, No. 541.

WILSON, O. C.

1959a   *Ap. J.*, **130**, 496.

1959b   *Ibid.*, p. 499.

1961   *Sci. American*, **204**, No. 1, 107.

WILSON, O. C., and
  BAPPU, M. K. V.

1957   *Ap. J.*, **125**, 661.

CHAPTER 21

The Absolute Magnitudes of
Classical Cepheids

ROBERT P. KRAFT

Mount Wilson and Palomar Observatories
Carnegie Institution of Washington, California Institute of Technology

§ 1. INTRODUCTION

OVER the years, the determination of extragalactic distances has been based on the assumption that cepheids of a given period were essentially alike, regardless of the stellar system in which they occurred. The first change in this outlook was forced by Baade's distinction between the cepheids of Populations I and II. It gradually emerged that the long-period cepheids of globular clusters were old stars of comparatively low mass (Arp 1955); their spectroscopic properties were similar to those of the nearby peculiar cepheid W Vir (cf. Wallerstein 1958). Thus the need for modification of the earlier assumption was very clear; it was replaced with the idea that the period-luminosity law could still be used, provided that only stars of type I (Population I) were considered.

Recent studies suggest, however, that the concept of "type I" and "type II" is a serious oversimplification. It is probably more useful to regard age and chemical composition as the basic parameters governing stars and stellar systems. Within our Galaxy, there appears to be a rough correlation between these two parameters. Thus, on quite general grounds, one supposes that the sequence of age, starting from halo globular clusters, on through nuclear globulars, old galactic clusters, and up through the familiar sequence of younger galactic clusters, also represents a sequence of increasing metal/H ratio, as well as of increasing flatness in galactic distribution. Spectroscopic observations seem generally to confirm this picture. However, the metal "enrichment" has not, at least among these clusters, proceeded so rapidly in the last 5×10^9 years as in the preceding period. Arp (1961) has also emphasized that the correlation between age and metal abundance may not be so sharp as might first be imagined. Thus one can find two globular clusters of the same age (M2 and M5)

421

but with spectra indicating rather different H/metal ratios. Apparently, local spatial irregularities in the degree of metal enrichment show up in the formation of clusters of different metal content at the same time.

This apparent uncoupling of age and metal content *may* lie behind the difference between the color-magnitude diagrams of galactic clusters in the Small Magellanic Cloud (SMC) and the Galaxy (Arp 1961). One finds SMC clusters with main-sequence breakoff points that are matched by clusters of the Galaxy, yet their Hertzsprung gaps are narrower and their luminosity functions "younger," i.e., richer in bright stars relative to faint. Similar effects may be operating to distinguish Large Magellanic Cloud (LMC) clusters as well from those of both the Galaxy and the SMC (cf., e.g., NGC 1783, Sandage and Eggen 1960).

The effect of these developments on our search for a cosmic distance scale may be significant. At first, the term "type I" was reserved for any cluster with a color-magnitude diagram younger than M67. Among these are clusters of age 10^7–10^8 years that contain "type I," i.e., "classical" cepheids (summarized by Irwin 1958). Suppose, however, that among clusters of this kind in different galaxies (or, indeed, within the Galaxy!) there should be a range of chemical composition. Would we then be justified in assuming universality of the period-luminosity law even among so-called classical cepheids? This question seems to be of more than academic interest because of (1) the differences between LMC, SMC, and galactic clusters cited in the preceding paragraph; (2) the marked differences between SMC and galactic cepheids (§ 4) (Arp and Kraft 1961); and (3) the small, but possibly significant, differences in chemical composition between the sun and stars of the Hyades (Wallerstein and Helfer 1959) and between the MK standards and stars of NGC 752 (Roman 1955) and M67 (Burbidge and Burbidge 1959).

Such a proposal is perhaps not unreasonable when viewed in the light of recent developments about the chemical composition of globular clusters and RR Lyrae stars. There is evidence that differences in chemical composition between globular clusters (Sandage, private communications; Arp 1962) induce a spread of about 1 mag. in the luminosities of the cluster variables. Preston (1959, 1961) has shown that a remarkable range of metal abundances probably exists among individual RR Lyrae variables of the general field; this is correlated with kinematic and space-distribution properties. One of the RR Lyrae variables studied by Preston (1961), viz., DX Del, has an H/metal ratio indistinguishable, within the errors, from that of the sun. While it is true that the RR Lyrae variables probably encompass a wide range of (old) ages and that this in itself would presumably induce a range in chemical composition, it is also probably the case that RR Lyrae variables in different parts of the Galaxy have the same age but different chemical compositions, owing to composition differences in the material out of which they were formed. This would seem to be confirmed by the results on M2 and M5 (Arp 1961) already cited.

It is this latter possibility that should be kept in mind when comparing the

"type I," i.e., young, cepheids in different stellar systems and, indeed, in different parts of the Galaxy. This has been stressed by Arp (1962) in a paper on
the place of variable stars in stellar evolution. As we shall see later in this chapter, there is evidence that the Galaxy contains "young" cepheids of low metal
content. However, we shall first review the observational status of the period-
luminosity and period-color relations for classical cepheids in the vicinity of the
sun. We are then in a position to compare these cepheids with those of other
galactic regions and of the SMC.

§ 2. THE PERIOD-COLOR AND PERIOD-LUMINOSITY RELATIONS FOR CEPHEIDS IN THE VICINITY OF THE SUN

The history of the determination of the period-luminosity law has been reviewed by Baade (1956) and need not be repeated at length here. It is sufficient
to recall that the slope had been taken from the Magellanic Cloud cepheids and
the zero point from a study of proper motions and radial velocities (statistical
parallaxes) of cepheids in the vicinity of the sun (cf. R. E. Wilson 1939). Current
developments (cited later) indicate that the Wilson study underestimated the
absorption of light by interstellar material. An early estimate (Joy 1939) of
about 0.85 mag. (pg)/kpc was used; for 40 classical cepheids within 1 kpc of
the sun, we now find an average value of 1.9 mag/kpc. Since the RR Lyrae
variables used in the analysis suffered little or no absorption, a zero point was
obtained for the classical cepheids that was too faint relative to the cluster variables. Unfortunately, the error was such that the identification of long-period
cepheids in ω Cen with the 16-day classical cepheids (Shapley 1918) seemed to
give reasonable absolute magnitudes for the RR Lyrae variables in ω Cen; this
unfortunate coincidence retarded for many years a true appreciation of the difference in brightness between globular-cluster and "type I" long-period
cepheids. It should be mentioned that Joy (1939), in his classical study of
galactic rotation from cepheids, had emphasized the possibility that the absorption might have to be considerably larger than 0.85 mag/kpc if the condition
$\langle z \rangle = \langle r \sin b \rangle = $ constant independent of r was to be maintained for cepheids
throughout the Galaxy. Joy (1940) was also the first to notice the profound spectroscopic differences between Barnard's variable ($P = 15$ days) in M3 and the
classical 16-day cepheids.

2.1. THE PERIOD-COLOR RELATION

The interstellar material is highly spotty and surprisingly thick even a few
hundred parsecs from the sun. The foregoing discussion shows clearly that cepheids cannot properly be used as distance indicators without a well-defined
star-by-star method for evaluating the visual absorption, $A_V = 3.0 \, E_{B-V}$, where
E_{B-V} is the color excess. The task is considerably simplified, however, because
the classical cepheids satisfy a period-color relation. Once this is set up, color

excesses can be obtained without recourse to spectroscopic or photometric techniques, given, of course, the light- and color-curves.

That the cepheids satisfy a period-color relation was shown in Code's (1947) investigation of spectral types. Figure 1 contains a slight revision (Kraft 1960*a*) of Code's original diagram; MK types at maximum and minimum light are shown as a function of log *P*. The appearance of the G band was used as the sole spectroscopic criterion, in order to avoid the phase-dependent kinematic widening of strong lines such as hydrogen and Ca I λ 4226 (cf. Kraft 1960*a, c*).

The diagram can be used to predict color excesses, provided that the intrinsic colors of a few cepheids can be found. It is reasonable to suppose that the intrinsic colors at maximum light are approximately constant with log *P*; alternatively, we might try to evaluate the period dependence of the color at mean or

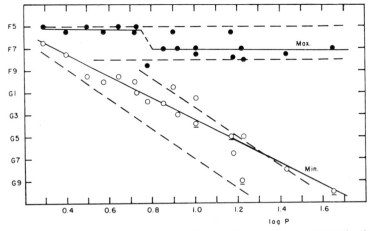

FIG. 1.—Period–spectral type diagram (after Code 1947; revised by Kraft 1960*a*). The MK spectral types at maximum and minimum light are derived from the appearance of the G band alone. Dashed lines outline the original boundaries given by Code.

minimum light. Kraft (1960*b*) has shown that the scatter about the mean color is less than the scatter about the color at maximum light.

Attempts to use the diagram were carried out by Eggen (1951), by Gascoigne and Eggen (1957), and by Walraven, Müller, and Oosterhoff (1958). In the first-named paper, it was found that the observed colors at maximum light of five nearby cepheids lay on a straight line, which was assumed to represent the locus of unreddened colors. Unfortunately, this proved to be a coincidence; it is now known that all nearby cepheids are reddened, some quite heavily. The other two papers assumed that the colors of field cepheids at maximum light were the same as those of Magellanic Cloud cepheids; the latter were assumed to be unreddened. Almost all field cepheids turned out to be redder than the Cloud cepheids, and the difference was attributed directly to galactic interstellar reddening. The method is subject to the criticism that the reddening between us and the Magellanic Clouds is unknown, that the reddening within the Clouds themselves was neglected, and that the assumed identity between the Cloud cepheids and the galactic cepheids is not necessarily justified.

Later studies considered only stars in the vicinity of the sun (Kron 1958; Kron and Svolopoulos 1959; Kraft 1960a, b, 1961a, b, c). For a number of F-, G-, and K-type (non-variable) supergiants classified by Bidelman, Kron plotted colors $(V - B)$ versus $(R - I)$ from the six-color photometry. Reddening trajectories were determined from color measurements of stars of the same spectral type but at different distances. An unreddened envelope was estimated for the body of these stars (see Fig. 2); movement of a given supergiant along the reddening trajectory to this envelope determined the color excess. Kron and Svolopoulos assumed that, during the cycle, classical cepheids had a correspondence between $(V - B, R - I)$ and spectral type identical with that of Ib supergiants. Actually, the stars describe skinny loops in the color-color diagram, but the spread is small enough for presumably meaningful average excesses to be obtained. One of these is illustrated in Figure 2. The period–mean color relation, following Kron and Svolopoulos but transformed to the MK B, V system, is illustrated in Figure 3.

Kraft's method made use of the intrinsic colors of classical cepheids that are members of galactic clusters (cf. Irwin 1958). It was assumed that, at any phase, a one-to-one correspondence could be found between intrinsic color, $(B - V)^0$, and the MK spectral type defined by the appearance or strength of the G band. For Ib supergiants of the MK system, the strength of the G band was measured, using narrow band-pass interference filters (Γ-photometry); this is illustrated in Figure 4. Γ-measurements were also made at many phases of U Sgr in M25 (Wampler, Pesch, Hiltner, and Kraft 1961) and DL Cas in NGC 129 (Arp, Sandage, and Stephens 1959), and consequently the MK types could be plotted against $(B - V)^0$. The spectral type–intrinsic color relation so obtained is illustrated in Figure 5.

The excess E_{B-V} for any field cepheid was then obtained at any phase by measuring Γ, predicting from this $(B - V)^0$, and comparing the latter with the observed $(B - V)$ for that phase. The intrinsic colors of the field cepheids were thus tied directly to the method of determining color excesses for cluster B-type stars that had been developed by Johnson and Morgan (1953). The period–mean color relation so obtained is illustrated in Figure 6. The mean color is slightly redder than that derived from the Kron-Svolopoulos data, but the difference is small. The fact that the agreement is good in spite of the rather different methods of analysis suggests that excesses derived by either technique must be substantially correct. Recent results by Kraft and Hiltner (1961) confirm this view. From U, B, V measurements of supergiants and a reasonable extrapolation to M2 Ib of the intrinsic color–spectral type relation of Figure 5, these authors obtained E_{B-V} for most of the supergiants observed by Kron (1958). A plot of excesses from one investigation versus the other is shown in

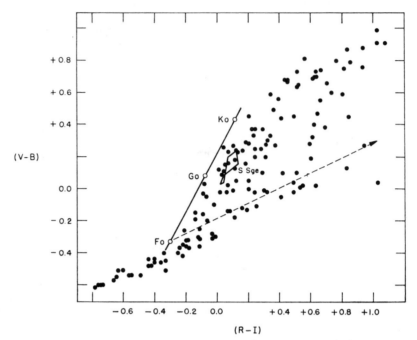

FIG. 2.—The $(V - B)$ versus $(R - I)$ diagram for MK supergiants (after Kron 1958). The solid line represents the thermal locus of unreddened supergiants. The dashed line is the reddening trajectory. The skinny figure 8 is the phase locus of S Sge ($P = 8^d.4$), according to Kron and Svolopoulos (1959).

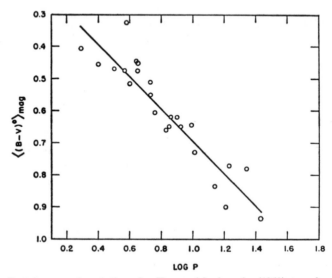

FIG. 3.—Period–mean color relation, after Kron and Svolopoulos (1959), transformed to the B, V system.

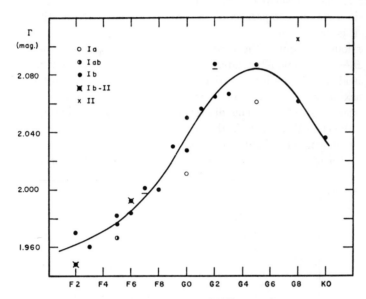

Fig. 4—Relation between Γ and MK spectral type

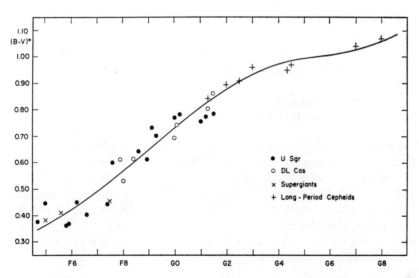

Fig. 5.—MK spectral type versus $(B - V)^0$ for Ib supergiants of the MK system, after Kraft (1961c).

Figure 7; the agreement is very satisfactory. A systematic effect is, however, found in a similar comparison of excesses for cepheids (Kraft 1961b); though small, it is unexplained.

A serious criticism of the Kraft method might be found in the assumption that $(B - V)^0$ is uniquely related to the MK type through the G band. Studies of cepheids in clusters indicate that $(U - B)^0$ for these stars bears, especially near maximum light, a slightly different relation to spectral type than that for non-variable supergiants. This discrepancy is in the sense that cepheids move toward the class V sequence in the $(U - B)^0$ versus $(B - V)^0$ diagram as they rise toward maximum light, (cf. Fernie 1961). This probably results from increased atmospheric pressure, owing to the passage of a running wave through

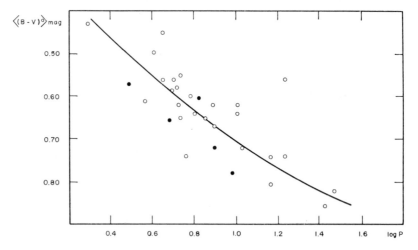

FIG. 6.—Period–mean color relation, after Kraft (1961c). Filled circles represent the five galactic cluster cepheids, EV Sct, CF Cas, U Sgr, DL Cas, and S Nor.

the atmosphere (cf. Kraft, Camp, Fernie, Fujita, and Hughes 1959). The colors thus imitate a star of luminosity lower than Ib on the rise to maximum light. The effect is seen almost entirely in $(U - B)^0$ (effect of the Balmer jump?) and only very slightly in $(B - V)^0$. An exaggerated version of this phenomenon is found in "type II" stars, such as RR Lyr (Oke and Bonsack 1960) and W Vir (Arp 1957). That the effect on $(B - V)^0$ is small seems justified by the agreement in the intrinsic color of a Per (F5 Ib), a member of I Per, with that of U Sgr in M25 at maximum light, which is also F5 Ib at that phase.

2.2. THE PERIOD-LUMINOSITY LAW

The empirically derived period-color relation is found to have a definite scatter, larger than would be expected from the errors in the color-excess determinations. Indeed, scatter in both the period-luminosity and the period-color relations is shown quite conclusively in the reddening-freed colors and absorption-freed absolute magnitudes of the cepheids in galactic clusters (see Table 1).

It is especially notable that U Sgr, DL Cas, and S Nor all have about the same mean absolute magnitude, but their periods and mean colors are quite different.

Sandage (1958), from a semitheoretical argument, has shown that the scatter in the period-color and period-luminosity relations is coupled and is intrinsic. Let any cepheid satisfy a period–mean density relation of the form

$$P \left(\frac{\langle \rho \rangle}{\langle \rho_\odot \rangle} \right)^{1/2} = Q , \qquad (1)$$

where $\langle \rho \rangle$ and $\langle \rho_\odot \rangle$ are the mean densities of the cepheid and the sun, respectively, and Q the pulsational constant. Since $\rho \sim \mathfrak{M}/R^3$, where $\mathfrak{M}$ is the mass and R the radius, this relation can be written in the form

$$f_1(\mathfrak{M}, L, T_e, P) = Q , \qquad (2)$$

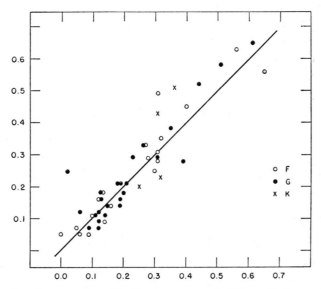

Fig. 7.—E_{B-V} for supergiants, Kron's system versus the Hiltner-Kraft system. The abscissa is E_{B-V} given by Kraft and Hiltner (1961).

TABLE 1

COLOR EXCESSES, ABSOLUTE MAGNITUDES, AND MEAN INTRINSIC COLORS FOR
5 GALACTIC CLUSTER CEPHEIDS (KRAFT 1961c)

Star	log P	E_{B-V}	$\langle (B-V)^0 \rangle_{\mathrm{mag}}$	$\langle M_V^0 \rangle$	log Q	log Q_{corr}	Wt.
EV Sct....	0.490	0.58	+0.57	−2.62	−1.3074	−1.3018	$\frac{1}{2}$
CF Cas....	.687	.555	+ .655	−3.45	−1.3585	−1.3510	$\frac{1}{2}$
U Sgr......	.828	.55	+ .605	−3.92	−1.3001	−1.3041	1
DL Cas....	.908	.50	+ .72	−3.84	−1.2768	−1.2700	1
S Nor......	0.989	0.205	+0.78	−3.96	−1.2578	−1.2457	1

where T_e is the effective temperature. Now, if it is possible to find the bolometric correction and effective temperature scales for cepheids as a function of $(B - V)^0$ and if, further, a suitable mass-luminosity law is employed, then this function can be replaced by

$$f_2[M_V^0, (B - V)^0, P] = Q. \tag{3}$$

Thus there is really no such thing as a period-luminosity law; actually, we are dealing with a period-luminosity-color relation. To put the matter another way, the period-luminosity and period-color relations are mean traces of equation (3) for the variables taken two at a time with P as the independent variable. The intrinsic scatter in the period-color relation *induces* a scatter in the period-luminosity law. It is for this reason that the five galactic cluster cepheids cannot, by themselves, determine the period-color and period-luminosity relations. Considering the observational inaccuracies, we find there are simply not enough points to determine with precision all the coefficients in equation (3), particularly if the degree of freedom of a variable Q is allowed.

Strictly speaking, equation (1) requires the evaluation of the mean density in some sense or other. Kraft (1961a) assumed that $\langle 1/R^3 \rangle$ over the time was required; thus we write

$$Q = P \left(\frac{\mathfrak{M}}{\mathfrak{M}_\odot} \right)^{1/2} \left[\frac{L_{bol}(\odot)}{\langle L_V \rangle} \right]^{3/4} \left\{ \int_0^1 \left[\frac{\langle L_V \rangle}{L_V(\phi)} \right]^{3/2} \left[\frac{L_V(\phi)}{L_{bol}(\phi)} \right]^{3/2} \right.$$

$$\left. \times \left[\frac{T_e(\phi)}{T_e(\odot)} \right]^6 d\phi \right\}^{1/2}, \tag{4}$$

evaluating Q by a timewise integration. It was shown that, for classical cepheids at least, adoption of $1/\langle R^3 \rangle$ or $1/\langle R \rangle^3$ as the appropriate mean did not change Q more than 0.3 per cent of itself.

Oke's (1961b) model atmospheres and Kraft's (1961c) reddening for δ Cep lead to the following effective temperature and bolometric correction scales:

$$\log T_e = 3.886 - 0.175 (B - V)^0, \quad 0.30 \le (B - V)^0 \le 1.15, \tag{5}$$

and

$$M_{bol} - M_V = -0.116 + 0.583 (B - V)^0 - 0.704 [(B - V)^0]^2. \tag{6}$$

From the galactic clusters containing cepheids, Kraft found that the mean difference in magnitude between the cluster "breakoff" and the cepheids was -0.05 ± 0.1 (p.e.) mag.; thus the appropriate mass-luminosity law is

$$M_{bol} = 2.96 - 8.25 \log \frac{\mathfrak{M}}{\mathfrak{M}_\odot}, \tag{7}$$

in which it is assumed that the evolutionary tracks are horizontal after an initial rise of 1 mag. from the zero-age main sequence. Finally, from the observed colors and magnitudes of the five galactic cluster cepheids, we can evaluate Q, using equations (5), (6), (7), and (4) (see Table 1).

The Q's can be used to deduce two physical quantities. The first of these is the physically appropriate mean color. Various observational mean colors can be defined; these are reviewed by Kraft (1961a). But which of these is physically significant? What is suggested is that we look for the color of the fictitious star representing the equilibrium configuration about which the pulsation perturbation is applied. Thus, in the limit of vanishingly small amplitude, we can substitute from equations (5), (6), and (7) directly in equation (4) and obtain

$$\log P - 0.3854\ (B - V)^0 - 0.1685\ [(B - V)^0]^2 + 0.2394\ M_V^0$$
$$= \log Q + 0.8958 . \tag{8}$$

Since there is no ambiguity in the mean of $\log Q$, $\log P$, or $\langle M_V^0 \rangle$, we can find for each of the five galactic cluster cepheids the appropriate mean color that will give the same $\log Q$ from equation (8) as from equation (4). This appears to be identifiable with $\langle (B - V)^0 \rangle_{mag}$ (cf. Kraft 1961a). In other words, we find from the reddening-corrected color-curve the mean magnitude just as the curve stands. Why this particular mean seems to be physically significant within the present context has not yet been explained. For some other kind of variable star, a different mean might be required.

A second physical result derived from the use of these equations is the distinct possibility that Q is not the same constant for all cepheids. The period–mean color relation illustrated in Figure 6 is represented in the mean by the equation

$$\langle (B - V)^0 \rangle_{mag} = -0.101\ (\log P)^2 + 0.5365\ (\log P) + 0.2644 . \tag{9}$$

Suppose the period–mean luminosity law can be represented by an expression of the form

$$\langle M_V^0 \rangle = a + b \log P . \tag{10}$$

Then, substituting equations (9) and (10) in equation (8), we obtain

$$-0.00172\ (\log P)^4 + 0.01833\ (\log P)^3 - 0.00093\ (\log P)^2$$
$$+ (0.74449 + 0.2394b) \log P + (0.2394a - 1.00948) = \log Q . \tag{11}$$

This relation is valid, of course, only along the mean locus of the instability strip in the H-R diagram. If the terms of order $(\log P)^2$ and higher are neglected as a rough approximation, the condition that Q is a constant independent of P is $b = -3.11$, i.e., the slope of the visual period-luminosity law would have to be considerably steeper than that given by the SMC (Arp 1960; Arp and Kraft 1961). In other words, a constant Q implies that the slope of the period-luminosity law is not a universal number.

This is probably not surprising. We recall that Q is an eigenvalue of the differential equations of pulsation. The conclusion that Q is the same for all cepheids results from the convenient assumption of homology (cf. Aller 1954). There is no a priori reason, however, why cepheids should be homologous to one another. Nevertheless, we should probably be careful in supposing that the variation of Q with P will be given exactly by equation (11). The derivation assumes that the scale of T_e and the bolometric correction given by Oke (1961b) for δ Cep are applicable over the entire range of cepheid periods and also that the form of the $\mathfrak{M}$-L law (eq. [7]) is the same for all P. These assumptions are not expected to be greatly in error, but more will be known when Oke completes his current model-atmosphere calculations for T Mon ($P = 27$ days).

The period-luminosity relation at present is derived best from the five cepheids in galactic clusters. However, because of the color dependence, i.e., the $f_2[(B - V)^0, M_V^0, P] = Q$ relation, the observational errors, and the fact that no galactic cluster cepheids are known with $P > 10$ days, we cannot determine with sufficient precision both the slope and the zero point. We take the slope from Arp's discussion of the SMC cepheids; we then derived the following equations from the five galactic cluster cepheids:

$$\langle M_V^0 \rangle = -1.67 - 2.54 \log P , \qquad (12a)$$

$$\langle M_B^0 \rangle = -1.33 - 2.25 \log P . \qquad (12b)$$

The mean error of each zero point is ± 0.06 mag.

Since the slope of equation (12b) is different from the early derivation by Shapley (1940), viz., $\langle M_{pg} \rangle = -0.28 - 1.74 \log P$, it makes no sense to speak of the "zero-point correction to Shapley's original period-luminosity law." If we fix our attention on a specific period, say $P = 6$ days, we find a correction of -1.4 mag. to the Shapley relation. It should also be emphasized at this point that the zero point of our period-luminosity law is based essentially on the absolute magnitudes of A- and F-type main-sequence stars, as given by the Yerkes system (Johnson and Morgan 1953; Johnson and Iriarte 1958).

As a check on the absolute magnitudes given by cepheids in clusters, we consider Oke's careful discussion of Wesselink's method for η Aql (Oke 1961a) and δ Cep (Oke 1961b). The success of the method for classical cepheids seems assured because the radius change is of the order of 50 times the atmospheric scale height, H (Abt 1959). Since H is of the same order as the optical thickness of the atmosphere, the question of the relative change in radius of line- and continuum-forming regions is probably a second-order consideration (cf. Whitney 1955a, b). Using model atmospheres given by Canavaggia and Pecker (1953), Oke compares the model emergent flux with the observed flux from $\lambda \sim 10,000$ to $\lambda \sim 3400$. The observations combine photoelectric spectrum scanning and high-dispersion spectrograms; corrections are made for reddening and for blanketing by metallic lines. The models turn out to be quite insensitive to gravity, so that, given the chemical composition, T_e is obtained. Thus, if subscripted values refer to some particular phase, we have, for any phase,

$$2.5 \log \left(\frac{L}{L_0} \right)_\lambda = 5 \log \left(\frac{R}{R_0} \right) + 2.5 \log \left(\frac{F}{F_0} \right)_\lambda \qquad (13)$$

for any wavelength λ. The left-hand side is known when some monochromatic light-curve is given, and the model atmosphere gives the last term on the right. One solves for R/R_0. But integration of the radial-velocity curves give $R - R_0$, the displacement-curve; thus the change in radius and the mean radius are determined. These quantities are plotted as functions of phase for η Aql in Figure 8 (Oke 1961a). The shapes of the computed and observed R/R_0-curves agree very well. For δ Cep and η Aql, Wesselink's method (after Oke) gives $\langle M_V^0 \rangle = -3.2$ and -4.1, respectively; Kraft's fit of the period-luminosity-color relation gives $\langle M_V^0 \rangle = -3.48$ and -3.86. The agreement is very satisfactory.

A second kind of check on the absolute magnitudes is given by Polaris,

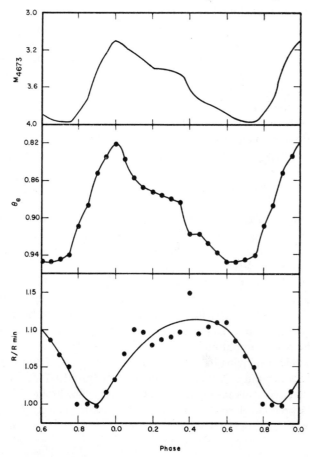

Fig. 8.—Wesselink's method for η Aql (after Oke 1961a). The panels give the monochromatic flux at $\lambda = 4673$, the effective temperature of the models (after line-blanketing corrections are applied), and the change in radius as a function of phase. In the bottom panel the dots are computed from the model fluxes and the monochromatic light-curves, and the curve is the displacement-curve derived from the radial velocities.

which is evidently a component of a visual binary system. The secondary is of type F2 V (reviewed by Gascoigne and Eggen 1957); if it is on the zero-age main sequence, the primary has $\langle M_V^0 \rangle = -3.05$. Again, the period-luminosity-color relation gives $\langle M_V^0 \rangle = -3.3$; the agreement is reasonably good. We shall not, however, consider δ Cep A and B. The secondary may not be on the main sequence, and there now seems to be some doubt that the pair forms an actual physical system (cf. Kraft 1961a).

§ 3. PROPERTIES OF THE COLOR-MAGNITUDE DIAGRAM FOR GALACTIC CEPHEIDS

As soon as the period-luminosity law is given by equation (12), log Q can be computed as a function of log P on the mean relation through equation (11). Then, for any assigned period, equation (8) generates the lines of constant period in the H-R diagram. Strictly speaking, Q may not be constant along a line of constant P. However, the total variation is presumably small because the slope of the lines of constant period in the SMC is not large (cf. Arp 1960) and the color width of the cepheid domain is only about 0.2 mag. Since the SMC results also indicate that the lines of constant period are probably straight, we absorb the quadratic term in equation (8) into the change in Q along a constant P-line. For the 31 cepheids used to define the period–mean color relation, we obtain the color-magnitude diagram in Figure 9. Here the stars are entered with intrinsic color and period and are located in accordance with their fit on the grid of period lines. The galactic cluster cepheids, however, are located by the colors and magnitudes of Table 1. Each of these fits its appropriate period line with a precision of 0.2 mag. or better. Thus we may expect to determine the photometric distance to a cepheid having known V and $B - V$ curves with a precision of the same order as that of a galactic cluster.

An important property of this diagram can be derived from the following considerations. Define a quantity ΔB which represents the total amplitude of the blue light-curve of a cepheid. (A similar quantity ΔV can be defined; since all results are seen more easily in ΔB, we shall make use of it alone in what follows.) The period-amplitude diagram (ΔB versus log P) is shown in Figure 10 for all cepheids belonging to the Cygnus-Carina arm (Kraft 1964) and having photoelectric magnitudes (Eggen, Gascoigne, and Burr 1957; Oosterhoff 1960; Irwin 1961; Weaver, Steinmetz, and Mitchell 1961). The broken line represents an assumed upper envelope. We define the amplitude "defect" f_B of a star by the equation

$$2.5 \log f_B = (\Delta B)_* - (\Delta B)_{max}, \qquad (14)$$

where $(\Delta B)_{max}$ is given by the upper envelope line. The quantity f_B measures the amount by which the amplitude of a cepheid is less than the maximum amplitude known for that period.

Returning to the 31 stars of the period–mean color relation, we can also define a quantity $\delta(B - V)^0$, which represents the deviation of a star from the mean curve; it is negative if the star is bluer than the relation and positive if the star is redder. In Figure 11 we have plotted f_B against the absolute value of $\delta(B - V)^0$ for the 28 cepheids of the group belonging to the Cygnus-Carina arm (Kraft 1964). Within the errors, there is a correlation in the sense that large-amplitude cepheids satisfy the relation closely, but the smaller the amplitude, the larger is $\delta(B - V)^0$ in absolute value. Note, too, that if the algebraic value of $\delta(B - V)^0$ had been plotted, Figure 11 would be replaced by a "roof-shaped" structure.

This result can be interpreted in the color-magnitude diagram to mean that a supergiant, on first entering the instability strip, pulsates with a small ampli-

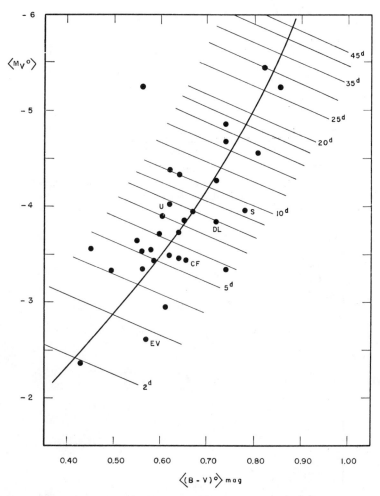

Fig. 9.—The color-magnitude-period diagram for 31 galactic cepheids. The cepheids in galactic clusters (Table 1) are identified by letters.

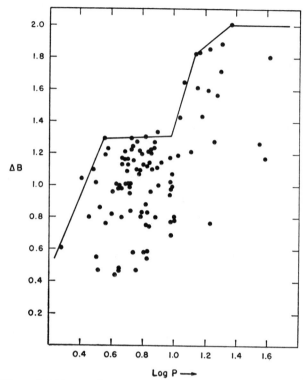

FIG. 10.—The period–blue amplitude diagram. The cepheids plotted are those having approximately the same distance from the galactic center as the sun, i.e., those belonging to the Cygnus-Carina arm (Kraft 1963).

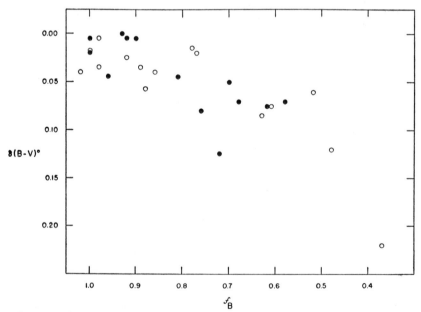

FIG. 11.—The deviation from the period–mean color relation $[\delta(B - V)^0]$ as a function of amplitude defect (f_B). The absolute value of $\delta(B - V)^0$ is plotted. Filled circles represent colors redder than average, and open circles, bluer.

tude. As evolution proceeds (say, from left to right), the amplitude increases, reaches a maximum near the center of the strip, and then again declines. A corresponding effect ought then to be found in the period-luminosity law as well as in the period-color relation; i.e., stars farthest from the mean line of the period-luminosity law should have smaller than maximum ΔB. Arp (1960) has independently discovered just such an effect (see § 4) for the SMC cepheids.

It is clear that the parameter f_B takes the place of the designation A, B, C (Eggen 1951; Gascoigne and Eggen 1957). Whatever the faults of the former may be, it has the advantage of being continuous, as opposed to discrete, and also appears to have some physical meaning.

§ 4. A COMPARISON OF CEPHEIDS IN THE SMALL MAGELLANIC CLOUD WITH THOSE IN THE VICINITY OF THE SUN

The photometric properties of cepheids in a region centered on the open cluster NGC 371 in the SMC have been summarized in a fundamental paper by Arp (1960). These have been compared with the cepheids within 1000 pc of the sun (Arp and Kraft 1961). The present discussion incorporates a few small modifications of the conclusions reached in the latter paper, owing to a slight subsequent revision of the galactic period-luminosity relation (Kraft 1961c).

The SMC and solar-vicinity cepheids can be compared in three respects: (1) the period-frequency function; (2) the period-amplitude diagram (ΔB versus log P); and (3) the period–mean color relation—$\langle (B - V)^0 \rangle_{mag}$ versus log P. These are shown in Figures 12, 13, and 14, respectively.

In Figure 12, the number of cepheids is given per unit volume of space (10^8 pc^3) on the assumption of $(m - M)_0 = 18.6$ for the SMC. If the modulus is correct, it follows that there are more cepheids per unit volume of space in the SMC than in the vicinity of the sun, but by less than one order of magnitude. However, the leading feature of the diagram is that the frequency function of the SMC has a mode at log $P = 0.5$, whereas the galactic (solar-vicinity) mode lies at log $P = 0.9$.

Figure 13 shows that the short-period cepheids of the SMC not only outnumber their galactic counterparts (relative to the long-period cepheids) but also have very much larger amplitudes. At the same time, the long-period cepheids of the SMC seem not to have amplitudes so large, on the average, as those in the vicinity of the sun. Clearly, the envelope used to define the amplitude defect f_B would have to be quite different in the two regions.

Figure 14 requires some additional explanation. We have already described the techniques employed to obtain the period–mean color relation for cepheids near the sun (Kraft 1961c). Arp (1960) has employed the period-luminosity analogue of the f_B versus $\delta(B - V)^0$ relation (§ 3) to estimate the reddening of the SMC cepheids. In the SMC, the period-luminosity relation, in the form $\langle B \rangle$ versus log P, can be directly observed. Arp found that the cepheids of largest ΔB most closely satisfied the relation; a star with small amplitude at a given

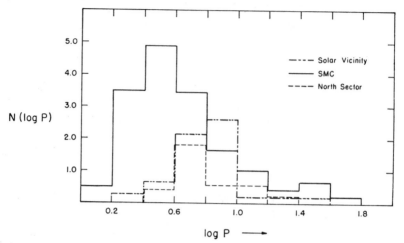

FIG. 12.—The period-frequency function for classical cepheids. The three regions represented are (1) all cepheids within 1000 pc of the sun; (2) Arp's (1960) region of the SMC; and
(3) the north sector discussed in § 5. Unit of the ordinate is number per 10^8 pc³.

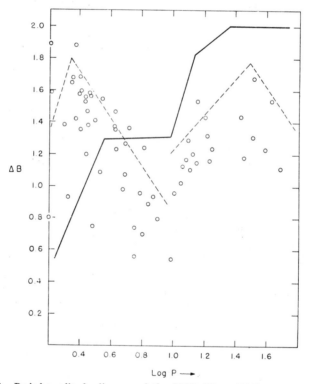

FIG. 13.—Period-amplitude diagram of the SMC. The solid line represents the solar-
vicinity relation of Fig. 10.

log P deviated by being either too bright or too faint. Let the deviation of such a star be denoted by δB. In Figure 15, we plot δB against ΔB.[1] We would expect this plot to be a "roof-shaped" structure, in analogy with the f_B versus $\delta(B - V)^0$ plot of galactic cepheids, provided that there is no appreciable *differential* absorption. In that case, the observed points will be shifted to the right in the diagram by the *average* absorption in such a way that the "roof-shaped" structure will retain its identity. We can then draw the envelope corresponding to the least absorption on the left-hand side of the distribution. Dividing the average blue absorption so found by 4.0, Arp obtained $E_{B-V} = 0.06$ mag. as a *minimum* average value of the reddening for the SMC cepheids. This agreed

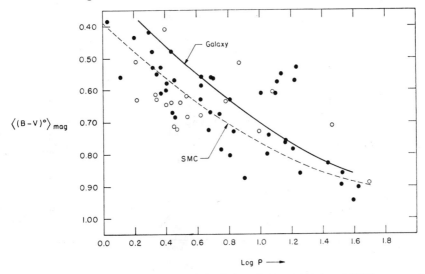

F ɪɢ. 14.—The period-color relations of the Galaxy (solar vicinity) and SMC compared. Dots and open circles are stars of the SMC; open circles denote low weight.

well with the mean excess of $E = 0.05$ mag. derived from three-color photometry of eight early-type supergiants in the field of the cepheids; the minimum value was therefore taken as the true average value.

The difference of about 0.1 mag. in color between the SMC and solar-vicinity cepheids exhibited by Figure 14 therefore seems to be real. If we had used the period-color relation for galactic cepheids derived from the work of Kron and Svolopoulos (1959) instead of Kraft, the agreement would have been no better. This means that we cannot obtain the distance modulus of the SMC entirely free from ambiguity. Thus, from the period-luminosity law alone, we have, for the Galaxy,

$$\langle M_B^0 \rangle = -1.33 - 2.25 \log P \quad \text{(eq. [12b])}$$

[1] The values of ΔB so plotted contain a zero point that is the mean value of ΔB as a function of P.

and, for the SMC (Arp 1960) (Fig. 16),

$$\langle m_B^0 \rangle = 17.45 - 2.25 \log P \; ;$$

whence

$$(m - M)_0 = 18.78 \; . \tag{15}$$

On the other hand, we might choose to superimpose the period lines in the H-R diagram, allowing for the difference in color between the SMC and the galactic cepheids. In that case, the SMC cepheids are 0.1 mag. redder and about 0.2 mag. fainter than galactic cepheids at a given period; thus the true modulus must be smaller by 0.2 mag., viz.,

$$(m - M)_0 = 18.58 \; . \tag{16}$$

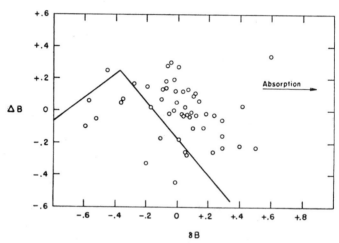

Fig. 15.—The deviation (δB) from the SMC period-luminosity relation as a function of blue amplitude (ΔB), after Arp (1960). The values of ΔB contain a zero point that is the *mean* ΔB for SMC cepheids at a given period.

The corresponding apparent moduli, therefore, are 19.02 and 18.82, respectively. On the assumption of $M_V \sim +0.5$ for RR Lyrae variables in the SMC, the apparent modulus is $(m - M) = 18.7 \pm 0.3$ mag. (Thackeray and Wesselink 1955; Arp 1959). On the other hand, the life-luminosity relation for novae implies $(m - M) = 19.2 \pm 0.3$ mag. (Schmidt 1957). Thus no variable-star method for determining distance yields a result in really close agreement with any other. The best we can say is that the true modulus probably lies in the range 18.6–19.0.

However, a word of warning is in order. We recall that the slope of the period-luminosity law for galactic cepheids cannot be derived from the five galactic cluster cepheids alone, primarily because the period range is too short ($3^d < P < 10^d$). We *assumed*, therefore, that the slope was the same as for the SMC cepheids and determined only the zero point. However, there is no a priori reason why the slope should be the same in all galaxies. Indeed, Hodge (private communication) suggests that the slope of the period-luminosity relation in the LMC may be steeper than the slope in the SMC. This is in the same direction as the difference between the SMC and LMC found many years ago by Shapley (cf. Arp 1960). Thus we must be prepared to accept the possibility that the slope of the period-luminosity relation is something different in each of the three galaxies under consideration. If that were true, no distance in the local group of galaxies would necessarily be free from ambiguity.

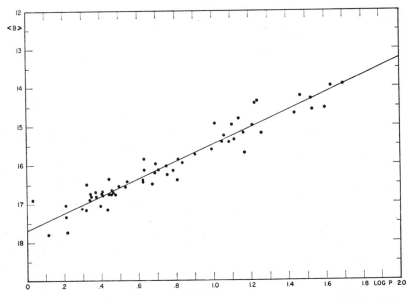

FIG. 16.—Period-luminosity diagram for cepheids of the SMC, after Arp (1960). Ordinate is ⟨B⟩, uncorrected for absorption.

Finally, there is another possible source of trouble. Considerations discussed elsewhere (Kraft 1964) suggest that the long-period cepheids of a galaxy lie, on the average, closer to their region of formation than do the short-period cepheids. We might then expect that the former would suffer greater average absorption than the latter if the dust lanes represented the regions of stellar birth. Consequently, an apparent period-luminosity relation derived for such a galaxy may have too shallow a slope. This means that no period-luminosity relation for galaxies of the local group can properly be derived without a study of color excesses for individual cepheids. Γ-photometry of these faint stars might be possible by using pulse-counting techniques, though the observations would necessarily be very time-consuming.

§ 5. SOME ANOMALOUS CLASSICAL CEPHEIDS OF THE DISTANT NORTHERN MILKY WAY

In Figure 12, we also illustrate the period-frequency function for cepheids of the northern Milky Way between $l^{I} = 67°$ and $l^{I} = 117°$. The data are taken from a study by Bahner, Hiltner, and Kraft (1962), and the sample is probably complete out to about $r = 3500$ pc. A few stars may be as far away as 5000

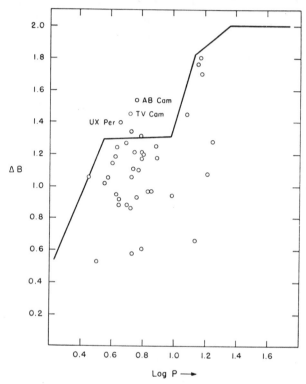

Fig. 17.—Period–blue amplitude diagram for stars of the northern Milky Way, after Bahner *et al*. (1962). AB Cam and TV Cam show evidence of weakened metallic lines. The full line corresponds to the stars of Fig. 10.

pc or more; all but three have $r > 1500$ pc. The mode of this frequency function is at log $P = 0.7$.

Thus there is a region of the Galaxy toward the "Per-Cas" arm (Bahner, Hiltner, and Kraft 1962; Kraft 1964) in which the mode of the distribution is intermediate between the SMC and the solar vicinity. There is a further property of this region which also has an intermediate characteristic. In Figure 17 we plot the period-amplitude diagram for these cepheids superimposed on the "local-arm" diagram of Figure 10. One is surprised to find three cepheids of short period having unusually large amplitudes, viz., AB Cam, TV Cam, and UX Per.

If these stars satisfy the classical period-luminosity relation, their distances are 5520, 5150, and 5150 pc; their distances from the galactic plane are 290, 530, and 180 pc, respectively. Thus we find, in this sector, distant cepheids having amplitudes intermediate between SMC and solar-vicinity cepheids.

A closer study has been made of TV Cam. Several small-scale spectrograms have been obtained by the writer, as well as one rather narrow 200-inch coudé exposure (dispersion 18 A/mm), at phase = 0.11 P (from max. light). It is reasonable to suppose that, because of the large amplitude, the star would satisfy the period-color relation rather closely; in that case, we predict a spectral type of F6 Ib at the phase in question. Figure 18 illustrates some portions of the spectrum, with stars of types F5 Ib and F8 Ib for comparison. All were obtained with the same spectrograph and slit width. The spectrum of TV Cam at this phase is, however, not that of a star of type F6 Ib. It can best be described as having hydrogen lines similar to F8–G0 Ib and metallic lines weaker than F5 Ib. If the hydrogen lines correctly indicate the temperature, then the metallic spectrum is too weak. This suggests a larger than normal H/metal ratio.

At first, one might suppose TV Cam to be a star of type II, but this is not at once obvious. In Figure 19 we compare the visual light-curves of δ Cep ($P = 5.4$ days), TV Cam ($P = 5.3$ days) (Bahner et al. 1962), and M13, No. 2 ($P = 5.1$ days) (Arp 1955). Aside from its larger amplitude, there is nothing about the shape of the light-curve of TV Cam to suggest that it is anything but a classical cepheid; the colors are also what one might expect for the distance. On the other hand, the distance above the plane is rather large. However, small-scale spectrograms obtained by the writer with the 60- and 200-inch telescopes indicate that other cepheids in this part of the sky may also have composition anomalies. Included here are DF Lac, UX Per, CH Cas, and AB Cam with z-values of -170, -180, $+130$, and $+290$ pc, respectively; all have $r > 3700$ pc (if the period-luminosity relation is applicable). These z-values are slightly, but not unusually, high compared with other cepheids and may only reflect the fact that, in selecting stars by apparent magnitude, near the limit one discriminates against stars with small $|z|$, owing to the heavy concentration of absorbing material in the plane. Relatively nearby cepheids with $|z| > 150$ pc and with apparently normal abundances are FM Cas, RY Cas, SY Cas, RW Cas, RW Cam, Y Lac, and BG Lac. This is not to say that the sector in question is free from traditional type II stars. Based on light-curve shape, CS Cas and perhaps IX Cas are of this type; $b^I = -12°$ and $-10°$, respectively, for these stars.

Thus it appears that classical cepheids may be more complicated than we originally believed. The stars TV Cam, AB Cam, UX Per, DF Lac, and CH Cas have no photometric characteristics that would distinguish them from ordinary type I cepheids, yet it is distinctly possible that their compositions are unusual. The extent to which this affects the period-luminosity law is not known and may, of course, be quite small. Cox and Whitney (private communi-

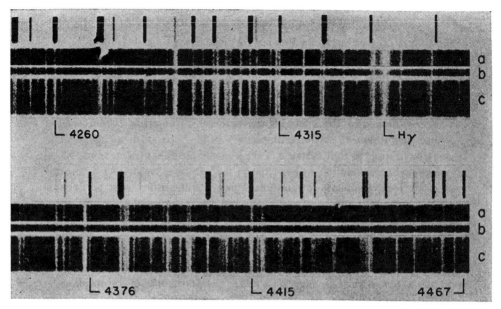

FIG. 18.—Spectrum of TV Cam ($\phi = 0.11\ P$) compared with MK standards. (a) α Per, F5 Ib; (b) TV Cam; (c) γ Cyg, F8 Ib.

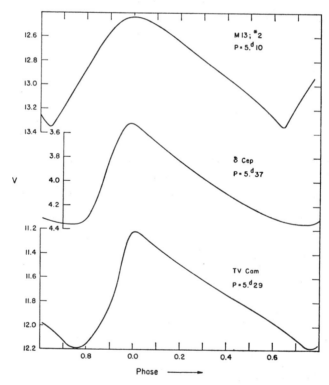

FIG. 19.—Visual light-curves of three cepheids

cation) have shown that large changes in the He abundance do not affect the period-luminosity law derived from theory by more than a few tenths of a magnitude. However, models of late-type stars with large convective envelopes seem considerably affected by atmospheric opacity (Hoyle and Schwarzschild 1955), which is controlled to a large extent by metallic abundances. For our present purposes, however, it would seem sufficient to be aware of the following possibilities: (1) the distant northern Milky Way may contain type I cepheids (i.e., young stars) with low metal content, presumably because they were formed from interstellar material of low metal content; (2) these stars may not readily be distinguishable by photometry alone; and (3) the cepheids of the SMC may represent an extension of stars of this kind.

Hence we may imagine that the SMC cepheids would have a reduced metal content. Against this is Feast's (Feast, Thackeray, and Wesselink 1960) conclusion that the spectra of SMC cepheids are normal, though the spectrograms were confined entirely to stars with $P > 48$ days, for which there are almost no galactic counterparts. Clearly, spectra of fainter SMC cepheids should be obtained if at all possible. In the meantime, composition analyses of some of these distant northern cepheids will go forward.

REFERENCES

Abt, H. A.	1959	*Ap. J.*, **130**, 824.
Aller, L. H.	1954	*Astrophysics* (New York: Ronald Press Co.), **2**, 120.
Arp, H. C.	1955	*A.J.*, **60**, 1.
	1957	*Ibid.*, **62**, 129.
	1959	*Ibid.*, **64**, 441.
	1960	*Ibid.*, **65**, 404.
	1961	*Science*, **134**, 810.
	1962	*La Plata Conference on Stellar Evolution* (National University of La Plata: Astronomical Observatory), p. 87.
Arp, H. C., and Kraft, R. P.	1961	*Ap. J.*, **133**, 420.
Arp, H. C., Sandage, A. R., and Stephens, C.	1959	*Ap. J.*, **130**, 80.
Baade, W.	1956	*Pub. A.S.P.*, **68**, 5.
Bahner, K., Hiltner, W. A., and Kraft, R. P.	1962	*Ap. J. Suppl.*, **6**, 319.
Burbidge, E. M., and Burbidge, G. R.	1959	*Ap. J.*, **129**, 513.
Canavaggia, R., and Pecker, J. C.	1953	*Ann. d'ap.*, **16**, 47.
Code, A. D.	1947	*Ap. J.*, **106**, 309.
Eggen, O. J.	1951	*Ap. J.*, **113**, 367.

Eggen, O. J., Gascoigne,
S. C. B., and Burr, E. J.   1957   *M.N.*, **117**, 406.
Feast, M. W.,
Thackeray, A. D., and
Wesselink, A. J.   1960   *M.N.*, **121**, 337.
Fernie, J. D.   1961   *Ap. J.*, **133**, 64.
Gascoigne, S. C. B., and
Eggen, O. J.   1957   *M.N.*, **117**, 430.
Hoyle, F., and
Schwarzschild, M.   1955   *Ap. J. Suppl.*, **2**, 1.
Irwin, J. B.   1958   *Trans. I.A.U.*, **10**, 680.
 1961   *Ap. J. Suppl.*, **6**, 253 (No. 58).

Johnson, H. L., and
Iriarte, B.   1958   *Lowell Obs. Bull.*, No. 91.
Johnson, H. L., and
Morgan, W. W.   1953   *Ap. J.*, **117**, 313.
Joy, A. H.   1939   *Ap. J.*, **89**, 356.
 1940   *Ibid.*, **92**, 396.
Kraft, R. P.   1960*a*   *Ap. J.*, **131**, 330.
 1960*b*   *Ibid.*, **132**, 404.
 1960*c*   "The Spectra of Supergiants and Cepheids of
Population I," in *Stellar Atmospheres*, ed. J. L.
Greenstein (Chicago: University of Chicago
Press), p. 370.
 1961*a*   *Ap. J.*, **133**, 39.
 1961*b*   *Ibid.*, p. 57.
 1961*c*   *Ibid.*, **134**, 616.
 1964   "Classical Cepheids and Galactic Structure," in
Galactic Structure, ed. A. Blaauw and M.
Schmidt (Chicago: University of Chicago
Press), in press.
Kraft, R. P., Camp,
D. C., Fernie, J. D.,
Fujita, C., and
Hughes, W. T.   1959   *Ap. J.*, **129**, 50.
Kraft, R. P., and
Hiltner, W. A.   1961   *Ap. J.*, **134**, 850.
Kron, G.   1958   *Pub. A.S.P.*, **70**, 561.
Kron, G., and
Svolopoulos, S.   1959   *Pub. A.S.P.*, **71**, 126.
Oke, J. B.   1961*a*   *Ap. J.*, **133**, 90.
 1961*b*   *Ibid.*, **134**, 214.

Oke, J. B., and
Bonsack, S. J.   1960   *Ap. J.*, **132**, 417.
Oosterhoff, P.   1960   *B.A.N.*, **15**, 199.
Preston, G.   1959   *Ap. J.*, **130**, 507.
 1961   *Ibid.*, **134**, 633.

ROMAN, N. G.   1955   *Ap. J.*, **121**, 454.
SANDAGE, A. R.   1958   *Ap. J.*, **127**, 513.
SANDAGE, A. R., and
  EGGEN, O. J.   1960   *M.N.*, **121**, 232.
SCHMIDT, TH.   1957   *Zs. f. Ap.*, **41**, 182.
SHAPLEY, H.   1918   *Ap. J.*, **48**, 89.
                                      1940   *Proc. Nat. Acad. Sci.*, **26**, 541.
THACKERAY, A. D., and
  WESSELINK, A.   1955   *Observatory*, **75**, 33.
WALLERSTEIN, G.   1958   *Ap. J.*, **127**, 583.
WALLERSTEIN, G., and
  HELFER, H. L.   1959   *Ap. J.*, **129**, 347.
WALRAVEN, T., MÜLLER,
  A., and OOSTERHOFF, P.   1958   *B.A.N.*, **14**, 81.
WAMPLER, J., PESCH, P.,
  HILTNER, W. A., and
  KRAFT, R. P.   1961   *Ap. J.*, **133**, 895.
WEAVER, H. F.,
  STEINMETZ, D., and
  MITCHELL, R.   1961   *Lowell Obs. Bull.*, No. 110.
WHITNEY, C.   1955a   *Ap. J.*, **121**, 682.
                                      1955b   *Ibid.*, **122**, 385.
WILSON, R. E.   1939   *Ap. J.*, **89**, 218.

CHAPTER 22

The Luminosities of Variable Stars

CECILIA PAYNE-GAPOSCHKIN AND SERGEI GAPOSCHKIN
Harvard College Observatory

§ 1. INTRODUCTION

THE problem of the luminosities of variable stars is neither simple nor single. We know in a rough way that supernovae are exceedingly luminous and that novae at maximum are of very high luminosity; that cepheids are supergiants and that long-period variables are red giants. The RR Lyrae stars are not far from zero in absolute visual magnitude. The T Tauri stars lie above the main sequence, and so (to a lesser extent) do the UV Ceti stars. The novae at minimum are blue stars in the subdwarf range, and so are the even less luminous U Geminorum stars.

The rough categories just named cover most, but not all, of the recognized types of variable stars, and many of them have been subdivided. There is no type of variable star for which we can today assign a single definite luminosity. The luminosities of the stars in these groups must be related to their other properties.

The superficial properties of stars are currently regarded (we cannot presume to say "understood") in terms of present ideas about stellar development. A star of given composition and initial mass is believed to undergo changes in luminosity and dimensions (and hence in surface brightness) at a rate dictated by its energy sources. These changes are directly inferred from the properties of the stars in clusters or associations, groups that are at least approximately coeval. Theories of stellar development are in reasonable accord with the observations and lead to the conclusion that differences in pattern between different groups are related to differences in initial composition.

In the course of its development (contraction to the main sequence, progress up the giant branch, across the horizontal branch, and downward toward the white dwarf domain) a given star may pass through the conditions that result in variability and may successively be a variable star of several types. Stars of different composition or initial mass (or both) will not necessarily (in fact, probably will not) have identical superficial properties when they become variables of a given sort. The fact that cepheid variables display a period-luminosity relation is a case in point. Also it may be expected that stars with certain values of initial mass and composition may not be observed to display variations of a given sort, either because their course of development does not cross the critical area or, if an upper limit to the age of stars in a given system is accepted, because they have not had the time to reach it.

The preceding description relates to stars whose development is governed by their own initial properties. The development of stars that are subject to outside influences, particularly the members of close binaries, may be profoundly affected, and the changes in their superficial properties must differ from those of undisturbed stars. In approaching the luminosities of variable stars, therefore, it is necessary not only to find the average luminosity for a group but also to

TABLE 1

TYPES OF VARIABLE STARS

Group	Designation	Description	Reference
Pulsating periodic......	C	Classical cepheids	3.1.*a*, 3.1.*b*, 3.1.*c*
	CW	W Virginis stars	3.4.*a*
	M	Mira stars	3.4.*a*, 3.5.*a*, 3.6
	RR*a*	RR Lyrae stars, asymmetrical light-curves }	3.2.*a*, 3.2.*b*, 3.2.*c*
	RR*c*	RR Lyrae stars, sinusoidal light-curves	
	RV*a*	RV Tauri stars, constant mean brightness }	3.4.*a*
	RV*b*	RV Tauri stars, varying mean brightness	
	β C	Beta Canis Majoris stars	3.7
	δ Sc	Delta Scuti stars (dwarf cepheids)	3.8
	α CV	Alpha Canum Venaticorum stars	
Semiregular.....	SR*a*	Red stars, appreciable periodicity }	3.3.*e*, 3.4.*a*
	SR*b*	Red stars, poor periodicity	
	SR*c*	Supergiant red variables	
	SR*d*	Yellow variables (spectrum F, G, K)	
Irregular.......	I*a*	Irregular variables, early spectral class }	3.3.*c*, 3.4.*a*
	I*b*	Irregular red variables	
	I*c*	Irregular red supergiants	
Eruptive.......	SN	Supernovae	3.3.*e**
	N*a*	Fast novae }	3.3.*a*, 3.3.*e*, 3.4.*b*
	N*b*	Slow novae	
	N*c*	Very slow novae	
	N*d*	Recurrent novae	3.5.*b*
	N*e*	Nova-like stars	
	UG	U Geminorum stars	3.4.*c*, 3.5.*c*
	Z	Z Camelopardalis stars	
	R CB	R Coronae Borealis stars	3.3.*d*
Spasmodic......	RW	RW Aurigae stars	
	T	T Tauri stars	
	UV	Flare (UV Ceti) stars	3.5.*d*

* See also Payne-Gaposchkin (1957*b*) and Zwicky (1958).

find the relation of the dispersion in luminosity to the dispersion in the properties of the individuals.

The current catalogue of variable stars compiled by Kukarkin, Parenago, *et al.* (1958) assigns them to about thirty subdivisions (excluding the eclipsing stars). These groups are arranged and summarized for reference in Table 1. Scarcely any of the subdivisions can be assigned a single luminosity. The "Reference" column in Table 1 serves as a key to the sections in this chapter in which the results for the various subdivisions of the variables are discussed. The omission of a few groups from the discussion indicates that satisfactory data are not available. In particular, the RW Aurigae class, though listed in the general catalogue (Kukarkin, Parenago, *et al.* 1958), has probably no physical significance, as was pointed out by Herbig (1952).

The astrometric determination of distance is still fundamental to the determination of luminosities of variable stars; in combination with accurate photometry (which gives apparent magnitude and evaluates the obscuration, if any), it yields absolute magnitudes on the chosen photometric system. Statistical methods, again in combination with accurate photometry, lead to the average luminosities of groups of stars.

Membership in systems of known distance (galaxies, open and globular clusters, or double stars) provides a powerful differential method for luminosities, but absolute values depend on the difficult evaluation of apparent and absolute moduli for the system, and this relies ultimately on astrometric methods.

Luminosities based on the physical properties of individual stars supplement the other determinations. Spectroscopic absolute magnitudes, the Wesselink method for pulsating stars, and expansion parallaxes for novae are three examples, all subject to some qualifications.

§ 2. VARIABLE STARS IN STELLAR GROUPS

Table 2 represents a schematic summary of the different types of variable stars associated with the various stellar groups. The key to the designation of the variables is found in Table 1.

2.1. LUMINOSITIES REFERRED TO GALACTIC CLUSTERS

A growing body of accurate photometric data has permitted the formation of a composite color-magnitude array for galactic clusters ranging from the very young groups like h and χ Persei to the "old" galactic clusters Messier 67 and NGC 188. Photometry on the U, B, V system permits the arrays to be fitted with confidence to the original main sequence. The transfer to absolute luminosity rests ultimately on the well-determined distance of the Hyades, based on transverse and radial motions.

The cepheid variables that are known to be members of galactic clusters are thus accurately placed in luminosity. If a large number of such cepheids were known, a zero point for the corresponding period-luminosity curve would be determinate. Unfortunately, only half a dozen are known at present, and, as period-luminosity curves have considerable dispersion in luminosity, the determination is not so precise as might be wished. Morever, it is commonly taken for granted that the period-luminosity curve derived for the cepheids in the Small Magellanic Cloud is representative, and it remains the only one determined from a body of data large enough for its course to be well known in spite of the dispersion. However, the cepheids of the Small Magellanic Cloud differ radically from those known in the Galaxy, both in frequency of period and in the relationship between period and amplitude, and it is open to question whether the curve determined from the former system is strictly applicable for the Galaxy. The excellent photoelectric material now available for galactic cepheids should be used to select Magellanic cepheids that have galactic counterparts in the form and amplitude of light- and color-curves, and a period-luminosity curve for galactic stars might be based on the latter.

TABLE 2

TYPES OF VARIABLE STAR ASSOCIATED WITH STELLAR GROUPS

Galactic clusters............	C, SRa, SRb, SRc
Stellar associations..........	T, C?
Globular clusters...........	CW, M, RVa, SRa, Na, UG?
Spiral galaxies..............	C, SRa, SRb, SRc, Ia, Ib?, Ic, SN, Na, Nb
Irregular galaxies...........	C, SRa, SRb, SRc, Ia, Ib, Ic, Na, Nb, R CB
Elliptical galaxies...........	RRa, RRb, CW
Double stars...............	C, M, SRa, Nb, Nd, UG, Z, UV

Stellar associations, like galactic clusters, can be fitted to the composite color-magnitude array, and the luminosities of the T Tauri stars and the associated stars of peculiar color and spectrum are thus determined; these stars lie well above the main sequence, with considerable dispersion in magnitude (subject to the proviso, which has been questioned, that they are members of the associations and not foreground or background objects).

2.2. LUMINOSITIES REFERRED TO GLOBULAR CLUSTERS

The many types of variable stars associated with globular clusters can be placed in luminosity if a method similar to that used for galactic clusters can be found for combining the color-magnitude arrays. The growing body of evidence that the globular clusters are not so homogeneous a group as the open clusters is currently regarded as reflecting a large range in composition, from extremely metal-poor to nearly "normal." In order to combine the color-magnitude arrays and, in particular, to refer them to the zero point defined by the main sequence of the Hyades, it is necessary to take account of the different effects of the absorption lines, as a function of metal abundance, on the magnitudes and colors themselves. Unlike the distances for galactic clusters, the distances for globular clusters therefore depend on theory as well as on observation, and hence the determinations are less certain by a few tenths of a magnitude.

Since globular clusters were first studied, their RR Lyrae stars have been recognized as powerful tools for the determination of distance. The new work on the color-magnitude arrays leads inescapably to different luminosities for the RR Lyrae stars in clusters of different properties (i.e., composition). The RR Lyrae stars of the galactic field are likewise found to possess a range of properties, again referable to composition, and it may be possible to base their luminosities on those of comparable globular cluster stars.

The most important group of variable stars in globular clusters, next to the RR Lyrae stars, are the W Virginis and RV Tauri stars. When referred to the RR Lyrae stars in the same cluster, they show a rough period-luminosity relation parallel to, but well below, that now accepted for classical cepheids. However, the accurate photometric and theoretical work necessary for determining the luminosities of the RR Lyrae stars in these clusters is only beginning, and the effect on the zero point and dispersion of the period-luminosity relation therefore cannot as yet be evaluated.

The other types of variable stars occur only sporadically in globular clusters: one possible U Geminorum star, two novae, a few long-period variables. The most striking group of the latter are the three in 47 Tucanae, a cluster of unusual properties, which contains two RR Lyrae stars. If these RR Lyrae stars have the conventional luminosity near to zero, the long-period variables have the exceptionally high absolute photographic magnitude of -3 at maximum. But the RR Lyrae stars are themselves of unusual period, and their own absolute magnitudes are at present unknown.

2.3. Luminosities of Variable Stars in Spiral Galaxies

The rich data on the variable stars in the Sb spiral Messier 31 open up the luminosities of a large range of bright variable stars. The two problems to be solved are those of the true and apparent modulus and of the effect of obscuration within the system.

Baade (1956) discussed the distance modulus of M31 from two standpoints. By adopting the revised period-luminosity relation, he obtained an apparent distance modulus of $24^{m}90$ from 237 cepheids in a field 50' from the nucleus and deduced a true distance modulus of $24^{m}32$. By adopting an absolute photographic magnitude of -1.50 for the brightest Population II stars in Messier 31 (apparent magnitude 22.75), he obtained the true modulus 24.25, in close agreement with the other value. But this determination actually rests on an assumed luminosity for the brightest Population II stars, based on the assumption of zero absolute magnitude of RR Lyrae stars in globular clusters. As had been shown, this luminosity is uncertain by a magnitude or more and so, therefore, is the distance modulus based on the brightest stars of Population II. We have therefore no independent determination of the luminosities of the cepheids in Messier 31. If the period-luminosity curve of the Small Magellanic Cloud is valid for Messier 31, the apparent modulus based on the cepheids can be used for the variable stars of other types. But the cepheids in Messier 31 seem to be counterparts of those in the Galaxy (also an Sb spiral) in frequency of period and in the relation between period and amplitude. If, as suggested above, the period-luminosity relations are not strictly similar in the Galaxy and the Small Magellanic Cloud, we may surmise that the relation for Messier 31 will be closer to that for the Galaxy.

2.4. LUMINOSITIES OF VARIABLE STARS IN IRREGULAR GALAXIES

A large number of variable stars, principally cepheids, are known in irregular galaxies: the two Magellanic Clouds, NGC 6822, and IC 1613. Each provides a determination of the course of the period-luminosity relation, which has roughly (but perhaps not exactly) the same slope in all. The determination of the zero points encounters the same ambiguity as was noted for Messier 31. The discovery of RR Lyrae stars in the globular clusters and in the field of the Small Magellanic Cloud by Thackeray (1958) confirmed the upward shift of the period-luminosity curve for cepheids that Baade had deduced from the brightest Population II stars of Messier 31, but the absolute magnitudes of these RR Lyrae stars are subject to the same uncertainty as before, and the accurate photometry also presents great difficulties. If the zero point of the period-luminosity curve is based on the cepheids in galactic clusters, the luminosities of the long-period and irregular variables and the novae can be derived.

2.5. LUMINOSITIES OF VARIABLE STARS IN ELLIPTICAL GALAXIES

Most of the very numerous variable stars known in the Sculptor and Draco systems are RR Lyrae stars, and the luminosities of the other variables depend on a decision as to the luminosities of the former. For the Draco system, an estimate can be made on the grounds that the color-magnitude array suggests extreme metal poverty. The resulting distance modulus can be used to determine the luminosities of the very few Population II cepheids; no other type of variable is represented.

2.6. VARIABLE STARS IN BINARY SYSTEMS

The most important group of intrinsic variables that are members of binary systems comprises the U Geminorum and Z Camelopardalis stars. Two Mira stars, several cepheids, and several semiregular red supergiants are also members of binary systems, and so are a number of the UV Ceti stars. In all these cases we deal with the star as an individual, and they will be discussed under the headings of the different types of variables.

§ 3. LUMINOSITIES OF INTRINSIC VARIABLES

3.1. CLASSICAL CEPHEIDS

As has been shown, the luminosities of the classical cepheids are fundamental to the determination of those of many other groups of variable stars. Only a brief survey will be given here, since the preceding chapter is devoted to this problem.

a) The statistical determinations have a long history, which has been summarized by Baade (1956). Corrections to the previously accepted zero point of the period-luminosity relation, foreshadowed by Mineur (1944), were evaluated from parallaxes and proper motions by Parenago (1954) and by Blaauw and Morgan (1954) from proper motions—the most authoritative such determinations yet made. Attention should be called to determinations based on galactic

TABLE 3

CEPHEIDS IN GALACTIC CLUSTERS AND ASSOCIATIONS

Name	Cluster	Reference*	M_B	Reference	$M_V^0 \langle (B-V)^0 \rangle$	Reference
XZ CMa.....	Anon	1	....		....	
OA CMa....	Anon	2	....		....	
ER Car.....	NGC 3532	3	....		....	
BY Cas.....	NGC 663	1	....		....	
CH Car.....	Tr 18	3	....		....	
CE Cas *a*....	NGC 7790	3, 4	....		....	
CE Cas *b*....	NGC 7790	3, 4	....		....	
CF Cas......	NGC 7790	4	-2.50 ± 0.15	4	$-3.45 + 0.655$	18
CG Cas.....	Anon	1	....		....	
DF Cas......	NGC 1027	1	....		....	
DL Cas......	NGC 129	2, 3, 5, 6	-2.91	13	$-3.84 + .72$	18
R Cru.......	NGC 4349?	3	....		....	
CV Mon.....	Anon†	2	-2.98	14	....	
S Nor.......	NGC 6087	3, 7, 8, 9	....		$-3.96 + .78$	18
U Sgr.......	M25	2, 3, 7, 10, 11	$-2.87, -3.3$	15, 16	$-3.92 + .605$	18
WZ Sgr......	III Sgr?	12	-4.5:	12	....	
EV Sct......	NGC 6664	2, 3, 5	-1.95	17	$-2.62 + 0.57$	18

* References are as follows:
1. Tifft (1959)
2. Van den Bergh (1957)
3. Kraft (1957)
4. Sandage (1958)
5. Kraft (1958*b*)
6. Lenham and Franz (1961)
7. Irwin (1955)
8. Irwin (1958)
9. Fernie (1961)
10. Doig (1925)
11. Wampler, Pesch, Hiltner, and Kraft (1961)
12. Fernie (1962)
13. Arp, Sandage, and Stephens (1959)
14. Arp (1960*a*)
15. Sandage (1960)
16. Johnson (1960*a*)
17. Arp (1958)
18. Kraft (1961) (see also chap. 21, Table 1)

† This cluster may be a fortuitous group of stars and the determination for CV Mon therefore invalid.

rotation, such as those of Parenago (1954) and Weaver (1954, 1955), and to their dependence on the Oort constants and the dimensions of the Galaxy.

b) As mentioned earlier, the most definite determination of the luminosities of cepheids rests on membership in galactic clusters. Table 3 contains the cepheids known or suspected to be members of galactic clusters and the results from some of them. The absolute magnitudes derived by Kraft are brighter than previous estimates because of the use of the method of Johnson (1960*b*) for fixing the breakoff point of the main sequence.

c) Four cepheids (Polaris, FF Aquilae, S Sagittae, and BM Cassiopeiae) are spectroscopic binaries of known period, and two more (Y Ophiuchi and U

Sagittarii) may possibly be so. The data concerning these stars are tabulated by Abt (1959a). If the properties of the companions were known, luminosities could be derived for the cepheids; but in none of the cases is the second spectrum observable, and such information as can be obtained relates to the masses of cepheids rather than to their luminosities.

Eggen (1951) attempted to derive the absolute magnitude of δ Cephei from the properties of the fainter companion, $40''$ distant. His result must be considered provisional, and -1.56 is much fainter than the photographic luminosity now ascribed to δ Cephei.

d) The determination of "pulsation parallaxes" by the Wesselink method furnishes an approach for the individual cepheid. Applications of this method are collected and discussed by Abt (1959b), who assesses the success for the various stars and discusses the limitations. Whitney (1955a, b) compared the results of the Wesselink and "absolute-photometric" methods (the latter based on six-color photometry) for δ Cephei and η Aquilae. He reduced a discrepancy between the results by making allowance for the distortion of the continuum by line absorption, and he concluded that the Wesselink method gives valid results for these stars. The correction to the old zero point of the period-luminosity curve was determined to be $M_V = -1.65 \pm 0.3$.

3.2. The RR Lyrae Stars

Second only to the cepheids as standards of luminosity, the RR Lyrae stars can be extensively studied as members of globular clusters, nearby elliptical galaxies, and our own galactic system.

a) The RR Lyrae population of different globular clusters runs from over 200 in Messier 3 to zero in a number of others. The average periods and the proportion of type c (sinusoidal) curves differ also from cluster to cluster. Careful photometry has revealed differences in the course of the color-magnitude array and the distribution of stars within it, and concurrent study of integrated spectra has shown that the globular clusters have great variety, which can be related to large differences in metal abundance. The work of Kinman (1959a, b, c) has demonstrated a range of several hundred in metal abundance. The non-homogeneity of the globular clusters has led to the recognition of differences in luminosity of their RR Lyrae stars, which greatly complicates their use as standards of luminosity, and the subject is still in a state of flux.

Table 4, taken principally from Sandage and Wallerstein (1960), summarizes the properties of a number of well-observed globular clusters. The column headed "D" contains the difference between the horizontal branch and the giant branch at $(B - V)_0 = +1.4$. The metal abundance by Deutsch (1955 and unpublished) is derived from individual stars: A denotes metallic lines slightly weaker than in Population I giants; B, definitely weaker, and C, very much weaker. The metal-abundance scale by Morgan (1959) runs from I (very weak

TABLE 4

PROPERTIES OF GLOBULAR CLUSTERS

CLUSTER NGC	Messier	D	METAL ABUNDANCE Deutsch	Morgan	No. OF RR LYR STARS	MEAN PERIOD (a, b)	PERCENTAGE TYPE a	HORIZONTAL BRANCH	REFERENCES COLOR-MAG. DIAGRAM
104	(47 Tuc)	2.15	A	(High met.)	2	0.737	50	r	Wildey (1961)
6356	......	2.15	......	VI	0	......	......	r	Sandage and Wallerstein (1960)
6838	71	2.1	......	VI	0	......	......	r	Arp (unpublished)
		2.17 ± 0.06 (m.e.)							
4147	......	2.45:	B	......	16	.531	66	?	Sandage and Walker (1955)
5272	3	2.64	AB	II	201	.550	88	e	Johnson and Sandage (1956)
5904	5	2.58	A	III	99	.546	70	e	Arp (1955, 1962)
6205	13	2.55	A	III	3	......	33	b	Arp and Johnson (1955)
6656	22	2.50	B	II	19	.651	61	b	Arp and Melbourne (1959)
		2.54 ± 0.06							
5024	53	3.10	B	III	45	.642	56	......	Cuffey (1958)
5053	......	......	C	......	10	.673	50	......	Cuffey (1943)
5139	(ω Cen)	......	(AB)	......	142	.629	50		Cuffey (1961)
5466	......	3.0	C	......	18	.636	50	be	Sandage and Schmidt (unpublished)
5897	......	3.10	B	......	4	......	......	b	Arp (1955)
6254	10	2.85	C	IV	0	......	82	b	Sandage and Walker (unpublished)
6341	92	2.92	C	I	15	.626	50	be	Arp (1955)
7078	15	3.10	C	I	93	.645	100	b	Arp (1955)
7089	2	2.98	B	II	13	0.629			
		3.01 ± 0.08							

metallic lines) to VIII (normal metallic lines). Kinman (1959b) gives the accompanying table relating metal abundance, relative to "normal," to the

Individual Giants	Integrated Spectrum	Metal Abundance	Individual Giants	Integrated Spectrum	Metal Abundance
A........	G5–G0	>0.1	B........	F7–F2	>0.01
B........	G0–F5	<0.1	C........	F5–F2	<0.01

Deutsch types and integrated spectra. Subsequent columns in Table 4 give the number of known RR Lyrae stars, the average period for those of types *a* and *b*, the percentage that are of type *a*, and the characteristics of the horizontal branch of the color-magnitude array (*b*: most of the stars on the blue side of the variable star gap; *e*: equal numbers on both sides of the gap; *r*: most of the stars on the red side of the gap).

TABLE 5

RR LYRAE STARS IN GALAXIES

Name of Galaxy	No. of Stars	Period (Days)	Magnitude	Reference
Sculptor........	40	....	19.6	Baade and Hubble (1939)
Sculptor........	216 (700?)	0.48–0.72	....	Thackeray (1950)
Draco..........	260	.613 (mean)	20.48	Baade and Swope (1961)
Small Magellanic Cloud........	7?	0.5–0.6	19:	Thackeray (1958)

The variety of properties of the tabulated globular clusters furnishes the background to the recognition that the luminosities of the associated RR Lyrae stars may differ. Arp (1959) gave values of M_V for the RR Lyrae stars in Messier 5, Messier 13, and Messier 2 as +0.8, +0.2, and +1.0, respectively, denoting the last as provisional. More recently, Arp (1962) suggests M_V = about +0.6 for the RR Lyrae stars in Messier 5, Messier 3, and RR Lyrae itself. The corresponding M_B is then about +1.0 for these stars, but could be a little fainter for those in Messier 2, and perhaps considerably fainter for those in Messier 92.

b) The RR Lyrae stars known in two dwarf elliptical galaxies and in the Small Magellanic Cloud would be extremely valuable luminosity standards if their own luminosities could be accurately determined.

The color-magnitude array for the Draco system ($D = 3^m$; cf. Table 5) suggests that the RR Lyrae stars might be comparable with those in Messier 92 or Messier 2, but the system may be of even lower metal abundance and the RR Lyrae stars accordingly less luminous. Both the Sculptor and the Draco systems contain short-period type II cepheids.

The RR Lyrae stars of our own Galaxy are known to contribute to a halo population, highly concentrated toward the galactic center. The use of this concentration to determine the distance of the galactic center depends, of course (after allowance for absorption), on a knowledge of absolute luminosity; and the uncertainty of the precise distance to the galactic center precludes a reversal of the argument to determine this luminosity. It would be necessary to use other properties to evaluate the luminosities of these RR Lyrae stars.

The spectra of galactic field RR Lyrae stars have been used by Preston (1959, 1961) to find such a criterion. Like the globular clusters themselves, these stars are found to differ in line character and hence probably in metal abundance, which ranges from "strong-lined" (i.e., normal) in the solar vicinity toward weaker-lined, far from the galactic plane. The strong-lined stars are relatively less concentrated toward the galactic center; it may be, therefore, that those near the galactic center are weaker-lined and hence of correspondingly lower luminosity. That color may also be used as a criterion of metal abundance has been shown by Spinrad (1959).

c) Pulsation parallaxes by the Wesselink method have been shown by Abt (1959*b*) to be less valid than for cepheids, both because of the comparability of the atmospheric scale height and the total expansion and because of the contribution of the shock front to the radiation during the rise in brightness. He devised a shock-wave model that led to results compatible with an average photographic luminosity of 0. More recently, Oke (1962) has shown that the original Wesselink method gives incorrect results for RR Lyrae stars, if the velocity-curve is interpreted literally at all phases. It can, however, be applied over a limited range of phases. In this way, Oke determines M_v at $+0.8 \pm 0.4$ for SU Draconis.

3.3. Intrinsic Variables Associated with Cepheids

If the zero point and slope of the period-luminosity curve for cepheids can be regarded as known, the luminosities of other types of variables follow, if they are found in systems containing cepheids. The Magellanic Clouds provide information on long-period and irregular variables, novae, and R Coronae Borealis stars. In Messier 31 we have one supernova, many novae, and some irregular variables, both blue and red.

If we assume that the period-luminosity curves for the Galaxy and the Small Magellanic Cloud are identical, we can use the determination by Kraft (chap. 21, eq. [12*b*]):

$$\langle M_B^0 \rangle = -1.33 - 2.25 \log P \text{ for the Galaxy,}$$

and the determination by Arp (1960*b*):

$$\langle B \rangle_0 = 17.45 - 2.25 \log P \text{ for the Small Cloud ,}$$

to obtain an apparent modulus of 19^m02 for the Small Cloud, the average absorption as evaluated by Arp being 0^m24. The apparent modulus of the Large Cloud is less well determined; we shall adopt the conclusion of Buscombe,

Gascoigne, and de Vaucouleurs (1954) that it is 0^m1 greater than that of the Small Cloud and, accordingly, 19^m12.

a) Data on the novae collected by Buscombe, Gascoigne, and de Vaucouleurs. Table 6 contains the name of the nova, the Cloud (Large or Small), the time of decline by 3 mag. (in days), the apparent photographic magnitude at maximum, and the deduced absolute magnitude at maximum. No revision of the published magnitudes has been made.

TABLE 6

NOVAE IN THE MAGELLANIC CLOUDS

Nova	Cloud Large/Small	t_3 (Days)	Apparent Magnitude	Absolute Magnitude
N Men 1951..........	L	7	11.9	−7.2
N Dor 1937..........	L	20	10.6	−8.5
VZ Tuc 1927.........	S	20	11.4	−7.6
N Hyi 1935..........	L	25	11.0	−8.1
N Dor 1936..........	L	30	10.5	−8.6
N Tuc 1897..........	S	40	11.0	−8.0
N Tuc 1951..........	S	50	11.5	−7.5
N Tuc 1952..........	S	....	11.0	−8.0
N Dor 1948..........	L	100	13.0	−6.1
RY Dor 1926........	L	200	12.0	−7.1

b) A number of long-period variables in the Magellanic Clouds can be fixed in the same manner, but the differentiation of foreground stars presents a problem. The frequency of long-period variables in the region of the Small Cloud is shown in the accompanying table.

Apparent m_{pg}	No. of Stars	Apparent m_{pg}	No. of Stars	Apparent m_{pg}	No. of Stars
Brighter than 10.....	1	12–13..............	7	15–16..............	7
10–11..............	0	13–14..............	4	16–17..............	5
11–12..............	3	14–15..............	6	Fainter than 17.....	3

All the brighter long-period variables have periods less than 400 days, and most of the fainter ones have longer periods. In the writer's judgment, the stars brighter than 13.5 mag. can be regarded as foreground stars, and they are marked by an "F" in Table 7. The magnitudes in Table 7 represent a rough revision to the new magnitude scale, as given by Arp (1960*b*).

The long-period variables in the Magellanic Clouds clearly differ from those in the Galaxy in period distribution, in being far more luminous, and in displaying a period-luminosity relation, the brightest being those of longest period.

c) The irregular variables of the Magellanic Clouds are a comparatively small group of red stars of small range. For example, the fourteen such stars near the Loop Nebula of the Large Cloud, as enumerated by Shapley and Nail (1948), when their magnitudes are approximately corrected for scale and obscuration and referred to the revised zero point, are found to have an average maximal absolute photographic magnitude of -4.2. Similar data for 28 stars in the bar of the Large Cloud, published by Shapley and Nail (1955), lead to an average maximal absolute photographic magnitude of -4.05.

d) The R Coronae Borealis star W Mensae lies in the Large Cloud, and SY Hydri is another possible member. Their absolute photographic magnitudes at

TABLE 7

LONG-PERIOD VARIABLES IN THE MAGELLANIC CLOUDS

HARVARD VARIABLE OR NAME	MAGEL-LANIC CLOUD LARGE/SMALL	PERIOD (DAYS)	APPARENT MAGNITUDES		ABSOLUTE MAGNITUDE (MAX. M_{pg})	REFER-ENCE
			M_{max}	M_{min}		
8039........	L	108.3	$+12.8$	$+15.5$	F	1
2882........	L	171.8	$+12.3$	$+15.6$	F	1
1956........	S	209	$+12.0$	$+14.0$	F	2
878........	L	233	$+13.2$	$+15.9$	F	3
8034........	L	250.4	$+12.2$	$+16.8$	F	1
11427........	S	254.4	$+16.8$	$+17.5$	-2.2	4
12439........	L	261.8	$+17.2$	$+17.5$	-1.9	5
12252........	L	283.6	$+11.7$	$+15.7$:	F	1
1645........	S	300.3	$+17.2$	$+17.5$	-1.8	4
5680........	L	303:	$+17.2$	$+17.5$	-1.9	4
RX Dor.....	L	335.4	$+11.4$	$+17.4$	F	
12247........	L	345.6	$+13.0$	$+17.5$	F	1
12249........	L	353.0	$+12.7$	$+17.5$	F	1
5810........	L	359:	$+16.1$	$+17.5$	-3.0	1
5820........	L	359.7	$+15.7$	$+17.5$	-3.4	1
11329........	S	388.1	$+15.8$	$+17.5$	-3.2	4
U Dor.......	L	393.3	$+ 9.28$	$+15.5$	F	
2763........	L	400	$+14.9$	$+17.5$	-4.2	6
1375........	S	510.2	$+16.5$	$+17.5$	-2.5	4
1719........	S	531.9	$+14.9$	$+17.5$	-4.1	4
12048........	L	540	$+15.3$	$+17.5$	-3.8	1
11303........	S	540	$+16.3$	$+17.5$	-2.7	4
1001........	L	541.2	$+14.4$	$+17.5$:	-4.7	1
1004........	L	548.3	$+13.5$	$+16.8$	F?	1
2493........	L	552.5	$+16.5$	$+17.5$	-2.6	6
1865........	S	562.4	$+16.4$	$+18$	-2.6	4
11295........	S	571.4	$+15.5$	$+17.5$	-3.5	4
859........	S	573.4	$+14.6$	$+17.5$	-4.5	4
12227........	L	591.7	$+15.4$	$+17.5$	-3.6	1
2112........	S	607.7	$+14.5$	$+17.5$	-4.5	4
12070........	L	613.5	$+15.9$	$+17.5$	-3.2	1
12149........	S	740.7	$+14.9$	$+18.5$	-4.1	4
Means: Period.		200–300 300–400 500–600 600–700 Over 700			$-2.05(2)$ $-2.92(6)$ $-3.46(10)$ $-3.85(2)$ $-4.1(1)$	

* References are as follows:
1. Nail (1952)
2. Hoffleit (1935)
3. Shapley and Nail (1940)
4. Shapley and Nail (1951)
5. Shapley (unpublished)
6. Shapley and Nail (1948)

maximum, based on the distance modulus mentioned earlier, would be -5.3 and -5.7, respectively. They thus seem comparable with the brightest galactic representatives of the type.

e) In addition to its cepheids, Messier 31 provides information on the luminosities of supernovae, novae, and irregular red variables.

The data on the novae have been placed on a firm foundation by Arp (1956), whose discussion contains all the necessary information, which need not be repeated here. The absolute photographic magnitudes at maximum range from -8.5 for the very fast novae to about -6 for the slow ones. These values depend on the distance modulus for Messier 31, which has been discussed above.

The one supernova in Messier 31, S Andromedae, reached an absolute photographic magnitude of -17.05.

According to Gaposchkin (1962), the red semiregular variables in Messier 31 have apparent photographic magnitudes between 19.2 and 23.3 or (using the apparent modulus 24.9 mentioned earlier) absolute photographic magnitudes from -5.7 to -1.6. They thus seem to be comparable with the red irregular stars in the Large Magellanic Cloud.

3.4. Intrinsic Variables Referred to RR Lyrae Stars

The recognition that all RR Lyrae stars are not of the same luminosity has greatly complicated the study of the luminosities of other variable stars in globular clusters and galaxies, comprising type II cepheids, W Virginis, and RV Tauri stars, long-period, semiregular, and irregular variables, two novae, and a U Geminorum star.

a) The current situation concerning the RR Lyrae stars in globular clusters has been discussed in § 2.2. In what follows, the material will be discussed in three groups: clusters of high, intermediate, and low metal content (see Table 4).

Tables 8 and 9 summarize the data on red variables and on type II cepheids in selected globular clusters. Successive columns give the metal-content group (as in Table 4), the cluster, the average apparent photographic magnitude of the RR Lyrae stars, the adopted absolute magnitude for these stars, the type of variable star, the number of the star in the cluster, period, logarithm of period, range of apparent magnitudes, and absolute magnitudes with the adopted modulus. The uncertainty of the latter in most cases cannot be overstressed.

We note that no cepheids are represented in the clusters of high metal content. The long-period and semiregular variables show a rough period-luminosity relation, the brightest being of longest period. The type II cepheids show the same tendency; perhaps the minimal absolute magnitudes show a better correlation than those at maximum or the averages. In view of the uncertainties for the RR Lyrae stars, which are basic to the luminosities, further discussion would be unprofitable.

b) The nova T Scorpii (1860) in the cluster M80 had an apparent maximum

TABLE 8
RED VARIABLES IN GLOBULAR CLUSTERS

Metal Content	Cluster	RR Lyrae Stars — Average m_{pg}	RR Lyrae Stars — Adopted M_{pg}	Type of Variable	No.	Period (Days)	Log P	Range m_{pg}	M_{pg}
High	47 Tuc	+14.16	0:	Long-period	3	192.34	2.28	+11.35 to +16.1	−2.81
	47 Tuc	+14.16	0:	Long-period	2	202.84	2.30	+11.55 +15.3	−2.61
	47 Tuc	+14.16	0:	Long-period	1	212.40	2.32	+11.4 +16	−2.86
	47 Tuc	+14.16	0:	Semiregular	4	150:	2.18	+12.0 +14.0	−2.16
	47 Tuc	+14.16	0:	Semiregular	8	150:	2.18	+12.7 +14.7	−1.46
Intermediate	M5	+15.11	+1.0	Semiregular	50	106:	2.02	+13.6 +14.0	−0.51
	M3	+15.57	+1.0	Semiregular	95	103.19	2.01	+13.31 +14.50	−1.26
	M13	+15.20	+1.0:	Semiregular	11	92.5	1.96	+12.92 +13.71	−1.28
	M13	+15.20	+1.0:	Irregular	10	.....	.....	+13.4 +13.7	−0.80
	M13	+15.20	+1.0:	Irregular	15	.....	.....	+13.32 +13.67	−0.88
	M22	+14.06	+1.0:	Semiregular	8	.....	.....	+12.0 +12.7	−1.06
	M22	+14.06	+1.0:	Irregular	9	.....	.....	+12.7 +13.3	−0.36
	M22	+14.06	+1.0:	Irregular	17	.....	.....	+14.6 +15	+1.54
Low	ω Cen	+14.65	+1.2:	Long-period	42	149.4	2.17	+12.5 +14.9	−0.95
	ω Cen	+14.65	+1.2:	Long-period	2	242	2.38	+13.06 +16.12	−0.39
	ω Cen	+14.65	+1.2:	Semiregular	17	60:	1.78	+14.18 +14.61	+0.73
	ω Cen	+14.65	+1.2:	Semiregular	138	74.6:	1.87	+12.5 +13.6	−0.95
	ω Cen	+14.65	+1.2:	Semiregular	53	87:	1.94	+13.30 +13.87	−0.15
	ω Cen	+14.65	+1.2:	Semiregular	148	90:	1.95	+12.9 +13.8	−0.55
	ω Cen	+14.65	+1.2:	Semiregular	152	124	2.09	+12.8 +13.7	−0.65
	ω Cen	+14.65	+1.2:	Irregular	129	.....	.....	+13.84 +15.24	+0.39
	ω Cen	+14.65	+1.2:	Irregular	161	.....	.....	+14.18 +14.74	+0.73
	ω Cen	+14.65	+1.2:	Irregular	162	.....	.....	+13.3 +13.8	−0.15
	ω Cen	+14.65	+1.2:	Irregular	163	.....	.....	+12.9 +13.6	−0.55
	ω Cen	+14.65	+1.2:	Irregular		.....	.....	+13.7 +14.0	+0.25

TABLE 9

Type II Cepheids in Globular Clusters

Metal Content	Cluster	RR Lyrae Stars		Type of Variable	No.	Period (Days)	Log P	Range	
		Average m_{pg}	Adopted M_{pg}					m_{pg}	M_{pg}
Intermediate.	M5	+15.11	+1.0	CW	42	25.738	1.41	+10.76 to +12.46	−3.35 to −1.65
	M5	+15.11	+1.0	CW	84	26.5	1.42	+11.00 +12.77	−3.11 −1.34
	M3	+15.57	+1.0	CW	154	15.283	1.18	+11.86 +13.5	−2.71 −1.07
	M13	+15.20	+1.0:	CW	1	1.459	0.16	+13.27 +14.61	−0.93 +0.41
	M13	+15.20	+1.0:	CW	6	2.113	0.32	+13.90 +14.73	−0.30 +0.53
	M13	+15.20	+1.0:	CW	2	5.110	0.71	+12.67 +13.90	−1.53 −0.30
	M22	+14.06	+1.0:	CW	11	1.690	0.23	+12.9 +13.8	−0.16 +0.52
	ω Cen	+14.65	+1.2:	CW	43	1.157	0.06	+13.41 +14.55	−0.04 +1.10
	ω Cen	+14.65	+1.2:	CW	78	1.168	0.06	+14.17 +14.84	+0.72 +1.39
	ω Cen	+14.65	+1.2:	CW	92	1.345	0.13	+14.10 +14.48	+0.65 +1.13
	ω Cen	+14.65	+1.2:	CW	60	1.349	0.13	+13.32 +14.48	−0.13 +1.03
	ω Cen	+14.65	+1.2:	CW	61	2.274	0.36	+13.72 +14.48	+0.27 +1.03
	ω Cen	+14.65	+1.2:	CW	29	14.724	1.17	+12.44 +13.50	−1.01 +0.05
	ω Cen	+14.65	+1.2:	RV	1	58.703	1.77	+10.7 +12.6	−2.75 −0.85
Low.........	M2	+16.10	+1.3:	CW	1	15.565	1.19	+13.29 +14.78	−1.51 −0.02
	M2	+16.10	+1.3:	CW	5	17.555	1.24	+13.30 +14.47	−1.50 −0.33
	M2	+16.10	+1.3:	CW	6	19.301	1.28	+13.07 +14.31	−1.73 −0.49
	M2	+16.10	+1.3:	RV	11	67.086	1.83	+12.12 +13.25	−2.68 −1.55
	M15	+15.63	+1.3:	CW	1	1.437	0.16	+14.39 +15.75	+0.06 +1.42

magnitude of 6.8, and if variables 3, 4, and 5 (for which no periods are known) are RR Lyrae stars, we may deduce an absolute magnitude of -8.6 ± 0.5, consistent with other determinations for very fast novae. If (as seems probable) V1148 Sgr (1930) was in NGC 6553, its luminosity could be deduced if RR Lyrae variables were established in the cluster, since its maximum magnitude is fairly well determined.

c) Variable No. 4 in NGC 7099 is considered to be a U Geminorum star of apparent magnitude 16.4 at maximum. The three known RR Lyrae stars in the cluster, with a mean average apparent magnitude of 15.54, lead to an absolute magnitude at maximum of $+1.46 \pm 0.5$ and a minimum fainter than $+2.5$. It is not impossible that a U Geminorum star may be as bright as this, but the information does not contribute much to our knowledge of these stars.

For reference to all the basic data see publication by Sawyer (1955).

3.5. Intrinsic Variables in Binary Systems

In addition to the cepheids already mentioned, it is possible to study long-period variables, novae, U Geminorum stars, and UV Ceti stars as individuals, through their membership in binary systems.

a) The long-period variables Mira and X Ophiuchi are known members of visual binaries; the former has a very unusual Be star for a companion, the latter an apparently normal K1 III star. Comparison with these stars provides an approach to the luminosities of the variables.

For X Ophiuchi, the luminosity of the K star has been determined spectrophotometrically by Fernie (1959); but the photometric separation of the two stars presents difficulties, and the luminosity can be regarded only as a rough confirmation of that derived by statistical methods.

The system of Mira presents even greater difficulties, since the companion is an abnormal, perhaps unique, star (which is itself variable). The determination of the orbit itself has presented difficulties, discussed and resolved by Van Biesbroeck (1959).

The unusually short period of 14 years, proposed several years ago, must be discarded; the period is definitely more than 100 years. This knowledge leaves a wide margin for speculation as to the properties of the system, as has been shown by Fernie and Brooker (1961).

The long-period variable R Aquarii is no doubt a member of a binary, but the whole system is so peculiar that it cannot be used as an approach to the luminosity.

b) The discovery by Walker (1956, 1958) that Nova DQ Herculis is an eclipsing binary has opened up new possibilities in the approach to novae. However, the unusual character of the system, as analyzed by Kraft (1958c), Greenstein and Kraft (1959), and Kraft (1959), makes it difficult to evaluate the luminosity of the nova at minimum.

The fast, recurrent nova T Coronae Borealis is a spectroscopic binary with a giant M3 companion; the system is discussed by Kraft (1958a). If the M star is normal (which may perhaps be doubted, if it fills one lobe of the zero-velocity surface), the minimal absolute photographic magnitude of the nova would be +4.0.

General discussions of the luminosities of novae at minimum are given by Payne-Gaposchkin (1957a) and by Greenstein (1957).

c) The U Geminorum stars, long suspected to be binaries, were first shown to be of very short period by Joy (1954, 1956). Here again the properties of the companion star (when observable, of spectrum G or K) are abnormal and can be used to evaluate the luminosity of the explosive component only with caution. Periods have been determined for AE Aquarii by Joy (1954), for SS Cygni by Joy (1956), and for RX Andromedae, SS Aurigae, U Geminorum, and RU Pegasi by Kraft (1962). Spectra of the companions have been observed for AE Aquarii (K5 IV–V) by Crawford and Kraft (1956), for SS Cygni (dG5) by Joy (1956), and for RU Pegasi (G8 IV) by Kraft (1962). As Kraft points out, the luminosity of the last of these is not that of a normal G8 IV star but is considerably lower (as might be expected if it filled the inner lobe of the zero-velocity surface).

From a study of the color of U Geminorum, Wallerstein (1961) deduced an absolute visual magnitude of +7 at minimum. Although the spectrum of the companion of U Geminorum was not observed by Kraft (1962) when he determined the orbital elements, the photometric observations of Krzeminski, reproduced by Mumford (1962), strongly suggest that eclipses occur. A provisional evaluation of this very peculiar light-curve by Gaposchkin (unpublished) leads to absolute visual magnitudes of +10.9 and +10.2 for the blue variable and the companion, respectively. An absolute parallax given by Jenkins (1952) leads to an absolute visual magnitude of +8.8 for the combined light of the two.

Kraft (1962) obtained a rough statistical parallax from the radial velocities and proper motions of U Geminorum, SS Cygni, RU Pegasi, and EY Cygni and deduced the average visual absolute magnitude +9.5, to be compared with the value of +9.5 given by the parallax of SS Cygni determined by Strand (1948) and the value of about +10.1 deduced photometrically for UZ Serpentis by Herbig (1944).

d) The UV Ceti stars, or flare stars, have several well-known members that are components of visual binaries. Five of the eleven members of the group listed by Kukarkin, Parenago, et al. (1958) and one additional star are given in Table 10. The parallaxes are taken from the General Catalogue of Trigonometric Parallaxes (Jenkins 1952).

3.6. Long-Period Variables

A recent rediscussion of the radial velocities, proper motions, magnitudes, and spectra of galactic long-period variables by Osvalds and Risley (1960) leads to the results of Table 11.

3.7. Beta Canis Majoris Stars

Table 12, based largely on work by McNamara (1953) and Struve (1955), gives a list of β Canis Majoris stars. The principal period is P_2, while the interfering period is P_1, giving rise to a beat phenomenon in both the radial-velocity and the light-curves. The remaining columns list the spectra, colors, and absolute visual magnitudes. As pointed out by McNamara, the stars show a period-luminosity relation.

TABLE 10

UV Ceti Stars as Visual Binaries

Star	Parallax	Source*	Reference
V 645 Cen=Proxima Cen....	+0″762	1	Shapley (1951)
DO Cep=Krüger 60 B......	+ .252	1	Lippincott (1953)
UV Cet=L 726-8 B........	+ .380	2	Luyten (1949)
EQ Peg=+19°5116 A......	+ .144	1	Petit (1955)
WX UMa=+44°2051 B.....	+ .173	1	Petit (1955)
.... +4°4048 B......	+0.168	1	Van Biesbroeck (1944); Herbig (1956)

* Sources: (1) Jenkins (1952); (2) van de Kamp (1959).

TABLE 11

Long-Period Variables

Mean Period (Days)	No. of Stars	Mean Spectrum	Mean M_{pg} at Maximum
131.........	14	M1.9	−1.94
176.........	29	M2.7	−3.16
223.........	55	M3.7	−2.80
273.........	65	M4.2	−2.90
324.........	73	M5.3	−2.25
376.........	42	M6.2	−2.85
419.........	23	M6.5	−2.31
508.........	18	M6.0	−2.82

TABLE 12

Beta Canis Majoris Stars

Star	P_1	P_2	Spectrum	$B-V$	M_v
β CMa.........	6ʰ00ᵐ	6ʰ02ᵐ	B1 II–III	−0.280	−4.7
σ Sco..........	5 45	5 55	B1 III	....	−4.3
ξ′ CMa........	5 02	....	B1 IV	− .280	−4.2
BW Vul........	....	4 49	B2 III	− .270	−4.1
HD 21803.......	4 48	....	B2 IV	....	−2.9?
DD Lac........	4 44	4 38	B2 III	− .265	−4.1
β Cep..........	4 34	....	B2 III	− .275	−4.1
ν Eri..........	4 16	4 10	B2 III	− .255	−4.1
EN Lac........	4 06	4 04	B2 IV	− .260	−3.3
δ Cet.........	3 52	....	B2 IV	− .245	−3.3
γ Peg.........	3 38	....	B2 IV	−0.240	−3.0

3.8. Delta Scuti Stars (Dwarf Cepheids)

The δ Scuti stars form a homogeneous group with a small spread in color. No attempt will be made here to survey the extensive literature relating to the individual variables, some of which is summarized by Fitch (1959).

Woltjer (1956) discussed the luminosities of some of these stars on the basis of their light-curves. More recently, McNamara and Augason (1962) have used a modification of the Strömgren (1958) method for determining the luminosities of several more. The results are summarized in Table 13. There is a tendency for those of shortest period to be the least luminous.

TABLE 13

Delta Scuti Stars (Dwarf Cepheids)

Star	Period (Days)	Spectrum	M_{pg}	Reference*
δ Sct.........	0.193770	F3 III–IV	+1.6	1
ρ Pup†.......	.141	F6 II	+0.9	1
δ Del†........	.13505	F2 IV	+1.3	1
CC And......	.124078	F3 IV–V	+1.9	1
AI Vel........	.1116	A2–F2	+2.2	2
DQ Cep......	.078865	F1 IV–V	+1.5	1
SX Phe.......	0.0550	sd A2	+4.5	2

* References are as follows: (1) McNamara and Augason (1962); (2) Woltjer (1956).
† Deficient in calcium.

REFERENCES

Abt, H. A.	1959a	*Ap. J.*, **130**, 769.
	1959b	*Ibid.*, p. 824.
Arp, H. C.	1955	*A.J.*, **60**, 317.
	1956	*Ibid.*, **61**, 15.
	1958	*Ap. J.*, **128**, 166.
	1959	*A.J.*, **64**, 441.
	1960a	*Ap. J.*, **131**, 322.
	1960b	*A.J.*, **65**, 404.
	1962	*Ap. J.*, **135**, 311.
Arp, H. C., and Johnson, H. L.	1955	*Ap. J.*, **122**, 171.
Arp, H. C., and Melbourne, W. G.	1959	*A.J.*, **64**, 29.
Arp, H. C., Sandage, A., and Stephens, C.	1959	*Ap. J.*, **130**, 80.
Baade, W.	1956	*Pub. A.S.P.*, **68**, 5.
Baade, W., and Hubble, E. P.	1939	*Pub. A.S.P.*, **51**, 40.
Baade, W., and Swope, H. H.	1961	*A.J.*, **66**, 300.
Bergh, S. van den	1957	*Ap. J.*, **126**, 323.

BLAAUW, A., and
  MORGAN, H. R.   1954   *B.A.N.*, **12**, 95.
BUSCOMBE, W.,
  GASCOIGNE, S. C. B.,
  and VAUCOULEURS,
  G. DE   1954   *Suppl. Australian J. Sci.*, Vol. **17**, No. 3.
CRAWFORD, J. A., and
  KRAFT, R. P.   1956   *Ap. J.*, **123**, 44.
CUFFEY, J.   1943   *Ap. J.*, **98**, 49.
                  1958   *Ibid.*, **128**, 219.
                  1961   *A.J.*, **66**, 71.
DEUTSCH, A. J.   1955   *Principes fondamentaux de classification stellaire*
                         (Coll. Int. Centre Nat. Rech. Sc., Vol. **55**), p.
                         25.
DOIG, P.   1925   *J. Brit. Astr. Assoc.*, **35**, 201.
EGGEN, O. J.   1951   *Ap. J.*, **113**, 367.
FERNIE, J. D.   1959   *Ap. J.*, **130**, 611.
                1961*a*   *Ibid.*, **133**, 64.
                1962   *Ibid.*, **135**, 298.
FERNIE, J. D., and
  BROOKER, A. A.   1961   *Ap. J.*, **133**, 1088.
FITCH, W. S.   1959   *Ap. J.*, **130**, 1022.
GAPOSCHKIN, S.   1962   *A.J.*, **67**, 334.
GREENSTEIN, J. L.   1957   *Ap. J.*, **126**, 23.
GREENSTEIN, J. L., and
  KRAFT, R. P.   1959   *Ap. J.*, **130**, 99.
HERBIG, G. H.   1944   *Pub. A.S.P.*, **56**, 230.
                1952   *Trans. I.A.U.*, **8**, 805.
                1956   *Pub. A.S.P.*, **68**, 531.
HOFFLEIT, D.   1935   *Harvard Bull.*, No. 900.
IRWIN, J.   1955   *M.N., Astr. Soc. South Africa*, **14**, 38.
                1958   *A.J.*, **63**, 197.
JENKINS, L. F.   1952   *General Catalogue of Trigonometric Stellar Paral-*
                         laxes (New Haven: Yale University Observa-
                         tory).
JOHNSON, H. L.   1960*a*   *Ap. J.*, **131**, 620.
                1960*b*   *Lowell Obs. Bull.*, No. 107.
JOHNSON, H. L., and
  SANDAGE, A. R.   1956   *Ap. J.*, **124**, 379.
JOY, A. H.   1954   *Ap. J.*, **120**, 377.
                1956   *Ibid.*, **124**, 317.
KAMP, P. VAN DE   1959   *A.J.*, **64**, 236.
KINMAN, T. D.   1959*a*   *M.N.*, **119**, 157.
                1959*b*   *Ibid.*, p. 538.
                1959*c*   *Ibid.*, p. 559.
KRAFT, R. P.   1957   *Ap. J.*, **126**, 225.
                1958*a*   *Ibid.*, **127**, 625.

1958*b* *Ibid.*, **128**, 161.
1958*c* *Pub. A.S.P.*, **70**, 598.
1959   *Ap. J.*, **130**, 110.
1961   *Ibid.*, **134**, 616.
1962   *Ibid.*, **135**, 408.

KUKARKIN, B. V.,
 PARENAGO, P. P.,
 EFREMOV, Yu. I., and
 KHOLOPOV, P. N.   1958   *General Catalogue of Variable Stars* (2d ed.; Moscow: Publishing House of the Academy of Sciences of the U.S.S.R.).

LENHAM, A. P., and
 FRANZ, O. G.   1961   *A.J.*, **66**, 16.
LIPPINCOTT, S. L.   1953   *Pub. A.S.P.*, **65**, 248.
LUYTEN, W. J.   1949   *Ap. J.*, **109**, 532.
MCNAMARA, D. H.   1953   *Pub. A.S.P.*, **65**, 155 and 286.
MCNAMARA, D. H., and
 AUGASON, G.   1962   *Ap. J.*, **135**, 64.
MINEUR, H.   1944   *Ann. d'ap.*, **7**, 160.
MORGAN, W. W.   1959   *A.J.*, **64**, 432.
MUMFORD, G. S., III   1962   *Sky and Telescope*, **23**, 137.
NAIL, V. McK.   1952   *Harvard Bull.*, No. 921.
OKE, J. B.   1962   *A.J.*, **67**, 278.
OSVALDS, V., and
 RISLEY, M.   1960   *A.J.*, **65**, 496.
PARENAGO, P. P.   1954   *Peremennye Zvezdy*, **10**, 193.
PAYNE-GAPOSCHKIN, C.   1957*a* *The Galactic Novae* (Amsterdam: North-Holland Publishing Co.; New York: Interscience Publishers), pp. 31 ff.
             1957*b* *Ibid.*, chap. 9.
PETIT, M.   1955   *Documentation des observateurs*, **8**, 9.
PRESTON, G.   1959   *Ap. J.*, **130**, 507.
             1961   *Ibid.*, **134**, 651.
SANDAGE, A. R.   1958   *Ap. J.*, **128**, 150.
             1960   *Ibid.*, **131**, 610.
SANDAGE, A. R., and
 WALKER, M. F.   1955   *A.J.*, **60**, 230.
SANDAGE, A. R., and
 WALLERSTEIN, G.   1960   *Ap. J.*, **131**, 598.
SAWYER, H. B.   1955   *Pub. David Dunlap Obs.*, **2**, 35.
SHAPLEY, H.   1951   *Harvard Repr.*, No. 344.
SHAPLEY, H., and
 NAIL, V. McKIBBEN   1940   *Harvard Circ.*, No. 439.
             1948   *Harvard Repr.*, No. 306.
             1951   *Ibid.*, No. 346.
             1955   *Ibid.*, No. 407.
SPINRAD, H.   1959   *Ap. J.*, **130**, 539.

STRAND, K. AA.   1948   *Ap. J.*, **107**, 106.
STRÖMGREN, B.   1958   *Stellar Populations*, ed. D. J. K. O'CONNELL
                                 (Amsterdam: North-Holland Publishing Co.;
                                 New York: Interscience Publishers), p. 245.
STRUVE, O.   1955   *Pub. A.S.P.*, **67**, 135.
THACKERAY, A. D.   1950   *Observatory*, **70**, 144.
                         1958   *M.N.*, **118**, 117.
TIFFT, W. G.   1959   *Ap. J.*, **129**, 241.
VAN BIESBROECK, G.   1944   *A.J.*, **51**, 61.
                         1959   *Pub. A.S.P.*, **71**, 462.
WALKER, M. F.   1956   *Ap. J.*, **123**, 68.
                         1958   *Ibid.*, **127**, 319.
WALLERSTEIN, G.   1961   *Ap. J.*, **134**, 1020.
WAMPLER, J., PESCH, P.,
  HILTNER, W. A., and
  KRAFT, R. P.   1961   *Ap. J.*, **133**, 895.
WEAVER, H. L.   1954   *A.J.*, **59**, 375.
                         1955   *Ibid.*, **60**, 202.
WHITNEY, C.   1955a   *Ap. J.*, **121**, 682.
                         1955b   *Ibid.*, **122**, 385.
WILDEY, R. L.   1961   *Ap. J.*, **133**, 430.
WOLTJER, L.   1956   *B.A.N.*, **13**, 62.
ZWICKY, F.   1958   *Hdb. d. Phys.* (Berlin: Springer-Verlag), **51**, 766.

APPENDIX I

Star Catalogues and Charts

G. VAN BIESBROECK

Yerkes Observatory

§ 1. EARLY STAR CATALOGUES

Among the earliest astronomical documents are the star catalogues. Apart from some earlier short lists of star positions, the first star catalogue according to the present definition is the list of 1025 bright stars found in Ptolemy's *Almagest*. The catalogue was constructed by Hipparchus for the year 128 B.C. and was later reduced by Ptolemy to the equinox 138 A.D. by means of a crude value for the precession.

Ptolemy's list was reproduced many times during the Middle Ages for later equinoxes. Al-Sufi added estimates of magnitudes to the catalogue, and Ulugh Beg, Tycho Brahe, and Hevelius improved the positions with their own observations.

These early catalogues have only historical interest, and it was not until Flamsteed (1646–1719) introduced the use of the telescope that the first star positions were obtained which remain of value to the present time. Since his time, a long list of star catalogues, which vary a great deal from one another, have been published.

§ 2. SURVEY CATALOGUES

The survey catalogues are also named *Durchmusterungen*, according to a designation introduced by Argelander, when he undertook to list all stars to the limiting magnitude of the 72-mm Bonn telescope. The catalogue named the *Bonner Durchmusterung*, or, in abbreviated form, the *BD*, contains 320,000 stars. The stars are grouped in zones of 1° declination from the North Pole to −2° declination and are numbered consecutively in order of increasing right ascension for the equinox 1855. The positions of the stars are given to the nearest 0^s1 in right ascension and $0''1$ in declination, and magnitudes are listed to the tenth.

Argelander estimated the magnitudes of the stars beyond the limiting magni-

471

tude for naked-eye observations to the faintest stars he could see in his telescope, which he gave a magnitude of 9.5. Although this system of magnitudes is entirely subjective, it has proved to be surprisingly reliable to the ninth magnitude, and it was used extensively in the early studies of stellar distribution until more precise photometric data became available, such as the *Henry Draper Catalogue.*

Schoenfeld, a student of Argelander, continued the survey beyond $-2°$ declination to $-23°$. The catalogue is called the *Southern Durchmusterung, SD,* and contains 133,000 stars.

Thome, in Córdoba, Argentina, carried the survey further to $-62°$ declination, and the resulting catalogue named the *Córdoba Durchmusterung, CDM,* lists 580,000 stars to a limiting magnitude of 10. The catalogue was extended to the south celestial pole by Perrine.

Another survey of the southern sky was carried out by photographic means at the initiative of Gill and Kapteyn. The resulting catalogue is named the *Cape Photographic Durchmusterung, CPD,* and includes 455,000 stars from declinations $-18°$ to the south celestial pole.

§ 3. ZONE CATALOGUES

The star catalogues designated as "zone catalogues" list accurate positions of the fainter stars. The positions are determined from meridian observations, using as a reference system a relatively small number of bright, so-called fundamental stars.

Typical of zone catalogues is the *Astronomische Gesellschaft Katalog,* designated the *AGK.* The catalogue, which has a limiting magnitude of about 9 on the Argelander scale, is the result of a large international undertaking which started in 1869 and involved the collaboration of 12 observatories, dividing the sky into 15 zones, as shown in Table 1. The catalogue contains the position of 144,128 stars referred to the equinox 1875 and was published between 1890 and 1910.

An extension of the catalogue beyond $-2°$ declination was started in 1887 and was carried out at the following observatories:

AG Zone	Extent in Declination	AG Zone	Extent in Declination
Strasbourg	$- 2°$ to $- 6°$	Washington	$-14°$ to $-18°$
Vienna (Ottakring)	$- 6$ to -10	Algiers	-18 to -23
Cambridge (Mass.)	-10 to -14		

The Southern zones were published between 1904 and 1924 and the star positions are given for the equinox 1900.

The more recent Córdoba catalogues can be considered as a further extension of the zone catalogues previously mentioned. They are as follows:

Zone Córdoba	Extent in Declination	Zone Córdoba	Extent in Declination
A.......	−22° to −27°	C......	−32° to −37°
B......	−27 to −32	D......	−37 to −47

These catalogues were published between 1913 and 1954 and contain 60,542 stars for the equinox 1900 for catalogues A–C and 1950 for catalogue D.

The Yale Observatory has repeated the zone catalogues, covering the important zones between +30° and −30° declinations. Details of this work are tabulated in chapter 4 (Table 1).

In the course of time the star positions in the *AGK* have become more and more uncertain because of the insufficient knowledge of the proper motions of

TABLE 1

THE ASTRONOMISCHE GESELLSCHAFT ZONES

AG Zone	Extent in Declination		AG Zone	Extent in Declination	
Kazan...............	+81° to	+75°	Cambridge, Eng......	+30° to	+25°
Berlin C.............	+75	+70	Berlin B.............	+25	+20
Christiania..........	+70	+65	Berlin A.............	+20	+15
Helsingford-Gotha....	+65	+60	Leipzig II...........	+15	+10
Cambridge, Mass......	+55	+50	Leipzig I............	+10	+45
Bonn................	+50	+40	Albany..............	+ 5	+ 1
Lund................	+40	+35	Nikolayev...........	+ 1	− 2
Leiden..............	+35	+30			

the individual stars. It was therefore decided in 1921 that the stars in the catalogue should be reobserved, using the photographic method, which would give more uniformly precise positions in a short time.

The plates were taken at the Bergedorf and Bonn observatories and were used to obtain the *Zweiter Astronomische Gesellschaft Katalog, AGK2*, which was published between the years 1951 and 1958.

A repetition of this catalogue was planned at the Astrometric Conference held at Evanston, Illinois, in 1953, and the catalogue *AGK3* is now near completion.

A great many other star catalogues covering lesser areas of the sky have been published. The long list of those published up to the year 1900 can be found in *Fehlerverzeichniss zu den Sterncatalogen*, published by Ristenpart (1909). Several hundred more catalogues are listed in the *Index der Sternörter* published by the Bergedorf Observatory in 1928. In 1922 the Berlin Academy began the publication of the *Geschichte des Fixsternhimmels, GFH*. This catalogue contains all the measures which have been published for a given star and was completed in 1952.

§ 4. THE *CARTE DU CIEL CATALOGUE*

4.1. GENERAL DESCRIPTION

The *Carte du Ciel Catalogue*, CdC, also designated as the *Astrographic Catalogue*, AC, is the result of an international undertaking which originated in Paris in 1887 following the success of the Henry brothers in producing a 13-inch photographic lens. With instruments of similar type, plates covering the whole sky were taken at 18 different observatories. Each plate covers $2° \times 2°$, and the scale is very nearly 1 minute of arc per millimeter. The program consists of two sets of plates, one with a shorter exposure on which stars down to the eleventh photographic magnitude are measured for the positions published in the catalogue, the other set with a longer exposure with a limiting magnitude (photographic) of 14 is used for the purpose of charting. A small section of this large undertaking still awaits publication.

In the *Carte du Ciel Catalogues* the positions of the stars are given in the form of rectangular co-ordinates, x and y, as measured on the plates. Only in two sections from declinations $+40°$ to $+46°$ (Helsingfors) and $+54°$ (Catania) has the transformation of the x, y co-ordinates into right ascension and declination been carried out.

The problem of transforming one system of co-ordinates into the other has been the subject of a large number of contributions, which are found in the Introduction to each volume. It has been a detriment to the general use of the CdC that the great diversity in methods of notation and auxiliary tables has not been standardized but has been left to the choice of the individual contributor. As an example, it can be mentioned that, for the transformation of x, y into a, δ in the Oxford zone, no less than 17 tables are given, differing for each degree zone.

This drawback has been removed by the auxiliary tables published by the Hamburg Observatory (Vick 1924). These tables apply uniformly to all zones of the CdC, thus avoiding for the user the necessity of reading the introductions to the volumes in order to be familiar with the notations used.

The transformation of the published rectangular co-ordinates into equatorial co-ordinates is carried out in two steps, as explained in § 4.2.

4.2. TRANSFORMATION OF CO-ORDINATES

The first step in transforming the published rectangular co-ordinates, x, y, into equatorial co-ordinates, a, δ, consists of a linear transformation of x, y into standard co-ordinates, ξ, η. In this process the published plate constants are used, according to the notations listed in Table 2, which has been brought up to date since the Hamburg tables were published.

The standard co-ordinates obtained by means of Table 2 are referred to the equinox 1900, with the exception of the Paris zones $+21°$ to $+24°$ declination,

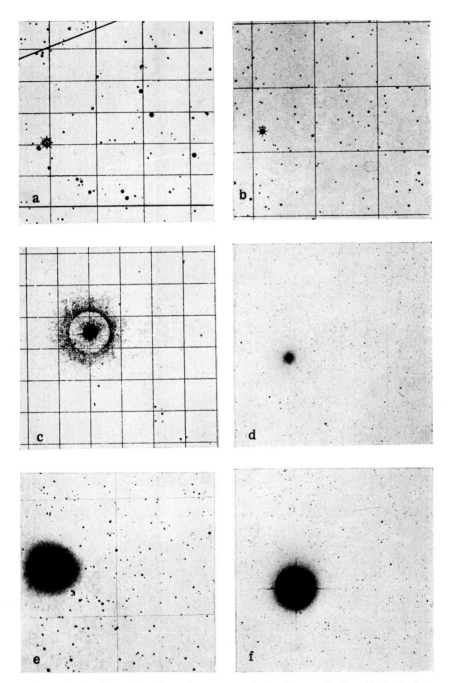

PLATE 1.—Region near Regulus as it appears on six star charts. *a:* Berliner Akademie chart. *b:* Argelander's *Bonner Durchmusterung* chart. *c: Carte du Ciel (Astrographic Chart). d:* Frank-lin-Adams chart. *e:* Wolf-Palisa chart. *f:* National Geographic Society–Palomar Observatory chart. All scales have been reduced to 85 per cent from originals. (Copyright National Geographic Society–Palomar Sky Survey.)

TABLE 2

NOTATIONS USED IN THE "ASTROGRAPHIC CATALOGUES"

Zones and Declinations of Plate Centers	Transformation of Measured into Standard Co-ordinates ξ, η Expressed in Minutes of Arc	Remarks
Greenwich 90° to +65°	$\begin{cases} \xi = 5(X + aX + bY + c - 14) \\ \eta = 5(Y + dX + eY + f - 14) \end{cases}$	Constants in Introduction in Vol. 3; ξ, η are given as XY on a plane tangent to the pole +87° to +90°
Rome-Vatican +64° to +55°	$\begin{cases} \xi = 5(X - AX - BY - C - 13) \\ \eta = 5(Y - DX - EY - F - 13) \end{cases}$	In Vols. 1 and 3 (zones +64° and +63°) A has to be replaced by $A - 0.00004$
Catania +54° to +47°	$\begin{cases} \xi = aX + bY + c \\ \eta = aY - bX + d \end{cases}$	a and δ are given for the first three hours of right ascension only
Helsingfors +46° to +40°	$\begin{cases} \xi = 0.998(X + a + bX + cY) \\ \eta = Y - 0.002Y + d + eX + iY \end{cases}$	The "Erreurs de div." have to be added to the "valeurs directes" XY; the a and δ are also given
Hyderabad +39° to +36°	$\begin{cases} \xi = 5(X - Ax - BY - C - 13) \\ \eta = 5(Y - DX - EY - F - 13) \end{cases}$	Sec. +39° to +32° originally attributed to Potsdam was more recently divided between Hyderabad and Oxford; revised constants for the Hyderabad zone found in *Pub. Nizamiah Obs.*, Vol. 13, Part 1, 1945
Oxford +35° to +25°	$\begin{cases} \xi = 5(X - AX - BY - C - 13) \\ \eta = 5(Y - DX - EY - F - 13) \end{cases}$	
Paris +20° to +18°	$\begin{cases} \xi = X_x + Yi_x \\ \eta = Y_y - Xi_y \end{cases}$	For sections +21° to +24° use the new constants for 1950 given in *A.J.*, **59**, 143, 1954
Bordeaux +17° to +11°	$\begin{cases} X_0 = X - 0.005X \\ Y_0 = Y - 0.005Y \\ \\ \xi = X_0 + p_x X_0 + r_x Y_0 + A \\ \eta = Y_0 + p_y Y_0 + r_y X_0 + A' \end{cases}$	
Toulouse +11° to +5°	$\begin{cases} \xi = (X + i_x Y)\tau_x \\ \eta = (Y - i_y X)\tau_y \\ \\ \xi = X\tau_x + i_x Y \\ \eta = Y\tau_y - i_y X \end{cases}$	For uneven degree centers For even degree centers
Algiers +4° to −2°	$\begin{cases} \xi = X + (A - 0.01112)X + 0.989B + 0.989C \\ \eta = Y + 0.989A'X + (B' - 0.01112)Y \\ \quad + 0.989C' \end{cases}$	Instead of the constants printed with the measures, use the corrected values in Vol. 4 B, pp. 22–39; those in turn have been partly replaced by the improved values, pp. 40–43
San Fernando −3° to −9°	$\begin{cases} \xi = X + aX + bY + c \\ \eta = Y + dX + eY + f \\ \\ \xi = X_0 + c_x +_x X_0 - i_x Y_0 \\ \eta = -(Y_0 + c_y +_y + i_x X_0) \end{cases}$	Tables in this form are available at the Yerkes Observatory Y is positive toward the south
Tacubaya −10° to −16°	$\begin{cases} \xi = 5(X + aX + bY + c) \\ \eta = 5(Y + dX + eY + f) \end{cases}$	In zone −15° from 0^h4^m to 5^h56^m the values of a and δ as well as ξ and η are given

TABLE 2—*Continued*

Zones and Declinations of Plate Centers	Transformation of Measured into Standard Co-ordinates ξ, η Expressed in Minutes of Arc	Remarks
Hyderabad $-17°$ to $-23°$..	$\begin{cases} \xi = 5(X-AX-BY-C-13) \\ \eta = 5(Y-BX-EY-F-13) \end{cases}$	Y is positive toward the south
Córdoba $-24°$ to $-31°$..	$\begin{cases} \xi = 5(X-AX-BY-C-14) \\ \eta = 5(Y-DX-EY-F-14) \end{cases}$	Constants at end of volume
Perth $-32°$ to $-40°$..	$\begin{cases} \xi = 5(X-AX-BY-C-13) \\ \eta = 5(Y-DX-EY-F-13) \end{cases}$	For the zones $-32°$ to $-36°$ measured at Perth
Perth $-32°$ to $-40°$..	$\begin{cases} \xi = 5(X+aX+bY+c-14) \\ \eta = -5(Y+dX+bY+f-14) \end{cases}$	For the zones $-37°$ to $-40°$ measured at Edinburgh
Cape of Good Hope $-41°$ to $-51°$..	$\begin{cases} \xi = X \\ \eta = Y \end{cases}$	
Sydney $-52°$ to $-64°$..	$\begin{cases} \xi = -5[X-A(X-1)-B(Y-30)-C-14] \\ \eta = +5[Y-D(X-1)-E(Y-30)-F-43] \end{cases}$	X decreases with increasing a
Melbourne $-65°$ to $-90°$..	$\begin{cases} \xi = X+aX+bY+c \\ \eta = Y+dX+eY+f \end{cases}$	

for which improved plate constants have been established for the equinox 1950 (Heckmann, Dieckvoss, and Kox 1954).

The standard co-ordinates, which are expressed in minutes of arc, can be transformed into equatorial co-ordinates by means of Vick's tables, which supersede all the tables published in the individual volumes of the *CdC*. In this way the computations become uniform and simple to carry out.

If a_0 and δ_0 are the equatorial co-ordinates of the center of the plates as listed in the catalogue, we have:

$$a = 4\xi(1-N) \sec d, \qquad a = a_0 + a - A,$$
$$d = d_0 + \eta - T, \qquad \delta = d - D \sin 2d,$$

for which N and T are found in Table 3, with η as argument; N is always positive and given in units of the sixth decimal; T is in units of the fourth decimal of a minute of arc and has the same sign as η; A and D are found in Table 4 with a as argument; A has the same sign as a, and D is always positive. For $\delta > 65°$, D is obtained with the argument $a - A$. For a larger than 600^s, the extension found under III in the Hamburg tables (Vick 1924) should be used.

By using the tables just described, the full value of the *CdC* catalogues has become available in a simple standardized form. There is no other system of catalogues that has such a wealth of high-precision positions of faint stars, and, with time, these data will become increasingly more valuable for determining proper motions of faint stars.

TABLE 3

AUXILIARY TABLES FOR COMPUTING RIGHT ASCENSION AND DECLINATION FROM STANDARD CO-ORDINATES

η	N	T	η	N	T	η	N	T	η	N	T	η	N	T
0...	0	0	15...	10	1	30...	38	8	45...	86	26	60...	152	61
1...	0	0	16...	11	1	31...	41	8	46...	90	27	61...	157	64
2...	0	0	17...	12	1	32...	43	9	47...	93	29	62...	163	67
3...	0	0	18...	14	2	33...	46	10	48...	97	31	63...	168	71
4...	1	0	19...	15	2	34...	49	11	49...	102	33	64...	173	74
5...	1	0	20...	17	2	35...	52	12	50...	106	35	65...	179	77
6...	2	0	21...	19	3	36...	55	13	51...	110	37	66...	184	81
7...	2	0	22...	20	3	37...	58	14	52...	114	40	67...	190	85
8...	3	0	23...	22	3	38...	61	15	53...	119	42	68...	196	89
9...	3	0	24...	24	4	39...	64	17	54...	123	44	69...	201	93
10...	5	0	25...	26	4	40...	68	18	55...	128	47	70...	207	97
11...	5	0	26...	29	5	41...	71	19	56...	133	50			
12...	6	0	27...	31	6	42...	75	21	57...	137	52			
13...	7	1	28...	33	6	43...	78	22	58...	142	55			
14...	8	1	29...	36	7	44...	82	24	59...	147	58			

TABLE 4

AUXILIARY TABLES FOR COMPUTING RIGHT ASCENSION AND DECLINATION FROM STANDARD CO-ORDINATES

a^s	A	D	a^s	A	D	a^s	A	D
0.....	0ˢ000	0″00	200....	0ˢ014	10″91	400....	0ˢ113	43″6
10.....	.000	0.03	210....	.016	12.03	410....	.121	43.6
20.....	.000	0.11	220....	.019	13.20	420....	.130	48.1
30.....	.000	0.25	230....	.021	14.43	430....	.140	50.4
40.....	.000	0.44	240....	.024	15.71	440....	.150	52.8
50.....	.000	0.68	250....	.028	17.04	450....	.160	55.2
60.....	.000	0.98	260....	.031	18.44	460....	.171	57.7
70.....	.001	1.34	270....	.035	19.88	470....	.183	60.3
80.....	.001	1.75	280....	.039	21.48	480....	.195	62.9
90.....	.001	2.21	290....	.043	22.93	490....	.207	65.5
100.....	.002	2.73	300....	.048	24.54	500....	.220	68.2
110.....	.002	3.30	310....	.053	26.2	510....	.234	71.0
120.....	.003	3.93	320....	.058	27.9	520....	.248	73.8
130.....	.004	4.61	330....	.063	29.7	530....	.262	76.7
140.....	.005	5.35	340....	.069	31.5	540....	.277	79.6
150.....	.006	6.14	350....	.076	33.4	550....	.293	82.6
160.....	.007	6.98	360....	.082	35.3	560....	.309	85.6
170.....	.009	7.88	370....	.089	37.3	570....	.326	88.7
180.....	.010	8.84	380....	.097	39.4	580....	.344	91.8
190.....	0.012	9.84	390....	0.105	41.5	590....	.362	95.0
						600....	0.381	98.3

§ 5. FUNDAMENTAL CATALOGUES

Only a summary will be given here of the fundamental catalogues which have been described in detail in earlier chapters of this volume (chaps. 2–4).

Fundamental catalogues give the position of the stars to the highest degree of accuracy, as determined from meridian observations referred to the sun. The stars are generally visible to the naked eye, and the brighter ones are observed in the daytime for comparison with the sun, so as to obtain fundamental positions with respect to the equator. Sometimes this is carried out through the intermediary of the planets.

The most difficult part in establishing a fundamental catalogue is the determination of the proper motions. In order to furnish the reference stars for the numerous fainter stars in the *AGK*, the need for a fundamental catalogue arose. Auwers (1869) made a new reduction of Bradley's observations from 1750 to 1762 and compared these with observations made in 1865 at Pulkovo and established the first *Fundamental Katalog, FK*, which contains 539 bright stars covering the Northern Hemisphere and the southern sky to $-10°$ declination (Auwers 1879). The catalogue was later supplemented by 83 stars to a declination of $-32°$ (Auwers 1883).

No matter how painstakingly such catalogues are worked out, improvements become necessary in the course of time, particularly in the proper motions, as new observations become available. The entire material in Auwers' catalogue was rediscussed by Peters, using Newcomb's constants of precession in preference to the Struve constants used by Auwers. The new catalogue, *NFK*, contains 905 stars and, in addition, 20 pole stars and was published in 1907 (Auwers 1907).

The *NFK* became the source of star positions published in the yearly ephemerides until Kopff (1934) produced a third improved fundamental catalogue, designated *FK3*, which is still being used in the present ephemerides. A further revision, designated the *FK4*, has been completed at the Heidelberg Rechen Institut and will be adopted with the 1964 edition of the international volume of *Apparent Places of Fundamental Stars*.

Independently of the fundamental catalogues previously mentioned, L. and B. Boss produced a much more extensive fundamental catalogue which included all the naked-eye stars, as well as those whose positions could be considered as well determined. The catalogue was first published in 1910 by the Carnegie Institution of Washington under the title *Preliminary General Catalogue of 6188 Stars*. The catalogue, designated the *PGC*, was the result of a discussion of all available material on star positions at the turn of the century. In its final form the catalogue was published in 1937 by the Carnegie Institution as the *Boss General Catalogue of 33,342 Stars*, also designated the *GC*. All observations up to 1925 were included, in order to obtain improved proper motions. The stars' positions are given for the equinox 1950 and for the same epoch, using the improved proper motions. The catalogue also lists the probable errors of the positions and the proper motions, and in the Introduction are found tables giving the systematic corrections to apply to most published catalogues to reduce them to the system of the *GC*, which has become the basis of most work done since in stellar dynamics.

When the *GC* positions are compared with those in the *FK3*, small systematic differences appear in the positions and the proper motions. A useful table has been published, giving the reduction of one system to the other (Kopff 1939).

§ 6. STAR CHARTS

The ancient celestial globes and charts represented the constellations in the form of mythological figures as seen from the convex side of the sphere. Bayer (1603) was the first to draw the constellations on the inside of the sphere as they appear in the sky.

Lists of star charts and atlases are in Houzeau's *Vade Mecum* (1881) and Wolf's *Handbuch der Astronomie*, **1**, 189, 1890.

In modern charts the symbolic figures of the constellations no longer appear. The stars are projected on a grid of meridians and parallels, and if the boundaries of the constellations are indicated, they are along the lines geometrically defined by the International Astronomical Union (Delporte 1930).

Plate 1 shows the region near Regulus as it appears on six modern charts. While charts *a* and *b* represent the very laborious charting based on visual observations, the remaining four charts are based on photographic charting. The Berliner Akademie chart is represented by Plate 1, *a*. It was undertaken at the suggestion of Bessel to help in the search for minor planets. It covers the ecliptic to a limiting visual magnitude of 11. It was never completed, but it should be remembered that it was this chart at 21 hours right ascension which enabled Galle in 1846 to locate Neptune in the position predicted by LeVerrier.

Plate 1, *b*, represents Argelander's *Bonner Durchmusterung* chart with a limiting visual magnitude of 9.5. Plate 1, *c*, is copied from the Bordeaux zone of the *CdC* or *AC* chart, which has a limiting photographic magnitude of 14.

Plate 1, *d*, is taken from the Franklin-Adams chart, which is the first photographic chart covering the whole sky. It has a limiting photographic magnitude of 15.

The Wolf-Palisa chart is shown in Plate 1, *e*. It covers most of the ecliptic belt and has a limiting magnitude (photographic) of 16.

Finally, in Plate 1, *f*, is represented the National Geographic Society–Palomar Observatory chart, which has a limiting magnitude of 20 (see Appendix 2 for further details).

REFERENCES

AUWERS, A.   1869   *Vierteljahrsschrift der astronomischer Gesellschaft*, **4**, 316, and Suppl. 2.

	1879	*Pub. A.G.*, No. 14.
	1883	*Ibid.*, No. 17.
	1907	*Veröff. Astr. Rechen Inst. Berlin*, No. 33.
BAYER, J.	1603	*Uranometria.*
DELPORTE, E.	1930	*Délimitation sci. d. constellations* (Cambridge: Cambridge University Press).
HECKMANN, O., DIECK-VOSS, W., and KOX, H.	1954	*A.J.*, **59**, 143.
KOPFF, A.	1934	*Berliner Astr. Jahrb.* 1936, Anhang.
	1939	*A.N.*, **269**, 160.
RISTENPART, F. W.	1909	*A. N. Ergänzungsheft*, No. 16.
VICK, C.	1924	*Hilfstafeln d. Hamburger Sternw.*, Abt. G.

APPENDIX **II**

The National Geographic Society–Palomar Observatory Sky Survey

R. L. MINKOWSKI[1] AND G. O. ABELL[2]

Mount Wilson and Palomar Observatories

Carnegie Institution of Washington, California Institute of Technology

§ 1. THE PROGRAM

THE National Geographic Society–Palomar Observatory Sky Survey was planned to cover the sky north of declination −27° with pairs of photographs in the blue and in the red (Wilson 1952). Experience gained during the progress of the survey showed that a slight lowering of the standards of quality for plates taken at large zenith distances permitted the inclusion of the declination zone −27° to −33°. Altogether, the survey covers the sky north of declination −33° on 935 pairs of plates.

§ 2. THE TELESCOPE

The 48-inch telescope is the standard Schmidt type (Harrington 1952). The spherical mirror is 72 inches in diameter and has a radius of curvature of 241 inches. The correcting plate has a clear aperture of 49.5 inches. The effective focal length of the system is 121 inches, giving a focal ratio of $f/2.44$ and a scale of 67″.14 per millimeter.

Chromatic aberration caused by the correcting plate is not entirely negligible in an instrument of the aperture and focal length of the 48-inch Schmidt telescope. For this reason, a careful selection had to be made of the wavelength for which the chromatic aberration would be zero.

The dependence of the image size on wavelength due to chromatic aberration alone is shown in Table 1, according to computations by F. E. Ross. With the correcting plate figured precisely for λ 4861 (Hβ), the table shows that the

[1] Now at the Radio Astronomy Laboratory and the Statistical Laboratory, University of California, Berkeley.

[2] Now at the Department of Astronomy, University of California, Los Angeles.

effect of chromatic aberration on image size becomes appreciable for wavelengths shorter than λ 3600 and longer than λ 10,000.

The ⅜-inch plate glass used for the correcting plate showed an unexpectedly high ultraviolet transmission. This, together with the difficulties encountered in using Hβ for testing, led to the choice of λ 4358 (Hg) for the precise figuring. The images are therefore slightly smaller in the ultraviolet and slightly larger in the infrared than shown in Table 1.

The photographic plates employed are 14 inches square and only 1 mm thick, so that they can be curved in the plateholder into a 121-inch radius along the focal surface, which is concentric with the spherical mirror. Under good seeing conditions the smallest stellar images have a diameter of about 30 μ, determined by the resolution of the photographic emulsions used. A focus difference of 0.05 mm, leading to a circle of confusion of 20 μ, causes a noticeable deterioration

TABLE 1

COMPUTED SMALLEST DIAMETERS OF IMAGES
MADE WITH THE 48-INCH SCHMIDT
TELESCOPE

Wavelength (λ)	Diameter μ	Wavelength (λ)	Diameter μ
3400........	50	4861......	0
3600........	40	5500......	5
3800........	30	6000......	13
4000........	21	7000......	24
4400........	10	10,000.....	34

of the images. The total field covered on a plate is 6°6 square. The non-vignetted field of the telescope, determined by the respective sizes of the mirror and correcting plate, is 5°4 in diameter. The computed loss in limiting magnitude because of vignetting at the extreme corners of a 14 × 14-inch plate is less than 0.2 mag.

The 48-inch Schmidt telescope is equipped with two 10-inch refracting guiding telescopes of 156 inches focal length mounted on opposite sides of the Schmidt tube. Guide stars have to be of magnitude 9 or brighter. The eyepiece and reticle assembly of each guiding telescope is mounted on a double slide with micrometric motion, so that a guide star at a position not coinciding with the center of the field can be used.

§ 3. THE SKY SURVEY

The centers of the 935 fields of the survey and its southern extension lie along declination circles at 6° intervals from +90° to −30°, inclusive, and are so spaced in right ascension that adjacent photographs overlap along a zone at least 0°6 wide on all four edges. The nominal positions of the field centers from −18° to +90° are for the equinox of 1855; those for −24° and −30° are for the equinox of 1875. It is thus easy to locate the survey field centers on the *BD* or *SD* charts (see Appendix 1, § 2).

Each field was photographed on both blue- and red-sensitive photographic emulsions. The two exposures were taken in immediate succession. The order of the exposures, however, was arbitrary, generally being dictated by convenience or efficiency in arranging the observing schedule.

All exposures were made on photometrically clear nights in the absence of moonlight and when the seeing disk of a stellar image was not more than 3 seconds of arc in diameter; somewhat poorer seeing was admitted for the $-30°$ declination zone. All exposures were made as near to the meridian as practicable (with very few exceptions, within 2 hours), to minimize the effects of extinction, differential refraction, and instrumental distortions.

The optimum exposure times to reach the faintest stars that can be recorded by the instrument under average observing conditions were determined by test exposures for each shipment of plates. They ranged from 10 to 15 minutes for the blue exposures and from 40 to 60 minutes for the red; they were about 20 per cent shorter for the declination zone $-30°$. It is fortunate that the survey could be completed during a period of sunspot minimum. A noticeable loss of limiting magnitude would have resulted from the unusual amount of solar activity in the few years following 1956 that approximately doubled the illumination of the night sky at Palomar, as compared with that during the survey period.

For the blue exposures, the Eastman 103a-O emulsion was used, and for the red exposures the Eastman 103a-E emulsion in combination with red Plexiglas 2444 as a filter. Red Plexiglas 2444 has transmission characteristics closely similar to those of the Wratten No. 29 filter and was used here because it can be obtained readily in the large sizes required. The spectral response-curves to a spectrum of constant intensity at all wavelengths for the combination of a 103a-O emulsion with the correcting plate and for the combination of 103a-E emulsion with the red Plexiglas are shown in Figure 1. Eastman catalogue data (Kodak Co. 1953) were used for the plate sensitivity. The transmission of the correcting plate has been measured by E. Pettit; that of the red Plexiglas by W. C. Miller.

All plates were processed in standard formula D-19 developer for 5 minutes, with constant agitation provided by an electrically operated mechanical rocking device designed to insure uniform development. Because of differences between individual shipments of plates the photographic contrasts (gammas) ranged between 1.5 and 2.0.

The particular plate-filter combination for the red exposures was chosen because it has peak sensitivity near Hα (λ 6563) and is well suited for the detection of faint, extended, emission nebulosities. Magnitudes of stellar images on the blue plates correspond to a color sensitivity that deviates in the ultraviolet from that of international photographic magnitudes. If, nevertheless, stellar magnitudes measured on the blue plates are assumed to correspond to international photographic, P, magnitudes, then the blue minus red, $P - R$, color indices are related to the international, $P - V$, color indices by the approximate linear color equation,

$$P - R = 1.6(P - V).$$

A star for which $P - V = 0.7$ appears about equally bright on the blue and red plates. The limiting magnitude, defined as the faintest magnitude for which every star produces a recognizable image on plates of average quality, is 21.1 mag. for P and 20.0 mag. for R. The limiting magnitudes are up to about 0.3 mag. brighter for the poorest plates included in the Sky Survey and up to 0.5 mag. brighter for the declination zone $-30°$. The limiting magnitudes quoted are based on the photoelectric measures in Selected Area 57 by W. A. Baum.

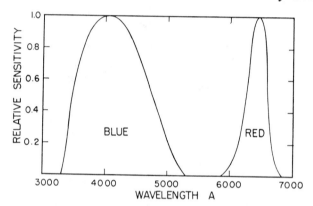

Fig. 1.—Response of the plate-filter combinations to light of constant intensity for all wavelengths.

Each pair of photographs of a field was inspected for quality. Plates were rejected because of meteorologic conditions, such as clouds, haze, excessive sky brightness, bad seeing; for misleading or too numerous emulsion defects; or for operational difficulties, such as poor focus, breakage, star trails due to improper alignment of the polar axis of the telescope, and airplane trails. Rejection of one member of a pair automatically caused rejection of the other. Many fields had to be photographed several times before acceptable pairs of plates could be obtained. Altogether, 1620 pairs of plates had to be exposed to obtain the 935 pairs included in the survey.

§ 4. THE REPRODUCTION

No known reproduction method can reproduce on paper the full density range obtained on a photographic plate. For the *Sky Atlas*, it was decided that the reproduction of the faintest details at the limit of the plates should be achieved, even at the expense of inadequate reproduction of bright objects, because the 48-inch Schmidt telescope permits the observation of faint stars, galaxies, and nebulosities that are beyond the limits of smaller instruments. Satisfactory preservation of the plate limit is possible only on negative reproductions; this was one reason for their choice for the production of the *Atlas*.

Experiments with various methods of reproduction showed that only photographic copies could preserve the faintest stellar images with diameters of about 0.03 mm. At least one intermediate step—the production of a positive—was necessary to avoid the risk of damaging the plates in printing large numbers of copies directly from the originals. Since positive reproduction would have necessitated the making of a duplicate negative as a second intermediate step, negative reproduction was to be preferred, for each intermediate step entails some deterioration of image quality.

Separate contact printers were used for the production of the glass positives and of the paper prints. The source of illumination in the positive printer was a projection lamp at a distance of 16 feet. A close approximation to illumination by a distant point source was thus obtained, which minimized the loss of definition because of imperfect contact. Diffuse illumination was used in the paper printer. Both printers were of the vacuum type, in which the plate to be copied and the duplication plate or paper were kept in nearly perfect contact by evacuation of the air between them.

After extensive tests and trials, Eastman Kodak Finegrain Positive glass plates were selected for the positives, and Eastman Kodak Unicontrast double-weight paper for the negative prints. The positive plates were processed 3 minutes with agitation in standard formula 16D developer to a photographic contrast of gamma 1.8. The paper reproductions were processed in standard formula D-72 developer. The contrast of the paper is gamma 2.0, practically independent of development.

The prints were fixed for 3 minutes in each of two fixing baths. They were then washed with agitation until a starch-iodine test indicated that every trace of the sodium thiosulfate from the fixing bath had been removed. They were finally treated with a commercial print-flattening solution that minimizes the danger of the emulsion cracking with handling. It is believed that every possible care has been taken to insure a long life for the prints.

The original plates show considerable variation in background density, which depends on the sky brightness. It was found that the most satisfactory reproduction could be obtained by printing all positives to a density of 1.4, without regard to the densities of the originals. This was achieved by measuring the background density of the originals and adjusting the exposure time for the positives with rigid control of the illumination and carefully standardized development. Originals with background densities below 0.3 or above 0.9 were found to give inferior results and were therefore rejected.

The paper prints were found to be most satisfactory with a background density of 0.2 or slightly higher. Because they could be processed in yellow light

of sufficient brightness for visual control of development and because the opera-
tors learned to control the development adequately, strict production controls
were not used for the development of the paper prints.

The reproduction of the Sky Survey photographs on positive transparencies
and the printing of the *Atlas* were carried out by the Graphic Arts Facilities
of the California Institute of Technology in Pasadena.

§ 5. THE *SKY ATLAS*

The National Geographic Society–Palomar Observatory *Sky Atlas* is distributed as a set of 1870 unbound photographic prints on double-weight paper
of 14 × 17-inch size. Each print has a margin of 1 inch on one side and 2 inches
on the other, with the wider margin on the west edge of photographs in the
blue and on the east edge of those in the red.

In one corner, usually the north-following one, of each print are given the
plate number with a letter "O" or "E," denoting, respectively, whether the
original exposure was on the Eastman 103a-O or 103a-E emulsion, the date, and
the 1950 co-ordinates of the field center. The 1855 co-ordinates of the field
center have been stamped on the back of each print.

A catalogue distributed with the *Atlas* gives for each exposure the date,
sidereal and Pacific Standard times, hour angle, exposure time, and seeing.

Throughout the entire program, every effort was made to maintain high
standards of quality. However, on photographic plates of the size used here,
some imperfections had to be allowed to pass. As an aid to users of the *Atlas*,
the more common of these imperfections are described in a pamphlet accompanying the *Atlas*, with references to prints where examples may be found.

§ 6. DISPOSITION OF THE PLATES

All plates taken for the Sky Survey, including the rejected plates, are stored
in a vault in the Robinson Laboratory of Astrophysics of the California Institute
of Technology, where they are available for use by staff members and guest
investigators of the Mount Wilson and Palomar Observatories.

One of the two sets of glass positive copies is in Pasadena, where it is used
in making copies of the plates; the other is stored, unused, in the dome of the
200-inch telescope on Palomar Mountain, where it will be available in the event
that the plates in Pasadena should be damaged or destroyed by some catas-
trophe.

The Sky Survey was made financially possible by grants from the National
Geographic Society. The society provided the photographic materials and special equipment required, the salaries of the personnel employed full or part time
on the survey, and the production of the two contact positives on glass of each
survey photograph.

The observing time with the 48-inch Schmidt telescope required to obtain the Sky Survey photographs was made available by the Palomar Observatory of the California Institute of Technology.

REFERENCES

HARRINGTON, R. G.   1952   *Pub. A.S.P.*, **64**, 275.
KODAK CO.   1953   *Kodak Photographic Plates for Scientific and Technical Use* (7th ed.; Rochester, N.Y.: Eastman Kodak Co.).
WILSON, A. G.   1952   *Trans. I.A.U.*, **8**, 335.

Subject Index

A stars
  absolute magnitudes (luminosities), 92 f.,
    106 f., 149 f., 158 f., 387, 393, 401
  bolometric corrections, 267 ff.
  effective temperatures, 90 f., 267, 270
  intrinsic colors, 128, 142, 213 ff., 249, 251–
    54
  photometric data, 208 ff., 219 f.
  radial velocities, 71 f.
  spectral classification, 84, 86, 95 f., 116 f.,
    135 ff., 145 ff., 150 f., 154 f., 157, 159,
    162, 170 ff., 209 f., 212, 268, 384–400
Aberration of light, 6 f.
Absolute bolometric magnitudes
  cepheids in Small Magellanic Cloud, 439 ff.
  classical (long-period) cepheids, 430 ff.
  eclipsing binaries, 288 ff.
  mass-luminosity relation, 284–91
  spectroscopic binaries, 286 f.
  visual binaries, 282 f.
  W Ursa Majoris systems, 289 f.
Absolute magnitude (luminosity) calibrations, 383–406
  in early Mount Wilson work, 384–98
    analyses of, 391 ff.
    modern use of, 394–97
    systematic errors in, 387–91
  MK (Yerkes) system, 397–401
    A stars, 400
    F5–K5 stars, 398 ff.
  modern systems, 400–405
    from H and K absorption lines, 404 f.
    from line strength, 402 ff.
  O and B supergiants, 406–17
    fundamental data, 406
    from hydrogen lines, 415–17
    main-sequence fitting procedure, 406–13
    MK system, 413 ff.
Absolute magnitude (luminosity) effects from
  Balmer line, 96 f., 146–50, 159 f., 170 ff.
  color difference, 250 f.
  cyanogen (CN) index, 97 f., 109–12, 146,
    173–76
  H and K line widths, 147 f., 179, 404
  intermediate-band photometry, 138, 140
  narrow-band photometry, 149 f., 155
  wide-band photometry, 130 f.
Absolute visual magnitudes; see also Luminosities
  and bolometric corrections, 265
  classical cepheids, 429–34
  from color difference (U, B, V system),
    250 ff.

giants, 92
from Hβ index, 165, 171
main-sequence stars, 92 f.
MK types, 90, 401, 404
Mount Wilson catalogue, 87 f., 394–400
Population I stars, 106 f.
Population II stars, 106 f.
red dwarfs, 195
spectroscopic binaries, 394–99
stars with CN bands, 111
subgiants, 92
supergiants, 92 f., 406
variable stars, 339 f., 344 f., 347, 354, 448–
  70
visual binaries, 282 f.
zero-age main sequence, 216, 407
Absorption; see Interstellar absorption
Algol type variables, 357
Alpha Orionis variables, 347 f.
Apparent places, reduction to mean places, 7

B stars; see O–B stars
Balmer discontinuity (Balmer jump), 107,
  126, 129, 137, 152 ff., 159 f., 162 ff., 241,
  243, 247 f., 252
Beta Canis Majoris type variables, 354 ff.,
  466
Beta Lyrae type variables, 357
Binaries; see Eclipsing binaries; Spectroscopic
  binaries; Visual binaries
Blink microscope, 46
Bolometric absolute magnitudes, 263 f.
Bolometric corrections, 263–72
  for early-type stars, 266, 269
  empirical values of, 264 f.
  for late-type stars, 265 f., 269
  theoretical values of, 266

Carbon stars
  classification of, 102–5
  sequence of, 104 f.
Catalogues
  AGK1 (Katalog der Astronomische Gesell-
    schaft), 24, 33 f., 42, 472 f.
  AGK2 (Zweiter Astronomische Gesellschaft
    Katalog), 24, 27, 34, 42, 473
  AGK2A, 34
  AGK3 (Dritter Astronomische Gesellschaft
    Katalog), 26 f., 34, 42
  AGK3R, 27, 43
  Astrographic (AC), 33 f., 43 f., 474 ff.

Catalogues—*Continued*
  Bonner Durchmusterung (BD), 471 f.
  Cape, 24, 42 f., 472
  Carte du Ciel (CdC), 33 f., 43 f., 474 ff.
  Catalogues of variable stars, 333 ff.
  Córdoba Durchmusterung (CDM), 472
  Fehlerverzeichniss zu den Sterncatalogen, 473
  FK (Fundamental-Katalog), 17, 478
  FK3 (Dritter Fundamental-Katalog des Berliner astronomischen Jahrbuchs), 15, 17 f., 20–23, 26, 32 ff.
  FK4, 17, 22 f., 26, 33 f.
  FKSZ (Fundamental Catalogue of Faint Stars), 34
  GC (General Catalogue of 33,342 Stars for the Epoch 1950), 17 ff., 23–26, 32, 478
  General Catalogue of Stellar Radial Velocities, 64–73, 76
  General Catalogue of Trigonometric Stellar Parallaxes, 55–61
  General Catalogue of Variable Stars, 334, 371
  GFH (Geschichte des Fixsternhimmels), 24, 473
  HD (Henry Draper Catalogue), 79, 83 ff., 472
  HDE (Henry Draper Extension), 84
  Index der Sternörter, 25, 473
  KSZ (Catalogue of Faint Stars), 34
  McCormick, 44
  New General Catalogue of Nebulae and Clusters of Stars, 36 f.
  NFK (Neuer Fundamental-Katalog), 17, 32, 478
  N30 (Catalogue of 5,268 Standard Stars, 1950.0), 17–23, 26, 33
  PFKSZ (Preliminary General Catalogue of Faint Fundamental Stars), 26, 34
  PGC (Preliminary General Catalogue of 6,188 Stars), 478
  of radial velocities, 64 f.
  of slitless spectrograms, 113 f.
  Southern Durchmusterung (SD), 472
  Washington catalogues, 15 f.
  Yale zone catalogues, 24, 33, 42 f.
Cepheids
  absolute magnitudes, 351, 429–35, 439 ff.
  amplitude, 351, 434 ff.
  classical, 350–54, 421–47
  cluster-type variables; *see* RR Lyrae stars
  color-magnitude diagram, 434 f.
  intrinsic colors, 429, 439
  light-curves, 351 ff., 355 f., 444
  long-period, 350–54, 421–47
  in Magellanic Clouds, 422 f., 437–41
  period-amplitude diagram, 436 ff., 442 f.
  period-color relation, 423–26, 428–32, 436, 439 f.
  period-density relation, 352
  period-frequency function, 438
  period-luminosity relation, 351, 423, 428–34, 440 f., 445
  period-spectral-type diagram, 424

  RR Lyrae stars, 354 f., 422 f., 428, 440, 442–45, 449, 452–58, 461 ff.
  short-period; *see* RR Lyrae stars
Charts, 479
Classifications
  of eclipsing variables, 357 f.
  of giants and supergiants, 98–101
  of stellar spectra; *see* Spectral classification
  of variable stars, 337–59, 449 f.
Cluster-type variables, 354 f., 428, 440, 442 f., 449, 452 ff., 461 ff.
Color difference, 126, 128, 136–46, 162–86, 231 f., 246–51, 253 f., 259 f.
Color excess, 127 f., 133, 226, 231 f., 237, 246
Color index
  intermediate-band photometry, 131–46
  narrow-band photometry, 162–79
  related to absolute magnitude, 250 ff.
  six-color photometry, 221
  wide-band photometry, 125–31, 204–20, 224–60
Color-magnitude diagram, 250 ff., 402 f., 407, 427, 435
Color temperature, comparison with effective temperature, 270
Co-ordinate systems
  apparent, 3
  celestial, 12 f.
  ecliptic, 1 f.
  equatorial, 1 f.
  fundamental, 11
  galactic, 1 f., 8
Cosmic distance scale, 422
Cyanogen (CN) bands
  anomalous intensities in, 111, 151
  discrepancy, 110 ff., 151
  in G–K stars, 97 f., 108–12, 151
  index, 97 f., 109–12, 146, 173–76
  population effects, 108–12, 151

Declination
  annual terms, 22
  apparent, 7
  systematic errors in, 14
Depolarization parameters, 313
Double stars; *see* Visual binaries

Eclipsing binaries
  absolute dimensions of, 377 f.
  Algol type, 357
  apsidal motions of, 376
  Beta Lyrae type, 357
  bolometric magnitude, 288 ff.
  catalogues, 371 f.
  change of period, 373 ff.
  classification, 357 f.
  definition, 356
  with displaced secondary minimum, 379
  distribution, 356
  with eccentric orbits, 379
  empirical data, 288–91, 370–82

history, 370 f.
Krat's classification, 358 f.
light-curves of, 357 f.
limb darkening, 375
mass, 288–91, 377 f.
period, 373 ff.
publications, 371 f.
radius, 288 f.
selected systems, 288–91, 380
tables, 375–82
variable periods, 376
W Ursa Majoris type, 357 f.
Eclipsing variables; see Eclipsing binaries
Ecliptic latitude, 1
Ecliptic longitude, 1
Effective temperatures, 90, 263, 266–72
comparison with color temperature, 270
fundamental, 266 f.
from model atmosphere, 267 f.
spectral-type relationship, 267–70
and theoretical bolometric corrections, 266
Effective wavelengths of photometric systems, 245
Epoch, 8
Equinox, 2, 8
Eruptive variables, 339–46
classification, 339
nova-like variables, 342 f.
novae, 339–42
recurrent novae, 342
RW Aurigae type, 345
supernovae, 339
T Tauri type, 345
U Geminorum type, 343 ff.
UV Ceti type, 345 f.
Extragalactic distances from cepheids, 421,
440

F–G–K stars
absolute magnitudes, 92 f., 106, 111, 151,
158 f., 179, 193 f., 384–405
bolometric corrections, 265, 269
effective temperature, 91, 267–70
intrinsic colors, 128, 142 ff., 196, 213 ff.,
249, 254
photometric data, 208 ff., 219 f.
radial velocities, 68 ff., 72, 197
spectral classification, 84, 86–93, 96 ff., 100,
108–11, 137, 139 ff., 145 ff., 151, 155,
157, 159, 161 f., 170–78, 195, 384–405
Fundamental observations, probable errors
of, 14

G stars; see F–G–K stars
Galactic longitude, 2, 8
Galactic rotation, 9
Galaxies
reference system of, 31, 35 f., 38
two-color diagrams, 257
Geometric variables; see Eclipsing variables

Giants and supergiants, spectral classification, 90, 93, 98–101, 406–17
Globular clusters
two-color diagram, 257
variables in, 451 f., 455 f., 461 ff.

Henry Draper (HD) Catalogue, 79, 83 ff., 472
classification of carbon stars, 102 f.
extension, 84
limiting magnitude, 85
system of, 79, 83 ff.
High-velocity stars, two-color diagram, 256
HR (Hertzsprung-Russell) diagram, 105–12,
116 ff., 386, 413

Intensity distribution in stellar spectra, 242
Interferometer measures; see Stellar radii
Interstellar absorption
ratio of total to selective, 226, 229–33,
235 ff.
sources of errors, 229 f.
variation in, 234
Interstellar polarization
by dust grains
absorption by, 302 ff., 314
alignment mechanisms, 308 f.
diamagnetic grains, 310
extinction by, 303–7, 313 ff.
ferromagnetic grains, 309
gas-flow alignment, 308
graphite flakes, 307, 310
iron needles, 306 f., 310
magnetic alignment, 308 ff.
optical properties, 302–8
paramagnetic absorptions, 308 ff.
quantum-mechanical grains, 307 f.
scattering effects, 304–7
extinction, related to, 301 f., 303–7, 313 ff.
galactic longitude dependence, 300, 310 f.
in galaxies, 311
in globular clusters, 311
in Milky Way, 299 ff.
observational results, 299 ff.
parameters, 293–96
photoelectric measurements, 297 ff.
photographic measurements, 296 f.
of starlight, 293–319
Stokes parameters, 394 ff.
synchrotron radiation, 301
wavelength dependence, 301 f.
Interstellar reddening, 225–39
measurements of, 231 f.
in the C_1 system, 231
of stars in the Orion Nebula, 236 ff.
from three-color photometry, 231 f.
from U, B, V photometry, 232
variation in, 233–36
Irregular variables, 347

K stars; see also F–G–K stars
radial velocities, 68
spectral surveys, 192–201
velocity dispersions, 198 f.

Kapteyn's Selected Areas, proper motion in, 44

Krat's classification of eclipsing variables, 358 f.

Limb darkening, 375

Longitude
    ecliptic, 1
    galactic, 8

Luminosities; *see also* Absolute visual magnitudes
    Beta Canis Majoris stars, 466
    in binary systems, 453, 464 ff.
    classical cepheids, 429–35, 453 ff., 458, 461 ff.
    Delta Scuti stars, 356, 467
    in galaxies, 452 f., 457 f., 461
    in globular clusters, 451 f., 455 f., 461 ff.
    irregular variables, 459, 462 f.
    in Magellanic Clouds, 458 ff.
    novae, 339 f., 458 f., 461, 465
    RR Lyrae stars, 354, 455 ff.
    semiregular variables, 462 f.
    supernovae, 339 f., 461
    U Geminorum stars, 465

Luminosity criteria, calibration of, 383–417

M dwarfs; *see also* M stars
    bolometric corrections to, 266
    counts of, 195
    spectral surveys, 192–201
    velocity dispersions, 198 f.
    velocity-vector diagrams, 199 f.

M stars; *see also* M dwarfs
    absolute magnitudes, 92 f., 106 f., 179, 193 f., 384–93
    bolometric corrections, 266
    effective temperature, 91, 267
    intrinsic colors, 128, 196, 213, 215
    photometric data, 208 ff., 219 f.
    radial velocities, 198 ff.
    spectral classification, 84, 86 ff., 98–101, 148, 195, 384–93

Magnitudes; *see* Absolute visual magnitudes; Luminosities

Main sequence, 216, 407
    two-color diagram, 216, 248 ff., 258 ff.

Mass-luminosity relation, 284 ff., 289 ff.

Mass ratios, 281–84

Masses; *see* Stellar masses

Mean places, reduction from apparent, 7 f.

Mira type stars, 329, 337, 348 ff., 361, 365, 449, 451, 464 f.

MK (Yerkes) system
    absolute magnitudes, 92
    bolometric corrections to, 265 ff., 269 ff.
    classification of giants and supergiants, 98–101
    effective temperatures, 91, 266–70
    intrinsic colors, 213 ff.
    luminosity classes, 88 f., 397–401

revised types, 88, 90
    temperature calibration, 90
    visual absolute magnitude of, 92, 401

Mount Wilson (MW) spectral classification, 85–88
    spectroscopic absolute magnitude, 87

Mu Cephei type stars, 347 f.

National Geographic Society–Palomar Observatory Sky Survey
    atlas, 486
    reproduction of, 484 ff.
    sky survey, 482 ff.
    telescope, 481 f.

Natural groups, in HR diagram, 116 ff.

Nova-like variables, 342 f.

Novae, 339–42

Nutation
    dynamical theory of, 4 f.
    in longitude, 3
    in obliquity, 3

O–B stars
    absolute magnitudes, 92 ff., 106 f., 149 f., 401
    bolometric corrections, 269 f.
    effective temperature, 91, 267 ff.
    intrinsic colors, 128, 213 ff., 249, 254
    photometric data, 208 ff., 219 f.
    radial velocities, 66 f., 72 ff.
    spectral classification, 84, 93 ff., 131 ff., 135, 147, 149 ff., 154, 162, 164–70

Observations, fundamental
    in declination, 13
    in right ascension, 13

Orbits of visual binaries; *see* Visual binaries

Period-color relation, 423 ff., 437 ff.; *see also* Cepheids

Period-luminosity relation, 349, 351, 428–34
    color dependence of, 430 ff.
    history of, 423
    universality of, 422, 440 f.
    zero point of, 423, 432

Perturbations, of sun's latitude, 3

Photoelectric photometry; *see also* Spectral classification
    intermediate-band width, 131–46
    narrow-band, 162–79
    wide-band, 125–31

Photometric parallaxes
    evolutionary effects on, 308
    from Hβ intensities, 417
    from Hγ intensities, 414 ff.
    main-sequence fitting, 416 ff.
    MK luminosity classifications, 413 f.
    O–B stars, 406–17
    supergiants, 406–17

Photometric systems, 204–22
    C₁ system, 218
    Cape systems, 217 f.

P, V system, 216 f.
$(P, V)_E$ system, 217
R, I system, 218 ff.
six-color photometry, 221, 244 f.
standards, 219 f.
U, B, V system, 130 f., 207–16, 242, 244–57
    bolometric corrections on, 268 f.
    comparisons between Northern and Southern Hemispheres, 211
    extinction coefficient, 211 f.
    intrinsic colors, 213 ff.
    primary standards, 208
    standard zero-age main sequence, 216, 251–54
    standards, 208 ff.
U, G, R system, 130, 242, 244 ff., 258 ff.
U_c, B, V system (Cape), 244 ff., 255
W, U, B, V system, 132 ff.

Photometry
    multicolor, 241–62
    spectral classification by
        R, G, U system, 130 f.
        U, B, V system, 127 f.
        U, V, B, Y system, 136 ff.

Physical variables; *see* Variable stars

Planetary precession, 3

Polar motion, 9

Polarization; *see* Interstellar polarization

Precession
    constant of, 5
    dynamical theory of, 4 ff.
    general, 3 f.
    geodesic, 5
    luni-solar, 3
    planetary, 3
    speed of, 5 f.

Proper motions
    absolute, 40 f., 44
    accidental errors of, 41, 43
    AGK3, 26 f., 42
    Astrographic Catalogues (AC), 44
    Cape catalogues, 24, 42 f.
    Carte du Ciel (CdC), 44
    centennial, errors of, 18 ff.
    detection by blink microscope, 47 f.
    FK3, 18, 20–23, 26
    FK4, 22
    fundamental, 11 f., 23 f.
    GC, 19, 23
    Kapteyn's Selected Areas, 44
    McCormick catalogues, 44
    magnitude-color error, 42
    magnitude errors, 41 f.
    N30, 19 ff., 22 f.
    photographic, 40 ff.
    reduction to absolute, 41 f., 44 f.
    relative, 40
    with respect to galaxies
        Lick program, 31, 35, 38
        Russian program, 31, 36, 38
    surveys, 46–51
        Bruce (by Luyten), 48, 50 f.
        by Innes, 49
        Lowell Observatory, 52
        miscellaneous, 51
        Palomar 48-inch Schmidt, 52
        by Ross, 50
        by Wolf, 49
    systematic errors, 26, 41
    Yale catalogues, 24, 42 f.

Pulsating variables, 346–56
    AF Cygni type, 347
    Alpha Orionis type, 347 f.
    Beta Canis Majoris type, 354 ff., 466
    Beta Cephei type, 354 f.
    cepheids, 350 ff.
    classification of, 347
    cluster-type variables, 354
    definition of, 346
    irregular variables, 347
    long-period cepheids, 350 ff.; *see also* Cepheids
    Mira type, 348 ff.; *see also* Mira type stars
    Mu Cephei type, 347 f.
    period-luminosity relation, 349 ff.
    RR Lyrae type, 354; *see also* RR Lyrae stars
    RV Tauri type, 347
    semiregular variables, 347 ff.
    short-period cepheids, 354; *see also* Cepheids; RR Lyrae stars

Q-method, 215 f., 246 ff.

Radial velocities, 64–76
    A stars, 66, 71 ff.
        systematic corrections, 66
    absolute accuracies, 69 ff.
    B stars, 72 f.
    catalogues of, 64
    General Catalogue, 64 ff., 76
    solar-type stars, 69 f.
    systematic corrections, 65 f., 68
    systematic differences
        B stars, 66 f., 73
        K stars, 68
    Taurus cluster, 70, 72
    zero point of *General Catalogue*, 68 ff.

Radii; *see* Stellar radii

Rayleigh's law, 225

Recurrent novae, 342

Red dwarfs
    colors of, 196 f.
    determination of absolute magnitudes, 193 f.
    discovery of, 192 f.
    kinematic characteristics, 197–201
    luminosity function, 194 f.
    population groups, 200 f.
    visual absolute magnitudes, 194 ff.

Reddening-curve, 225, 239
    extension into the infrared, 228
    from observations with spectrum scanner, 228 f.
    schematic, 226

Reddening-curve—*Continued*
from six-color photometry, 229 f., 233, 237
spectrophotometric studies of, 233
variations in, 233 ff.
Reddening line, 215
for O stars, 234
Reference systems
astronomical, 1 f.
bright stars, 31 f.
ecliptic, 1 f.
equatorial, 1 f.
faint stars, 31, 35 f.
galaxies
Lick program, 31, 35–38
Russian program, 31, 36 ff.
intermediate stars, 30, 33 ff.
stars and galaxies, 30–39
Right ascension
apparent, 7
periodic errors, annual type, 22
systematic errors in, 14
Rotation, galactic, 9
RR Lyrae stars, 354 f., 422 f., 428, 440, 442–45, 449, 452–58, 461 ff.
RV Tauri stars, 347
RW Aurigae stars, 345

S stars, MK classification of, 102
Selective absorption, ratio of total absorption to, 226, 229 f., 232 f., 235 ff.
Semiregular variables, 347 ff.
Sky survey; *see* National Geographic Society–Palomar Observatory Survey
Small Magellanic Cloud
cepheids in, 422 ff.
distance modulus of, 440
Space distribution of variables, 363 ff.
Spectral characteristics
population groups, 105–12
Population I stars, 105–12
main-sequence, 107 f.
Population II stars, 105–12
giants, 108–12
horizontal branch, 107
main-sequence, 107 f.
subdwarfs, 107 f.
subgiants, 108 f.
Spectral classification; *see also* Absolute magnitude (luminosity) calibrations
A stars, 95
accuracy of quantitative methods, 180 ff.
application to theory of model stellar atmospheres, 184 f.
B stars, 95
from Balmer discontinuity, 152 ff., 159 f.
from CN absorption, 151, 172–76
criteria, 80 ff., 124
from equivalent widths of Balmer lines, 149 f., 159 f., 162–72
F stars, 96
G–K stars, 96 ff.

from H and K emission lines, 179
Henry Draper system, 79, 83 ff.
by intermediate-band photometry, 131–46
limiting magnitude of quantitative methods, 180 ff.
Lindblad criteria, 146 f.
from line ratios, 94–99, 101–4, 161 f.
M stars, 98 f.
from metal content, 139–46, 158, 176 ff.
MK, 88–93, 99 ff.
Mount Wilson (MW), 85–88, 384–98
analysis of, 391 ff.
modern use of, 394–97
systematic errors in, 387–91
by narrow-band photometry, 146–79
natural groups, 116 f.
O stars, 93 f.
physical theory, 80–83
principles of, 78 f.
quantitative methods, 123–86
of short spectra, 112–18
systems of, 83–93
technique of, 118
two-dimensional, 82, 85, 87, 123–86
ultraviolet criteria of Barbier and Chalonge, 151–59
by wide-band photometry, 125–31
Spectral type
bolometric correction, 265 ff., 269
effective temperature, 267–70
Spectroscopic binaries
frequency of, 73 ff.
masses, luminosities, and radii of, 286 f.
Spectroscopic parallaxes; *see also* Absolute magnitude (luminosity) calibrations
accidental errors, 388 ff.
early Mount Wilson work, 384–97
luminosity parameter, 387 ff.
systematic errors, 388 ff.
Standard (zero-age) main sequence, 216, 251 f., 254, 406–17
Stellar luminosities; *see also* Absolute visual magnitudes, etc.
empirical data, 273–92
mass-luminosity relation, 284 ff., 290
Stellar masses
accuracy and errors of, 274
determination of, 273–84
of eclipsing binaries, 288–91
empirical data, 273–92
mass-radius relation, 290 f.
sources of, 273
of spectroscopic binaries, 286 f.
of visual binaries, 273–84
Stellar parallaxes; *see* Trigonometric stellar parallaxes
Stellar radii
eclipsing binaries, 377 f.
empirical data, 273–92, 377 f.
interferometric determination of, 289 ff.
mass-radius relation, 290 f.
methods of determining, 288 ff.
sources of, 288 ff.

Stellar spectra, quantitative classification methods, 123–86; *see also* Spectral classification

Stellar temperature scale, 263–72

Stereocomparator, 46

Stokes parameters, 294 f.

Supergiants, two-color diagram, 255

Supernovae, 339

Synchrotron radiation, 301

Systematic errors
in meridian-circle work, 14
proper motions, 41

T Tauri stars, 345

Temperature; *see* Bolometric correction; Effective temperatures; Stellar temperature scale

Temperature scale, stellar, 263–72

TiO bands, in M stars, 99 f.

Transit circle, precision of, 2

Trigonometric stellar parallaxes, 55–62
accidental errors, 57 f.
bibliography, 62
external probable error, 58 f.
general catalogue, 55–61
median parallax of, 56
reduction to absolute, 60 f.
systematic corrections, 60 f.
internal accuracy, 56 ff.
internal probable error, 56
relation to external error, 58 f.
night error, 57 f.
shift error, 57
systematic errors, 60 f.

Two-color diagram
cepheids, 426
galaxies, 257
globular clusters, 257
high-velocity stars, 256
main-sequence stars, 258 ff.
supergiants, 255
white dwarfs, 255

U Geminorum type stars, 343 ff., 465

Ultraviolet extinction, related to spectral type, 212

UV Ceti type stars, 345 f.

Variable stars, 328–69
Beta Canis Majoris stars, 354 ff.
bibliography of, 336 f.
catalogues and lists of, 333 ff.
cepheids; *see* Cepheids
classification of, 337–59
eclipsing variables, 328, 356–59; *see also under* separate entries
eruptive variables, 339–46

frequency distribution of types, 360 f.
general catalogues of, 334
history of, 329–32
importance of, 328 f.
literature of, 333 ff.
luminosities of, 448–70
Mira type, 329, 337, 348 ff., 361, 365, 449, 451, 464 f.
nomenclature, 332 f.
nova-like variables, 342 f.
novae, 339–342
number of, 334 ff., 364 f.
physical variables, 328–69
probability of discovery, 359 f.
pulsating variables, 346–56
RR Lyrae type, 354 f., 422 f., 428, 440
special surveys, 360–64
statistics of, 359–66
supernovae, 339
surveys and observations of, 328–69
types of, 329, 449
types associated with stellar groups, 350 f.
U Geminorium variables, 343 ff., 465

Vernal equinox, 2

Visual absolute magnitudes, 394–407; *see also* Absolute magnitude (luminosity) calibrations; Absolute visual magnitudes
evolutionary effect, 408
from main-sequence fitting procedures, 406–13
MK luminosity classes, 397, 401
related to H and K absorption lines, 404 f.
from related line strength, 402 ff.
zero-age main sequence, 406–13

Visual binaries
card catalogue of measures, 326
early surveys, 320 ff.
general catalogues, 325 f.
index catalogue, 325 f.
Lick survey, 322 f.
luminosities of, 282 ff.
mass-luminosity relation, 284 ff.
mass ratios of, 281 ff.
masses, 282 f.
orbits for determination of stellar masses, 274–83
random searches, 320 f.
southern surveys, 323
special surveys, 324 f.
surveys and observations of, 320–27

Visual double stars; *see* Visual binaries

W Ursa Majoris stars, 289 f., 357 f.

White dwarfs, two-color diagram, 255

Yale catalogues, proper motion of, 42 f.

Zero-age main sequence; *see* Main sequence

Zone catalogues, 472 f.